INVESTIGATIONS IN NUMBER, DATA, AND SPACE®

Tables and Graphs

Patterns of Change

Grade 5

Also appropriate for Grade 6

Cornelia Tierney
Ricardo Nemirovsky
Tracy Noble
Doug Clements

Developed at TERC, Cambridge, Massachusetts

Editorial Offices: Glenview, Illinois • Parsippany, New Jersey • New York, New York
Sales Offices: Needham, Massachusetts • Duluth, Georgia • Glenview, Illinois
Coppell, Texas • Ontario, California • Mesa, Arizona

http://www.scottforesman.com

TERC

This project was supported, in part, by the
National Science Foundation
Opinions expressed are those of the authors
and not necessarily those of the Foundation

The *Investigations* curriculum was developed at TERC (formerly
Technical Education Research Centers) in collaboration with Kent State
University and the State University of New York at Buffalo. The work
was supported in part by National Science Foundation Grant No. ESI-
9050210. TERC is a nonprofit company working to improve mathematics
and science education. TERC is located at 2067 Massachusetts Avenue,
Cambridge, MA 02140.

Managing Editor: Catherine Anderson
Series Editor: Beverly Cory
Manuscript Editor: Nancy Tune
Revision Team: Laura Marshall Alavosus, Ellen Harding, Patty Green Holubar,
Suzanne Knott, Beverly Hersh Lozoff
ESL Consultant: Nancy Sokol Green
Production/Manufacturing Director: Janet Yearian
Production/Manufacturing Supervisor: Karen Edmonds
Production/Manufacturing Coordinator: Joe Conte
Design Manager: Jeff Kelly
Design: Don Taka
Illustrations: Susan Jaekel, Carl Yoshihara
Cover: Bay Graphics
Composition: Archetype Book Composition

ISBN 0-328-16768-1
This product may appear as part of package ISBN 0-328-17406-8.

T E R C

INVESTIGATIONS IN NUMBER, DATA, AND SPACE®

Principal Investigator   Susan Jo Russell

Co-Principal Investigator   Cornelia Tierney

Director of Research and Evaluation   Jan Mokros

Curriculum Development
Joan Akers
Michael T. Battista
Mary Berle-Carman
Douglas H. Clements
Karen Economopoulos
Claryce Evans
Marlene Kliman
Cliff Konold
Jan Mokros
Megan Murray
Ricardo Nemirovsky
Tracy Noble
Andee Rubin
Susan Jo Russell
Margie Singer
Cornelia Tierney

Evaluation and Assessment
Mary Berle-Carman
Jan Mokros
Andee Rubin
Tracey Wright

Teacher Support
Kabba Colley
Karen Economopoulos
Anne Goodrow
Nancy Ishihara
Liana Laughlin
Jerrie Moffett
Megan Murray
Margie Singer
Dewi Win
Virginia Woolley
Tracey Wright
Lisa Yaffee

Administration and Production
Irene Baker
Amy Catlin
Amy Taber

Cooperating Classrooms for This Unit
Jo-Ann Pepicelli
Boston Public Schools
Boston, MA

Barbara Fox
Cambridge Public Schools
Cambridge, MA

These teachers worked in concert with Marlene Kliman, Tracey Wright, David Carraher, and Steve Monk to carry out the research and planning for this unit.

Technology Development
Douglas H. Clements
Julie Sarama

Video Production
David A. Smith
Judy Storeygard

Consultants and Advisors
Deborah Lowenberg Ball
Marilyn Burns
Mary Johnson
James J. Kaput
Mary M. Lindquist
Leslie P. Steffe
Grayson Wheatley

Graduate Assistants
Richard Aistrope
Kathryn Battista
Caroline Borrow
William Hunt
Kent State University

Jeffrey Barrett
Julie Sarama
Sudha Swaminathan
Elaine Vukelic
State University of New York at Buffalo

Dan Gillette
Irene Hall
Harvard Graduate School of Education

Revisions and Home Materials
Cathy Miles Grant
Marlene Kliman
Margaret McGaffigan
Megan Murray
Kim O'Neil
Andee Rubin
Susan Jo Russell
Lisa Seyferth
Myriam Steinback
Judy Storeygard
Anna Suarez
Cornelia Tierney
Carol Walker
Tracey Wright

CONTENTS

Investigations in Number, Data, and Space® is a K–5 mathematics curriculum with four major goals:

- to offer students meaningful mathematical problems
- to emphasize depth in mathematical thinking rather than superficial exposure to a series of fragmented topics
- to communicate mathematics content and pedagogy to teachers
- to substantially expand the pool of mathematically literate students

The *Investigations* curriculum embodies a new approach based on years of research about how children learn mathematics. Each grade level consists of a set of separate units, each offering 2–8 weeks of work. These units of study are presented through investigations that involve students in the exploration of major mathematical ideas.

Approaching the mathematics content through investigations helps students develop flexibility and confidence in approaching problems, fluency in using mathematical skills and tools to solve problems, and proficiency in evaluating their solutions. Students also build a repertoire of ways to communicate about their mathematical thinking, while their enjoyment and appreciation of mathematics grows.

The investigations are carefully designed to invite all students into mathematics—girls and boys, members of diverse cultural, ethnic, and language groups, and students with different strengths and interests. Problem contexts often call on students to share experiences from their family, culture, or community. The curriculum eliminates barriers—such as work in isolation from peers, or emphasis on speed and memorization—that exclude some students from participating successfully in mathematics. The following aspects of the curriculum ensure that all students are included in significant mathematics learning:

- Students spend time exploring problems in depth.
- They find more than one solution to many of the problems they work on.

- They invent their own strategies and approaches, rather than rely on memorized procedures.
- They choose from a variety of concrete materials and appropriate technology, including calculators, as a natural part of their everyday mathematical work.
- They express their mathematical thinking through drawing, writing, and talking.
- They work in a variety of groupings—as a whole class, individually, in pairs, and in small groups.
- They move around the classroom as they explore the mathematics in their environment and talk with their peers.

While reading and other language activities are typically given a great deal of time and emphasis in elementary classrooms, mathematics often does not get the time it needs. If students are to experience mathematics in depth, they must have enough time to become engaged in real mathematical problems. We believe that a minimum of 5 hours of mathematics classroom time a week—about an hour a day—is critical at the elementary level. The scope and pacing of the *Investigations* curriculum are based on that belief.

We explain more about the pedagogy and principles that underlie these investigations in Teacher Notes throughout the units. For correlations of the curriculum to the NCTM Standards and further help in using this research-based program for teaching mathematics, see the following books:

- *Implementing the* Investigations in Number, Data, and Space® *Curriculum*
- *Beyond Arithmetic: Changing Mathematics in the Elementary Classroom* by Jan Mokros, Susan Jo Russell, and Karen Economopoulos

This book is one of the curriculum units for *Investigations in Number, Data, and Space*. In addition to providing part of a complete mathematics curriculum for your students, this unit offers information to support your own professional development. You, the teacher, are the person who will make this curriculum come alive in the classroom; the book for each unit is your main support system.

Although the curriculum does not include student textbooks, reproducible sheets for student work are provided in the unit and are also available as Student Activity Booklets. Students work actively with objects and experiences in their own environment and with a variety of manipulative materials and technology, rather than with a book of instruction and problems. We strongly recommend use of the overhead projector as a way to present problems, to focus group discussion, and to help students share ideas and strategies.

Ultimately, every teacher will use these investigations in ways that make sense for his or her particular style, the particular group of students, and the constraints and supports of a particular school environment. Each unit offers information and guidance for a wide variety of situations, drawn from our collaborations with many teachers and students over many years. Our goal in this book is to help you, a professional educator, implement this curriculum in a way that will give all your students access to mathematical power.

Investigation Format

The opening two pages of each investigation help you get ready for the work that follows.

What Happens This gives a synopsis of each session or block of sessions.

Mathematical Emphasis This lists the most important ideas and processes students will encounter in this investigation.

What to Plan Ahead of Time These lists alert you to materials to gather, sheets to duplicate, transparencies to make, and anything else you need to do before starting.

INVESTIGATION 1

Number Patterns in Changing Shapes

What Happens

Sessions 1 and 2: Analyzing Tile Patterns
Students explore tile patterns and analyze how they "grow," deciding how to extend each pattern. In a table and on graphs, they show the number of new tiles added at each step and the total number of tiles used in the pattern so far. They create a tile pattern of their own and make a table and graphs that reflect the pattern.

Sessions 3 and 4: Four Growing Tile Patterns
Students analyze four tile patterns with these growing totals: 2, 4, 6, 8,…; 1, 4, 9, 16,…; 1, 3, 6, 10,…; and 2, 6, 14, 30,…. In tables and on graphs, students show how the tile patterns and the number series grow (whether at a steady or accelerating rate). Small groups investigate one of the four patterns in depth. They make a poster that shows the tile pattern shapes, a table, two graphs, and a written description of how their pattern grows.

Mathematical Emphasis

- Building designs that change in a regular way
- Building designs that grow according to number patterns
- Predicting later steps of number patterns and designs
- Making tables and graphs to display number patterns
- Investigating changes in the number of new tiles and the total number of tiles
- Using the language of speed and motion to describe number patterns

---

INVESTIGATION 1

What to Plan Ahead of Time

Materials

- Square tiles in mixed colors: 1 bucket of 400 per 6–8 students (all sessions)
- Markers, colored pencils, or crayons in the colors of the tiles (all sessions)
- Overhead projector (all sessions)
- Blank transparency (Sessions 1–2, optional)
- Pens for overhead projector, in colors of tiles (Session 1, optional)
- Transparent tiles for overhead projector: 10 each of four colors (all sessions, optional)
- Large paper for posters: 1 sheet per group of 3–4 students (Sessions 3–4)
- Scissors and tape for each group (Sessions 3–4)

Other Preparation

- Duplicate student sheets and teaching resources (located at the end of this unit) as follows. If you have Student Activity Booklets, copy only the items marked with an asterisk.

For Sessions 1–2
Student Sheet 1, Tile Pattern Template (p. 109): 1 per pair and 2 transparencies*
Student Sheet 2, Growing Tile Patterns (p. 110): 1 per student (homework)
Student Sheet 3, Growing and Graphing Tile Patterns (p. 111): 1 per student (homework)
One-centimeter graph paper (p. 146): 1 sheet per pair
Family letter* (p. 108): 1 per student. Remember to sign it before copying.

For Sessions 3–4
Student Sheet 4, Growing Tile Patterns (p. 112): 1 per student, and transparencies* of first two patterns (Twos Tower and Squares)
Student Sheet 5, Same Numbers, Different Pattern (p. 116): 1 per student (homework)
One-centimeter graph paper (p. 146): 2 sheets per 3–4 students

---

Sessions Within an investigation, the activities are organized by class session, a session being at least a one-hour math class. Sessions are numbered consecutively through an investigation. Often several sessions are grouped together, presenting a block of activities with a single major focus.

When you find a block of sessions presented together—for example, Sessions 1, 2, and 3—read through the entire block first to understand the overall flow and sequence of the activities. Make some preliminary decisions about how you will divide the activities into three sessions for your class, based on what you know about your students. You may need to modify your initial plans as you progress through the activities, and you may want to make notes in the margins of the pages as reminders for the next time you use the unit.

Be sure to read the Session Follow-Up section at the end of the session block to see what homework assignments and extensions are suggested as you make your initial plans.

While you may be used to a curriculum that tells you exactly what each class session should cover, we have found that the teacher is in a better position to make these decisions. Each unit is flexible and may be handled somewhat differently by every teacher. Although we provide guidance for how many sessions a particular group of activities is likely to need, we want you to be active in determining an appropriate pace and the best transition points for your class. It is not unusual for a teacher to spend more or less time than is proposed for the activities.

Ten-Minute Math At the beginning of some sessions, you will find Ten-Minute Math activities. These are designed to be used in tandem with the investigations, but not during the math hour. Rather, we hope you will do them whenever you have a spare 10 minutes—maybe before lunch or recess, or at the end of the day.

Ten-Minute Math offers practice in key concepts, but not always those being covered in the unit. For example, in a unit on using data, Ten-Minute Math might revisit geometric activities done earlier in the year. Complete directions for the suggested activities are included at the end of each unit.

Sessions 1 and 2

Analyzing Tile Patterns

Materials

- Overhead projector and blank transparency
- Transparent tiles for overhead (optional)
- Student Sheet 1 (2–3 per student and transparencies)
- Overhead pens in colors of tiles (optional)
- One-centimeter graph paper (1 per pair)
- Square tiles in mixed colors (1 bucket of 400 per 6–8 students)
- Markers, pencils, or crayons in the colors of the tiles (optional)
- Family letter (1 per student)
- Student Sheet 2 (1 per student, homework)
- Student Sheet 3 (1 per student, homework)

What Happens

Students explore tile patterns and analyze how they "grow," deciding how to extend each pattern. In a table and on graphs, they show the number of new tiles added at each step and the total number of tiles used in the pattern so far. They create a tile pattern of their own and make a table and graphs that reflect the pattern. Their work focuses on:

- predicting later steps in tile patterns and in number patterns
- building designs that change in a regular way
- making tables and graphs that describe growing tile patterns
- finding patterns in step numbers and totals

Activity

Exploring Tile Patterns

To introduce the idea of making a pattern that grows in a regular way, use transparent tiles on an overhead projector or make tile designs on a flat surface where students can gather around. Build the beginning of a Threes Tower—a growing stack of rows of three tiles. Start with one color at the bottom and build up, changing the color for each new row. (Throughout this investigation, we will illustrate patterns with tiles in four colors, red (R), blue (B), green (G), and yellow (Y), in no particular order.)

| Y | Y | Y |

As you make the first three rows, talk about what you are doing.

I'm building a pattern. For each new step of the pattern, I'll change the tile color so the step is clear.

| R | R | R |
| Y | Y | Y |

Activities The activities include pair and small-group work, individual tasks, and whole-class discussions. In any case, students are seated together, talking and sharing ideas during all work times. Students most often work cooperatively, although each student may record work individually.

Choice Time In some units, some sessions are structured with activity choices. In these cases, students may work simultaneously on different activities focused on the same mathematical ideas. Students choose which activities they want to do, and they cycle through them.

You will need to decide how to set up and introduce these activities and how to let students make their choices. Some teachers present them as station activities in different parts of the room. Some list the choices on the board as reminders or have students keep their own lists.

Tips for the Linguistically Diverse Classroom At strategic points in each unit, you will find concrete suggestions for simple modifications of the teaching strategies to encourage the participation of all students. Many of these tips offer alternative ways to elicit critical thinking from students at varying levels of English proficiency, as well as from other students who find it difficult to verbalize their thinking.

The tips are supported by suggestions for specific vocabulary work to help ensure that all students can participate fully in the investigations. The Preview for the Linguistically Diverse Classroom (p. I-21) lists important words that are assumed as part of the working vocabulary of the unit. Second-language learners will need to become familiar with these words in order to understand the problems and activities they will be doing. These terms can be incorporated into students' second-language work before or during the unit. Activities that can be used to present the words are found in the appendix, Vocabulary Support for Second-Language Learners. In addition, ideas for making connections to students' languages and cultures, included on the Preview page, help the class explore the unit's concepts from a multicultural perspective.

Session Follow-Up: Homework In *Investigations,* homework is an extension of classroom work. Sometimes it offers review and practice of work done in class, sometimes preparation for upcoming activities, and sometimes numerical practice that revisits work in earlier units. Homework plays a role both in supporting students' learning and in helping inform families about the ways in which students in this curriculum work with mathematical ideas.

Depending on your school's homework policies and your own judgment, you may want to assign more homework than is suggested in the units. For this purpose you might use the practice pages, included as blackline masters at the end of this unit, to give students additional work with numbers.

For some homework assignments, you will want to adapt the activity to meet the needs of a variety of students in your class: those with special needs, those ready for more challenge, and second-language learners. You might change the numbers in a problem, make the activity more or less complex, or go through a sample activity with those who need extra help. You can modify any

student sheet for either homework or class use. In particular, making numbers in a problem smaller or larger can make the same basic activity appropriate for a wider range of students.

Another issue to consider is how to handle the homework that students bring back to class—how to recognize the work they have done at home without spending too much time on it. Some teachers hold a short group discussion of different approaches to the assignment; others ask students to share and discuss their work with a neighbor; still others post the homework around the room and give students time to tour it briefly. If you want to keep track of homework students bring in, be sure it ends up in a designated place.

Session Follow-Up: Extensions Sometimes in Session Follow-Up, you will find suggested extension activities. These are opportunities for some or all students to explore a topic in greater depth or in a different context. They are not designed for "fast" students; mathematics is a multifaceted discipline, and different students will want to go further in different investigations. Look for and encourage the sparks of interest and enthusiasm you see in your students, and use the extensions to help them pursue these interests.

Excursions Some of the *Investigations* units include excursions—blocks of activities that could be omitted without harming the integrity of the unit. This is one way of dealing with the great depth and variety of elementary mathematics—much more than a class has time to explore in any one year. Excursions give you the flexibility to make different choices from year to year, doing the excursion in one unit this time, and next year trying another excursion.

Materials

A complete list of the materials needed for teaching this unit follows the Unit Overview. Some of these materials are available in kits for the *Investigations* curriculum. Individual items can also be purchased from school supply dealers.

Classroom Materials In an active mathematics classroom, certain basic materials should be available at all times: interlocking cubes, pencils, unlined paper, graph paper, calculators, things to

count with, and measuring tools. Some activities in this curriculum require scissors and glue sticks or tape. Stick-on notes and large paper are also useful materials throughout.

So that students can independently get what they need at any time, they should know where these materials are kept, how they are stored, and how they are to be returned to the storage area. For example, interlocking cubes are best stored in towers of ten; then, whatever the activity, they should be returned to storage in groups of ten at the end of the hour. You'll find that establishing such routines at the beginning of the year is well worth the time and effort.

Student Sheets and Teaching Resources Student recording sheets and other teaching tools needed for both class and homework are provided as reproducible blackline masters at the end of each unit. We think it's important that students find their own ways of organizing and recording their work. They need to learn how to explain their thinking with both drawings and written words, and how to organize their results so someone else can understand them. For this reason, we deliberately do not provide student sheets for every activity. Regardless of the form in which students do their work, we recommend that they keep their

work in a mathematics folder, notebook, or journal so that it is always available to them for reference.

Student Activity Booklets These booklets contain all the sheets each student will need for individual work, freeing you from extensive copying (although you may need or want to copy the occasional teaching resource on transparency film or card stock, or make extra copies of a student sheet).

Assessment Sourcebook The *Assessment Sourcebook* provides sets of End-of-Unit Assessment Tasks and Assessment Masters designed to assess students' understanding of the most important mathematical ideas of the unit. The *Sourcebook* also provides information about the mathematical significance of each assessment task; suggestions on how to observe students and evaluate their work; and unit checklists of mathematical emphases. Each checklist provides space to make short notes about individual students.

Calculators and Computers Calculators are used throughout *Investigations*. Many of the units recommend that you have at least one calculator for

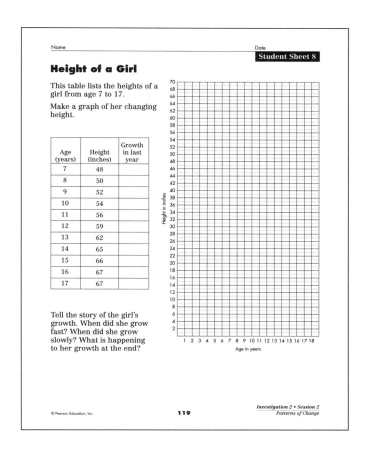

each pair. You will find calculator activities, plus Teacher Notes discussing this important mathematical tool, in an early unit at each grade level. It is assumed that calculators will be readily available for student use.

Computer activities are offered at all grade levels. How you use the computer activities depends on the number of computers you have available. Technology in the Curriculum discusses ways to incorporate the use of calculators and computers into classroom activities.

Children's Literature Each unit offers a list of related children's literature that can be used to support the mathematical ideas in the unit. Sometimes an activity is based on a specific children's book, with suggestions for substitutions where practical. While such activities can be adapted and taught without the book, the literature offers a rich introduction and should be used whenever possible.

Investigations **at Home** It is a good idea to make your policy on homework explicit to both students and their families when you begin teaching with *Investigations*. How frequently will you be assigning homework? When do you expect homework to be completed and brought back to school? What are your goals in assigning homework? How independent should families expect their children to be? What should the parent's or guardian's role be? The more explicit you can be about your expectations, the better the homework experience will be for everyone.

Investigations at Home (a booklet available separately for each unit, to send home with students) gives you a way to communicate with families about the work students are doing in class. This booklet includes a brief description of every session, a list of the mathematics content emphasized in each investigation, and a discussion of each homework assignment to help families more effectively support their children. Whether or not you are using the *Investigations* at Home booklets, we expect you to make your own choices about homework assignments. Feel free to omit any and to add extra ones you think are appropriate.

Schools and Families: Creating a Math Partnership This book suggests ways schools and districts can encourage family participation in students' mathematics education.

Family Letter A letter that you can send home to students' families is included with the blackline masters for each unit. Families need to be informed about the mathematics work in your classroom; they should be encouraged to participate in and support their children's work. A reminder to send home the letter for each unit appears in one of the early investigations. These letters are also available separately in Spanish, Vietnamese, Cantonese, Hmong, and Cambodian.

Help for You, the Teacher

Because we believe strongly that a new curriculum must help teachers think in new ways about mathematics and about their students' mathematical thinking processes, we have included a great deal of material to help you learn more about both.

About the Mathematics in This Unit This introductory section (p. I-17) summarizes the critical information about the mathematics you will be

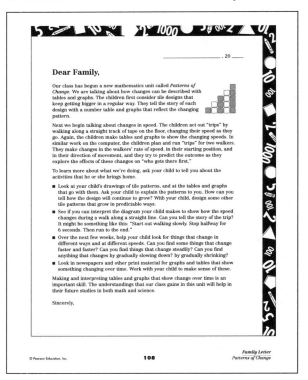

teaching. It describes the unit's central mathematical ideas and the ways students will encounter them through the unit's activities.

About the Assessment in This Unit This introductory section (p. I-19) highlights Teacher Checkpoints and assessment activities contained in the unit. It offers questions to stimulate your assessment as you observe the development of students' mathematical thinking and learning.

Teacher Notes These reference notes provide practical information about the mathematics you are teaching and about our experience with how students learn. Many of the notes were written in response to actual questions from teachers or to discuss important things we saw happening in the field-test classrooms. Some teachers like to read them all before starting the unit, then review them as they come up in particular investigations.

Dialogue Boxes Sample dialogues demonstrate how students typically express their mathematical ideas, what issues and confusions arise in their thinking, and how some teachers have guided class discussions.

These dialogues are based on the extensive classroom testing of this curriculum; many are word-for-word transcriptions of recorded class discussions. They are not always easy reading; sometimes it may take some effort to unravel what the students are trying to say. But this is the value of these dialogues; they offer good clues to how your students may develop and express their approaches and strategies, helping you prepare for your own class discussions.

Where to Start You may not have time to read everything the first time you use this unit. As a first-time user, you will likely focus on understanding the activities and working them out with your students. For a quick way to become familiar with the unit, see the **Where to Start** suggestions on the inside front cover.

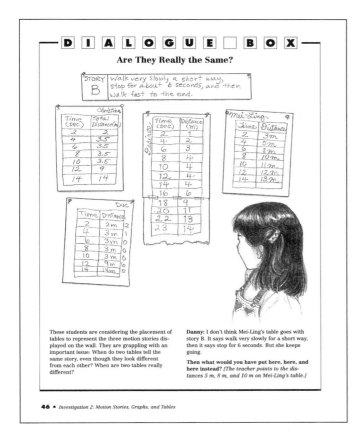

The *Investigations* curriculum incorporates the use of two forms of technology in the classroom: calculators and computers. Calculators are assumed to be standard classroom materials, available for student use in any unit. Computers are explicitly linked to one or more units at each grade level; they are used with the unit on 2-D geometry at each grade, as well as with some of the units on measuring, data, and changes.

Using Calculators

In this curriculum, calculators are considered tools for doing mathematics, similar to pattern blocks or interlocking cubes. Just as with other tools, students must learn both *how* to use calculators correctly and *when* they are appropriate to use. This knowledge is crucial for daily life, as calculators are now a standard way of handling numerical operations, both at work and at home.

Using a calculator correctly is not a simple task; it depends on a good knowledge of the four operations and of the number system, so that students can select suitable calculations and also determine what a reasonable result would be. These skills are the basis of any work with numbers, whether or not a calculator is involved.

Unfortunately, calculators are often seen as tools to check computations with, as if other methods are somehow more fallible. Students need to understand that any computational method can be used to check any other; it's just as easy to make a mistake on the calculator as it is to make a mistake on paper or with mental arithmetic. Throughout this curriculum, we encourage students to solve computation problems in more than one way in order to double-check their accuracy. We present mental arithmetic, paper-and-pencil computation, and calculators as three possible approaches.

In this curriculum we also recognize that, despite their importance, calculators are not always appropriate in mathematics instruction. Like any tools, calculators are useful for some tasks but not for others. You will need to make decisions about when to allow students access to calculators and when to ask that they solve problems without them so that they can concentrate on other tools and skills. At times when calculators are or are not appropriate for a particular activity, we make specific recommendations. Help your students develop their own sense of which problems they can tackle with their own reasoning and which ones might be better solved with a combination of their own reasoning and the calculator.

Managing calculators in your classroom so that they are a tool, and not a distraction, requires some planning. When calculators are first introduced, students often want to use them for everything, even problems that can be solved quite simply by other methods. However, once the novelty wears off, students are just as interested in developing their own strategies, especially when these strategies are emphasized and valued in the classroom. Over time, students will come to recognize the ease and value of solving problems mentally, with paper and pencil, or with manipulatives, while also understanding the power of the calculator to facilitate work with larger numbers.

Experience shows that if calculators are available only occasionally, students become excited and distracted when they are permitted to use them. They focus on the tool rather than on the mathematics. In order to learn when calculators are appropriate and when they are not, students must have easy access to them and use them routinely in their work.

If you have a calculator for each student, and if you think your students can accept the responsibility, you might allow them to keep their calculators with the rest of their individual materials. Alternatively, you might store them in boxes on a shelf, number each calculator, and assign a corresponding number to each student. This system can give students a sense of ownership while also helping you keep track of the calculators.

Using Computers

Students can use computers to approach and visualize mathematical situations in new ways. The computer allows students to construct and manipulate geometric shapes, see objects move according to rules they specify, and turn, flip, and repeat a pattern.

This curriculum calls for computers in units where they are a particularly effective tool for learning mathematics content. One unit on 2-D geometry at each of the grades 3–5 includes a core of activities that rely on access to computers, either in the classroom or in a lab. Other units on geometry, measuring, data, and changes include computer activities, but can be taught without them. In these units, however, students' experience is greatly enhanced by computer use.

The following list outlines the recommended use of computers in this curriculum. The software is available for download at http://investigations.scottforesman.com.

Kindergarten
Unit: *Making Shapes and Building Blocks*
    (Exploring Geometry)
Software: *MS_Shapes*

Grade 1
Unit: *Quilt Squares and Block Towns*
    (2-D and 3-D Geometry)
Software: *QS_Shapes*

Grade 2
Unit: *Mathematical Thinking at Grade 2*
    (Introduction)
Software: *MT_Shapes*

Unit: *Shapes, Halves, and Symmetry*
    (Geometry and Fractions)
Software: *SH_Shapes*

Unit: *How Long? How Far?* (Measuring)
Software: *HL_Geo-Logo*

Grade 3
Unit: *Flips, Turns, and Area* (2-D Geometry)
Software: *Tumbling Tetrominoes*

Unit: *Turtle Paths* (2-D Geometry)
Software: *TP_Geo-Logo*

Grade 4
Unit: *Sunken Ships and Grid Patterns*
    (2-D Geometry)
Software: *SS_Geo-Logo*

Grade 5
Unit: *Picturing Polygons* (2-D Geometry)
Software: *PP_Geo-Logo*

Unit: *Patterns of Change* (Tables and Graphs)
Software: *Trips*

The software for the *Investigations* units uses the power of the computer to help students explore mathematical ideas and relationships that cannot be explored in the same way with physical materials. With the *Shapes* (grades K–2) and *Tumbling Tetrominoes* (grade 3) software, students explore symmetry, pattern, rotation and reflection, area, and characteristics of 2-D shapes. With the *Geo-Logo* software (grades 2–5), students investigate rotation and reflection, coordinate geometry, the properties of 2-D shapes, and angles. The *Trips* software (grade 5) is a mathematical exploration of motion in which students run experiments and interpret data presented in graphs and tables.

We suggest that students work in pairs on the computer; this not only maximizes computer resources but also encourages students to consult, monitor, and teach one another. However, asking more than two students to work at the same computer is less effective. Managing access to computers is an issue for every classroom. The curriculum gives you explicit support for setting up a system. The units are structured on the assumption that you have enough computers for half your students to work on the machines in pairs at one time. If you do not have access to that many computers, suggestions are made for structuring class time to use the unit with fewer than five.

Assessment plays a critical role in teaching and learning, and it is an integral part of the *Investigations* curriculum. For a teacher using these units, assessment is an ongoing process. You observe students' discussions and explanations of their strategies on a daily basis and examine their work as it evolves. While students are busy recording and representing their work, working on projects, sharing with partners, and playing mathematical games, you have many opportunities to observe their mathematical thinking. What you learn through observation guides your decisions about how to proceed. In any of the units, you will repeatedly consider questions like these:

- Do students come up with their own strategies for solving problems, or do they expect others to tell them what to do? What do their strategies reveal about their mathematical understanding?

- Do students understand that there are different strategies for solving problems? Do they articulate their strategies and try to understand other students' strategies?

- How effectively do students use materials as tools to help with their mathematical work?

- Do students have effective ideas for keeping track of and recording their work? Do keeping track of and recording their work seem difficult for them?

You will need to develop a comfortable and efficient system for recording and keeping track of your observations. Some teachers keep a clipboard handy and jot notes on a class list or on adhesive labels that are later transferred to student files. Others keep loose-leaf notebooks with a page for each student and make weekly notes about what they have observed in class.

Assessment Tools in the Unit

With the activities in each unit, you will find questions to guide your thinking while observing the students at work. You will also find two built-in assessment tools: Teacher Checkpoints and embedded Assessment activities.

Teacher Checkpoints The designated Teacher Checkpoints in each unit offer a time to "check in" with individual students, watch them at work, and ask questions that illuminate how they are thinking.

At first it may be hard to know what to look for and what kinds of questions to ask. Students may be reluctant to talk; they may not be accustomed to having the teacher ask them about their work, or they may not know how to explain their thinking. Two important ingredients of this process are asking students open-ended questions about their work and showing genuine interest in how they are approaching the task. When students see that you are interested in their thinking and are counting on them to come up with their own ways of solving problems, they may surprise you with the depth of their understanding.

Teacher Checkpoints also give you the chance to pause in the teaching sequence and reflect on how your class is doing overall. Think about whether you need to adjust your pacing: Are most students fluent with strategies for solving a particular kind of problem? Are they just starting to formulate good strategies? Or are they still struggling with how to start? Depending on what you see as the students work, you may want to spend more time on similar problems, change some of the problems to use smaller numbers, move quickly to more-challenging material, modify subsequent activities for some students, work on particular ideas with a small group, or pair students who have good strategies with those who are having more difficulty.

Embedded Assessment Activities Assessment activities embedded in each unit will help you examine specific pieces of student work, figure out what they mean, and provide feedback. From the students' point of view, these assessment activities are no different from any others. Each is a learning experience in and of itself, as well as an opportunity for you to gather evidence about students' mathematical understanding.

The embedded Assessment activities sometimes involve writing and reflecting; at other times, a discussion or brief interaction between student and teacher; and in other instances, the creation and explanation of a product. In most cases, the assessments require that students *show* what they did, *write* or *talk* about it, or do both. Having to explain how they worked through a problem helps students be more focused and clear in their mathematical thinking. It also helps them realize that doing mathematics is a process that may involve tentative starts, revising one's approach, taking different paths, and working through ideas.

Teachers often find the hardest part of assessment to be interpreting their students' work. We provide guidelines to help with that interpretation. If you have used a process approach to teaching writing, the assessment in *Investigations* will seem familiar. For many of the assessment activities, a Teacher Note provides examples of student work and a commentary on what it indicates about student thinking.

Documentation of Student Growth

To form an overall picture of mathematical progress, it is important to document each student's work. Many teachers have students keep their work in folders, notebooks, or journals, and some like to have students summarize their learning in journals at the end of each unit. It's important to document students' progress, and we recommend that your keep a portfolio of selected work for each student, unit by unit, for the entire year. The final activity in each *Investigations* unit, called Choosing Student Work to Save, helps you and the students select representative samples for a record of their work.

This kind of regular documentation helps you synthesize information about each student as a mathematical learner. From different pieces of evidence, you can put together the big picture. This synthesis will be invaluable in thinking about where to go next with a particular child, deciding where more work is needed, or explaining to parents (or other teachers) how a child is doing.

If you use portfolios, you need to collect a good balance of work, yet avoid being swamped with an overwhelming amount of paper. Following are some tips for effective portfolios:

■ Collect a representative sample of work, including some pieces that students themselves select for inclusion in the portfolio. There should be just a few pieces for each unit, showing different kinds of work—some assignments that involve writing as well as some that do not.

■ If students do not date their work, do so yourself so that you can reconstruct the order in which pieces were done.

■ Include your reflections on the work. When you are looking back over the whole year, such comments are reminders of what seemed especially interesting about a particular piece; they can also be helpful to other teachers and to parents. Older students should be encouraged to write their own reflections about their work.

Assessment Overview

There are two places to turn for a preview of the assessment opportunities in each *Investigations* unit. The Assessment Resources column in the Unit Overview Chart (pp. I-13–I-15) identifies the Teacher Checkpoints and Assessment activities embedded in each investigation, guidelines for observing students, and any Teacher Notes and Dialogue Boxes that explain what to look for and what types of student responses you might expect to see in your classroom. Additionally, the section About the Assessment in This Unit gives you a detailed list of questions for each investigation, keyed to the mathematical emphases, to help you observe student growth.

Assessment Sourcebook   The *Assessment Sourcebook* complements and supports the embedded assessments of *Investigations* by offering further opportunities to gather information about students' growing mathematical understanding.

The *Assessment Sourcebook* provides you with sets of Assessment Tasks and Masters designed to assess your students' understanding of the most important mathematical ideas of the unit. The *Sourcebook* also provides information about the mathematical significance of each assessment task; suggestions on how to observe students and evaluate their work; and unit checklists of mathematical emphases. Each checklist provides space to make short notes about individual students.

The assessments in the *Sourcebook* should be used in addition to other assessments that are presented in each unit. The combination of these assessments, along with samples of student work, will offer a picture of a student's understanding of the mathematical concepts and skills presented in the unit.

Patterns of Change

Content of This Unit   Using plastic tiles, students experiment with forms of geometric growth that express number patterns. Students show their growing patterns in number tables and on graphs, and distinguish between growth, shrinkage, and oscillation, as well as between steady and accelerated growth.

Students then use number tables, graphs, and written "motion stories" to describe walks along a straight line or "track," noting the patterns that show increasing or decreasing speed. In the *Trips* software, which simulates a boy and a girl walking along two tracks, and in parallel off-computer activities, students explore the trade-off between factors that influence the outcome of a trip, including step size (which, at 1 step per second, represents speed) and starting position. The unit culminates with the analysis of the relationship between graphs of position vs. time and graphs of step size vs. time.

Connections with Other Units   If you are doing the full-year *Investigations* curriculum in the suggested sequence for grade 5, this is the seventh of nine units. It builds on ideas developed in the grade 3 unit *Up and Down the Number Line* and the grade 4 unit *Changes Over Time*. If your students have not made line graphs to show something changing over time, such as plant growth, you might use the grade 4 unit before starting *Patterns of Change*.

This unit can also be used successfully at grade 6, depending on the previous experience and needs of your students.

Investigations Curriculum ■ Suggested Grade 5 Sequence

Mathematical Thinking at Grade 5 (Introduction and Landmarks in the Number System)

Picturing Polygons (2-D Geometry)

Name That Portion (Fractions, Percents, and Decimals)

Between Never and Always (Probability)

Building on Numbers You Know (Computation and Estimation Strategies)

Measurement Benchmarks (Estimating and Measuring)

▶ *Patterns of Change* (Tables and Graphs)

Containers and Cubes (3-D Geometry: Volume)

Data: Kids, Cats, and Ads (Statistics)

Investigation 1 ▪ Number Patterns in Changing Shapes

Class Sessions	Activities	Pacing
Sessions 1 and 2 (p. 4) ANALYZING TILE PATTERNS	Exploring Tile Patterns Other Patterns and Their Graphs From Tables to Groups Teacher Checkpoint: Designing a Growing Tile Pattern Homework: Growing Tile Patterns Homework: Growing and Graphing Tile Patterns	minimum 2 hr
Sessions 3 and 4 (p. 14) FOUR GROWING TILE PATTERNS	Making Tables and Graphs for Tile Patterns Comparing Graph Shapes Investigating a Pattern in Depth Presenting the Posters Homework: Same Numbers, Different Pattern Homework: Reviewing Work Extension: Tile Designs to Fit Descriptions	minimum 2 hr

◔ **Ten-Minute Math** ▪ **Nearest Answer**

Mathematical Emphasis

- Building designs that change in a regular way

- Building designs that grow according to number patterns

- Predicting later steps of number patterns and designs

- Making tables and graphs to display number patterns

- Investigating changes in the number of new tiles and the total number of tiles

- Using the language of speed and motion to describe number patterns

Assessment Resources

Teacher Checkpoint: Designing a Growing Tile Pattern (p. 8)

The Relationship of Step Size to Total (Teacher Note, p. 11)

Finding General Rules for Step Size and Total (Teacher Note, p. 12)

Four Patterns (Teacher Note, p. 22)

Finding General Rules for the Staircase Patterns (Dialogue Box, p. 24)

Materials

Square tiles in mixed colors

Markers, crayons, or colored pencils

Overhead projector

Blank transparency

Overhead pens

Transparent tiles

Large poster paper

Scissors

Tape

Student Sheets 1–5

Teaching resource sheets

Family letter

Investigation 2 ■ Motion Stories, Graphs, and Tables

Class Sessions	Activities	Pacing
Session 1 (p. 28) DESCRIBING CHANGING SPEEDS	Describing Fast and Slow Trips Representing Changes of Speed Homework: Describing a Straight Line Trip	minimum 1 hr
Session 2 (p. 33) FROM BEANBAGS TO TABLES	Comparing Fast and Slow Trips Marking and Guessing Trips Making Tables to Show Trips Homework: Height of a Girl	minimum 1 hr
Session 3 (p. 41) TABLES FOR STORIES	Interpreting the Table of Heights Teacher Checkpoint: Making Tables for Stories Matching Tables to Stories Similarities Among Tables Homework: Graph of a Trip	minimum 1 hr
Session 4 (p. 48) GRAPHS FOR TABLES	Homework Review: Graph of a Trip Making Graphs from Tables Interpreting Graphs Homework: Planning and Graphing a Trip Extension: Change Over Time	minimum 1 hr
Session 5 (p. 52) STORIES, TABLES, AND GRAPHS	Assessment: Matching Stories, Tables, and Graphs Homework: Reviewing Work Extension: *Trips* Software	minimum 1 hr

◔ Ten-Minute Math ■ Nearest Answer

Mathematical Emphasis

- Exploring relationships among distance, time, and speed

- Exploring irregular increases and decreases in speed

- Exploring ways that speed, time, and distance can be represented with tables, graphs, stories, and informal representations

- Interpreting intervals in a table and reflecting speed

- Interpreting steepness in a distance vs. time graph as reflecting speed

- Associating tables, graphs, and stories of the same event

Assessment Resources

Invented Representations of Trips (Teacher Note, p. 32)

Marking and Guessing Trips: Observing the Students (p. 38)

Tables That Show Changing Speeds (Teacher Note, p. 40)

Teacher Checkpoint: Making Tables for Stories (p. 43)

Are They Really the Same? (Dialogue Box, p. 46)

Making Graphs from Tables: Observing the Students (p. 49)

Assessment: Matching Stories, Tables, and Graphs (p. 52)

Materials

Wide masking tape

Unlined paper

Markers, crayons, or colored pencils

Timepieces with second hands

Beanbags

Shallow containers

Stick-on notes

Overhead projector

Scissors

Tape or glue sticks

Students Sheets 6–14

Teaching resource sheets

Investigation 3 ▪ Computer Trips on Two Tracks

Class Sessions	Activities	Pacing
Session 1 (p. 57) WAYS OF MAKING TRIPS	Showing Speed with Step Size Trips Along a Meterstick Trips on the Computer On Computer: Exploring the *Trips* Software	minimum 1 hr
Session 2 (p. 69) TRIPS ON TWO TRACKS	Working with Motion Stories Teacher Checkpoint: Running and Recording *Trips* Homework: Story of a Trip Extension: Another Motion Story	minimum 1 hr
Session 3 (p. 75) DIFFERENT KINDS OF TRIPS	How Settings 2 and 3 Work Running *Trips* in Setting 2 and Setting 3 Homework: Story of a Trip with Varying Step Sizes Extension: The Challenge	minimum 1 hr
Session 4 (p. 81) MORE MATCH-UPS	Comparing Tables and Graphs Extension: Creating Challenges	minimum 1 hr
Sessions 5 and 6 (p. 83) TWO TYPES OF GRAPHS	Showing a Walk with Two Graphs Graphing and Guessing Mystery Walks Assessment: Graphs: What Story Do They Tell? Homework: Graphing a Motion Story Extension: Comparing Graphs on the Computer Screen	minimum 2 hr
Session 7 (Excursion)* (p. 90) ANIMATION	Animated Flip Books Flip Books with Two Changes Choosing Student Work to Save Homework: Sharing Flip Books Extension: Another Flip Book	minimum 1 hr

🕐 **Ten-Minute Math ▪ Graph Stories**

* Excursions can be omitted without harming the integrity or continuity of the unit, but offer good mathematical work if you have time to include them.

Mathematical Emphasis

- Representing motion with number tables, graphs, and verbal descriptions

- Exploring the relationships between time, distance, and speed

- Connecting slope in a graph with rate of change

- Comparing relative motions

- Relating number patterns to graph shapes

- Exploring the relationship between graphs of distance vs. time and step size vs. time

Assessment Resources

About the *Trips* Software (Teacher Note, p. 64)

Teacher Checkpoint: Running and Recording *Trips* (p. 72)

Using the Three *Trips* Settings (Teacher Note, p. 73)

"The Boy Is Going to Win . . ." (Dialogue Box, p. 74)

Changing the Step Size in Setting 2 (Teacher Note, p. 80)

Assessment: Graphs: What Story Do They Tell? (p. 87)

Choosing Student Work to Save (p. 92)

Materials

Adding machine tape

Metersticks

Masking tape

Overhead projector

Colored markers

Computers with *Trips* installed

Timepiece that shows seconds

Cuisenaire® rods

Stick-on notes

Scissors

Glue or paste

Student Sheets 15–26

Teaching resource sheets

Following are the basic materials needed for the activities in this unit.

- Square color tiles in mixed colors: 1 bucket of 400 per group of 6–8 students

- Overhead projector and blank transparencies

- Overhead pens, in colors of tiles (optional)

- Transparent tiles for overhead: 10 each of four colors (optional)

- Metersticks: 1 per 8–12 students

- Stopwatches or wall clock that shows seconds: 1 per 4–6 students

- Small beanbags in two colors (see p. 27 for ideas for making these): 12 per 4–6 students

- Shallow containers to hold 12 beanbags: 1 per 4–6 students

- Cuisenaire® rods: 3–4 sets of 10. If you do not have these, substitute centimeter cubes taped together in varying lengths or narrow strips of tagboard cut in 1- to 10-centimeter lengths.

- Computers

  Macintosh: PowerPC processor running OS 7.6 or higher, 32 MB RAM, 10 MB hard drive space, 13" color monitor (256 colors), and 2x CD-ROM drive.

  Windows: 100 MHz Pentium processor or greater running Win 95 or 98, 32 MB RAM, 10 MB hard drive space, SVGA monitor (256 colors), and 2x CD-ROM drive.

  [Note: Minimum system requirements may change as software is updated. Review the minimum system requirements listed in the readme file for your software.]

  For suggestions on how to structure the unit to match your computer availability, see the **Teacher Note**, Managing the Computer Activities, p. 67.

- *Trips*, software written to accompany *Patterns of Change*. The software is available for download at http://www.scottforesman.com/investigations/software/.

- Large-screen monitor or computer projector for whole-class viewing (optional)

- Computer disks or hard drive space for students to save their work

- Stick-on notes: 2 pads for the class to share; 1 pad per student of 2" by 3" size (light colored, for making flip books)

- Wide (2-inch) masking tape: about 50 meters

- Adding machine tape: 5–6 meters

- Colored markers or crayons for every student

- Scissors: 1 per pair

- Tape or glue sticks: 1 per pair

- Large paper for posters: 1 sheet per 3–4 students

- Chart paper

- Calculators: always available

- Unlined paper

The following materials are provided at the end of this unit as blackline masters. A Student Activity Booklet containing all student sheets and teaching resources needed for individual work is available.

Family Letter (p. 108)

Student Sheets 1–26 (p. 109)

Teaching Resources:
    One-Centimeter Graph paper (p. 146)
    Graph Shapes (for Ten-Minute Math) (p. 147)

Practice Pages (p. 149)

Related Children's Literature

Anno, Mitsumasa. *Anno's Magic Seeds.* New York: Philomel, 1995.

Birch, David. *The King's Chessboard.* New York: Dial Books for Young Readers, 1988.

Guiberson, Brenda. *Cactus Hotel.* New York: Henry Holt, 1991.

Things change over time—sometimes steadily, sometimes at varying rates. Figuring out how quickly something grows or declines is essential not just in higher mathematics, but in the sciences and social sciences as well. Elementary students need some experience in describing, representing, and comparing *rates of change;* that is the focus of this unit. Following are some of the major mathematical ideas that students encounter:

Understanding the relationship between rate of change and accumulated change. An appreciation of the connections between rate of change and accumulated change is a foundational skill for students as they proceed through their study of mathematics toward calculus. Students explore these ideas about that relationship:

■ A constant positive rate of change corresponds to a steady increase in the accumulated changes. In terms of the "trips" students explore, moving at a constant speed implies that the distance traveled increases steadily.

■ We can accumulate the same total change with many small successive changes or a few big ones. In "trips" terms, we can travel the same distance in the same time with many small steps or a few big steps.

These ideas have profound mathematical implications that can be expressed in the shape of graphs, in number patterns, and in geometric growth.

Using the language of motion to describe mathematical behavior. Motion, with its pervasive presence in daily life, offers powerful metaphors and language to use in considering symbolic expressions. For example, consider two number series:

  1, 3, 5, 7, 9, ...

  1, 2, 4, 8, 16, ...

We can compare them by saying that the first increases at a steady rate and the second grows faster and faster. Even though nothing is actually moving, the language of motion *(steady, faster and faster)* allows us to communicate the change and the overall trends in these number patterns. A crucial part of mathematical understanding is

being able to look at symbolic expressions and "see" in these static forms the dynamics of events changing over time.

Seeing connections between graphs, number tables, and stories. To make sense of a mathematical model, we need to be able to tell stories that express events as symbolic features. For example, we can show one person catching up to another (an event) as two graphs crossing each other (a symbolic feature).

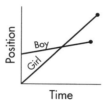

We can show climbing a particular staircase (an event) as numbers in a table increasing by 2's (a symbolic feature).

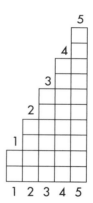

Step	Total
1	2
2	4
3	6
4	8
5	10

Students experiment with the notion that the same story can be told in many mathematical forms, such as graphs, patterns of marks along a line, and number tables, which are equivalent precisely because they tell the same story.

Distinguishing across-time and simultaneous relationships. In observing something that changes, we can take a *diachronic* (across-time) perspective or a *synchronic* (simultaneous) perspective. For example, we can study someone's growth across the years, perhaps by looking at the person's height in each past year. Or, we can compare someone's height to the height of others at a given time, perhaps by arranging the names of a group of people according to their height.

In symbolic terms, we can describe the number table below by noticing that N increases by 1's and P by 2's (a diachronic view). Or, we can point out that P is always $2 \times N$ (a synchronic view).

N	P
1	2
2	4
3	6
4	8
5	10

Fluency in moving back and forth between these two perspectives is central to the mathematical analysis of change.

At the beginning of each investigation, the Mathematical Emphasis section tells you what is most important for students to learn about during that investigation. Many of these understandings and processes are difficult and complex. Students gradually learn more and more about each idea over many years of schooling. Individual students will begin and end the unit with different levels of knowledge and skill, but all will become more able to make, interpret, and compare graphs and tables that show something changing over time.

Throughout the *Investigations* curriculum, there are many opportunities for ongoing daily assessment as you observe, listen to, and interact with students at work. In this unit, you will find three Teacher Checkpoints:

Investigation 1, Sessions 1–2:
Designing a Growing Tile Pattern (p. 8)

Investigation 2, Session 3:
Making Tables for Stories (p. 43)

Investigation 3, Session 2:
Running and Recording *Trips* (p. 72)

This unit also has two embedded Assessment activities:

Investigation 2, Session 5:
Matching Stories, Tables, and Graphs (p. 52)

Investigation 3, Sessions 5–6:
Graphs: What Story Do They Tell? (p. 87)

In addition, you can use almost any activity in this unit to assess your students' needs and strengths. Listed below are questions to help you focus your observations in each investigation. You may want to keep track of your observations for each student to help you plan your curriculum and monitor students' growth. Suggestions for documenting student growth can be found in the section About Assessment.

Investigation 1: Number Patterns in Changing Shapes

- How do students build designs that change in a regular way? Is it clear where the next tiles in the sequence should go? Do students remember to change colors with each new step?

- How effectively do students build designs that grow according to number patterns? What strategies do they use to design a pattern that matches a certain pattern?

- How do students predict later steps of number patterns and designs? What strategies do they use? On what information do they base their predictions? Do they make use of the design itself, the number table, and/or the graphs?

- How reflective of the tile patterns are the tables and graphs students make? How do they double-check their work? Do they refer back to the design to keep the tables and graphs accurate?

- How do students determine the number of new tiles to add? Can they look at a pattern and determine how many tiles were added? How do they determine the total number of tiles in a pattern? How do they relate the changes in the number of new tiles to the total of accumulated tiles?

- Can students interpret the shape of a graph? Can they distinguish between and describe graphs that show no growth, steady growth, accelerating growth, or alternating fast and slow growth? What language do they use to describe speed and motion of number patterns, as reflected in a graph?

Investigation 2: Motion Stories, Graphs, and Tables

- What is students' understanding of relationships among distance, time, and speed? Do they associate the length of the interval between beanbags with the speed at which the dropper was moving?

- How do students determine step size? total distance traveled? How do they relate the changes in the former to the total distance?

- In what ways do students represent speed, time, and distance in their own diagrams or drawings? How do they show length of time, distance, changes of speed, and stopping?

- How do students understand, find, and interpret the size of intervals in a table? Do they understand that the size of these intervals reflects speed when the intervals are regular? Do they understand that distances farther apart reflect a faster speed and distances closer together show a slower speed?

- How do students interpret the slope of a distance vs. time graph? Do they understand that when a graph becomes steeper, it represents an increase in speed? Do they understand that to show slowing down, the graph continues to go up, just less steeply? What is their understanding of how a stop is represented on a graph?

- How do students understand the relationship between tables, graphs, and stories of the same event?

Investigation 3: Computer Trips on Two Tracks

- How effectively do students represent motion with number tables, graphs, and/or verbal descriptions? Do they realize that a single motion story can be expressed with many number tables and graphs, and yet that all of those tables and graphs have to share some essential characteristics of the motion story?

- How do students explore and understand relationships between time, distance, and speed?

- How do students make sense of and compare the motion of two different objects (or people) that move along parallel tracks?

- How do students relate number patterns and graph shapes? What features do they attend to in trying to match examples of one to the other? Do they look for particular speeds? stops? points at which speeds change? the size of steps?

- How do students relate graphs of distance vs. time and step size vs. time? How do they understand the relationship between the steepness of the line on a position graph with the size of a bar on a step-size graph? Are they able to identify and explain how each type of graph represents a stop in the motion? What is their understanding of ways in which each type of graph represents a change in direction?

Assessment Sourcebook

In the *Assessment Sourcebook* you will find End-of-Unit Assessment Tasks and Assessment Masters available in English and Spanish. You will also find suggestions to help you observe and evaluate student work and checklists of mathematical emphases with space for you to record individual student information.

In the *Investigations* curriculum, mathematical vocabulary is introduced naturally during the activities. We don't ask students to learn definitions of new terms; rather, they come to understand such words as *factor* or *area* or *symmetry* by hearing them used frequently in discussion as they investigate new concepts. This approach is compatible with current theories of second-language acquisition, which emphasize the use of new vocabulary in meaningful contexts while students are actively involved with objects, pictures, and physical movement.

Listed below are some key words used in this unit that will not be new to most English speakers at this age level, but may be unfamiliar to students with limited English proficiency. You will want to spend additional time working on these words with your students who are learning English. If your students are working with a second-language teacher, you might enlist your colleague's aid in familiarizing students with these words, before and during this unit. In the classroom, look for opportunities for students to hear and use these words. Activities you can use to present the words are given in the appendix, Vocabulary Support for Second-Language Learners (p. 98).

grow, shrink Students note whether the regular patterns they are studying are growing, shrinking, or doing both in turns.

change, speed, faster, slower, increase, steady Throughout the unit, students note the way in which patterns or trips change, and whether the rate of change is getting faster or slower or remaining steady.

steep, flat, slope Students graph the patterns they discover, noting when the patterns are growing or shrinking rapidly, resulting in a steep slope, and when they are not changing, resulting in a flat horizontal line.

position, start, end As students represent trips in various ways, they discuss the start and end positions of people or markers as they move along a path.

Multicultural Extensions for All Students

Whenever possible, encourage students to share words, objects, customs, or any aspects of daily life from their own cultures and backgrounds that are relevant to the activities in this unit. For example, students might bring in tables and graphs from foreign-language magazines and newspapers and work together as a class to attempt to interpret them.

Investigations

INVESTIGATION 1

Number Patterns in Changing Shapes

What Happens

Sessions 1 and 2: Analyzing Tile Patterns
Students explore tile patterns and analyze how they "grow," deciding how to extend each pattern. In a table and on graphs, they show the number of new tiles added at each step and the total number of tiles used in the pattern so far. They create a tile pattern of their own and make a table and graphs that reflect the pattern.

Sessions 3 and 4: Four Growing Tile Patterns
Students analyze four tile patterns with these growing totals: 2, 4, 6, 8,...; 1, 4, 9, 16,...; 1, 3, 6, 10,...; and 2, 6, 14, 30,.... In tables and on graphs, students show how the tile patterns and the number series grow (whether at a steady or accelerating rate). Small groups investigate one of the four patterns in depth. They make a poster that shows the tile pattern shapes, a table, two graphs, and a written description of how their pattern grows.

Mathematical Emphasis

- Building designs that change in a regular way
- Building designs that grow according to number patterns
- Predicting later steps of number patterns and designs
- Making tables and graphs to display number patterns
- Investigating changes in the number of new tiles and the total number of tiles
- Using the language of speed and motion to describe number patterns

What to Plan Ahead of Time

Materials

- Square tiles in mixed colors: 1 bucket of 400 per 6–8 students (all sessions)
- Markers, colored pencils, or crayons in the colors of the tiles (all sessions)
- Overhead projector (all sessions)
- Blank transparency (Sessions 1–2, optional)
- Pens for overhead projector, in colors of tiles (Session 1, optional)
- Transparent tiles for overhead projector: 10 each of four colors (all sessions, optional)
- Large paper for posters: 1 sheet per group of 3–4 students (Sessions 3–4)
- Scissors and tape for each group (Sessions 3–4)

Other Preparation

- Duplicate student sheets and teaching resources (located at the end of this unit) as follows. If you have Student Activity Booklets, copy only the items marked with an asterisk.

For Sessions 1–2

Student Sheet 1, Tile Pattern Template (p. 109): 1 per pair and 2 transparencies*

Student Sheet 2, Growing Tile Patterns (p. 110): 1 per student (homework)

Student Sheet 3, Growing and Graphing Tile Patterns (p. 111): 1 per student (homework)

One-centimeter graph paper (p. 146): 1 sheet per pair

Family letter* (p. 108): 1 per student. Remember to sign it before copying.

For Sessions 3–4

Student Sheet 4, Growing Tile Patterns (p. 112): 1 per student, and transparencies* of first two patterns (Twos Tower and Squares)

Student Sheet 5, Same Numbers, Different Pattern (p. 116): 1 per student (homework)

One-centimeter graph paper (p. 146): 2 sheets per 3–4 students

Analyzing Tile Patterns

Materials

- Overhead projector
- Blank transparency, (optional)
- Transparent tiles for overhead (optional)
- Student Sheet 1 (1 per pair and 2 transparencies)
- Overhead pens in colors of tiles (optional)
- One-centimeter graph paper (1 per pair)
- Square tiles in mixed colors (1 bucket of 400 per 6–8 students)
- Markers, pencils, or crayons in the colors of the tiles (optional)
- Family letter (1 per student)
- Student Sheet 2 (1 per student, homework)
- Student Sheet 3 (1 per student, homework)

What Happens

Students explore tile patterns and analyze how they "grow," deciding how to extend each pattern. In a table and on graphs, they show the number of new tiles added at each step and the total number of tiles used in the pattern so far. They create a tile pattern of their own and make a table and graphs that reflect the pattern. Their work focuses on:

- predicting later steps in tile patterns and in number patterns
- building designs that change in a regular way
- making tables and graphs that describe growing tile patterns
- finding patterns in step numbers and totals

Activity

Exploring Tile Patterns

To introduce the idea of making a pattern that grows in a regular way, use transparent tiles on an overhead projector or make tile designs on a flat surface where students can gather around. Build the beginning of a Threes Tower—a growing stack of rows of three tiles. Start with one color at the bottom and build up, changing the color for each new row. (Throughout this investigation, we will illustrate patterns with tiles in four colors, red (R), blue (B), green (G), and yellow (Y), in no particular order.)

As you make the first three rows, talk about what you are doing.

I'm building a pattern. For each new step of the pattern, I'll change the tile color so the step is clear.

Explain that *where* the new tiles are added is important, but the order of the colors is not.

B	B	B
R	R	R
Y	Y	Y

What do you think my next step will be? How many new tiles will I add?

Take suggestions about how many tiles to add and where to put them. When students have the idea of how to continue this pattern, start a three-column table on a blank overhead transparency or on the board, showing the step number, the number of new tiles added at each step, and the total number of tiles used thus far. With students' suggestions, continue the table for a few rows.

Step number	New tiles (step size)	Total so far
1	3	3
2	3	6
3	3	9
4		
5		

Making a table is a way of seeing if there is a number pattern in the way this design is growing. What patterns do you see? As we continue adding tiles to this pattern, what numbers will we put in the column for new tiles? We will call this number the *step size*. What numbers will we put in the column for total tiles used so far?

To encourage students to read across rows in the table, ask questions about some steps you have not reached yet and perhaps about some steps that are beyond the table. You might cover the row just above the one you are asking about so that students can't build onto it to get the answer.

What will the *number of new tiles* be for the fifth step? for the seventh step? for any step?

What will the *total number of tiles* be for the fifth step? for the seventh step? If I kept on building, what would be the total after the tenth step? the twentieth step? If I tell you the step number, what calculations would you do to get the total?

When students identify the patterns in the step size and total, add notes at the bottom of the table columns to describe the patterns.

Step number	New tiles (step size)	Total so far
1	3	3
2	3	6
3	3	9
4	3	12
5	3	15
6	3	18
7	3	21
8	3	24
	always 3	multiply step number x 3

When you have completed the table through step 8, ask about the overall pattern.

How is this pattern growing? Is the step size growing? (No, it stays constant at 3.) **Is the total growing? Is it growing steadily, by the same amount every step, or is it growing faster and faster?** (The total grows steadily, adding 3 more for each step.)

Other Patterns and Their Graphs

Start another tile design, as shown below (at left). We call this one the Double-Step Staircase, but students may see it differently and want to call it by another name. Use whatever name they are comfortable with.

Describe each step as you build:

In the first step I'm placing two reds. In the second step I'm placing four greens. For the third step I'm taking six blues. How do you think I should place the blues?

What do you think the fourth step will be? How many yellows should I use? How should I place them?

On a transparency of Student Sheet 1, Tile Pattern Template, draw the Double-Step Staircase tile design. Ask students to describe how the general shape of the design is growing as you add tiles. Is it getting wider? taller? In what direction is it growing? Some students may observe that the design is growing taller at a faster rate than it is growing wider; some may even notice that it is growing taller exactly twice as fast as it is growing wider (that is, it grows 2 tiles taller for every 1 tile that it grows wider).

Point out the table below the pattern grid on Student Sheet 1. With students' suggestions, fill in the table with numbers that describe the pattern.

Start two more tile pattern designs. As necessary, remind students that each color change represents a new step.

Step number	New tiles (step size)	Total so far
1	2	2
2	4	6
3	6	12
4	8	20
5		
6		
7		
8		

Again, encourage students to describe generally how the patterns are growing. (The pattern on the left is growing equally taller and wider in all directions at once. The pattern on the right is growing longer but not taller.)

After students have established how these tile patterns are to be continued, hand out a sheet of centimeter graph paper to each pair. Pairs copy one of the two patterns and continue it on the graph paper, then make a table to go with it.

From Tables to Groups

When everyone has copied a design and begun the table, return to the overhead to demonstrate how patterns like these can be represented on graphs.

Show again your transparency of the Double-Step Staircase design on Student Sheet 1. Ask students to read numbers from the table as you draw the corresponding graphs: first the smaller graph showing how many tiles are in each new step (step size), then the graph on the right, showing how the total number of tiles grows. As students read each column, draw dots where graph lines intersect, showing (on the step-size graph at left) the number of new tiles used at each step (2, 4, 6, 8, 10...), and (on the totals graph at right) the total number of tiles in the pattern after each step (2, 6, 12, 20...).

If I continued the graph of the total number of tiles, on and on, how would it look? How does it compare with the graph of step size? Can you explain why these two graphs are different?

See the **Teacher Note,** The Relationship of Step Size to Total (p. 11), for a discussion of this issue.

How do the lines in these graphs show that the steps grow steadily, but the total grows faster and faster? (The step size graph is a straight line, but the total graph curves, getting steeper and steeper.)

Associating shapes of graphs with the story of growth for a pattern can be difficult; some students may need a lot of experience before the associations are clear. Students who have graphed plant growth in the grade 4 *Investigations* unit *Changes Over Time* will have made these kinds of connections.

Steady growth

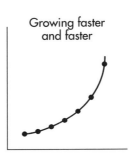
Growing faster and faster

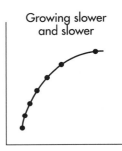
Growing slower and slower

Activity

Teacher Checkpoint

Designing a Growing Tile Pattern

Distribute the buckets of tiles. Explain that students will now be making their own designs that change in a regular way, so that someone else could continue the pattern just by looking at it.

Work in pairs to make up your own growing pattern of tiles. After you do about three steps, ask other students near you to guess how tiles should be added to your design for the next few steps. Your pattern should be regular enough so that they can predict how it will grow.

As students work, check their patterns to see if you can understand where to place the next tiles. As necessary, remind them to change colors at each new step. When a pair of students have a design that grows in a regular way, give them a copy of Student Sheet 1 to record it. They draw their design on the grid, then work together to fill out the table and the two graphs. Suggest that they check their table with another pair before starting to make the graphs (if the table has errors, the graphs will, too).

Use this activity as a checkpoint to see if students are developing the idea of making a table and graphs based on a growing tile design. Watch for students who fill out their table by continuing a number pattern they think they see in the table but that does not reflect the design. Help them refer back to the design to keep the table accurate.

Look for the following as students work:

■ Can students derive step size from the design?
■ Can they derive the total directly from the design and also from adding the new step to the previous total?
■ Can they make both graphs from the entries in their table?
■ Can they interpret the shape of a graph as showing no growth, steady growth, accelerating growth, or alternating fast and slow growth?

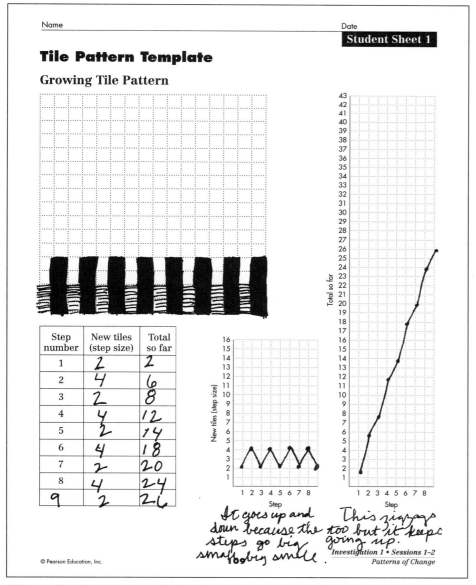

This student has created a design that grows in an oscillating pattern.

During the next two sessions, check on students who are having difficulty with the tables and graphs. Students will be making and analyzing tables and graphs throughout this unit, so it is worth taking time in this first investigation to give them a solid footing.

Before the end of class, ask students working near each other to look at each other's designs and decide how they are changing.

Does the step size grow, or stay the same, or change in some other way? Does the total grow steadily, or faster and faster, or change in some other way?

Students write a general description of the growth patterns of their tile design—both for the steps and for the overall design.

❖ **Tip for the Linguistically Diverse Classroom** Students may describe the growth patterns orally to you, pointing to the elements they have recorded on Student Sheet 1.

If students feel ready, they might write general rules for the step size and the total. See the **Teacher Note**, Finding General Rules for Step Size and Total (p. 12), for more information.

Sessions 1 and 2 Follow-Up

🏠 **Homework**

Growing Tile Patterns After Session 1, send home the family letter or *Investigations* at Home booklet. Students also take home Student Sheet 2, Growing Tile Patterns. They draw another pattern that changes in a regular way. They can color the patterns if they wish. They also make a table showing the step size—the number of new "tiles" (squares on the grid) they added to the pattern at each step—and the total number of tiles (squares) in the pattern after each step. They also describe generally how their tile pattern grows.

Growing and Graphing Tile Patterns After Session 2, students take home Student Sheet 3, Growing and Graphing Tile Patterns. They draw one tile pattern and fill in the tables and graphs. They may use any of the tile patterns discussed in class or one of their own.

The Relationship of Step Size to Total

As students investigate tile designs, they identify patterns as designs that change with a predictable regularity—that is, there is a pattern to the size of the steps. We can call the number of new tiles added at each subsequent step the *step size,* and the number of tiles in the whole design after any step the *total.*

The use of these terms here prepares students for the terminology they will be using as they graph motion and varying speed in Investigations 2 and 3. The *step size* for the tile patterns (how many tiles we add in a step) is analogous to the *step size* for a "trip" along a straight track (the distance traveled in one unit of time). The total number of tiles is analogous to the position reached by the traveler, or the total distance traveled.

For any tile pattern, the step size and the total are related but grow differently from one another. In the tile design we called the Threes Tower, the *step size* does not grow at all. It stays constant (the graph is flat), so the *total* grows at a steady rate (the graph of the total is a straight line with slope 3).

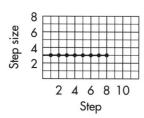

Threes Tower tile pattern

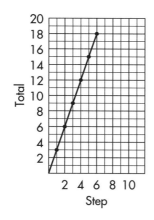

In the Double-Step Staircase design, the step size grows at a steady rate, increasing by 2 each time (the graph is a straight line with slope 2). Because each step is 2 larger than the step before, the total grows faster and faster (the graph is a curve with a steeper and steeper slope).

Double-Step Staircase tile pattern

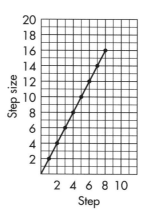

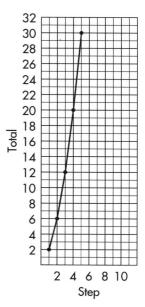

It is possible to have a decreasing step size while the total continues to increase. If we use fewer and fewer tiles each time, the step size decreases, but the total number of tiles continues to increase—although by less and less each time. If the step size continues to decrease, it will eventually reach zero and fall below zero, making the total growth stop and then decrease.

For example, imagine that we used this decreasing sequence of number of tiles:

$$4, 3, 2, 1, 0, -1, -2,\ldots$$

At first the total number of tiles would increase by 4, 3, 2, and 1; then it would stop, having an increase of 0; and finally it would decrease, because using $-1, -2,\ldots$ would mean that instead of adding tiles to the pattern, we would be taking tiles away.

Finding General Rules for Step Size and Total

As students make tables to reflect their growing tile designs, they look for patterns in the numbers that enable them to predict what the step size and the total for later steps will be. In their later study of mathematics, students will be expected to find a general rule that will work for any step number of a series (often called *n* for *number*) without finding all the terms in between. Many fifth grade students may be able to do this already for some patterns.

For example, students at this level may find general rules in the Threes Tower for both the step size (always 3) and the total (3 × step number), and in the Double-Step Staircase for step size (2 × step number). Encourage them to write the general rules they find in any informal way that makes sense. Do not push them to use *n* at this time.

When students are looking for general patterns in the tile designs, they will get different information from each of the representations: the design itself, the number table, and the graphs. The graph of totals gives an overview of the growth, showing *increase* or *decrease* or *oscillation*. It displays steady growth with a straight line and accelerating growth with a curved line.

The number table can be analyzed to see how early numbers can be used to find later ones. Students are likely to recognize patterns within columns first. For example, they may see in the table that the steps in the Threes Tower are always 3, and that for the total, we count by 3's. Later they may see that each total is made by adding the new step size to the previous total. Last of all, they may figure out how the numbers within one row are related—that we can get the total for the Threes Tower by multiplying the step number by 3, or we can get the step size in the Squares pattern (Student Sheet 4, page 2) by doubling the step number and subtracting 1.

To find a general pattern, it is often most helpful to look at the design itself. For example, to make the next larger step in the Squares pattern, we add a row of tiles along the top, a column along the side, and one additional tile in the corner; this is doubling the previous step number and adding 1. We might get a slightly different rule from the table: double the current step number and subtract 1. Both rules are equally descriptive of relationships in the pattern.

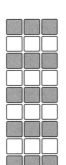

Step number	New tiles (step size)	Total so far
1	3	3
2	3	6
3	3	9
4	3	12
5	3	15
6	3	18
7	3	21
8	3	24
9	3	27

Threes Tower tile pattern

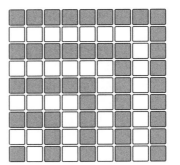

Step number	New tiles (step size)	Total so far
1	1	1
2	3	4
3	5	9
4	7	16
5	9	25
6	11	36
7	13	49
8	15	64
9	17	81

Square tile pattern

Continued on next page

Finding the general rule for the total number of tiles is difficult for the Double-Step Staircase pattern and for the Staircase pattern on Student Sheet 4. Avoid posing this as a question for the whole class or you will be off on a detour that may prove frustrating for many students. However, some students may be interested in these patterns; in one class, one pair worked for 20 minutes on the rule for the Double-Step Staircase total instead of going on to make a pattern of their own. They came to the conclusion (from analyzing the table) that you multiply each step number by the next step number to get the total.

One way to look into the totals for the Double-Step Staircase is to move tiles from taller columns to shorter ones to get the same number in all columns (see the diagram).

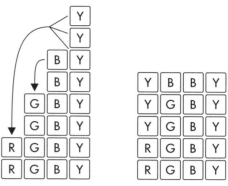

If you put 3 yellows with the reds and 1 blue with the greens, you make 4 columns of 5 tiles.

After step 2, we have an average of 3 tiles in each column and a total of 6 (2 × 3); after step 3 we have an average of 4 tiles in each column and a total of 12 (3 × 4); after step 4 we have an average of 5 tiles in each column and a total of 20 (4 × 5). Each total continues to be the product of the step number and the step number plus 1.

If any students find a pattern for the Double-Step Staircase and present their method to the class, you might show this averaging as another way to approach the pattern; or you might show it just to the students who worked out their own approach.

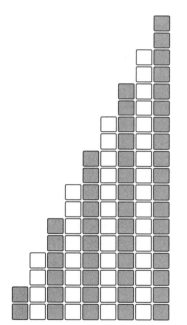

Step number	New tiles (step size)	Total so far
1	2	2
2	4	6
3	6	12
4	8	20
5	10	30
6	12	42
7	14	56
8	16	72
9	18	90

Double-Step Staircase tile pattern

Four Growing Tile Patterns

Materials

- Student Sheet 4 (four pages: 1 set per student plus transparencies of the Twos Tower and Squares patterns)
- Square tiles in mixed colors (1 bucket per 6–8 students)
- Markers, pencils, or crayons in the tile colors
- One-centimeter graph paper (2 sheets per group of 3–4)
- Overhead projector
- Transparent tiles for overhead (optional)
- Large paper for posters, scissors, tape
- Student Sheet 5 (1 per student, homework)

What Happens

Students analyze four tile patterns with these growing totals: 2, 4, 6, 8,...; 1, 4, 9, 16,...; 1, 3, 6, 10,...; and 2, 6, 14, 30,.... In tables and on graphs, students show how the tile patterns and the number series grow (whether at a steady or accelerating rate). Small groups investigate one of the four patterns in depth. They make a poster that shows the tile pattern shapes, a table, two graphs, and a written description of how their pattern grows. Student work focuses on:

- extending tile patterns
- making tables and graphs of step size and totals
- comparing graph shapes and explaining the differences
- investigating number sequences
- making several growing designs to fit the same table of numbers
- finding the nth term of a series

 Ten-Minute Math: Nearest Answer   In any spare 10 minutes outside of the regular math instruction period, do this Nearest Answer activity for ongoing practice with percents.

Select two or three Nearest Answer percent problems from p. 94 or prepare a few of your own, including answer choices, for display on a transparency or at the board. For example:

| 26% of 77 = | 20 | 40 | 50 | 100 |

| 38% of 21 = | 5 | 8 | 11 | 60 |

Keeping the answer choices covered at first, show the problem for 20 to 30 seconds. Students work mentally, using familiar percents to help them arrive at an estimated answer for the problem. For example, they might think:

26% of 77 is about 25% (¼) of 80, or 20.

38% of 21 is about 40% (⅖) of 20, or a bit larger than 33⅓% (⅓) of 21—close to 8.

Uncover the answer choices. Students choose the answer they think is the closest. Ask a few students to share their strategies for estimating an answer.

For complete instructions and variations on this activity, see p. 93.

Making Tables and Graphs for Tile Patterns

Hand out the four pages of Student Sheet 4, Growing Tile Patterns, to each student and distribute the tiles for groups to share. Students extend each tile pattern and fill out the tables and graphs as they did in the last session.

Students will have the rest of this session and part of the next one to work on the four pages. Caution them not to rush, and encourage them to consult with their classmates frequently or even work together throughout the activity. Students tend to be more careful with this work when they have to explain their thinking and get the agreement of a partner.

Before you draw a graph, check with your neighbors to be sure you agree about the numbers you have written in the table.

Circulate to help as students get started. Refer to the **Teacher Note,** Four Patterns (p. 22), for information about each pattern. Check to be sure students are extending the patterns correctly. For the Staircase pattern, some students may predict totals of 1, 3, 6, 9, 12,... instead of 1, 3, 6, 10, 15,... because from a quick look at the table, they have decided the totals are multiples of 3.

As students work, find out how they are filling in the tables. Pick out a row of a table and ask a student to tell you what the three entries mean. For example, in the fifth step of the Squares pattern, we use 9 new tiles (4 each for the top and side of the 4 by 4 square and 1 for the corner), and have a total of 25 tiles (5 rows of 5). In the fifth step of the Staircase, we take 5 (the same as the step number) and have a total of 15 (1 + 2 + 3 + 4 + 5).

When students seem ready, ask them if they can think of a way to get the *step size* and the *total* for any number without filling in all the steps on the table. Ask about steps beyond those on the table.

In the Squares pattern, how many new tiles will you use in the twentieth step? What will the total be? How did you figure it out?

The **Dialogue Box,** Finding General Rules for the Staircase Patterns (p. 24), illustrates how students in one class began thinking about general rules.

Although the names we have given to these four patterns suggest specific shapes, let students know that the tile patterns they are investigating do not *have* to look exactly like these. In the next session, they will have a chance to build different growing shapes that fit these same tables of numbers.

For example, the Staircase pattern is the "triangle" numbers (1, 3, 6, 10, 15,...), growing in larger and larger steps each time. When we make a column of each new step, the pattern looks like a staircase. Students often arrange the same numbers of tiles to make diagonals instead.

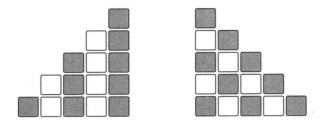

Rearranging the tiles in a pattern might help students find a general rule. However, when they do this, they must be sure to use the same step sizes in the same order as in the original design.

Comparing Graph Shapes

Toward the end of Session 3, bring students together to discuss their work on the four patterns on Student Sheet 4. Put the transparency of the Twos Tower on the overhead. With students' guidance, continue the pattern on the grid and fill out the table and graphs. Then ask about the shapes of the two graphs.

How do the different graphs show growth? Does either graph show no growth? Why is that? Which graph shows steady growth?

Do the same for the Squares pattern, and ask students to compare the two graphs for this pattern.

Which graph shows growth that is accelerating—growing faster and faster? How does that look different from the graph that shows steady growth?

This analysis is the heart of this activity. All these problems have a fixed solution, but how students think about the patterns and compare them shows their understanding of the important concepts presented here.

Suggest that students write under each graph how the pattern is changing: not growing at all, growing steadily, or growing faster and faster.

Which graphs look similar? Why are they similar?

Ask students to write about any general rules they have figured out. They can write on the backs of the student sheet pages if they need more room.

How would you figure out the step size and total for the next step? How would you figure out the step size and total for a much bigger step number, such as 20 or 100? Write anything you can say about this.

❖ **Tip for the Linguistically Diverse Classroom** Pair English-proficient students with those for whom English is a second language and let them do this task together.

Investigating a Pattern in Depth

Write on the board the first four numbers of the step-size sequence for the four patterns students have been exploring:

Twos Tower	Squares	Staircase	Doubling
2, 2, 2, 2,...	1, 3, 5, 7,...	1, 2, 3, 4,...	2, 4, 8, 16,...

Ask students how you could continue each series for a few more steps.

Explain that students will be working in groups to continue to investigate one of these four number series. You will tell them which series their group will explore. They will make a poster displaying information about the series.

One of the things each group must show on their poster is different tile patterns that grow with the same series of numbers. To illustrate this, recall the Double-Step Staircase from an earlier session, with the step-size number series 2, 4, 6, 8... Here are three other designs that grow in the same number pattern:

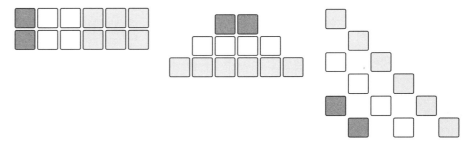

You might illustrate these alternative patterns at the overhead with transparent tiles or draw them on transparent grids.

Provide each group with large paper for the poster background. Also make available crayons, markers, or colored pencils in the tile colors, centimeter graph paper, scissors, and tape. Students can use these to make tile patterns and graphs, cutting them out and taping them on the poster. Tables might be drawn directly on the poster.

List on the board or on chart paper some of the things students could include on their posters to show how their series changes as it grows.

On your poster, try to teach something about growing tile patterns to someone who is not in this class. Think about how you might teach a parent or a brother or sister. Your poster might include the following:

- Pictures of several tile patterns that grow with this same series (the one on the student sheet plus others).

- A table, showing number of new tiles added (step size) and total tiles used so far, up to 10 steps. If you know how to find step size and/or total for higher numbers, such as 20 or 50 or 100, show them on your table, too.

- A graph of step size vs. step number

- A graph of total (tiles) so far vs. step number

- A written description of how the pattern grows, using your tile designs, table, and graphs. Does it grow taller? wider? both? Does the pattern increase in size steadily, or faster and faster, or slower and slower? How can you tell by looking at the table? How can you tell by looking at the graphs?

- A description of any methods you used to find next numbers in the table, or to find step size or totals if you skipped to higher numbers.

❖ **Tip for the Linguistically Diverse Classroom** Students might use symbols to represent steady growth, faster and faster growth, and slower and slower growth. They could work out their own symbols, making sure you understand, or work as a group to establish symbols they are satisfied with. Students can circle key parts of their graphs and tables to show what the symbols relate to. The whole class will give thought to this kind of symbolic representation in Investigation 2.

Assign the four patterns so that each pattern is investigated by one or more groups. You may want to take into account level of difficulty (from easiest to most difficult: Twos Tower, Squares, Doubling, and Staircase). If some students are reluctant to do the Twos Tower because it seems boring, or if you need *more* easy patterns, suggest students do a Ones Tower, a Twos Tower, and a Threes Tower, and compare the graphs for all three. If you need an additional difficult series, include the Double-Step Staircase from Session 1 or suggest that students investigate a Triple-Step Staircase (adding 3, 6, 9, 12,…).

As groups begin work on their poster, check to be sure they understand the task and that they are all participating and making an effort to share the work. Once students have made a table up to the tenth step, suggest they make a row for the twentieth step and try to fill it in without counting all the steps between 10 and 20. This may be too difficult for some of the patterns, so avoid pressuring students to do this. If they can explain how to find the twentieth step, ask them how they could find the numbers for any step (the nth step). To demonstrate, they write in their own words how to get the step size and the total for the nth step.

Presenting the Posters

At the end of these sessions, or when all the groups have had time to make their posters, arrange for groups to present their posters to the whole class. Groups who investigated the same series might make their presentations together, taking turns showing what they found out about that series.

Display the posters in the hall where other classes can see them.

Sessions 3 and 4 Follow-Up

 **Homework**

Same Numbers, Different Pattern   After Session 3, students staple together and take home their work on Student Sheet 4, Growing Tile Patterns, and a copy of Student Sheet 5, Same Numbers, Different Pattern. They choose one pattern from Student Sheet 4 and draw different growing patterns on Student Sheet 5 that also fit the numbers in the table. Students may be able to use some of their new tile patterns on their posters in Session 4. They must be sure to bring all of Student Sheet 4 back to class for discussion during Session 4.

Reviewing Work   After Session 4, students take home their folder of work from Investigation 1. They spend time checking it over, making corrections and finishing any incomplete pages. They might select their favorite tile pattern to keep in their work portfolio.

Tile Designs to Fit Descriptions   Write on the board phrases that describe ways that a growing tile pattern can change, either in its step size or in its totals. For example:

 **Extension**

Grows steadily   Grows faster and faster   Grows slower and slower

Shrinks steadily   Shrinks slower and slower   Shrinks faster and faster

Grows and then shrinks   Oscillates between growing and shrinking

Distribute centimeter graph paper. Students use this to make (1) a tile design whose total or step size changes in a way that fits one of the descriptions, and (2) a graph that fits the same description. They then write a description of the overall pattern they have made.

The Two Towers, Squares, Staircase, and Doubling patterns are intriguing examples of the fusion between geometry and numbers. As students experiment with them, they will see the patterns from many different perspectives. For some patterns, they will be able to verbalize a general rule for finding step size and total at the nth step; for other patterns, this will be too difficult.

Twos Tower   The general rules for the Twos Tower are similar to the rules for the Threes Tower presented in Session 1. The pattern has a horizontal line graph for the step size (step size = 2 always) and a straight line graph for the totals (total = 2 × step number).

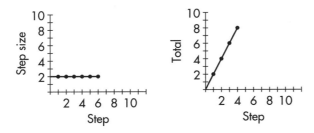

Step number	New tiles (Step size)	Total so far
1	2	2
2	2	4
3	2	6
4	2	8
step number n	always 2 2	twice the step number $2n$

Students are likely to figure out the general rules for this pattern. You can use the totals in this example to help students understand the idea of finding a general rule that can be used for any step.

If you know the step number, what calculation can you do to find the total? What is the total for step 100? for step 50? How did you figure that out?

Squares   In the Squares pattern, the step size (number of tiles added each time) grows at a steady rate, while the total number of tiles grows at an increasing rate.

Step number	New tiles (Step size)	Total so far
1	1	1
2	3	4
3	5	9
4	7	16
step number n	1 less than twice the step number $2n - 1$	step number multiplied by itself n^2

Finding the totals (the step number multiplied by itself, or squared) may be easier than finding the step size. Refer the students to the actual tiles, or to the picture on grid paper, to explore the number of tiles added at each step.

When you add new tiles to make a bigger square, where do you put them? How can you know how many you need by looking at the square that is already there?

Staircase   For the Staircase pattern, the numbers for the totals (1, 3, 6, 10, 15,...) are often called triangle (or triangular) numbers because the steps of the pattern can be arranged as a triangle.

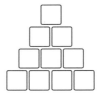

Continued on next page

Step number	New tiles (Step size)	Total so far
1	1	1
2	2	3
3	3	6
4	4	10

step number n	same as step number n	multiply the step number by the *next* step number, then divide by 2 $\frac{n \times (n + 1)}{2}$

As is true of the Squares pattern, the total number in the Staircase pattern grows at an increasing rate, while the step size grows steadily. The number of tiles added at any step is the same as the step number, but the general rule for the total is much more difficult to figure out, and students should not be expected to find it.

If some students want to figure out the general rule for the Staircase total, suggest that they first try finding the general rule for the total in the Double-Step Staircase, then compare the numbers for the two patterns. The numbers for step size and total in this Single-Step Staircase are half as big. In the Double-Step Staircase, the total was the step number multiplied by the *next* step number: $n \times (n + 1)$.

Alternatively, suggest that students investigate the size of the rectangle that the Staircase is half of. (It is half of a rectangle made by *that* step number multiplied by the *next* step number; for example, if you put two of the staircases with three steps together, you can make a 4×3 rectangle.)

Doubling The Doubling pattern is an example of one for which both the total and the step size grow exponentially. A related example of exponential growth would be as follows: One person tells a story to two others, and each of them tells two others, and each of them tells two others, and so on. The step-size numbers are powers of two: $2 = 2^1$, $2 \times 2 = 2^2$, $2 \times 2 \times 2 = 2^3$, ..., 2^n.

Step number	New tiles (Step size)	Total so far
1	2	2
2	4	6
3	8	14
4	16	30

step number n	2 raised to the power of the step number 2^n	2 raised to the power of the *next* step number, then subtract 2 $2^{n + 1} - 2$

Both general rules for the Doubling table are too difficult for most fifth grade students to figure out on their own. However, once students see the pattern of multiplying by 2 again and again, they may enjoy it and want to go on doubling to get higher and higher step sizes.

You might take suggestions from students for a title for this shape. The name "Doubling" describes what is happening to the step size, but is not descriptive of the overall shape.

Finding General Rules for the Staircase Patterns

These students have been working on Student Sheet 4, Growing Tile Patterns. The teacher stops them to hold a brief discussion on the Staircase pattern. When asked how they are deciding what numbers to fill in, the students offer a variety of approaches and generalizations.

Staircase

Step number	New tiles (Step size)	Total so far
1	1	1
2	2	3
3	3	6
4	4	10
5	5	15
6	6	21

Tai: The step size is like the same as the step number, because you take one more every time. It starts from 1, and then 2, and 3, and then 4, and then 5, and then 6, and then 7, and 8, and then 9. Whoa [*indicating there's no more room on the table*]—way overboard!

Jeff: The total is 1, 3, 6, 9, and stuff. Threes, remember?

Look at your tile pattern again. How many tiles are there, total, after you add yellow [*the fourth step*]? How many after you add red again? Count carefully to check your totals. Amy Lynn?

Amy Lynn: First I saw a pattern. The total just goes up by 1, 2, 3, 4, 5, 6, 7. See the 1; it has no number on top of it, so it just equals 1. And then 1 from here [*indicates total column*] with 2 from here [*indicates step size column*] equals 3, and then 3 and 3 equals 6, so you just keep adding [*the previous total to the new step size*].

Katrina: Another pattern we saw is, look up here [*indicates totals*]. To get from 1 to 3 is 2. Then it'd take 3 to get to 6, and then 4 to get to 10. So add 2 to get from 1 to 3, then add 3 to get from 3 to 6, then add 4, and then add 5. And it keeps going.

Anything else about the totals?

Noah: It'll be curved on the graph. 1, 3, 6, 10, 15 and then it would just go bigger and bigger off the top.

Is there a way to find the numbers at the tenth step?

Marcus: I wrote *n* plus previous *n*'s equal the total.

If you know this pattern, you can do that, absolutely. I guess my question is, What if it were the 126th step? Is there a way to figure it out no matter what step it is?

Yu-Wei: Yeah. You'd hafta know the step before. I sorta thought I found a pattern too, but it doesn't really work because you need to know what the last step was.

Articulating a general rule is difficult for these students. Following the rule that they generated would require a lot of computation for higher-numbered steps. The teacher thinks some of the students are ready to investigate a complicated general rule, but not one as difficult as the Staircase pattern.

While the rest of the class continues to work on the patterns on Student Sheet 4, the teacher has a special project for those who are ready: Look for a general rule for the Double-Step Staircase pattern they talked about in the previous session. After about half an hour, one pair finds a general rule that doesn't quite work.

Continued on next page

Double-Step Staircase

Step number	New tiles (Step size)	Total so far
1	2	2
2	4	6
3	6	12
4	8	20
5	10	30
6	12	42
7	14	56

Jasmine: We think we've got it. Yeah, because *[without looking at the table]* 1 times 2 is 2. Then 2 times 3 is 6 for the total up to that row. 3 times 4 is 12. 4 times 5 is 20. 5 times 6 is 30. 6 times 7 is 42. 7 times 8 is 56. And 8 times whatever. 9 times 10 would be 90.

What about the twentieth step? What arithmetic should I do to find the total after the twentieth step?

Marcus: 19 times 20'd be…

[The teacher covers the seventh row with her hand.] **What if *n* is 7?**

Marcus: 42.

Jasmine *[looking at the now uncovered table]:* No, it's 56. Oh, it's 7 times 8.

Take some more time to think about the rule.

Jasmine *[a little later]:* We got it this time. Say the step number is 50, you do 50 times 51, which'd be… 50 times 50 is 2500 and then 1 more 50'd be 2550. So if 50 is *n*, then 51 is $n + 1$, so it's *n* times *n* plus 1.

How did you figure that out?

Jasmine: Well, before we were doing the step number times the number on the line above it, but we were going the wrong way. You have to do it by the *next* number. That's the one below it on the table, but it comes after it. It's a higher number.

Motion Stories, Graphs, and Tables

What Happens

Session 1: Describing Changing Speeds
Students plan and act out trips of varying speeds along a straight line track. They develop ways to record the trips, without using words, clearly enough so that someone who has not seen the action can describe the trip. Students interpret and critique one another's representations.

Session 2: From Beanbags to Tables Students record their trips along a track by dropping beanbags at two-second intervals. They make tables and diagrams showing where the beanbags landed. Students then exchange their work and try to describe each other's trips by interpreting the tables and diagrams.

Session 3: Tables for Stories Each student makes a table for one of three motion stories, showing where beanbags might have dropped at regular time intervals. Students exchange tables and decide which motion story belongs with the table they receive.

Session 4: Graphs for Tables Working from the table they made in Session 3, students make a line graph of distance versus time. As they did with the tables, they exchange graphs and decide which motion story best fits the graph they receive. Students compare graph shapes that represent the same story to identify common characteristics.

Session 5: Stories, Tables, and Graphs
Students match motion stories, tables, and graph shapes that describe the same trip. They make a table to go with one of the graphs and write a motion story to go with another.

Mathematical Emphasis

- Exploring relationships among distance, time, and speed
- Exploring irregular increases and decreases in speed
- Exploring ways that speed, time, and distance can be represented with tables, graphs, stories, and informal representations
- Interpreting intervals in a table as reflecting speed
- Interpreting steepness in a distance vs. time graph as reflecting speed
- Associating tables, graphs, and stories of the same event

What to Plan Ahead of Time

Materials

- Wide (2-inch) masking tape (see Other Preparation): about 50 meters (Session 1)
- Unlined paper (Sessions 1, 3, and 5)
- Markers, crayons, or colored pencils (Session 1)
- Timepieces that show seconds: 1 per 4–6 students (Sessions 1–2)
- Beanbags (see Other Preparation): place about 12 of one color in a shallow container for each 4–6 students. (Session 2)
- Stick-on notes: 1 pad (Sessions 3–4)
- Overhead projector (Sessions 3–4)
- Scissors and tape or glue sticks: 1 each per pair (Session 5)

Other Preparation

- Before Session 1, find four or more places where you can lay out straight lines (or tracks) of masking tape, 8 to 10 meters long. One track must be in the classroom; others can be in the hall or outside. Mark (or have students mark) these tracks by meters and half-meters.
- Before Session 2, prepare small "beanbags" in two different colors. You can wrap beans in scraps of fabric, closed with staples or stitching. Or fill small plastic bags, doubled for strength, with beans or sand; close them with rubber bands.
- Plan some wall space to display students' tables and graphs in Session 3. Write the three motion stories from Student Sheet 9, in large lettering, as titles for the displays.

- Duplicate student sheets and teaching resources (located at the end of this unit) as follows. If you have Student Activity Booklets, copy only the items marked with an asterisk.

For Session 1
Student Sheet 6, Describing a Straight Line Trip (p. 117): 1 per student (homework)

For Session 2
Student Sheet 7, Template for Tables (p. 118): 1 per pair

Student Sheet 8, Height of a Girl (p. 119): 1 per student (homework), plus 1 transparency* (for Session 3)

For Session 3
Student Sheet 9, Three Motion Stories (p. 120): 1 per student

Student Sheet 10, Graph of a Trip (p. 121): 1 per student (homework), plus 1 transparency* (for Session 4)

For Session 4
Student Sheet 11, Graph Template (p. 122): 1 per student

One-centimeter graph paper (p. 146): 1 per student (homework, optional)

Student Sheet 12, Planning and Graphing a Trip (p. 123): 1 per student (homework)

Student Sheet 13, Another Graph Template (p. 124): 1 per student (homework)

For Session 5
Student Sheet 14, Matching Stories, Tables, and Graphs (p. 125): 1 per student

Describing Changing Speeds

What Happens

Students plan and act out trips of varying speeds along a straight line track. They develop ways to record the trips, without using words, clearly enough so that someone who has not seen the action can describe the trip. Students interpret and critique one another's representations. Student work focuses on:

- describing trips with changing speed along a straight line path
- making visual representations to describe trips
- interpreting representations of trips

Materials

- Masking tape tracks laid out on the floor (at least 4, marked by half and whole meters)
- Timepieces that show seconds (1 per 4–6 students)
- Unlined paper; markers, crayons, or colored pencils
- Student Sheet 6 (1 per student, homework)

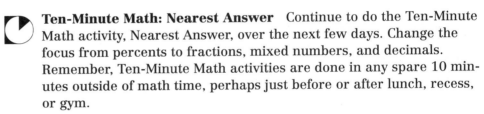

Ten-Minute Math: Nearest Answer   Continue to do the Ten-Minute Math activity, Nearest Answer, over the next few days. Change the focus from percents to fractions, mixed numbers, and decimals. Remember, Ten-Minute Math activities are done in any spare 10 minutes outside of math time, perhaps just before or after lunch, recess, or gym.

Follow the same procedure as for Nearest Answer percent problems, but choose from the fraction, mixed number, and decimal problems suggested on p. 94 or make up your own. Students are to round the numbers in the problems to the nearest whole or "landmark" numbers and estimate.

For complete instructions and variations on this activity, see p. 93.

Describing Fast and Slow Trips

Students sit where they will be able to see the motion of a person traveling along a "track" (one of the lines of masking tape you have laid out and marked by half and whole meters). Choose a volunteer to demonstrate the activity. Explain that students will move alongside the tape according to a plan that involves changing their speed.

Prepare a plan for the first trip and tell it to *only* the student who will act it out. For example: "Walk slowly about halfway, then stop for a few seconds, then run to the end."

While Sofia moves along this track, watch carefully so that afterward you can describe the trip to me. In particular, pay attention to *how* her speed changes, and *where* it changes. Watch the meter marks on the track. Where does she go fast? Where does she go slow? Where does she change speeds?

After your volunteer acts out the plan, students take turns describing the speeds in the trip.

Tell the story of the different speeds that Sofia went. Be as exact as you can. Tell at which meters she changed speeds.

If there are different interpretations, the same student acts out the trip again, and the rest of the students decide which of their descriptions is most accurate. Students discuss the trip until they agree.

For more practice, choose another volunteer to do a different trip. For example: "Run for three steps, then stop for 5 seconds, run three more steps, stop for 5 seconds, then walk slowly to the end." Again, students share their descriptions of the trip.

Representing Changes of Speed

Working in pairs or groups of three, students plan a trip along the tape track, different from the trips you just demonstrated. Instead of a verbal description, they create a visual representation of their trip. Explain the activity to the whole class, writing key instructions on the board.

With your partner, secretly plan a trip along the track. Be sure your trip has some changes of speed. Then invent a way of showing the changing speeds on paper, *without words* and *without a key*. You may make a table if you wish.

When you have shown your trip on paper, exchange papers with another pair. Try to figure out each other's trips.

While students are planning their trips, the pair that they will exchange with should not be watching. Thus, if two or three pairs must share a track, they should exchange their representations with a pair working at another track. If two pairs working at the same track will be exchanging representations, they must be careful to keep their trips secret.

Allow no more than 10 minutes for making the representations. Suggest that students keep them simple, avoiding elaborate drawings or symbols that take a long time to make. While students are working, observe and try to understand the trip they are describing. Ask for more clarity when you think it is needed, but do not expect or encourage any kind of conventional graphs.

Although students made conventional graphs to show the growth of tile patterns in Investigation 1, they are not expected to make similar graphs for this new situation. See the **Teacher Note,** Invented Representations of Trips (p. 32), for some observations about the issues students focus on and the kind of representations they typically make.

In other sessions in this investigation, students will use line graphs and tables to represent trips, just as they did for the growing tile patterns. But in this activity, students should be thinking about their *own* ways to communicate distance and speed. This is not an easy task, and it will help students appreciate the efficiency of the standard line graphs they will be making later, although they may regret the loss of some of the detail they included in their own more personalized graphs.

Tell students when time is almost up so they can finish and be ready to show their representation to the other pair.

Describing the Other Pair's Trip After each pair has had some time to discuss and interpret the representation they have received, they take turns trying to describe *and act out* the motion of the trip along the track. The pair who produced the drawing must refrain from giving any verbal hints, but they can write labels, make tables, or draw directly on their representations to make them clearer for the readers.

When both pairs have done their best to interpret each other's trip, students fix their representations to make them clearer.

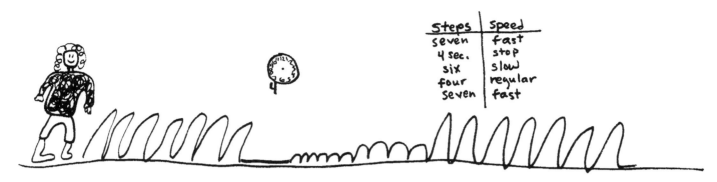

steps	speed
seven	fast
4 sec.	stop
six	slow
four	regular
seven	fast

Large-Group Sharing If there is time, arrange for students to come together in groups of eight to ten students (or as a whole class, if the class is small) to look at one another's trip representations. Student pairs take turns presenting their diagrams or drawings. They ask other students to guess what the representations mean and then explain what they were trying to communicate. Suggest that students look for good ways to show length of time, distance, changes of speed, and stopping. Look especially for ways of showing speed that can be varied easily to show different speeds.

Keep the tape tracks in place for the next session.

Displaying Representations as a Puzzle You might make a display of the students' trip representations in the hall, with all of the corresponding "stories" typed up on a separate piece of paper. Students from other classes can guess which story goes with which representation. They could write their guesses on a piece of paper tacked to the wall for this purpose.

Session 1 Follow-Up

Describing a Straight Line Trip Students take home Student Sheet 6, Describing a Straight Line Trip. They make a drawing of a straight line trip with changing speeds and ask someone at home to act it out. They make changes, if necessary, to make the trip easier to interpret, and ask the person to try again until the reader can interpret the trip correctly, working from the representation alone.

Students write a few notes on their representation about what the person did and didn't understand, and describe the changes they made to their representation.

 **Homework**

❖ **Tip for the Linguistically Diverse Classroom** Students who are not comfortable writing in English might write their notes in their primary language.

Invented Representations of Trips

Fifth grade students have many intuitions about and experiences with motion. When they are asked to represent motion on paper, they express what they regard as the important aspects of a particular trip. Students tend to include and combine the following elements in their work:

- starting position
- speed (fast, slow, steady)
- reference points (halfway, or at the sink)
- length of time
- stops along the way
- direction of the trip (forward, backward)
- final position

Students often combine pictorial and graphic aspects of motion in their representations. Some typical characteristics of students' spontaneous work include the following:

- They often represent a trip along a line drawn as if the line were the path (and may include a stick figure of a person taking the trip). Even students who have worked with two-dimensional coordinate graphs in other contexts do not think to use that technique here. They tend to use a line as one dimension to show distance, and add symbols of various sorts to show speeds. Most use a special symbol, such as a stop sign, to show no motion.

- They sometimes use discrete symbols or colors to show different speeds. Students may develop a scheme that can vary for different speeds: for example, a wavy line with higher or lower waves, larger and smaller dots, or footprints farther apart or closer together to show faster or slower motion.

- Students are most likely to use a variety of symbols, such as colors, that do not by themselves indicate speeds, and then provide a key to show meanings. They seldom use a scale to indicate speeds; if they use numbers, it is usually to indicate miles per hour.

Whether they use graphics, pictures, or both, students are symbolizing aspects of motion that they consider important in describing and understanding their trip.

One important goal of this activity is that students consider representations as a form of communication. Thinking of their graphing and use of symbols as a way to inform someone else about their trip is likely to be new for many students. By grappling with the task of representing motion, students will encounter for themselves the many problems that people have attempted to deal with by using conventional graphs and number tables.

Like language, representations exist to inform and communicate; and, like language, they can be ambiguous. In fact, when we step back to look at our representations, we may find some surprises. There may be aspects of the trip we thought we'd expressed that are not really discernible. For example, drawing a line quickly does not leave an indication of fast motion. Through revising their representations, students make them more consistent and often improve their ability to communicate. For example, in the work shown below, the students at first used numbers only to show the order of events. Later they decided to put numbers on the stop sign symbols to show how long the stops were between each set of 3 steps (the stops increase by one second each time).

From Beanbags to Tables

What Happens

Students record their trips along a track by dropping beanbags at two-second intervals. They make tables and diagrams showing where the beanbags landed. Students then exchange their work and try to describe each other's trips by interpreting the tables and diagrams. Their work focuses on:

- interpreting spacing of dropped objects as speed
- collecting and recording data in regular time intervals
- making a table of time and distance
- interpreting a table that shows accumulated distance and time
- measuring or computing intervals

Materials

- Timepieces that show seconds (1 per 4–6 students)
- Student Sheet 7 (1 per pair)
- Student Sheet 8 (1 per student, homework)
- Beanbags in two colors (12 of one color per 4–6 students, placed in shallow containers)
- Tape tracks from Session 1

Activity

Comparing Fast and Slow Trips

Ask students to gather around a marked tape track. Invite two volunteers to demonstrate the activity. Each volunteer takes a container of beanbags (each a different color so you can identify which beanbags have been dropped by each student).

Explain to the two volunteers, out of other students' hearing, that when you say "start," they will both move along the track, starting at the same end, one on each side of the track, but at different speeds. Together they agree who will walk slowly and who will walk quickly. Every time you say "drop," they will both drop a beanbag from their container. Both stop when they reach the end of the tape.

Before you begin the trips, ask the other students to turn their backs or close their eyes, but to listen carefully when you say "start" and try to figure out what you and the two demonstrators are doing. You will need a timepiece that shows seconds as you run the trips.

After you say "start," say "drop" every 2 seconds. Continue this until both students have reached the end of the tape.

Because there will be a delay in the students' reaction time, the interval from the start to the first beanbag drop will be longer than the other intervals, which should be quite regular. The fast walker's intervals (space between beanbags) will be longer than the slow walker's intervals.

At the end of the trips, the rest of the class can open their eyes and look at the track.

What do you think we were doing?

After some students guess, tell them that the demonstrators dropped a beanbag every 2 seconds.

How do you think Corey and Heather were moving along the tape? Which line of beanbags was dropped by someone moving fast? Which was dropped by someone moving slowly? How do you know?

Some students may find it confusing that the person moving fast dropped fewer beanbags with larger spaces in between (• • • • •) than the person moving slowly (• • • • • • •). One way to make sense of this is to note that the number of beanbags is a measure of time. The greater number for the slower trip shows that it took *more* time for the slower person to go the whole length; that person's time was *more* multiples of 2 seconds.

How can we figure out how long the faster walker took to go the whole length? How many seconds altogether? (It may not be possible to answer precisely; for example, in the table below, the fast walker took somewhere between 6 and 8 seconds to complete a 10-meter trip.)

How can we tell how long the slower walker took?

On the board, draw two tables like the ones below. As you fill in the 2-second intervals, students tell you the measures (to the nearest half meter) where beanbags were dropped. Record these distances in order, first for the slow trip and then for the fast trip. You might have the demonstrators re-enact each trip in 2-second segments as you record.

After the first 2 seconds, where are you? *[The walker moves to the first beanbag at the same speed as in the original trip and, with help from other students, tells you what distances to record.]* **In another 2 seconds, where are you?** *[The walker moves to the next beanbag, other students decide what the measure is, and you record.]*

Continue to the end of the trip. The measurements may resemble these, although they are unlikely to be this regular:

Slower Trip			Faster Trip	
Time	Total distance so far		Time	Total distance so far
2 sec.	1.5 m		2 sec.	3 m
4 sec.	2.5 m		4 sec.	6 m
6 sec.	3.5 m		6 sec.	9 m
8 sec.	4.5 m		8 sec.	end
10 sec.	5.5 m			
etc.	etc.			

Corey, the slower walker, dropped more beanbags because he went slower. How far apart are most of his beanbags? About how far did he usually travel in 2 seconds?

As students figure the length of the intervals (space) between beanbags for the slower walker, write them in just to the right of the table (as shown on the next page).

Heather, the faster walker, dropped fewer beanbags. About how far apart are her beanbags?

Repeat the process of figuring and noting the intervals between beanbags, this time for the faster walker.

Slower Trip		Space between beanbags
Time	Total distance so far	
2 sec.	1.5 m	1.5m
4 sec.	2.5 m	1m
6 sec.	3.5 m	1m
8 sec.	4.5 m	1m
10 sec.	5.5 m	1m
etc.	etc.	etc.

Faster Trip		Space between beanbags
Time	Total distance so far	
2 sec.	3 m	3m
4 sec.	6 m	3m
6 sec.	9 m	3m
8 sec.	end	end

As needed, clarify what you are doing here by relating it to a car trip students might have taken. Ask them to imagine that they are taking a car trip to a city that is about 4 hours away. At the start of the trip, they reset the trip odometer on the car's dashboard to 0. After every hour, they look at it. At the end of the first hour, the odometer reads 40 miles; then at the end of the next hour, it reads 98 miles; after the third hour, 151 miles; and after the fourth hour, 175 miles.

Write the numbers in a table. Ask students to tell the story of when the car went fast and when it went slowly by finding the number of miles driven each hour. Ask students to speculate about why the speed on the trip might have varied this way. For example, perhaps in the first hour they drove along streets with lots of stoplights, so they went more slowly; then they got on the highway where they could travel faster for two hours; then in the last hour, maybe they stopped for a snack.

Car Trip		miles each hour
Time	Total distance so far	
1 hr.	40 mi.	40 mi.
2 hr.	98 mi.	58 mi.
3 hr.	151 mi.	53 mi.
4 hr.	175 mi.	24 mi.

Comparing Another Two Trips Invite two students who are unsure of how to interpret the close-together and far-apart beanbags to make another trip along the tape track. Again, secretly tell the walkers how they are to move. One will walk quickly but then stop for 4 to 6 seconds and drop two or three beanbags on the same spot; the other will change speed in the middle of the trip (for example, start slowly and end quickly).

For these trips, either you or a student can time and say "drop" every 2 seconds. The rest of the students again look away or close their eyes while the trips are carried out.

After the trips, ask students to read the measures where the beanbags landed. Demonstrate again how to fill out tables with the intervals of time (every 2 seconds) and the position reached, or total distance traveled so far (in meters), and how to compute the distance traveled in each 2-second interval by finding the difference between adjacent total distances.

Briefly make clear some conventions about tables:

- **When you make tables, you start the story at the top and read down.**
- **Tables can be two or more columns. Each column needs a title telling what the numbers in it mean.**
- **Across any row of a table, the numbers are related. For example, the table for the slower walker shows that after 6 seconds, he had reached the ___-meter mark. Where was the faster walker at 6 seconds?**

See the **Teacher Note,** Tables That Show Changing Speeds (p. 40), for a discussion of the tables students typically make on their own compared to the kind of table you are teaching them to make.

Marking and Guessing Trips

For this activity, students practice making trips and guessing speeds from the placement of dropped beanbags. They work in small groups at the different tape tracks in and outside of the classroom. Designate a Group A and a Group B at each track, with two or three students in each group.

At the tape tracks, the students will first practice timing, dropping beanbags, and guessing speeds from the placement of the beanbags; then they will make tables from which others can guess the relative speeds in their trip. Four to six students (two pairs or groups of three) will work together at one tape track, taking turns acting out trips and guessing speeds. Then each pair or group of three will make a table of a trip for other students to interpret.

The two groups at each track will take turns. When it's your turn, your group makes up a trip, changing speeds along the way and dropping beanbags every 2 seconds. One person in each group will be the timer; you will say "drop" every 2 seconds. Only one traveler will take the trip and drop the beanbags. Everyone in the other group will look away while you do your trip.

When the trip is finished, the other group looks at where your dropped beanbags are and guesses where you moved fast, where you moved slowly, and whether you stopped anywhere. Take turns doing this until you are good at guessing how a trip went.

Take some time to plan your trips, secretly, before you act them out. Each group makes at least one trip and guesses at least once. Practice together reading the meters where the beanbags landed.

Be sure every group has a watch that shows seconds or a wall clock they can see clearly. When students start working, help anyone who is not clear on how to do the timing. Remind them as necessary that these trips are for just one person moving along a track, not two people as in the demonstration activity.

Observing the Students   Observe the students to see what sense they are making of this activity.

- Can students read the measures where the beanbags are dropped?
- Can they determine the lengths of the intervals? (Many students have difficulty finding the size of an interval that is not whole meters, for example, from 3.5 meters to 5 meters.)
- Can students associate the length of the interval between beanbags with the speed at which the dropper was moving?
- Can they make sense of two beanbags dropped almost in the same place, showing that the dropper stopped or went very slowly?

Students will need to be able to read distances along the tape track and interpret the intervals between beanbags in order to make and interpret tables. To encourage students to relate the intervals between beanbags to varying speeds, ask:

About how long is the interval between beanbags when you walk slowly? Show me how you know.

About how long is the interval between beanbags when you run?

How do the beanbags look when they were dropped while someone was stopped?

If some students are not getting clear patterns, advise them to work on simpler motion stories; for example, "Go fast most of the way and then finish very slowly."

Encourage groups to move on to making tables (the next activity) as soon as they are ready.

Making Tables to Show Trips

As students are ready, give each group a copy of Student Sheet 7, Template for Tables. Each group plans a trip and makes a table for the trip, showing the landing place of each beanbag. Students have several choices:

- making a table that shows where the beanbags dropped during a practice trip in the previous activity
- running another actual trip and recording measurements in a table
- inventing a trip by laying out beanbags and recording in the table where they place them along the tape track.

At least 10 minutes before the end of the session, gather everyone back in the classroom.

Now, each of you will exchange your table with another group. Before you give your table to someone else, be sure that you could figure out your own trip from your table. You might want to make some changes to the places where the beanbags fell, to make the intervals more regular, if you think that would help someone understand your trip.

When each group has a data table they are happy with, they exchange it with another group. They guess how each other's trip goes and perhaps act it out. Then they discuss how accurately the trips were described and acted out, and what the groups had intended their tables to convey.

The group who is trying to guess the trip may want to use the track on Student Sheet 7, marking with dots where the beanbags landed, to help them understand details of the trip. If there is time, groups can do more than one trip.

Note: You will not need the tape tracks for the remainder of this investigation, but try to leave the one in the classroom in place for use at the beginning of Investigation 3. If you cannot leave it, plan to replace it for use in the first session of that investigation.

Session 2 Follow-Up

Height of a Girl   Students take home Student Sheet 8, Height of a Girl. They fill in the third column in the table and make a graph of the data. They use their work to write the story of how fast the girl grew at different ages. Students will compare their interpretations in Session 3.

 **Homework**

❖ **Tip for the Linguistically Diverse Classroom**   Instead of writing a story, students can create a pictorial or symbolic representation of the girl's growth.

Showing Trips in Episodes (What Fifth Grade Students Typically Do) While we were developing this unit, we asked students to make tables for trips along the tape tracks without demonstrating a particular kind of table to them. These students had not worked with growing tile patterns (Investigation 1), so they hadn't seen those tables, either.

Most students spontaneously made tables like A, B, or C below (each shows the same trip). They thought of a trip in pieces as they planned it: "Shakita went real slow to 2 meters. Then she went fast for 4 meters and stopped. Then she went slow to the end." They timed and recorded each piece of the trip separately.

For tables A–C, they timed someone walking from 0 to 2 meters, then going faster from 2 meters to 6 meters, then stopping, then going slowly from 6 meters to 11 meters.

Table A

Meters	Time
2	4 sec.
4	2 sec.
0	3 sec.
5	10 sec.

Table B

Meters	Steps in a meter
2	4
4	1
0	0
5	4

Table C

Meters	Speed
2	slow
4	fast
0	stop
5	slow

It is important to avoid saying that any of these tables are "wrong." There are many ways of showing a trip with number tables, and there is no general criterion to say that one is right and another is wrong; it depends on what information we want to convey. The convention that we use in this unit (explained below) is convenient and commonly used, but it is one possibility among many.

Showing Accumulated Time and Distance (What We Are Teaching) Very few fifth graders spontaneously make a table based on one unit at regular intervals, such as the 2-second intervals in table D, or the 1-meter intervals in table E. We use a model with regular

intervals so that students can interpret tables by finding time or distance in each interval, and so they can graph the numbers from the tables to show change over time.

In tables D and E, both the time and the distances accumulate so that reading across at any level shows the time passed and the distance traveled since the start. In this investigation, students make graphs that show changes in distance vs. time. In the third investigation, they also make graphs that show speed (expressed in terms of step size) vs. time.

By finding how much distance was traveled in a regular interval of time (2 seconds in table D) or how much time it took to go a certain distance (1 meter in table E), students can decide whether a person was moving slowly or quickly or was stopped.

Table D

Time	Total distance so far	Space between beanbags
2 sec.	1 m	1 m (slow)
4 sec.	2 m	1 m (slow)
6 sec.	6 m	4 m (fast)
8 sec.	6 m	0 m (stopped)
10 sec.	7 m	1 m (slow)

Table E

Distance	Total time so far	Time for last meter
1 m	2 sec.	2 sec. (slow)
2 m	4 sec.	2 sec. (slow)
3 m	4.5 sec.	0.5 sec. (fast)
4 m	5 sec.	0.5 sec. (fast)
5 m	5.5 sec.	0.5 sec. (fast)

Tables for Stories

What Happens

Each student makes a table for one of three motion stories, showing where beanbags might have dropped at regular time intervals. Students exchange tables and decide which motion story belongs with the table they receive. Student work focuses on:

- making tables of total distance in periods of 2 seconds
- analyzing intervals in tables to match tables to stories
- comparing tables of distances that fit the same story

Materials

- Completed Student Sheet 8
- Transparency of Student Sheet 8
- Overhead projector
- Student Sheet 9 (1 per student)
- Three motion stories from Student Sheet 9, written in large print for wall display
- Student Sheet 10 (1 per student, homework)
- Stick-on notes (available)
- Large, unlined paper (1 sheet per student)

Activity

Interpreting the Table of Heights

Spend five or ten minutes reviewing the homework. Begin by asking students to compare their interpretations of the table for Height of a Girl (Student Sheet 8). Show the transparency of the student sheet while you discuss it with the class. You might uncover only a few lines of the table, for example, ages 7, 8, 9, and 10, and ask students how they would describe the girl's growth during that period (steady growth, 2 inches each year). From these entries, what might they predict for the next few years if they hadn't already looked at the whole table?

Fill in the third column with the number of inches the girl grew each previous year (the first row is blank because we do not know her 6-year-old height, then 2, 2, 2,...). Slowly uncover more lines and ask students what change they see in her growth pattern. When you have uncovered the whole table, ask if the pattern makes sense.

Is this the way an actual person might grow? What is happening at the end?

Graph the heights from the table on the transparency. Use a ruler to connect the first five heights (48–56 inches) with a straight line; then shift the ruler to connect the next three heights (59–65 inches). Connect the last three points one by one; the result will be a "curve" showing that the girl's growth is slowing down.

When is the girl tallest? At what age does she reach her greatest height? How can you tell? How can you tell on the graph at what ages the girl grew fastest? Is this the same as when she was tallest?

How is the part of the graph that shows where she grew fastest different from the part that shows where she grew 2 inches a year? How can you tell that her growth slows down?

If no students point out the changes in steepness, point them out yourself.

When is the graph steepest? What does this mean?

Students should notice that when the girl is growing 3 inches a year, the graph is steeper—climbing faster—than when she is growing 2 inches a year. When she has almost reached her full height, her rate of growth slows down, and the graph becomes less steep. Don't worry if students don't seem to understand all the details at this time. Consider this an introduction to distance (or, in this case, *height*) vs. time graphs, in which changes of slope reflect changes in speed.

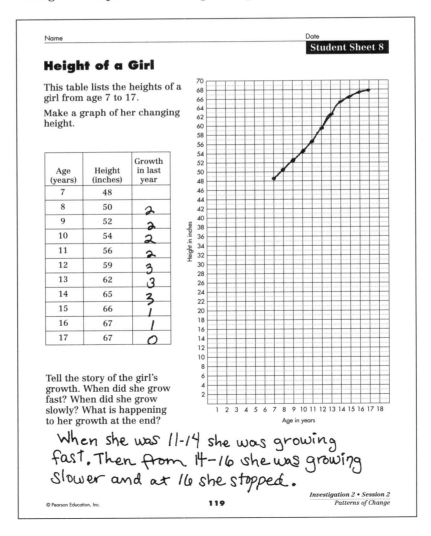

Name _____   Date _____

Height of a Girl

This table lists the heights of a girl from age 7 to 17.

Make a graph of her changing height.

Age (years)	Height (inches)	Growth in last year
7	48	
8	50	2
9	52	2
10	54	2
11	56	2
12	59	3
13	62	3
14	65	3
15	66	1
16	67	1
17	67	0

Tell the story of the girl's growth. When did she grow fast? When did she grow slowly? What is happening to her growth at the end?

When she was 11-14 she was growing fast. Then from 14-16 she was growing slower and at 16 she stopped.

© Pearson Education, Inc.   **119**   *Investigation 2 • Session 2*
Patterns of Change

Post the large prepared copies of the three motion stories. Leave space under each story for students to display the tables (and later, graphs) they make to fit the stories. Give a copy of Student Sheet 9, Three Motion Stories, to each student. Note that story C may be a challenge for some students, because the end of that trip could involve fractions of meters.

Choose one of these three stories. Imagine where the beanbags might fall along the track for that trip. Draw the beanbags on the track. Then fill in the table. If you work with a partner, do two different stories.

Observing the Students While students are working, observe to be sure their tables show the distance accumulating, rather than the distance between beanbags. Ask students to explain how their table shows each part of the story. Use this activity as a checkpoint to see how well students understand using tables of positions at regular time intervals to show speed.

■ Do students make total distances farther apart to show faster speed and closer together to show slower speed?

■ Do they make the total distance remain the same to show a stop?

After completing Student Sheet 9, each student makes a large-size copy of the table on an unlined sheet (it can be the back of used paper). They use dark ink and make the table large enough to fill the whole page, so the numbers can be seen from a distance. Then they put away Student Sheet 9 to use in the next session. Remind students to put their name on both the student sheet and their large-size table.

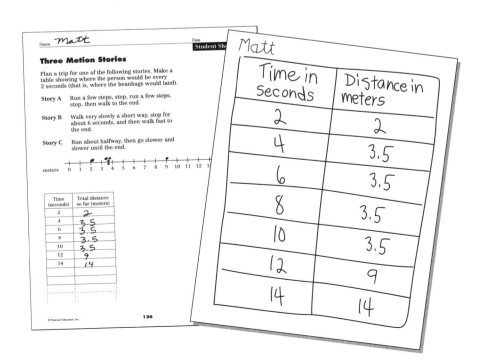

Matching Tables to Stories

Collect all the large-size tables, mix them up, and hand them out again, making sure that no students get their own or their partner's. Students figure out which story the table they received goes with and post the table under that story.

To interpret the tables, students may find it helpful to make a third column showing the intervals, titled something like "Space between beanbags" or "distance in last 2 seconds." They can compute the intervals by subtracting each distance on the table from the next. Some students may want to place beanbags along a track or sketch a track with beanbags to help them visualize the trip.

Check to see if students are able to interpret the intervals between distances to describe portions of the trip as fast, slow, or stopped.

| Story A | Run a few steps, stop, run a few steps, stop, then walk to the end. |

| STORY B | Walk very slowly a short way, stop for about 6 seconds, and then walk fast to the end. |

Kevin

Time (sec.)	Distance (m)	
2	4	4
4	4	0
6	8	4
8	8	0
10	10	2
12	12	2

Alani

Time	Distance
2	3
4	6
6	6
8	9
10	12
12	12
14	12
16	13
18	14
20	15

Ann

Time	Distance

Tai

Time in seconds	Distance meters
2	1
4	2
6	3
8	4
10	4
12	4
14	4
16	6
18	9
20	11
22	13
23	14

MARICEL

TIME	DISTANCE	
2	.5	.5
4	1.0	.5
6	1.5	.5
8	1.5	0
10	1.5	0
12	1.5	0

Similarities Among Tables

When all the tables are posted, students gather around the displays to see what the tables for each story have in common. If students are not sure that a table is placed correctly, or if they think part of a table doesn't fit the story, they can write a question on a stick-on note to place on the table.

When students have had a chance to look at the three groups of tables, they come together for a discussion of similarities in the tables. Start by drawing students' attention to one of the stories and its tables.

How do you know these tables belong with this story? What do they have in common?

Is there any table that does not belong in this group? Why do you think so? What part of the pattern of that story is missing?

Students are most likely to notice the presence or absence of stops, when the space between beanbags is 0 meters (that is, the total distance so far does not change).

Repeat this comparison of the tables for the other two stories in turn. See the **Dialogue Box,** Are They Really the Same? (p. 46), for points that students in one class discussed.

In preparation for graphing in the next session, allow time for students to correct their tables as needed to better fit the story they chose.

Session 3 Follow-Up

Graph of a Trip   Students take home Student Sheet 10, Graph of a Trip. They write the story of the trip shown by the graph. They may write notes directly on the graph to tell how the person was moving for each part—fast, slowly, or stopped. They may make a table from the graph if that would be helpful. Students will share their interpretations of the graph at the beginning of the next session.

 **Homework**

❖ **Tip for the Linguistically Diverse Classroom**   Students can draw pictures or symbols instead of writing notes to describe the speed.

Are They Really the Same?

STORY B — Walk very slowly a short way, stop for about 6 seconds, and then walk fast to the end.

Christine

Time (sec.)	Total Distance (m)
2	2
4	3.5
6	3.5
8	3.5
10	3.5
12	9
14	14

Desiree

Time (sec.)	Distance (m)
2	1
4	2
6	3
8	4
10	4
12	4
14	4
16	6
18	9
20	11
22	13
23	14

Mei-Ling

Time	Distance
2	3 m
4	5 m
6	8 m
8	10 m
10	11 m
12	12 m
14	13 m

Duc

Time	Distance	
2	2 m	2
4	3 m	1
6	3 m	0
8	3 m	0
10	3 m	6
12	9 m	6
14	14 m	5

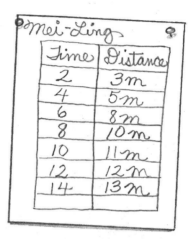

These students are considering the placement of tables to represent the three motion stories displayed on the wall. They are grappling with an important issue: When do two tables tell the same story, even though they look different from each other? When are two tables really different?

Danny: I don't think Mei-Ling's table goes with story B. It says walk very slowly for a short way, then it says stop for 6 seconds. But she keeps going.

Then what would you have put here, here, and here instead? [*The teacher points to the distances 5 m, 8 m, and 10 m on Mei-Ling's table.*]

Danny: Threes.

Mei-Ling: But I didn't make my table for story B!

OK, then this table tells a different story. Who knows which story it belongs with?

Rachel: I think it's story C: "Run about halfway, then go slower and slower until the end." But yours doesn't really go slower and slower at the end. It's the same speed.

Mei-Ling: That's right. I meant story C. I'll have to fix it.

Take a look at Christine's, Duc's, and Desiree's tables. They're all with story B. How do the tables compare to each other?

Christine: Me and Duc's are the same. We were in different parts of the room, but somehow it got the same.

How does Desiree's table differ? What does she point out?

Duc: There's more time. She figured that to get to 14 meters she needed 23 seconds. We only took 14 seconds.

Desiree's table is a bit different. But it has similarities to Christine's and Duc's too. Desiree has the person stopped for four chunks of time, just as Christine and Duc do. But what part of the story did Desiree take very seriously?

Danny: The first 6 seconds.

Zach: It has her going only 1 meter in 2 seconds, and theirs show 2 meters for the same time.

So they went a little farther when they were walking slowly.

Christine: I think it's the part where she walked fast. She went 6, 9, 11, 13, 14, and those are not sort of far apart like me and Duc's. So I think she made it more seconds.

Duc: Her trip took a longer time. Her going slow was really slow.

Desiree: It says "very slowly." I was trying to show that.

Do you agree that all three tables are ways of telling this same story with slow, stop, then faster?

Christine: Yes, but Desiree's slow is really slow, and our fast is faster than hers.

Graphs for Tables

Materials

- Transparency of Student Sheet 10
- Overhead projector
- Completed Student Sheet 9
- Student Sheet 11 (1 per student)
- Stick-on notes
- One-centimeter graph paper (1 per student, homework, optional)
- Student Sheet 12 (1 per student, homework)
- Student Sheet 13 (1 per student, homework)

What Happens

Working from the table they made in Session 3, students make a line graph of distance versus time. As they did with the tables, they exchange graphs and decide which motion story best fits the graph they receive. Students compare graph shapes that represent the same story to identify common characteristics. Student work focuses on:

- making graphs of total distance from tables of points
- matching graphs to stories and tables
- comparing graphs that fit the same story

Activity

Homework Review: Graph of a Trip

Display the transparency of Student Sheet 10, Graph of a Trip. For a couple of minutes, students explain their interpretations to their neighbors. Then a few students briefly share with the class how they knew when the person on this trip was going fast or slow or had stopped. Encourage students to describe differences in steepness or direction in their own words. Do they see two places where the person goes the same speed? Use this as an introduction to the next activity, in which students make their own graphs.

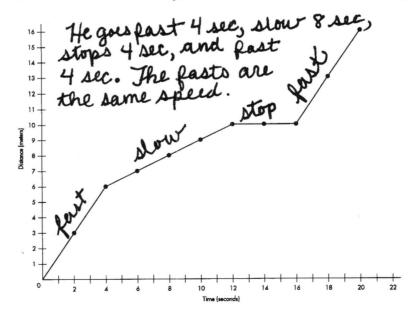

Making Graphs from Tables

Students will need their work on Student Sheet 9, Three Motion Stories, as they will be making graphs to go with their tables on that sheet. Distribute Student Sheet 11, Graph Template, to each student. Discuss with students that the numbers along the distance axis (vertical) represent accumulated distance, or distance from the beginning of the trip.

Yesterday you chose a motion story and made a table for it. Today you will use this grid to make a graph from your table.

Observing the Students   As you observe students working, ask them to explain how they show a slow speed compared to a fast speed, and how they show stopping. Check to see if students who are graphing stories A and B use a horizontal line to represent the stops. Do they understand that to show slowing down, the graph continues to go up, just less steeply? A line going down would mean *going backward.* Look for this also in graphs for story C (run, then go slower and slower). Do students' graphs continue to go up, only changing slope? If they go down when the traveler slows down, take some time to address this misunderstanding.

As students finish their graphs, encourage them to consult with partners to see that their graphs make sense.

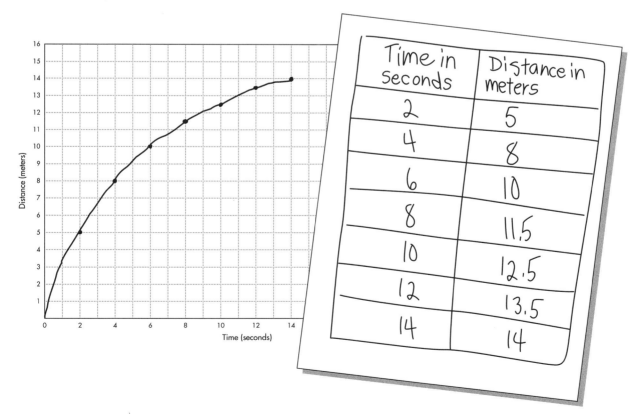

Interpreting Graphs

As you did for the tables, collect all the graphs students have made to go with the stories, mix them up, and hand them out again so that nobody gets back his or her own graph. Students post the graphs under the stories they believe they go with. Allow time for students to look at the posted graphs and to comment on them (using stick-on notes).

When students have looked over the graphs, bring them together for a discussion. Find out who thinks their own graph was misplaced. Talk with the whole class about these graphs and others that are controversial. Look for similarity of shape among graphs that go with the same story.

How can you tell when the person was going fastest? going slowest? stopped?

Session 4 Follow-Up

 **Homework**

Planning and Graphing a Trip Distribute Student Sheet 12, Planning and Graphing a Trip, and Student Sheet 13, Another Graph Template. Students plan a story of any sort of trip—walking, sailing, train, car, or other ideas they have. They write the story, then make a graph to go with it and explain how the graph shows the changes of speed that happen in the story. If they like, they might add a table to make the description of the trip clearer.

The goal is to make the story, graph, and explanation clear enough that they could be used together to teach a fourth grade student how to read the graph. You might provide centimeter graph paper to those who would prefer to use it.

❖ **Tip for the Linguistically Diverse Classroom** Let students know that they can write the story of their trip in their primary language, supplementing it with the symbols they have developed for varying speeds.

Extension

Change Over Time Students look in newspapers and other printed matter to find graphs or tables that show change over time and bring them in for display and for discussion. They might find some in foreign language newspapers and see if they can interpret them, even if they cannot read the foreign language text. Make a bulletin board of these graphs and tables. If some students bring in graphs that are not about change, designate a separate area of the bulletin board for those graphs and ask students to decide which graphs go in which area.

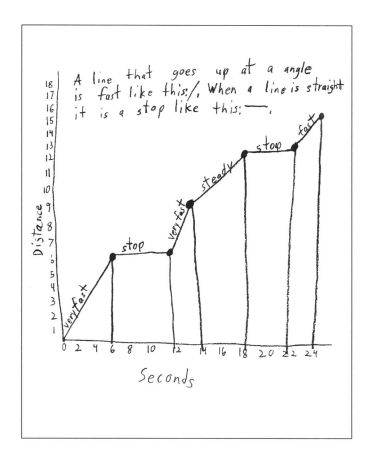

A line that goes up at a angle is fast like this:/. When a line is straight it is a stop like this:—.

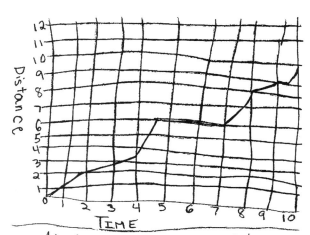

At first it's medium speed because you go 2 meters in 2 seconds. Then it's slower, a little over 1 meter in 2 seconds. Then in less than 1 second you go almost 3 meters, so it's fast. Then you stop for 2½ seconds. In the next 1 second, you go 2 meters, which is pretty fast. Then medium again, 1 m. in 1 second. You stop for a bit and then go 1m. in 1sec.

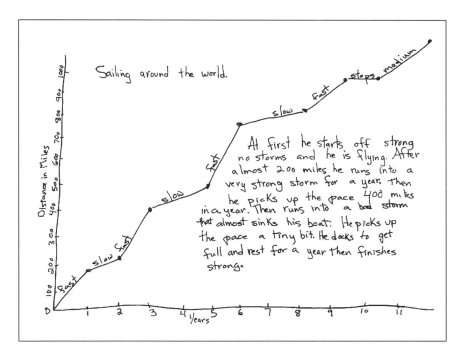

Sailing around the world.

At first he starts off strong no storms and he is flying. After almost 200 miles he runs into a very strong storm for a year. Then he picks up the pace 400 miles in a year. Then runs into a bad storm that almost sinks his boat. He picks up the pace a tiny bit. He docks to get full and rest for a year then finishes strong.

Session 4 Homework These students are explaining how to read graphs showing changes of speed. In the third example, the student's story is communicated appropriately by the graph. Despite his unrealistic choice of numbers (miles covered in a year), it is clear that this student can correctly use the conventions of graphing changes over time.

Stories, Tables, and Graphs

Materials

- Student Sheet 14 (1 per student)
- Unlined paper (3 sheets per student)
- Scissors (1 per pair)
- Tape or glue sticks (1 per pair)

What Happens

Students match motion stories, tables, and graph shapes that describe the same trip. They make a table to go with one of the graphs and write a motion story to go with another. Student work focuses on:

- relating tables and graphs of distance traveled to stories of trips
- creating a table of accumulated distance to fit a given graph and story
- writing a motion story to fit a given table and graphs

Activity

Assessment

Matching Stories, Tables, and Graphs

Hand out the two pages of Student Sheet 14, Matching Stories, Tables, and Graphs. Also make available scissors, tape or glue sticks, and unlined paper (the back of used paper is fine).

I have a puzzle for you. On these pages, you'll see three graphs, but only two stories and two completed tables. One graph has both a table and a story to go with it. One has only a table. One has only a story. The puzzle is to figure out how the stories, graphs, and tables go together. Then finish Table A and Table B, fill out Table C to fit the graph that needs a table, and write a story for the graph that needs a story.

Students cut apart the graphs, stories, and tables. They find the elements that go together and tape or glue them down in groups on the plain paper, then complete the missing parts, and fill in the table for the story that does not have one. The missing story, which goes with Graph △ and Table B, should be something like this: "Walk about halfway, then turn around and walk back." Table C goes with Graph ○ and Story 2.

Note: If you think this will be too difficult for your students to do individually, they may work in pairs or small groups and confer.

Assess individual students during the activity or after they have finished by asking them to explain how they decided a group of representations fits together. Ask students to interpret some of the tables and graphs provided by telling the story of the changing speeds.

Observing the Students   Following are some things to look for:

■ Do students look at intervals between table entries to determine speed? Do they recognize that covering larger distances in 2 seconds means greater speed? Do they show this on the table they invent, as well as when they interpret the tables provided?

■ Do students recognize steeper lines on distance vs. time graphs as representing greater speed? Do they recognize a straight ascending line as showing steady speed? Do they recognize a horizontal line as showing zero speed, or being stopped?

Session 5 Follow-Up

Reviewing Work   Before going on to the next investigation, students might collect all their work from Investigations 1 and 2, including Student Sheets 1–14 and the graph they made of a trip, and put them together in a folder. They could use these materials to explain to an adult friend or family member what they have done in these investigations.

Homework

Trips **Software**   In Investigation 3, students will begin using the *Trips* software on computers. If there is time available before the next session, invite students to explore Setting 1 on the software, trying different starting points and step sizes for the two figures to see what happens when they run their trips.

Extension

Computer Trips on Two Tracks

What Happens

Session 1: Ways of Making Trips Students discuss how we can walk faster and slower when the number of steps per second stays the same. They look at two ways of making and recording trips: marking successive "steps" along a meterstick on a paper track, and using *Trips*—a computer program with which students can vary the speed of a boy and a girl moving along parallel tracks.

Session 2: Trips on Two Tracks Students explore what happens when they change the speed and the start positions of two travelers along parallel tracks. They create graphs, tables, and lists of commands that correspond to one of three given motion stories. Students work alternately with *Trips* on the computer and with trips along metersticks.

Session 3: Different Kinds of Trips Students continue to work with the *Trips* software and with metersticks, exploring two new types of trips: one in which they can change the speed of either person at some position on the track, and one in which a person's step size can change at every step. Groups use the new trip rules to enact the same three motion stories they explored in the previous session.

Session 4: More Match-Ups Students match each other's tables and graphs (from Sessions 2 and 3) to the three motion stories, then as a whole group discuss any questions and observations about the match-ups.

Sessions 5 and 6: Two Types of Graphs
Students explore a different kind of graph, step size vs. time, discussing how to interpret different examples. Working in pairs, they prepare a set of distance vs. time and step size vs. time graphs to represent a "mystery" trip for the rest of the class to guess.

Session 7 (Excursion): Animation Students create two animated flip books, one showing a change over time, and another showing two simultaneous changes that take place at different rates. Students discuss the relationship between successive differences and rate of change.

Mathematical Emphasis

- Developing a vocabulary to discuss motion, e.g., *speed, fast, slow, steady, speed up, slow down, rate*
- Representing motion with number tables, graphs, and verbal descriptions
- Exploring the relationships between time, distance, and speed
- Connecting slope in a graph with rate of change
- Comparing relative motions
- Relating number patterns to graph shapes
- Exploring the relationship between graphs of distance vs. time and step size vs. time

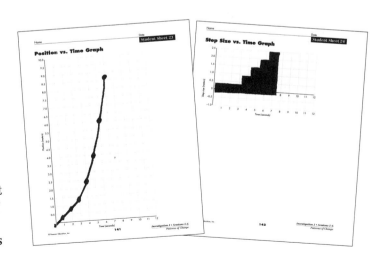

What to Plan Ahead of Time

Materials

- Adding machine tape: 5–6 meters; see Other Preparation (Sessions 1–3)
- Metersticks: 1 per group (Sessions 1–3)
- Masking tape (Sessions 1–3)
- Overhead projector (Sessions 1, 3)
- Colored markers: 2 (Sessions 1–3)
- Timepiece that shows seconds (Session 1)
- Computers with *Trips* installed
- Cuisenaire rods: 1 set of 10 for demonstration (Session 1) and 4–5 sets for student use (Sessions 2–3). Alternatively, use centimeter cubes taped together in trains from 1 to 10 cm long, or narrow strips of tagboard cut in those same centimeter lengths.
- Stick-on notes: 1 pad to share (Session 4)
- Scissors and glue or paste (Sessions 5–6)
- Stick-on notes in light colors for making flip books (2" by 3" size works well): 1 pad per student (Session 7, Excursion)

Other Preparation

- Duplicate student sheets (located at the end of the unit) in the following quantities. If you have Student Activity Booklets, copy only the items marked with an asterisk.

For Session 1

Student Sheet 15, *Trips* Computer Screen (p. 127): 1 per student and 1 transparency*

For Session 2

Student Sheet 16, *Trips* in Setting 1 (p. 128): 1 per group of 2–4

Student Sheet 17, Story of a Trip (p. 130): 1 per student (homework). Also make copies as needed for Session 3 homework (1 per student) and a Session 4 extension (1 per student).

For Session 3

Student Sheet 18, Using the *Trips* Settings (p. 132): 1 per student and 1 transparency*

Student Sheet 19, *Trips* in Setting 2 (p. 133): 1 per group of 2–4

Student Sheet 20, *Trips* in Setting 3 (p. 135): 1 per group of 2–4

For Sessions 5–6

Student Sheet 21, Two Kinds of Graphs (p. 137): 1 per student

Student Sheet 22, Mystery Walks (p. 139): 1 per pair plus some extras*

Student Sheet 23, Position vs. Time Graph (p. 141): 1 per pair

Student Sheet 24, Step Size vs. Time Graph (p. 142): 1 per pair

Student Sheet 25, What's the Story? (p. 143): 1 per student

Student Sheet 26, Graphing a Motion Story (p. 145): 1 per student (homework)

- Cut the adding machine tape into 110-cm lengths, making 2–3 demonstration strips and 6 strips per group of 2–4 students. (Sessions 1–3)

Continued on next page

■ To set up a demonstration track, lay a 110-cm length of adding machine tape on a table or the floor where everyone can gather around. Center a meterstick on the strip and lightly tape it in place. Have additional paper strips available. (Session 1)

■ Each of the Cuisenaire rods, cube trains, or tagboard strips you will be using to run trips along the metersticks need to be marked at one end to indicate the front. (Sessions 2–3)

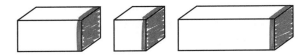

■ On the three large sheets of paper, write in large print the three motion stories found on p. 69. (Sessions 2 and 4)

■ Cut apart one copy of Student Sheet 22 so that each Mystery Walk is on a separate strip. Each pair needs one story, so for a class larger than 30, duplicate some of the strips. (Sessions 5–6)

■ To make a demonstration flip book, use about 20 pages of a 2" by 3" pad of stick-on notes. Show something changing, such as a flower getting taller and taller, or a person walking from left to right across the page. Starting with the last page and working forward is a good strategy. (Session 7, Excursion)

Computer Preparation

■ Install *Trips* on each available computer. See p. 99.

■ Read the **Teacher Note,** About the *Trips* Software (p. 64). Spend some time experimenting with the program and its three different settings before presenting it to your class. Familiarize yourself with the options available. As needed, refer to the Appendix, Computer Help for *Trips* (p. 99), for further information.

Session 1

Ways of Making Trips

What Happens

Students discuss how we can walk faster and slower when the number of steps per second stays the same. They look at two ways of making and recording trips: marking successive "steps" along a meterstick on a paper track, and using *Trips*—a computer program with which students can vary the speed of a boy and a girl moving along parallel tracks. Student work focuses on:

■ predicting trip outcomes based on step size

■ predicting how step size and starting position affect trip outcomes

 Ten-Minute Math: Graph Stories During Investigation 3, do the Graph Stories activity a few times for Ten-Minute Math.

Display a graph on the overhead (see p. 147, or use one that you have prepared or that a student has made). What story could this graph be telling? Students talk with a partner about possible stories that fit the graph and generate a story to share with the class. They identify the variable shown and tell how it changes. For example:

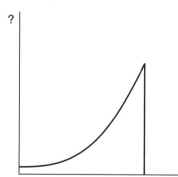

"The balloon was quickly blowing up bigger and bigger and suddenly it popped."

"The weed was growing taller and taller and then I pulled it and it stopped."

If students are having difficulty, offer some guidance: "What could be changing as time goes by? What might be growing or shrinking? going faster or slower? becoming more or less?"

Ask a few students to share their stories, explaining or showing how the story fits the shape of the graph and what is changing with time.

For complete instructions to this activity and variations on it, see pp. 96–97.

Materials

■ Student Sheet 15 (1 per student plus 1 transparency)

■ Overhead projector and pen

■ Several 110-cm strips of adding machine tape and meterstick for demonstration

■ Masking tape

■ 1-, 2-, 3-, 5-, and 8-cm Cuisenaire rods, cube trains, or tagboard strips for demonstration

■ Computers with *Trips* installed

■ Timepiece that shows seconds

■ Markers (2 colors)

Showing Speed with Step Size

Gather students around the masking-tape track left on the floor from Investigation 2. Recall the beanbag trips in that investigation.

When you took trips along these tracks before, you went at different rates of speed. Sometimes you took 1 or fewer steps per second, and sometimes you took many steps per second. This time we're going to take exactly 1 step every 1 second. Who wants to demonstrate with me?

You and a student volunteer walk side by side on either side of the tape track. Using a timer, call out "step" every 1 second. Match your step size to the student's so that you both reach the end of the track at the same time. Ask another student to keep track of the number of steps you take.

How many steps did we take to get to the end? Did we both take the same number? With both of us walking at the same rate, 1 step per second, is there any way one of us could go faster than the other? At 1 step per second, how could Leon get to the end of the track before me?

If no one suggests that the student could take *longer* steps, whisper to your student partner to do just that while you take the same size steps as before. Do the trip again, saying "step" every 1 second. Stop when the student reaches the end of the track.

Why did Leon get to the end before me that time? If I wanted to be sure that *I* reached the end first, how would I tell Leon to walk?

Students should understand that when the frequency of the steps remains the same (1 per second), the only way to show slower or faster speed is to change the step size: longer steps for faster speed, and shorter steps for slower speed.

For all the trips in this investigation, we will always use 1 step per second, and only the step size will change.

Note: Although this 1-step-per-second pace may seem artificial to students, we want to establish such a pace in this activity to simplify the way that speed can vary on a walking trip. Once we decide we will always take 1 step per second, then the only way to change our speed is to change our step size. This is the way the *Trips* program works, so this activity helps prepare the students for their work with trips on the computer.

Trips Along a Meterstick

Gather the class around your demonstration track, with the meterstick centered and taped on top of the 110-cm length of adding machine tape. Select a 5-cm and an 8-cm Cuisenaire® rod (or cube train, or tagboard strip). Be sure you have marked one end of each rod to indicate the "front end." Place one rod on each side of the meterstick.

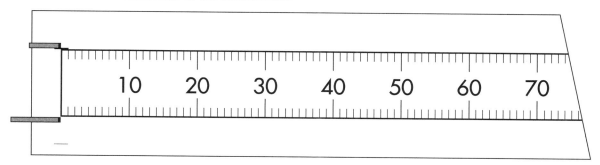

Explain that, for this activity, the rods represent two people taking trips. Each rod will take a series of "steps" equal to its length. At the start of a trip, the front of the rods will be placed just at the 0 end of the meterstick (see figure above). Mark both starting positions on the paper strip. When both rods have taken one step, they will be alongside the meterstick.

Demonstrate how students will show trips along the meterstick by moving each rod one length (one step) for each "second" (see figure below).

The shorter rod represents someone taking small steps and the longer one represents someone taking large steps. To move the rods, slide them along both sides of the meterstick to their next position, rather than turning them end-over-end or picking them up. Once you've moved the rod, put a mark at the front of it. You and your partner need to take the same number of steps, so be sure both people are ready to take a step at the same time.

Invite students to run trips the same way, with one person in the group taking responsibility for calling out "Step" to indicate when both rods should be moved. Otherwise, there may be problems with the two students moving the two rods at different rates. After each step, students pause to record the position of the front of the rod with a mark on the paper strip, using a different color for each rod.

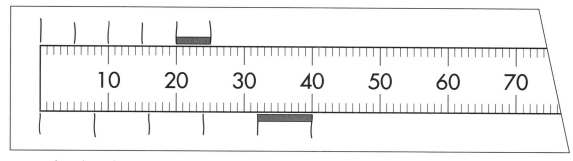

Meterstick, rods, and paper strip after 5 "steps"

After taking several steps, ask students to describe how this trip relates to the walking trips you took with the student volunteer. Also ask them to describe any patterns in the marks you have made on the paper strip. Some of the patterns they may notice include the regular spacing of the marks on both sides of the meterstick, the difference in the size of the spacing of marks on the two sides, and the way marks on the two sides of the meterstick may sometimes coincide. Students may see other patterns as well.

What will happen as the trip continues?

To mark a new pair of trips, remove the meterstick from the paper demonstration strip and turn the strip over (or use another strip). Tape the meterstick, centered, on the clean strip. Now demonstrate another kind of trip, in which one of the rods does not start at the beginning of the meterstick, but partway along it (see figure below). The trip that starts later will have marks only from its starting place.

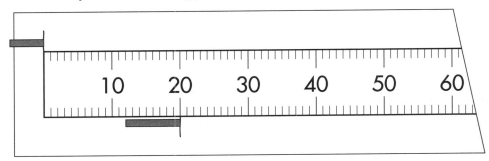

Trip with one starting position at 0, the other at 20

In the next session, you will be planning trips both on and off the computer. When you are working off the computer, you'll use a meterstick on a strip of paper, just as I've shown you. You'll put a rod on either side of the meterstick. Two students will move the rods, sliding them along the stick as one of them calls out "Step." They must make sure to take their steps at the same time, so that both are taking the same number of steps per "second." After each step, you'll mark the rod's progress on the paper strip.

As necessary, reassure the students that it doesn't matter if they take longer than 1 real second to move the rods and make the marks, as long as they keep moving both rods together at the same time. In other words, both rods take exactly the same number of steps in the same amount of time. Remind them to keep the marked end of each rod at the front and to mark the rod's progress after each step.

Trips on the Computer

Note: Be sure you have read the **Teacher Note**, About the *Trips* Software (p. 64), and have experimented with the program yourself before presenting it to the students.

Introduce the computer program *Trips* to the class using a computer and a projection device for screen display. If you do not have a projection device, gather students around the largest monitor available. If your computer display is very small or you do not have access to a computer for this activity, display a transparency of Student Sheet 15, *Trips* Computer Screen.

Distribute copies of Student Sheet 15. This illustration reproduces the *Trips* screen as it appears in Setting 1. The title bar in the main window indicates that you are in Setting 1 (Boy & Girl Start & Step); it will say "Untitled" unless you save your work.

On the computer, you are going to work with a program called *Trips*. You'll see two tracks where a boy and a girl walk, taking steps at exactly the same time, 1 step per second.

You'll notice that time runs fast in *Trips*, so 1 second for the boy and the girl is much shorter than it is for us in real time. This makes it easier for us to watch, because it all happens faster. But for the purpose of the tables and graphs, we will pretend that both the boy and girl are walking exactly 1 step per second.

Direct students' attention to the Command window on the computer or on Student Sheet 15.

The words and numbers in this window are commands. They are setting up a trip for the boy and girl, telling them how to move along the tracks from the house to the tree. Let's talk about how this trip will go.

```
startboyposition 0
startboystep 2
startgirlposition 10
startgirlstep 1
```

What do you think the boy and girl would do to follow the instructions in the Command window?

As students give their ideas, demonstrate with the meterstick and paper track, using 1-cm and 2-cm Cuisenaire rods for the boy's and girl's steps. According to the commands, the boy starts at position 0 and walks with a step size of 2. The girl starts *not* at 0, but at 10 on the track. Her step size is 1.

Show this by placing the 2-cm rod (for the boy) on one side of the meterstick, with the marked end of the rod at 0. Place the 1-cm rod (for the girl) on the other side, with the marked end of the rod at 10 cm. Mark each starting position on the paper strip, and mark a few steps as you move each rod to demonstrate the trip. If possible, run the trip on the computer by clicking on the **Go** button. Discuss the results of the trip.

Next, show how to set up a new trip by changing commands. Demonstrate on the computer or use the transparency of Student Sheet 15.

We can change the step size and the starting position of both the boy and the girl just by changing the numbers in the commands. We put the cursor at the end, like this:

```
startboyposition 0|
```

Then we use <Delete> or <Backspace> to erase the number, and then type a new one. Suppose that I change it like this:

```
startboyposition 50
startboystep 1
startgirlposition 0
startgirlstep 3
```

What will the boy and the girl do now? Who will get to the tree first with this set of commands?

Set up 1-cm and 3-cm Cuisenaire rods on the meterstick according to these commands: The 1-cm rod for the boy (small steps) starts at 50, and the 3-cm rod for the girl (larger steps) starts at 0. Ask the class to count seconds as you take steps along the meterstick with the two rods. Mark the steps as you move the rods, using a different color pen for each rod. After a few steps, ask:

Who do you think will get to the end first?

Volunteers move the rods through the rest of the trip to see whose prediction is correct. As necessary, remind them that the boy and girl take their steps at exactly the same time.

Could you tell me the story of that trip, from your point of view, as an observer?

One possible response would be: The girl is going really fast. She catches up to and passes the boy, who is going slow.

Now let's think about the story of the same trip from the point of view of the *girl*. If I were the girl, I might tell the story of the trip this way:

I started out way behind the boy, who was already halfway to the end by the time I got going. So I went really fast and caught up to him more and more. Finally, at 75, I passed him. Then I kept going really fast and got to the end first.

Ask for a volunteer to retell the story once again, this time from the point of view of the *boy*. Make sure that students understand the idea of talking as if they were the boy rather than speaking as an observer.

On Computer

Exploring the *Trips* Software

Note: For information on how you might structure students' access to computers depending on computer availability, see the **Teacher Note**, Managing the Computer Activities (p. 67).

Students spend the rest of Session 1 getting acquainted with the *Trips* software. Two to three pairs of students gather around a computer and take turns running the trips. The first pair plans a trip for the boy and girl by filling in different values in the Command window. Before starting any trip, all the students at the computer guess who will get to the end of the track first. After all guesses are in, students press the **Go** button to start the trip.

When one pair of students has planned and run two trips, another pair takes control of the computer, and the first pair joins in guessing and watching. Students continue with this rotation until the end of class.

The goals of this first interaction are to learn how to run trips on the computer and how to change the *step size* and *start positions*. Suggest that students sometimes have the boy get to the end first, and sometimes the girl. They could also try for a tie with the boy and girl starting at different places.

Point out that as the boy and girl walk at varying speeds, a little arrow appears under their feet every 2 "seconds," as if a beanbag had been dropped at that point. The students can use the pattern of little arrows to understand what happened during their trip, just as they used the patterns of beanbags left on the floor to recreate and understand their walking trips in Investigation 2.

Trips is a computer program designed for mathematical exploration of motion. In the *Trips* activities, students control the movement of two people simulated on the computer screen, a boy and a girl. They walk along parallel tracks, numbered from 0 to 100, between a house and a tree. Their travel along these tracks is termed a "trip."

Students can define the initial position, direction, and speed of both figures with commands such as "startgirlposition 10" (meaning that the girl will start her walk at position 10 on her track). To make the girl or boy go faster or slower for a particular trip, students change the size of their steps.

Students see the data for any trip displayed in several ways: along the number-line tracks, in the table that records the boy's and the girl's changing position over time, and in a graph showing either position vs. time or step size vs. time for both walkers. These representations are connected so that when one is manipulated, changes in the others can be observed.

Using *Trips,* students investigate relationships involving change and motion: What happens if we change the speed of the girl? What happens if we change the starting position of the boy? What if we change the girl's speed part way through the trip? What if we change direction?

Starting Up Trips To open the *Trips* program, double-click on the *Trips* icon located in the Patterns of Change folder (Macintosh) or click on the Start menu and select Programs\Investigations\Patterns of Change\Trips (Windows).

Trips

When the opening screen appears, click on the window to proceed. The *Trips* program will open with the Trips window, Command window, Graph window, and Table window displayed.

Running a Trip Students have a choice of three "settings" that run different kinds of trips (further described in the **Teacher Note,** Using the Three *Trips* Settings, p. 73). *Trips* always opens in Setting 1, which is the first setting students use for their work in this unit. The illustration on p. 65 shows the *Trips* screen as it appears in Setting 1. (If you have a computer with a small screen, you will see the same four windows in a slightly different arrangement.)

When *Trips* opens, you will see that a particular trip has already been described in the Command window. A boy is shown at position 0 and a girl is shown at position 10 on the numbered tracks. Run the trip by clicking on the **Go** button.

When the trip starts, the **Go** button toggles into a **Stop** button. If you want to stop the boy and girl while they are moving, click on this button.

When a trip is running, the elapsed time and the positions and step sizes of the boy and the girl are displayed on the screen. For the purposes of the activities, we say time on these trips is measured in "seconds." However, to speed things up, these are simulated seconds that run many times faster than actual time.

The **Step** button lets you "step through" a trip to observe it one step at a time. Click on the **Step** button to start a trip if you want to step through the trip from the start, or click on it *during* a trip to step the remainder of the trip from that point on. Each subsequent click will advance the time by 1 "second." While you are stepping, you can click on the **Go** button to resume the trip, or click on the **Stop** button to stop it. After running a trip, you can click on the **Set** button to move the boy and girl back to their starting positions.

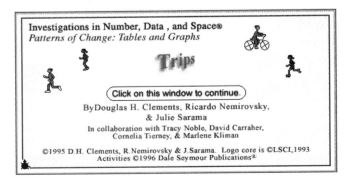

Investigations in Number, Data , and Space®
Patterns of Change: Tables and Graphs

Trips

Click on this window to continue.

ByDouglas H. Clements, Ricardo Nemirovsky,
& Julie Sarama
In collaboration with Tracy Noble, David Carraher,
Cornelia Tierney, & Marlene Kliman

©1995 D.H. Clements, R.Nemirovsky & J.Sarama. Logo core is ©LSCI,1993
Activities ©1996 Dale Seymour Publications®

Continued on next page

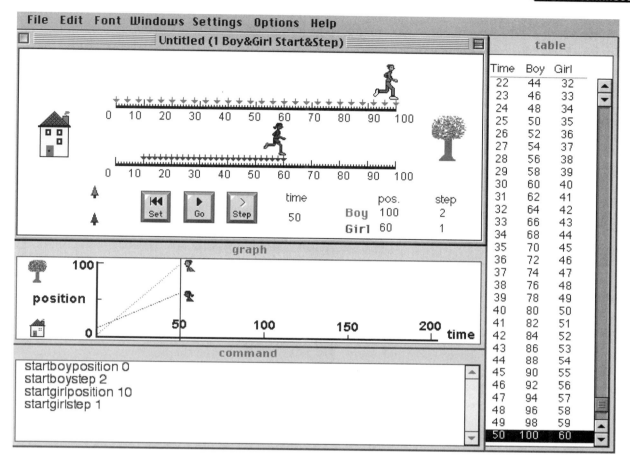

File   Edit   Font   Windows   Settings   Options   Help

Untitled (1 Boy&Girl Start&Step)

Time	Boy	Girl
22	44	32
23	46	33
24	48	34
25	50	35
26	52	36
27	54	37
28	56	38
29	58	39
30	60	40
31	62	41
32	64	42
33	66	43
34	68	44
35	70	45
36	72	46
37	74	47
38	76	48
39	78	49
40	80	50
41	82	51
42	84	52
43	86	53
44	88	54
45	90	55
46	92	56
47	94	57
48	96	58
49	98	59
50	100	60

time 50   pos.   step
Boy   100   2
Girl   60   1

command

startboyposition 0
startboystep 2
startgirlposition 10
startgirlstep 1

Editing the Commands   For each setting, the basic commands are provided in the Command window. The students' task is to change the inputs to these commands (that is, the numbers) to create a certain kind of trip. For example, in the trip that is described when you open in Setting 1, the boy reaches the tree before the girl does. Students are asked to change the inputs to the commands to create a trip in which the girl gets to the tree way ahead of the boy.

To change the inputs to the commands, students can simply click directly to the right of the number, use the **<Delete>** or **<Backspace>** key to erase the number, and then type a new one.

Analyzing Your Trips   After running a trip, you can click on the Graph or Table window to see a graph or table of that trip. The graph is initially set to show position vs. time. To graph step size instead of position, select **Graph Step** from the **Options** menu. If you wish to see the graph or table built during the trip, as the boy and girl are moving along the tracks, select **Graph During Trip** or **Table During Trip** from the **Options** menu.

After a trip, you can use the Graph or Table window to examine individual points in that trip, looking for correspondences between points in the graph or the table and the various positions of the boy and girl. Click on a row in the table (you can also use the arrow keys to select rows in the table). The boy and girl will return to the positions they were in at that time, and the graph and table will show the data for that time: the graph with a vertical line, and the table with a highlighted row.

Continued on next page

For a visual record of each trip similar to that provided by the beanbags dropped in classroom activities, students can mark the positions of the boy and girl at regular intervals with little arrows (termed **Marks** in the **Options** menu) just below the track. In the initial set-up, arrows appear every 2 steps. You can change the interval between them by typing in the Command window marksevery, space, and the interval you want. To get marks at intervals of four steps, for example, type marksevery 4. (This would be useful, for example, when the boy and girl are walking very slowly, as with a smaller interval, marks every 2 seconds would fall on top of each other.)

Other Options   In the main Trips window, two pointers (red for the boy and blue for the girl) are stored just below position 0 on the tracks.

You can drag these pointers to any position that you wish to mark. These are useful for making predictions before running a trip. For example, students might predict where the boy will be when the girl reaches the tree, or at what point one figure will pass the other.

When you have placed a pointer somewhere along the track, its position appears in the Command window (for example, boypointer 20). You can change the position of the pointer either by dragging it where you want it or by changing the numerical input to this command.

Any time you would like to verify the position of a pointer, you can shift-click on it (hold the <Shift> key down while you point at the object and click the mouse button); the object's name and position on the path are then shown. You can also use this feature to check the position of the boy or the girl when they are stopped along the track.

To hide the boy and girl during a trip (as students may want to do for the extension activity, The Challenge, p. 79), select **Screen** from the **Options** menu. Four square screens will appear, covering the tracks and the figures. Clicking on the individual square screens shrinks them to reveal what's behind; clicking again makes them grow to their original size. To remove them entirely, select **Screen** again from the **Options** window.

For variety, students can change the two "runners" into a biker (the boy) and a skater (the girl) by selecting **Biker and Skater** from the **Options** menu. This choice makes no change in how the trips operate.

Other Commands   For classes or individual students who want to explore the *Trips* software further, refer to Making Your Own Trip: Commands (p. 102) in the Appendix: Computer Help for *Trips*. This section provides information on other commands students can use to create trips.

Managing the Computer Activities

The grade 5 *Investigations* curriculum uses *Trips* and *Geo-Logo* software developed especially for the curriculum. *Geo-Logo* is used in grades 2 through 5 and is introduced in fifth grade in the unit *Picturing Polygons*. *Trips* is used solely in the grade 5 unit *Patterns of Change*. Although the software is explained in these units, we recommend that students use and explore the programs throughout the year. As students use the software over time, they develop skills and insights into important mathematical ideas.

The logistics of incorporating computer activities into your classroom depend on the number of computers you have available. Your computer setup may not be realistic for students to use the computers during math class. For example, you may have a computer lab available once a week. Or, if you have only one or two computers in your classroom, you may want to schedule students to use computers throughout the day. This Teacher Note will help you integrate the software effectively into your classroom by exploring several different scheduling possibilities that depend on the number of computers you have available. Included in this unit are several off-computer activities to be done in parallel with the on-computer activities.

Regardless of the number of computers you can use, let students work in pairs on the computer. Working in pairs not only maximizes computer resources, but also encourages students to consult, monitor, and teach one another. Generally, more than two students at one computer is difficult to manage; in most such cases, one or several students will end up having limited experience with the machine and the activity. However, if you have an odd number of students, you can form a threesome.

Three common computer access situations in elementary schools are three to six computers in the classroom, one or two computers in the classroom, and a computer lab. The computer activities can be coordinated for each of these situations.

Three to Six Computers The curriculum is written for this case and, in many ways, it is the simplest to coordinate. If you have several computers in your classroom, you might introduce the computer and software to the whole class using a large-screen monitor or projection device, or to small groups gathered around the computer. Then pairs of students can cycle through the computers, each pair spending 15–20 minutes at the computer in one session. It is important that every student gets a chance to use the computer, so you may need to allow students to use the computers at other times of the day. Be sure to monitor who uses the computers carefully so that all students get time at the computers.

One or Two Computers If you have only one or two computers in your classroom, students will definitely need to cycle through the computers throughout the school day, so that every pair of students has sufficient opportunities to do the computer activities.

Computer Lab If you have a computer laboratory that has one computer for each pair of students, you will need to let all the students do the computer activities at the same time. In order for students to have sufficient time to work with the software, plan to have students use the computer lab for one or two periods a week.

Students who are using computers and the *Trips* or *Geo-Logo* software for the first time will need assistance. Many of their questions will require only a short answer or a demonstration (see Computer Help for *Trips* on pp. 99–105). You do not have to be the only source of help for these students. Often students who are familiar with computers can assist those who need help. Encourage students to experiment and see if they can figure out what they need to do, and then to share what they've discovered with one another and with you. It is not unusual for students to discover things about the software that the teacher doesn't know.

Continued on next page

Saving Student Work   Students will need to save their work in some of the computer activities. This can be done in several ways: (1) Students can use the same computer each time and save their work on the computer's hard drive; (2) students can save their work on a disk; or, (3) with computers connected to a network, students can save their work to a folder on a shared server. Instructions for saving work are on p. 100 of Computer Help for *Trips*.

Demonstrating Computer Activities   You might use a computer with the whole class to demonstrate computer activities and to share results during whole-group discussions. It is helpful if a computer has, or is connected to, a large screen monitor or projection device—a "large display." If no large display is available, gather the students as close as possible around the computer. Increasing the font size when entering commands will make the commands more visible. To increase the font size, choose **All Large** from the **Font** menu. When you are finished demonstrating, return the font to its regular size by choosing **Plain Size** from the **Font** menu.

If your computer display is very small and it is difficult for students to see the demonstrations, you might make transparencies of student sheets and use the overhead to show and discuss the commands you might enter.

Trips on Two Tracks

Materials

- Display copies of three Motion Stories
- Student Sheet 16 (1 per group)
- Adding machine tape (3 strips per group)
- Metersticks (1 per group), masking tape
- Cuisenaire rods, cube trains, or tagboard strips (4–5 sets in 1-cm to 10-cm lengths)
- Computers with *Trips* installed
- Student Sheet 17 (1 per student, homework)
- Markers (at least 2 colors)

What Happens

Students explore what happens when they change the speed and the start positions of two travelers along parallel tracks. They create graphs, tables, and lists of commands that correspond to one of three given motion stories. Students work alternately with *Trips* on the computer and with trips along metersticks. Student work focuses on:

- understanding the relationship between speed, distance, and time
- combining discrete and continuous descriptions of motion

Motion Story 1

The girl gets to the tree way ahead of the boy.

Motion Story 2

The girl starts behind the boy, but she passes him and gets to the tree frist.

Motion Story 3

The boy starts at the tree and the girl starts at the house. The boy gets to the house before the girl gets to the tree.

Activity

Working with Motion Stories

We're going to be planning more trips for the boy and girl you saw yesterday in the *Trips* program. Half of you will work on the computer while the rest of you work with the meterstick-and-paper tracks. Then you'll switch places. The goal of this activity, whether you are working on or off the computer, is to have the boy and the girl move according to the three motion stories posted on the wall.

Ask volunteers to read the three stories.

Call attention to story 3, in which the boy starts at the tree at the right end of the track. For most of the trips so far, students will probably have had the boy and girl walking from left to right (from the house to the tree). In order to turn a figure around so it will walk in the opposite direction (from the tree to the house), a special command has to be entered.

If you put a minus sign in front of the number that tells the step size, the computer will make the boy or girl turn around and walk in the other direction, toward the house. On the computer, we can use a hyphen for the minus sign.

As an example, write on the board these four commands:

```
startboyposition 50        startgirlposition 0
startboystep -1             startgirlstep 3
```

How would the boy and the girl walk with these instructions? (The boy starts the trip halfway between the tree and the house and walks toward the house slowly. The girl starts at the house and walks toward the tree, moving faster.)

Put students in groups of 2 to 4, depending on computer availability; half the groups should be able to use the computers at the same time. Distribute a copy of Student Sheet 16 to each group. Designate which groups will work first at the computer.

When students successfully move the boy and the girl in a way that matches one of the motion stories, either at the computer or with the meterstick, they fill in their starting commands on the first page of Student Sheet 16 and go on to the next story. Explain that when they have recorded a set of commands for all three motion stories, they are to choose their favorite story and use it on the second page of Student Sheet 16, filling in the table, making a graph, and writing a description of the trip.

Note: You may want to discuss two features of Student Sheet 16 (2 pages): the story description of the trip and the time intervals. Point out that the description they write should tell how the trip would look from the point of view of either the boy or the girl. Emphasize that this description should be more specific than the corresponding motion story. For example, a version of story 2 from the boy's point of view might be:

> I started *well* ahead of the girl and went to the tree really slow. She passed me at around 70. I saw her getting to the tree first.

Students will find no numbers beyond 0 in the time column of the table and along the time axis in the graph. This allows them to create their own scale by choosing time intervals, based on the length of the trip they want to show. They will need to choose intervals that enable them to show the whole trip clearly in their table and graph. For example, Lindsay (student work, p. 71) wanted to show a trip that took 25 seconds. She could not show the whole trip using 1-second intervals, so she chose 2 seconds. Because the last interval in her table is just 1 second, the last data point in her graph falls midway between two vertical grid lines.

A student who is showing a very fast trip—say, one that is over in 6 seconds—may want to number alternate lines on the time axis (two vertical lines equal 1 second), to stretch out the graph. Circulate to help students as needed with the selection of appropriate time intervals when they begin making their tables and graphs.

For Trips with Metersticks As the computer groups begin work, hand out materials for the rest of the class. Each group will need 1 meterstick, paper strips, and masking tape to lightly fasten the meterstick in place on a paper strip. Also make available 4–5 sets of Cuisenaire rods, cube trains, or tagboard strips in 1-cm to 10-cm lengths, each marked to show a "front" end.

Whether you are working at the computer or with the meterstick track, you will fill in the same information on the student sheet. When you use the meterstick and rods, mark your trips along the paper strips on each side of the meterstick, using a different color for each "traveler."

Advise students that there is more than one way of working out these trips, so different groups may get different answers that are both right.

Divide the remaining time in the session in half. Halfway through, students at the computer switch with those at the meterstick tracks.

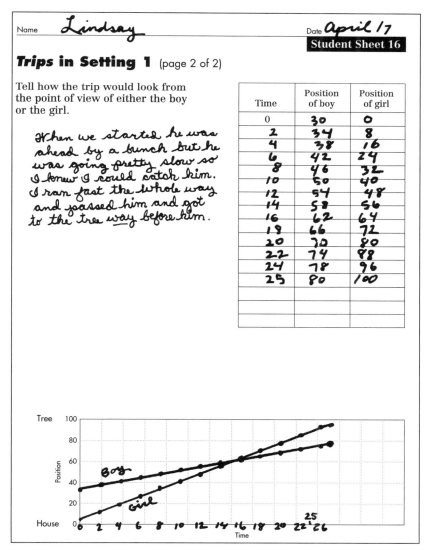

Name Lindsay   Date April 17

Student Sheet 16

Trips in Setting 1 (page 2 of 2)

Tell how the trip would look from the point of view of either the boy or the girl.

When we started he was ahead by a bunch but he was going pretty slow so I knew I could catch him. I ran fast the whole way and passed him and got to the tree way before him.

Time	Position of boy	Position of girl
0	30	0
2	34	8
4	38	16
6	42	24
8	46	32
10	50	40
12	54	48
14	58	56
16	62	64
18	66	72
20	70	80
22	74	88
24	78	96
25	80	100

Teacher Checkpoint

Running and Recording *Trips*

Observe students as they work. At the end of this session, collect all copies of Student Sheet 16, *Trips* in Setting 1, along with the paper strips students have used. Use these as a guide to determine the following:

- Are students able to create lists of commands that are appropriate to each story?
- Are students recording data accurately on the tables? Step size is constant for all these trips, so increments in the table should be constant. The numbers in the time column should match the numbers written along the time axis in the graph.
- Can students create graphs for their chosen stories? Are the lines on the graphs straight, reflecting constant step size?
- Are students making good choices of time intervals, so they can fit all their data in the table and graph? Are the intervals small enough that the data fill more than half the table and are not all squeezed into a corner of the graph?

Return the work to the students with comments. Be sure they save their work on Student Sheet 16 for Session 4, when they will be using the tables and graphs in another activity.

Session 2 Follow-Up

 **Homework**

Story of a Trip   Students take home the two pages of Student Sheet 17, Story of a Trip. They write their own motion story for the girl and boy and fill in the tracks, tables, and graph according to the story.

❖   **Tip for the Linguistically Diverse Classroom**   Students with limited English proficiency can illustrate their story, perhaps using frames to show where the girl and boy begin, how their positions change as they race, who reaches the end first, and where the other one is at that point.

Extension

Another Motion Story   If some students need a more challenging motion story, propose the following:

The boy and the girl start together at one place along the track that is *not* at either end or in the middle. The boy walks toward the house and the girl toward the tree. The boy gets to the house the same time the girl gets to the tree.

Using the Three Trips Settings

Students begin their work with the *Trips* software in Setting 1. As they continue working through Investigation 3, other activities require them to use Setting 2 and Setting 3. Changing the setting (with the **Settings** menu) changes the set of commands that appears in the Command window, making different types of trips.

```
Settings
✓1 Boy & Girl Start & Step
  2 Change Step at a Position
  3 Change Step Constantly
```

Setting 1: Boy & Girl Start & Step In this setting, you can change the starting position and step size of both the boy and the girl. The setting opens with these commands:

```
startboyposition 0
```
   (Boy starts at position 0.)
```
startboystep 2
```
   (Boy has step size of 2.)
```
startgirlposition 10
```
   (Girl starts at position 10.)
```
startgirlstep 1
```
   (Girl has step size of 1.)

Setting 2: Change Step at a Position In Setting 2, you can still change the starting position and step size of both the boy and the girl. In addition, you can change their step size when they reach a certain position on the track. Setting 2 opens with these commands:

```
startboyposition 0
startboystep 1
startgirlposition 0
startgirlstep 2
changeboystepto 4 [when
boyposition = 25]
```
   (Change boy's step size to 4 at position 25.)
```
changegirlstepto 3 [when
girlposition = 25]
```
   (Change girl's step size to 3 at position 25.)

Setting 3: Change Step Constantly In the third setting, you can again change the starting position and step size of both figures. In addition, you can change their step size constantly, once each second, so they are going increasingly faster throughout the trip. Setting 3 opens with these commands:

```
startboyposition 0
startboystep 0
startgirlposition 0
startgirlstep 1
changeboystepby 2 [always]
```
   (Increase the boy's step size by 2 at every step.)
```
changegirlstepby 1 [always]
```
   (Increase the girl's step size by 1 at every step.)

Students may find it useful to increase step size by small decimal numbers such as 0.1 or 0.25 so that the figures increase speed slowly. They might also experiment with *decreasing* speed by using negative inputs.

Student Sheet 18, Using the *Trips* Settings, provides examples of the three different types of trips with unfinished tables of the boy's and girl's step size and position changing over time. You can use this sheet in Session 3 to introduce the settings. As students finish the tables and share their results, you can check their understanding of how the three settings work.

For the remainder of Investigation 3, students explore how changing the numerical inputs in the different settings affects the outcome of the trips. They see that the three settings can be used to set up a variety of trips that match the same three motion stories about the boy and girl.

"The Boy Is Going to Win..."

Matt and Tai are using the *Trips* software. Before they run a trip, the teacher asks them what they think will happen. These are the commands:

```
startboyposition 0
startboystep 2
startgirlposition 50
startgirlstep 1
```

Tai: The boy will get creamed.

Matt: The boy is going to win, 'cause he's got a step of 2. Win! Win!

Tai: The girl's got to win because she's so far ahead.

Matt *[a few seconds before the trip ends]*: It's going to be a tie.

How did that happen?

Matt: It makes sense. The girl had a halfway of the distance head start, and she's only half the speed of the boy.

Tai: The boy can go twice as fast as the girl.

What is happening here? *[The teacher points to the graph window.]*

Matt: This line *[indicates girl's position]* goes up high right away because she got a head start.

Tai and Matt are figuring out the trade-off between step size and head start. Initially Tai expected that the girl would win because she started much closer to the tree. Matt, on the other hand, expected that the boy would win because of his larger step size. Tai and Matt interpreted the tie as a result of the exact compensation of the girl's head start for her smaller step size.

This kind of mutual compensation between factors—generally speaking between speed, distance, and time—is a central aspect of this unit. Encourage students to think and talk about the ways the factors of a trip interact. For example, they might reason, "If you keep the same number of steps per second, the larger the step size, the faster you go."

Different Kinds of Trips

What Happens

Students continue to work with the *Trips* software and with metersticks, exploring two new types of trips: one in which they can change the speed of either person at some position on the track, and one in which a person's step size can change at every step. Groups use the new trip rules to enact the same three motion stories they explored in the previous session. Student work focuses on:

■ describing differences between trips with constant step size and trips with changing step size

■ interpreting position vs. time graphs with straight, broken, and curved lines

 Ten-Minute Math: Graph Stories   Continue to present the Graph Stories activity, using graphs from p. 147 or your own. Encourage the class to interpret the graphs both in terms of varying speed on walking trips and in terms of other things that change over time. For complete instructions and variations on this activity, see pp. 96–97.

Materials

■ Overhead projector
■ Student Sheet 18 (transparency and 1 per student)
■ Demonstration paper tape, meterstick, and Cuisenaire rods
■ Student Sheet 19 (1 per group)
■ Student Sheet 20 (1 per group)
■ Adding machine tape (3 strips per group)
■ Masking tape
■ Metersticks, rods, and markers from Session 2
■ Computers with *Trips* installed
■ Student Sheet 17 (1 per student, homework)

Activity

How Settings 2 and 3 Work

Before you begin, divide the students into two groups: one that will use the computer first and another that will use the metersticks first. The students at the metersticks will work with the type of trip described by Setting 2, and those at the computer should start with the type of trip run in Setting 3. Students who did not have time to complete the activity in Session 2 should continue to use Setting 1.

In all the trips we have done so far, the step size stayed the same throughout the trip for both the girl and the boy. Now we are going to learn some ways of changing the step size along the way.

In the *Trips* program, you have three settings to choose from. Setting 1 is the one that you have been using: step size is set at the beginning of the trip and doesn't change. In Settings 2 and 3, you can change the step size during the trip and thereby change the boy's or girl's speed.

Hand out Student Sheet 18, Using the *Trips* Settings. Show the transparency of this sheet on the overhead projector as you help students understand the three settings.

At the top of this sheet, you'll see commands for a trip in Setting 1. You used this kind of command yesterday when you did trips at the metersticks and on the computer. The boy's step size for this trip is –1. What does that mean?

Ask a volunteer to explain how the entries in the first table were established. Following student suggestions, fill in one or two more entries. Students then complete this first table before you explain Settings 2 and 3.

In Setting 2, the step sizes of the boy and the girl can be changed when they reach a certain position on the track. In the example on Student Sheet 18:

> The boy starts with step size of 2 and changes it to 8 when he reaches the position 4 on the track.

> The girl's step size starts at 4 and changes to 6 when she reaches the position 12 on the track.

Demonstrate the use of the meterstick and rods to represent this trip in Setting 2. Note that you will have to change the size of the rods you are using partway through the trip. Have at hand the 2-cm and 8-cm rods for the boy and the 4-cm and 6-cm rods for the girl.

Using your demonstration meterstick centered over a strip of paper, start the trip with the 2-cm and 4-cm rods. As students refer to the table to tell you the step size and position of each walker at each second, slide the rods along the meterstick and make colored marks that correspond to positions of the boy and the girl. Change to the larger rods when students tell you to.

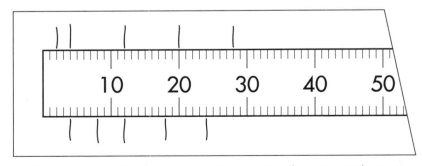

Marks showing step size changes at postion 4 (top) and position 12 (bottom)

Do not continue past step 5; ask students to complete the Setting 2 table on Student Sheet 18 and to share their results and any patterns they see.

In Setting 3, the step size is changed at every step. In the example on Student Sheet 18:

The boy's step size increases by 1 every step.

The girl's step size *decreases* by 1 every step.

In Setting 3, the boy or the girl can change direction as they walk. If their step size goes down to 0 and then becomes negative, they will slow down, stop, then start again in the opposite direction.

Using the reverse side of your paper strip, demonstrate how you could try using rods and the meterstick to run the Setting 3 trip on Student Sheet 18. Start with no rod (0-cm) for the boy's step and use the next larger rod (1-cm, then 2-cm) for each successive step. At the same time, start with the 10-cm rod for the girl's first step and decrease the size of the rod by 1 for each step. This process will be cumbersome; explain that for this reason, students will be doing trips in Setting 3 only on the computer, not at the metersticks. At the same time, watching you change the rods at each step will help the students visualize what is happening in Setting 3.

Ask students to complete the table for Setting 3 and to share their results.

Running *Trips* in Setting 2 and Setting 3

Make copies of Student Sheet 19, *Trips* in Setting 2, and Student Sheet 20, *Trips* in Setting 3, for each group as they go to work on the metersticks (in Setting 2) or the computer (in Setting 3). Students will recognize the three motion stories on both sheets as the same stories they worked with in Setting 1. Here they will discover different trips that match the same stories.

Students work in small groups creating trips for the setting they have been assigned. As in Session 2, students fill in the first page of their student sheets for every motion story. They then choose their favorite story to make a table, draw a graph, and write a more specific account of the trip on the second page.

Half of the groups work on the computers and the other half on the metersticks and paper strips. About halfway through the session, the groups working on the computers with Setting 3 should switch to the metersticks and try Setting 2. The groups who have been at the metersticks should move to the computers. They may first want to check their Setting 2 trips (done on the paper strips) on the computer. If there is time, they should also try at least one trip using Setting 3.

Note: In Setting 2, students might set up a trip in which the step size of the boy or the girl changes at a point that does not coincide with his or her position at any particular second, because the boy or girl *steps over* that position instead of landing on it. If this happens on the computer, students may find the boy or girl taking one step with a step size that is neither the original step size nor the new step size, but a number halfway in between these two. See the **Teacher Note,** Changing the Step Size in Setting 2 (p. 80), for a discussion of how to handle this in your class.

Students need to keep their completed Student Sheets 19 and 20 with their previously completed copies of Student Sheet 16 for use in the next session.

Name   Maricel   Date April 18

Student Sheet 20

Trips in Setting 3 (page 2 of 2)

Tell how the trip would look from the point of view of either the boy or the girl.

The boy was running towards me faster and faster and I was going the other way (tree to house). Then we passed each other and a little later I looked back and he had got to the tree and I wasn't to the house yet so he won I guess.

Time	Position of boy	Position of girl
0	0	100
1	0	95
2	1	90
3	3	85
4	6	80
5	10	75
6	15	70
7	21	65
8	28	60
9	36	55
10	45	50
11	55	45
12	66	40
13	78	35
14	91	30
14.6	100	26.79

Session 3 Follow-Up

Story of a Trip with Varying Step Sizes   Hand out another copy of Student Sheet 17, Story of a Trip. Earlier, students created a trip for the boy and girl using constant step sizes. This time, they are to create a trip that involves a *change* of step size. As before, they write a description (story) of the trip, show their trip on the tracks, fill in the tables, and draw a position vs. time graph of the trip.

 **Homework**

The Challenge   The *Trips* software allows users to hide one or more of the windows on the screen: the main Trips window, the Table window, the Graph window, and the Command window. This enables students to find out how well they understand the relationships between the various representations of a trip.

 **Extension**

For this activity, the class continues to work in groups. To start, half the groups create computer challenges, selecting which window they want to hide. The Command window must be hidden for all challenges. On a sheet of paper, students write down the setting they are using and the values of the starting positions, step sizes, and any changes in step size for the boy and girl.

To hide any window, students may either click on the close box in the title bar of the window or select **Hide (name of window)** from the **Windows** menu. To reopen a window, they select **Show (name of window)** from the **Windows** menu. Another way to hide the girl and the boy is to select **Screen** from the **Options** menu, as described in the **Teacher Note,** About the *Trips* Software (p. 64).

Once the first challenges have been created, the other groups rotate through the computers, trying to list the commands and describe the hidden window to the challengers. Then the groups switch roles. At the end of the activity, students discuss all the challenges.

Which challenges were difficult? Which were easy? Why? What clues helped you reconstruct the missing windows?

When the students are working at the computer in *Trips* Setting 2, they may sometimes get decimal numbers in their table. This is probably because one step size was set to change at a point where the boy or girl figure does not land—a point that is stepped over.

Here's an example: Suppose the girl has a step size of 2 and is set to change her step size to 3 at position 5. With a step size of 2, starting from 0, she would never land on 5, stepping instead on 0, 2, 4, 6, and so on. If she has to change step size at 5, she cannot continue from 4 to 6, or go from 4 to 7.

Instead, at 4, the girl will take a half-step of the initial size. Half of 2 is 1, which will take her from 4 to 5. Her next half-step will be half of the new step size. Half of 3 is 1.5, which takes her from 5 to 6.5.

Thus, when her step size changes, the girl will go from 4 to 6.5, or a step size of 2.5, for just one step. Thereafter, her step size will be 3.

This may be confusing to students running trips at the computer, and those working at the meter-sticks may not know when to actually make the change of step size. The best way to avoid this problem is to suggest that students always change the step size at a position where the boy or girl will land. Alternatively, you might discuss the issue with the class so they have some sense of why decimal numbers sometimes appear in the table on the computer.

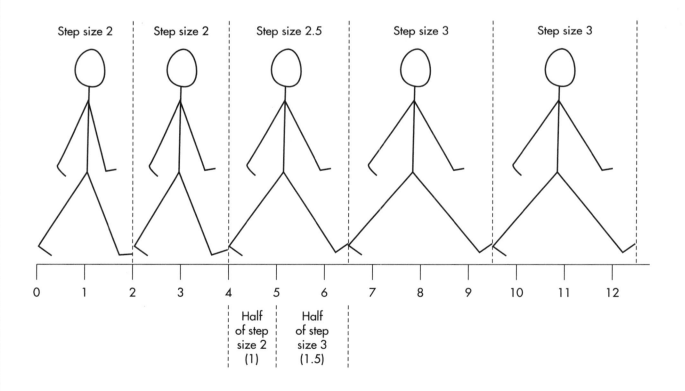

More Match-Ups

What Happens

Students match each other's tables and graphs (from Sessions 2 and 3) to the three motion stories, then as a whole group discuss any questions and observations about the match-ups. Student work focuses on:

■ describing relationships between number tables, graphs, and motion stories

Materials

■ Posted display of Three Motion Stories

■ Students' completed stories, tables, and graphs from Student Sheets 16, 19, and 20

■ Stick-on notes (available)

■ Student Sheet 17 (1 per student, Extension)

Activity

Comparing Tables and Graphs

Collect the work students have done during this investigation on the second page of Student Sheets 16, 19, and 20. Then redistribute the sheets to pairs or groups of three, being sure that no one gets his or her own work back.

Allow time for groups to discuss the work and decide which of the three motion stories each sheet represents. Students post the sheets under the corresponding motion stories on display. Then give students time to look over the postings and add stick-on notes with any questions or comments they may have about the classification or about particular graphs, tables, or stories. Finally, gather the class together for discussion.

Are there any tables and graphs that don't seem to go with the story they are posted under?

Pick out particular examples from student work for discussion:

■ **How do you know that these two tables both correspond to the same story?**

■ **How do you know that these two graphs both correspond to the same story?**

■ **How can you tell from this table what story it corresponds to? If the table and graph weren't on the same page, how could you tell that they go together? What features would you look for?**

■ **How can you tell from this graph what story it corresponds to?**

Pick some tables or graphs that have stick-on notes on them, and discuss students' questions.

The aim of this discussion is to focus on ways of seeing the correspondences among motion stories, number tables, and graphs. It is important to realize that a single motion story can be expressed with infinitely many number tables and graphs; all of those tables and graphs, however, have to share some essential characteristics of the motion story. For example, for motion story 2, there must be a row in the number table under which the numbers indicating the girl's positions become greater than the numbers indicating the boy's positions, and the graphs of position vs. time have to cross.

Session 4 Follow-Up

Extension

Creating Challenges   Distribute one more copy of Student Sheet 17, Story of a Trip. This time each student or pair makes up a story and marks the tracks for the story, leaving the tables and graphs blank. They turn in their work as a challenge for another student or pair, who must fill in the tables and draw a graph to go with the story. The challenger assesses whether the proposed solution is correct, explaining why or why not.

Two Types of Graphs

What Happens

Students explore a different kind of graph, step size vs. time, discussing how to interpret different examples. Working in pairs, they prepare a set of distance vs. time and step size vs. time graphs to represent a "mystery" trip for the rest of the class to guess. Student work focuses on:

■ making step size vs. time graphs

■ exploring the relationship between position vs. time and step size vs. time graphs

■ interpreting graphs of step size vs. time and position vs. time

Materials

■ Student Sheet 21 (1 per student)

■ Mystery Walk strips cut from Student Sheet 22 (1 strip per pair)

■ Student Sheet 22 (whole copy, 1 per pair)

■ Student Sheet 23 (1 per pair)

■ Student Sheet 24 (1 per pair)

■ Student Sheet 25 (1 per student)

■ Student Sheet 26 (1 per student, homework)

■ Scissors

■ Glue, paste, or tape

Activity

Note: When running trips on the computer, students deal with numbers for position and step size that are not specifically identified by a particular unit of measure; for example, a step size of 2, and a starting position of 15. When they use the meterstick and rods for a trip, the numbers correspond to centimeters. In Sessions 5 and 6, we link the numbers to meters. In order to show somewhat reasonable step sizes, the basic unit on each graph's vertical axis is 0.5 meter instead of 1 meter. Provide guidance as needed to clarify the decimal numbers. Also, in their graphing, students need to recognize that they will go up 2 "boxes" for 1 meter while they go right only 1 "box" for 1 second.

Distribute Student Sheet 21, Two Kinds of Graphs. Ask a volunteer to "walk" the first graph at one step per second, while the rest of the class gives suggestions and comments about the relationship between the graph and the walk.

It may be useful to discuss the corresponding table, raising issues such as the fact that position numbers can be large when the corresponding step size numbers are small—even 0.

Showing a Walk with Two Graphs

Point out to students that on the second graph on Student Sheet 21, the vertical axis is labeled *step size* instead of *position.*

How big was the first step? (1 meter) **the second step?** (also 1 meter) **How big was the step taken during the third second?** (0 meters)

How can we see the size of each step on the graph of position vs. time? If we wanted to show the size of each step more directly, we could graph step size vs. time.

Suggest a bar graph in which the height of the bar for each second shows the size of the corresponding step. Discuss with students how this convention can be used to indicate step size. Then ask them to add bars to the step size graph to fit the story shown on the position graph.

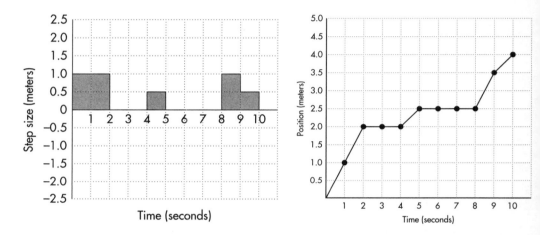

Ask students which of these graphs they find more useful: step size vs. time or position vs. time. If they need a more specific question, ask:

Which of these graphs do you think would be more useful to tell someone how to take a trip? Which graph would be more useful to determine how far you would go for a certain trip? Which graph would best help you to tell how fast you would have to go to act out the trip?

Can you reproduce a walk using either one of the graphs alone? Is it easy to create one graph from the other?

Follow the same procedure for the second page of Student Sheet 21, which describes a trip that includes a change of direction. Ask a volunteer to demonstrate the walk based on the position vs. time graph.

In the table, be sure students understand that step-size numbers are positive whenever the position numbers increase and negative when the position numbers decrease. (They will be familiar with this convention from the *Trips* program, where negative step-size numbers made the figures turn around and walk back.)

Students fill in the step size on the table and put bars on the second graph to show step size.

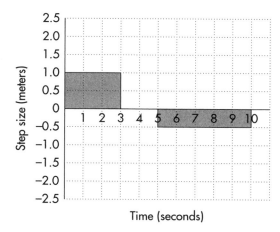

Time (seconds)

Note: The relationship between a position vs. time graph and its corresponding step size vs. time graph involves some of the most important ideas of the mathematics of change. As you discuss these graphs and the ideas they illustrate, it's important to stress the following dynamic aspects of that relationship:

The steepness of the line in a position vs. time graph corresponds to the height of a bar in a step size vs. time graph. The steeper the line in the position graph, the taller the corresponding bar or bars in the step-size graph.

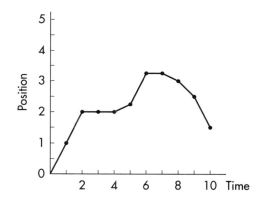

The correspondence can be seen in terms of movement: the "up and down" movement of the bars on a step-size graph corresponds to the changing direction and steepness of the position line.

A position vs. time graph "going up" corresponds to a positive step size, and a position vs. time graph "going down" corresponds to a negative step size. A horizontal line in a position vs. time graph corresponds to a zero step size.

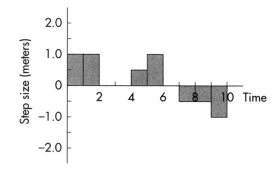

Graphing and Guessing Mystery Walks

In this activity, students work in pairs making two kinds of graphs to go with one of the Mystery Walks. They will post their two graphs together, and the rest of the class will guess which Mystery Walk the graphs show.

Give each pair one of the Mystery Walk strips you have prepared. Students should be careful not to let anyone else know which story they have. For their graphs, provide copies of the two blank graph templates: Student Sheet 23, Position vs. Time Graph, and Student Sheet 24, Step Size vs. Time Graph. Some students might create stories that don't fit on these graph templates; it's fine if they make their own.

Note: Some of the Mystery Walks include larger-than-normal step sizes; it is also likely that as students work out their graphs, they may include step sizes that are unrealistic for people. Keep in mind that the purpose here is to explore more generally the relationships between the two types of graphs; grant students creative license to include wide variation in step size, which may yield a variety of graphs for the same story.

After drawing their two graphs, student pairs post them on the wall, one just below the other. When their graphs are posted, they come to you to get a copy of *all* the Mystery Walks (Student Sheet 22). Allow time for everyone to look at the posted graphs and figure out which Mystery Walk each pair of graphs matches.

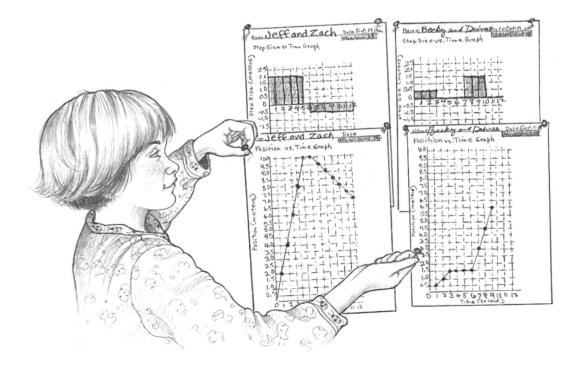

Then gather the class together. Student pairs take turns showing the graphs they have drawn while their classmates discuss which is the corresponding story. Any student who makes a guess must explain his or her choice. Encourage students to discuss several possibilities before the pair that is presenting their graphs reveals their Mystery Walk. Ask the presenters and the class the following questions:

Are these graphs a good match for their Mystery Walk story? Are any other stories that have been suggested also a possible match for these graphs?

Give each student a copy of Student Sheet 25, What's the Story? Have available scissors and glue, paste, or tape.

On the first page here, you'll see some graphs that show walking trips. There are three graphs showing how position changes throughout the walk, and four graphs showing how step size changes.

Your first task is to match each position graph to the step-size graph for the same trip. Cut out the graphs and put them in matching pairs. There will be one extra step-size graph that doesn't go with any of the position graphs.

Circulate and observe students as they work. Some features that students should notice in pairing graphs are the following:

■ The steeper the line on the position graph, the higher the bar on the step-size graph, and the faster the motion. Similarly, less steeply sloped lines on the position graph correspond to shorter bars on the step-size graph, and slower motions.

■ A horizontal line (the least steep line possible) on the position graph corresponds to a 0-height bar (no bar at all) on the step-size graph, and to a stop in the motion.

■ When the line on a position graph goes up, the step size bars are positive (above the horizontal axis), and the motion is forward. When the line on the position graph goes down, the step-size bars are negative (below the horizontal axis), and the motion is backward.

Allow 5 to 10 minutes for this task before continuing. Then direct attention to the second page, and ask for volunteers to read the three stories aloud.

Decide which pair of graphs from the first page goes with each motion story. Paste the graphs under that story. Then, beside the graphs, explain in writing how you would convince someone that these two graphs go with this story. Describe the specific features of each graph that tell you that it goes with the story.

❖ **Tip for the Linguistically Diverse Classroom** Students who are not writing proficiently in English might make their explanation orally, pointing to specific parts of the graph to support their thinking.

Advise students that you are looking for more explanation than "I guessed that this was the right story" or "There was only one pair of graphs left, so I picked them." If there is enough time, students can work on this in class. Otherwise, they can do the writing for homework.

If some students finish early, ask them to imagine that someone disagrees with their choices. Suggest that they also write the reasons why none of the graphs except the pair they picked could go with each story.

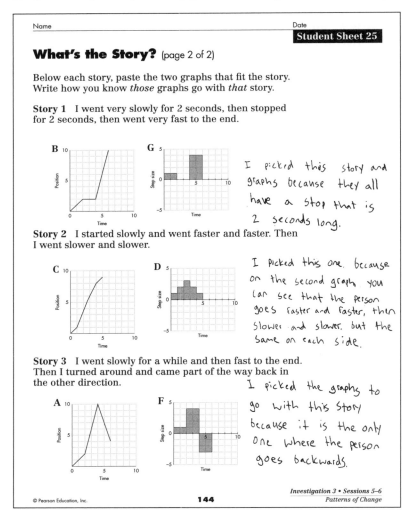

Name _____   Date _____

Student Sheet 25

What's the Story? (page 2 of 2)

Below each story, paste the two graphs that fit the story.
Write how you know *those* graphs go with *that* story.

Story 1 I went very slowly for 2 seconds, then stopped for 2 seconds, then went very fast to the end.

I picked this story and graphs because they all have a stop that is 2 seconds long.

Story 2 I started slowly and went faster and faster. Then I went slower and slower.

I picked this one because on the second graph you can see that the person goes faster and faster, then slower and slower, but the same on each side.

Story 3 I went slowly for a while and then fast to the end. Then I turned around and came part of the way back in the other direction.

I picked the graphs to go with this story because it is the only one where the person goes backwards.

© Pearson Education, Inc.   **144**

Investigation 3 • Sessions 5–6
Patterns of Change

In their writing, encourage students to describe in some detail how they related features of the graphs to parts of the story. For example:

In this story, the person walked slow, stopped, and then walked faster. So, I chose graph B that has a flat place for a stop. It has the second slanted line steeper than the first slanted line because the person went faster then. I also picked Graph G that had small steps, then no steps for a stop, then bigger steps for faster. No other graph has a stop, except for the one that goes backward.

Sessions 5 and 6 Follow-Up

Graphing a Motion Story   After Session 6, distribute Student Sheet 26, Graphing a Motion Story. Students draw graphs of step size vs. time and position vs. time for the following motion story:

The lioness was hunting. She walked very slowly for 4 seconds. Then she stood perfectly still for 5 seconds. Suddenly, she pounced, moving very fast for 3 seconds.

Comparing Graphs on the Computer Screen   Students use the *Trips* program to run some trips on the computer with graphs of step-size vs. time instead of position vs. time. This is done by choosing **Graph Step** from the **Options** menu.

Suggest that students first plan a trip and sketch a step-size graph for that trip. After they run the trip, they can compare the computer's graph with their sketch.

 **Homework**

 **Extension**

Animation

Materials

- Demonstration flip book
- Stick-on notes in light colors (1 pad per student)

What Happens

Students create two animated flip books, one showing a change over time, and another showing two simultaneous changes that take place at different rates. Students discuss the relationship between successive differences and rate of change. Their work focuses on:

- showing relative change or motion

Activity

Animated Flip Books

Show students the flip book you have made and ask what change it demonstrates. Brainstorm with the class other kinds of changes over time that they could show in a flip book that they will be drawing. Encourage them to imagine motions that would be simple to draw, such as a ball bouncing, a stick falling, or a wheel turning.

The students will work individually to produce a flip book that shows some kind of change over time. Suggest that they design books of 10 to 20 pages, tearing off this many notes (as a chunk) from their pad of stick-on notes. Explain that it is helpful to start from the back of the flip book and work forward; that way they can see through each page the image that follows. Stress the importance of using simple drawings so students can create their books in a reasonable amount of time without unnecessary complications.

After they finish their flip books, they exchange them and identify the change over time that each book shows.

Successive images from a student's flip book

Gather the class to share their experiences.

What was difficult about making the flip books? What was easy? Did your readers figure out the change that you had in mind? How do you make something that changes quickly or slowly?

Flip Books with Two Changes

This activity is more challenging: Students create a flip book that shows two things changing together, but at different rates.

Note: In a flip book, the rate of change is affected by two factors: the flipping rate (the more pages flipped per second, the faster the change seems to occur), and the differences between successive images (the more similar they are, the more slowly the change seems to occur). Since the flipping rate will be the same for both of the elements in these flip books, students should focus on the differences between successive images.

Write three possibilities on the board:

Story A: One thing changes slowly, and another thing changes fast.

Story B: One thing changes at a constant rate, and another thing starts to change slowly and then gets faster.

Story C: One thing changes at a constant rate, and another thing changes quickly at first and then slowly.

Each student chooses one of these three possibilities and designs a flip book that shows the story as clearly as possible. After students complete their flip books, they exchange them with a partner. Each student tries to recognize the story portrayed in the flip book they received—not only which type of story is shown (A, B, or C), but also the specific changes. For example, "It's story A. The sunflower grows tall really fast while the boy grows hardly at all."

You might collect the flip books for an exhibit that students and classroom visitors can explore at another time.

Choosing Student Work to Save

As the unit ends, you may want to use one of the following options for creating a record of students' work on this unit.

- Students look back through their folders or notebooks and write about what they learned in this unit, what they remember most, and what was hard or easy for them. Students might do this during their writing time.

- Students select one or two pieces of their work as their best, and you also choose one or two pieces, to be saved in a portfolio for the year. Students can create a separate page with brief comments describing each piece of work.

- You may want to send a selection of work home for families to see. Students write a cover letter, describing their work in this unit. This work should be returned if you are keeping year-long portfolios.

Session 7 Follow-Up

Homework

Sharing Flip Books   Students show their second flip book to someone at home and ask that person to guess the story and talk about the differences in how fast the changes take place.

 **Extension**

Another Flip Book   Students make up another motion story, and make a flip book to go with it. They might take the necessary materials home and make a flip book with someone at home.

Nearest Answer

Basic Activity

Students estimate answers to computation problems by rounding numbers in the problems and computing mentally. They pick the closest answer among the choices that are provided. In a variation, students choose an approximate number for a place marked on a number line between two given numbered points.

Nearest Answer provides practice with rounding numbers and estimating answers. This kind of thinking helps in checking answers found using a calculator. Students' work focuses on:

- rounding numbers
- calculating mentally
- comparing possible answers to find the closest one

Materials

- Overhead projector
- Overhead transparencies of the problems you will use in the session; choose from the examples in the discussion that follows, or design similar problems yourself.
- Pieces of paper or cardboard for covering parts of the problems
- Calculators (optional)

Procedure

Step 1. Prepare a problem and four answer choices. Keep it hidden from the students. If you are writing your own, include as one answer a fairly round number that is a good estimate, and three other answers that you think might be tempting if students are not thinking carefully. For example:

2,897,897 + 37 =
5,000,000   3,000,000   2,000,000   29,000,000

Tell students that you are going to show them an arithmetic problem for only a few seconds. They are to round the numbers in the problem to make them easier to compute with, and estimate the answer.

Note: If an overhead is not available, problems can be written on the board or chart paper.

Step 2. Present the problem, keeping the answers covered, for 20 to 30 seconds. Decrease this time to 15 seconds as students become accustomed to the activity and problem type. It is important not to show the problem so long that students have time to work it out in writing.

Step 3. Cover the problem, and show the choice of answers. Students write down the answer they think is closest. (In the example problem, they might round the numbers to 3,000,000 + 0, or 2,900,000 + 40, and choose 3,000,000 as the closest answer.)

Step 4. Uncover the problem and discuss. One or two students tell how they rounded and why they chose their answer.

Following are some whole-number problems to get you started. Plan to supplement these with problems that you or your students write.

29 + 52 =			
40	60	80	100

545 − 240 =			
200	300	400	700

50,102 − 2898 =			
10,000	20,000	40,000	50,000

32,010 − 934 =			
12,000	23,000	31,000	51,000

36,010 − 19,999 =			
1600	16,000	18,000	56,000

5210 + 298 =			
5400	5500	7000	8000

591,000 + 211,000 =			
700,000	800,000	900,000	10,000,000

3,928,012 − 43 =			
28,000	350,000	3,000,000	4,000,000

3,051,860 + 815 =			
5,000,000	4,000,000	3,000,000	2,000,000

$7108 - 141 =$			
5000	6000	7000	8000

$5982 + 978 =$			
6000	7000	14,000	15,000

$608 \times 980 =$			
5000	50,000	600,000	690,000

$9 \times 211 =$			
20	200	2000	20,000

$50,300 \div 4926 =$			
1	10	100	1000

$59 \times 11 =$			
60	500	600	6000

Variations

Nearest Answer Decimal Problems Students round the decimals to the nearest whole number or, for large numbers, to a landmark number. For example, $527.9 - 2.1321$ can be thought of as $528 - 2$ or $530 - 0$. The accuracy needed will depend on the answer choices. Sample problems:

$1.1 \times 54 =$	5.4	54	540	5400
$342 + 0.999 =$	14,000	13,000	12,000	340
$82 \div 4.2 =$	0.5	2	20	40
$24.8 + 3.1 =$	29	28	27	270
$498 \times 10.13 =$	5.00	50.0	500	5000
$59.3 \times 1.1 =$	60	600	6000	60,000
$435.4 \div 0.98 =$	4.4	44	440	4400
$268 \div 9.9 =$	25	250	2.5	2500
$402 \times 2.96 =$	400	800	1200	8000
$25 - 2.1 =$	4	12	23	30
$4.3 - 1.412 =$	0	1	3	6
$29.93 - 2.1 =$	9	20	25	28
$80.5 \div 3.97 =$	4	10	20	80
$311 + 3.71 =$	11	300	600	800

Nearest Answer Fraction and Mixed Number Problems Students round the fractions to the nearest whole number or, occasionally, to one-half, and estimate. Sample problems:

$8\frac{1}{13} \times 2\frac{9}{11} =$	16	18	24	64
$15\frac{7}{8} + 2\frac{6}{7} =$	17	18	19	29
$5\frac{9}{11} - 2\frac{7}{8} =$	2	3	$3\frac{2}{3}$	32.3
$3\frac{7}{8} + \frac{1}{15} =$	3	4	38.23	50
$\frac{32}{66}$ of $22 =$	$\frac{1}{3}$	7	10	45
$\frac{3}{4}$ of $83 =$	20	60	240	560
$\frac{3895}{39} =$	0.10	10	100	1000
$\frac{1}{11} + \frac{8}{9} =$	1	2	10	18
$\frac{1}{3} + \frac{4}{7} =$	$\frac{1}{2}$	1	2	3
$\frac{11}{4} =$	0.5	2.8	15	44

Nearest Answer Percent Problems Students use a nearby familiar percent to help them choose an answer. For example, 26% of 77 could be thought of as close to 25% (or 1/4) of 80. Sample problems:

33% of $15.85 =$	5	45	450	500
198% of $15 =$	7.5	15	30	3000
51% of $69 =$	16	35	4	100
98% of $14.3 =$	1400	143	14	0.143
25.9% of $774 =$	0.2	2	20	200
73% of $406.2 =$	50	100	200	300
24% of $83.6 =$	2	20	27	100

A bicycle listed at $210 is on sale at a 30% discount. The sale price is about:

$70	$150	$180	$200

With an increase of 10% per year, an article now costing $49 may be expected, in 12 months time, to cost:

$54	$57	$100	$200

Nearest Answer Number Line Problems

A number line is provided with three points labeled—two with numbers, and the third with the letter A. Students decide what number A is nearest to. Sample problems:

```
 2      A        5
 |___|_____|
```
A is nearest:
3   3.5   4   4.5

```
0.7         A    0.8
 |____|_____|
```
A is nearest:
0.6   0.15   0.76   0.79

```
0           A    1
 |_____|_____|
```
A is nearest:
−1   ¼   ⅖   ¾

```
−3     −1        A
 |___|_____|
```
A is nearest:
−5   −2   0   1

```
6            A  10
 |_____|__|
```
A is nearest:
6   7   8   9

```
8            A   9
 |_____|___|
```
A is nearest:
8.5   8.21   8.36   8.7

```
800           A      900
 |_____|_____|
```
A is nearest:
8.6   8.7   840   870

```
580 A              590
 |__|_____|
```
A is nearest:
5.82   58.2   582

Comparing Estimation in Addition and Multiplication

Pose addition and multiplication problems that use the same numbers. Working in pairs, students decide what four or five answers to provide for other students to choose among. They are likely to find that the answers for addition problems cannot range in size as much as answers for multiplication problems if they are to stump people. For example:

726 + 977 =   1700   1800   1900   8100

726 × 977 =   8400   80,000   700,000   800,000

Looking at the Effects of Rounding Different Factors

Pose multiplication problems with the requirement that students round only one of the factors to a number they can multiply by mentally. Students investigate this using calculators. Which number should they round? By how much can they round and still get a reasonably accurate answer?

Students will probably find that if the factors are close in size, rounding either factor has approximately the same effect. For example, for 38 × 52 [answer 1976], either 38 × 50 or 40 × 52 will give a reasonable approximation. Rounding both numbers to 40 × 50 gives a closer approximation because the numbers are rounded in opposite directions.

However, if the factors are of very different size, rounding the larger factor will result in a closer answer than rounding the smaller number. For example, for 8 × 389 [answer 3112], 8 × 400 produces a closer answer than 10 × 389, even though only 2 was added to the 8, whereas 11 was added to the 389.

■ **Students Invent Their Own Problems**
Students prepare problems with a choice of answers. They write about how they would do their own problems. Guide students to use numbers that are near landmark numbers or, in the case of fractions, near whole numbers. At another Ten-Minute Math time, students might exchange their problems with others and compare strategies.

Graph Stories

Basic Activity

Students look at a graph shape and try to imagine the story it is telling. In looking at graph shapes without numbers on either axis, students interpret qualities of the shape: relative heights, steepness of slope, pointed or gradual turns, going up or going down. Student work focuses on:

■ attending to important features of a graph

■ imagining the stories behind graphs that show change over time

■ drawing a graph to fit a particular story

Materials

■ Overhead projector

■ Graph shapes on transparency film

■ Squares of transparency film (for students to draw their own graph shapes)

Procedure

Step 1. Show a graph on the overhead. Choose one of those provided (p. 147) or another that you or a student has made. Ask questions to start students thinking: "What could be happening in this graph? What could be changing as time goes by? What might be growing and shrinking? going faster or slower? becoming more or less?"

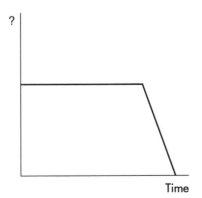

Step 2. Students talk in pairs about stories that might fit the graph. They could each invent one story, being sure it makes sense to the other person, or partners might collaborate on one story. In their story, students tell what variable is being shown and how it changes.

Step 3. Share students' stories. A few students tell their stories, explaining or showing how the story fits the shape. There are endless possibilities. For example:

■ The graph shows how fast I went: I started running very fast, but then I got tired and slowed down until I stopped.

■ The graph shows how much sunlight there was: There was a lot of sunshine in the room. Then later in the afternoon a storm came and the room got darker and darker until it was night.

■ The graph shows how many people: A lot of people were in the room. People started leaving. People kept leaving until there was no one left.

Variations

Making Graphs to Go with Stories   Prepare (or ask a student to prepare) a story; have in mind a graph that fits it. Tell the story, or show it on the overhead for students to read. Students draw graph shapes that fit the story, perhaps on pieces of transparency so they can be easily shared. Share the graphs in small groups and then a few of them with the whole class.

Making Graphs to Describe a Personal Change   On a topic you select, students draw a graph of their changing feelings. Topics might include these:

■ How awake I feel as I go through a day.

■ How much I have liked school since the beginning of the year.

■ How hungry I feel as I go through the day.

■ How I have felt about math over my years at school.

■ How my skill at (playing an instrument, playing a sport, reading, drawing, or the like) has changed over the years.

Comparing Stories for Two Graphs Draw two graphs on the same grid. Students tell stories about the graphs that bring out the similarities and differences. For example:

Time

This is the food in our dogs' dishes at mealtime. The dotted line is the food in Tipsy's dish. She gets more food and eats it super fast. The plain line is the food in Max's dish. He eats slowly and we have to keep Tipsy from pushing him away and getting her nose in his dish.

Inventing Graphs and Stories That Go Together Students write brief stories of something changing and make a graph to go with it. You might use some of these stories for the variation Making Graphs to Go with Stories.

The following activities will help ensure that this unit is comprehensible to students who are acquiring English as a second language. The suggested approach is based on *The Natural Approach: Language Acquisition in the Classroom* by Stephen D. Krashen and Tracy D. Terrell (Alemany Press, 1983). The intent is for second-language learners to acquire new vocabulary in an active, meaningful context.

Note that *acquiring* a word is different from *learning* a word. Depending on their level of proficiency, students may be able to comprehend a word upon hearing it during an investigation, without being able to say it. Other students may be able to use the word orally, but not read or write it. The goal is to help students naturally acquire targeted vocabulary at their present level of proficiency.

We suggest using these activities just before the related investigations. The activities can also be led by English-proficient students.

Investigation 1

grow, shrink

1. Blow a balloon up a little way, commenting that it is growing. Do this a few more times until the balloon is inflated.

2. Ask students how to make the balloon shrink. Let the air out a little at a time and have students use the word *shrink* as they describe what is happening. Use a large rubber band, stretching it out and letting it shrink back to reinforce the idea if needed.

3. Ask if students can name other things that grow and shrink (clothes can shrink, children grow, the moon grows and shrinks alternately).

change, speed, faster, slower, increase, steady

1. At a time when you can take the students outside, invite them to play Follow the Leader on a trip with changing speeds. Model for them a moderate walking speed, a slower walk, and a faster walk, using the vocabulary above.

2. Next, model changes from moderate to slow to fast, calling out, for example, "Change speed; go slower," then, "No change; steady speed," then, "Change speed," or "Increase speed; go faster."

3. Put groups of students through their paces, asking them to walk according to the patterns you call out to them. Let students proficient in English help to model the paces and changes as you use the vocabulary.

steep, flat, slope

1. Draw on the board sketches of two hills, one with a steep slope and one with a gentle slope, and a horizontal line. Identify the hillsides as being steep or not steep and as having a steep slope or a slope that is not as steep. Identify the line as flat.

2. If there are steep and gentle hills in your area, discuss them with the students, asking, for example, which ones are easier to walk up, or what it is like to ride a bike down them. How do the flat stretches compare with the hills?

Investigation 2

position, start, end

1. Direct a group of about five students to form a line. Name the first student in line and say that he or she is at the *start* of the line. Name the last student and say that he or she is at the *end* of the line. Ask other students to repeat what position each of those students has.

2. When you call "Change places," the students change their order in the line. Discuss who now has the *start* position and who has the *end* position in the line. You might assign a number to each student in line and ask the class to name the student in position 1 (the start), in position 2, and so on, to whatever is the last position (the end).

How to Install *Trips* on Your Computer

The *Trips* software for *Patterns of Change* is available for download at http://www.scottforesman.com/investigations/software/. If you do not have Internet access, call 1-800-552-2259 to request a CD-ROM.

To download *Trips* from the Internet and install it:

1. Type this address into your browser window: http://www.scottforesman.com/investigations/software/.

2. Select **Patterns of Change** from the drop-down menu.

3. Instructions on the screen will guide you to download and install the *Trips* software. It is recommended that virus protection, e-mail, disk security, and other open programs be turned off before installing this application.

To install *Trips* from the CD-ROM, follow these steps:

Macintosh installation:

1. Insert the CD-ROM into your CD-ROM drive.

2. Launch the installer by double-clicking on the *Trips Installer* icon.

3. Follow the instructions on your screen to install the program. The CD-ROM does not need to be in your CD-ROM drive to run the program after installation.

Windows installation:

1. Insert the CD-ROM into your CD-ROM drive.

2. Select Run from the Start menu and type X:\SETUP.EXE (where "X" stands for the name of your CD-ROM drive). Then click OK.

3. Follow the instructions on your screen to install the program. The CD-ROM does not need to be in your CD-ROM drive to run the program after installation.

Getting Started with *Trips*

After installing *Trips*, follow these steps to start the program:

1. Open *Trips*

   Macintosh: Locate and open the Investigations folder. Then open the Pattern of Change folder and double-click the *Trips* application icon.

   Windows: Click on the Start menu and go to Programs\Investigations\Patterns of Change\Trips to launch the application. Some versions of Windows put the Investigations icon at the bottom of the Programs menu and not in alphabetical order.

2. When the opening screen appears, click on the window to proceed. The Trips window, Command window, Graph window, and Table window will appear on the screen.

3. Click on the Go button in the Trips window to run a trip. You can enter or edit commands in the Command window to change the trip.

Creating an Alias or a Shortcut

For ease at startup, you might create an alias (Macintosh) or a shortcut (Windows) for the *Trips* program. An alias or a shortcut is connected to the original file that it represents, so when you open an alias or a shortcut, you are actually opening the original file.

To create an alias or a shortcut:

Macintosh:

1. Select **Trips** in the **Patterns of Change** folder.

2. Choose **Make Alias** from the **File** menu.

3. Click the *Trips alias* that appears and drag it to any location on the desktop.

4. For startup, double-click the *Trips alias*.

Windows:

1. Select **Trips.exe** in the **Patterns of Change** folder.

2. Choose **Create Shortcut** from the **File** menu.

3. Click the *Trips* shortcut that appears and drag it to any location on the desktop.

4. For startup, double-click the *Trips* shortcut.

Using the Menus in *Trips*

Menus look a little different on Macintosh and Windows computers. On both platforms, some menu commands have a shortcut and can be selected from the keyboard. The shortcut key for Macintosh is the **Command (⌘)** key. The shortcut key for Windows is the **Control (Ctrl)** key. For example, the **New Work** command in the **File** menu can be selected by pressing <⌘> and <N> (Macintosh) or <Ctrl> and <N> (Windows).

A menu item may be dimmed, indicating it is not available in a particular situation.

The File Menu

The **File** menu deals with documents and quitting.

File	
New Work	⌘N
Open My Work...	⌘O
Close My Work	⌘W
Save My Work	⌘S
Save My Work As...	
Page Setup...	
Print...	⌘P
Quit	⌘Q

New Work starts a new document.

Open My Work... opens previously saved work.

Close My Work closes present work.

Save My Work saves the work.

Save My Work As... saves the work with a new name or to a different disk or folder.

Page Setup... allows you to set up how the printer will print your work.

Print... prints your work.

Quit or **Exit** quits *Trips*.

Saving Your Work

When you save your work for the first time, a dialog box opens. Type a name for your work. You may want to include your name or initials, a brief description of the work, and the date.

For the remainder of that session, you can save your work simply by selecting **Save** from the **File** menu or pressing <⌘> and <S> (Macintosh) or <Ctrl> and <S> (Windows) on the keyboard.

If you are sharing the computer with others and it's their turn, save your work. Then choose **Close My Work**. Later, to resume your work, choose **Open My Work** and select the work you saved.

To save work on a floppy disk, see p. 104.

The Edit and Font Menus

The choices on the **Edit** and **Font** menus are similar to those you may have encountered in word processing programs.

Edit	
Cut	⌘X
Copy	⌘C
Paste	⌘V
Clear	

Font
Arial
Courier
Smaller Size
Bold Style
All Large

The **Edit** menu contains choices to use when editing text. **Cut** deletes selected text and saves it to the clipboard. **Copy** copies selected text to the clipboard. **Paste** puts the contents of the clipboard in the cursor location. **Clear** deletes the selected text.

The **Font** menu is used to change the appearance of text. If you are using the Notes window, you may want to use the **Font** menu to change the typeface, size, and style of your text.

All Large changes the text in the Command, Notes, and Print windows to a large-size font. This is useful for demonstrations.

The Windows Menu

When you open *Trips*, the Trips window, Command window, Graph window, and Table window appear on the screen. In the Trips window, the boy and girl take trips along tracks from the house to the tree. The file name and setting are shown in the title bar of the window. The Command window is where students enter or edit commands to set up different trips. The Graph window shows a graph of a trip, and the Table window shows a table of the changing positions over time for both the boy and the girl.

The **Windows** menu allows you to show or hide any of these windows separately. The selection toggles between **Hide [Name of Window]** and **Show [Name of Window]**. That is, when you select **Hide Trips,** the menu item changes to **Show Trips**. You can also hide a window by clicking in the "close box" in the title bar of the window. To make it reappear, you need to use the Windows menu.

```
Windows
  Hide Trips
  Hide Command
  Hide Graph
  Hide Table

  Show Print
  Show Notes
```

The Print window (initially hidden) is where the commands "print" and "pr" put their text.

The Notes window (initially hidden) can be opened and used to record thoughts and observations. Students might use it, for example, to describe their strategy for solving a certain problem, or to write a note about how they plan to continue the next day.

The Help Menu

The Help menu provides some onscreen assistance while you are working in the *Trips* program.

```
Help
  Windows...
  Vocabulary...
  Hints...    ⌘H
```

Windows... shows an illustration of the screen with basic information explaining the Trips window, the Command window, the Graph window, and the Table window.

Vocabulary... provides a list of the commands in *Trips,* with definitions and examples.

Hints... gives a series of hints for the present activity. It is dimmed when there are no available hints.

Settings and Options Menus

Each of the three settings in the **Settings** menu selects a set of commands that are placed in the Command window. The three settings are described in the **Teacher Note,** Using the Three *Trips* Settings (p. 73).

```
Settings
  ✓1 Boy & Girl Start & Step
   2 Change Step at a Position
   3 Change Step Constantly
```

```
Options
  ✓Graph Position
   Graph Step
   Graph During Trip
   Table During Trip
  ✓Marks
   Screen
  ✓Runners
   Biker and Skater
```

The **Options** menu allows you to customize *Trips*. For example, you may choose whether you will graph position or step size over time. You can also choose whether you will have the graph drawn and table filled in while the boy and girl are moving on their trip, or after the trip is completed. A check mark indicates which options you have selected.

You also have the option of showing or not showing the arrows (**Marks**) that appear below each track at certain intervals throughout a trip. These are initially set to appear every 2 steps. You can change the interval between marks with a command; for example, marksevery 4 will place an arrow every four steps.

Screen offers the option to place screens over the tracks, hiding the boy and girl. Clicking on the screens shrinks them to reveal what's behind; clicking on the screens again makes them grow to their original size.

You can choose either **Runners** or **Biker and Skater** to change the animation used for the boy and girl.

Making Your Own Trip: Commands

Whatever setting you are working in, you can change the commands in the Command window to change the trip. You can also add commands.

You do not need to start a new line for each command. However, when you want to start a new line, hitting the **<Return>** or **<Enter>** key simply reruns the trip. After the trip, the cursor appears on a new line after your last command.

Some possible commands are described below. While you are working in *Trips,* choose **Vocabulary** from the **Help** menu for a list of the commands you can use.

always

Used in a *"when list"* (see p. 103), this causes the action given to be taken at every step.

boypointer 20

Places the boy's pointer at 20 (or other position specified).

boyposition

Reports, or outputs, the boy's position (i.e., print boyposition).

boystep

Reports, or outputs, the boy's step size (i.e., print boystep).

changeboystepby 1 [when time = 25]

Adds 1 (or other specified amount) to the boy's present step size when the condition in the list (information in square brackets) is true.

changeboystepto 2 [when girlposition = boyposition]

Changes the boy's step size to 2 (or other specified size) when the condition in the list (information in square brackets) is true.

changegirlstepby 3 [when time = 10]

Adds 3 (or other specified amount) to the girl's present step size when the condition in the list (information in square brackets) is true.

changegirlstepto -1 [girlposition = 20]

Changes the girl's step size to –1 (or other specified size) when the condition in the list is true.

marksevery 10

Changes to 10 (or other specified amount) the interval at which arrows appear on the tracks below the boy and girl. The interval is initially set at 2.

girlpointer 55

Places the girl's pointer at 55 (or other specified position).

girlposition

Reports, or outputs, the girl's position (i.e., print girlposition).

girlstep

Reports, or outputs, the girl's step size (i.e., print girlstep).

startboy [when girlposition = 10]

Starts the boy when the condition in the list (information in square brackets) is true.

startboyposition 20

Starts the boy at 20 (or other specified position).

startboystep .5

Sets the boy's starting step size at 0.5 (or other specified size).

startgirl [when time = 20]

Starts the girl when the condition in the list (information in square brackets) is true.

startgirlposition 35

Starts the girl at 35 (or other specified position).

startgirlstep 4

Sets the girl's starting step size at 4 (or other specified size).

stop [when girlposition = 10]

Stops everything when the condition in the list (information in square brackets) is true. Because both the boy and girl stop at the same time, there is only one "stop" command.

***When* Lists** Many of the commands need a "*when* list" (the words shown in brackets) as an input. At the point at which the input in the *when* list is true, the command performs some action. For example:

```
stop [when boyposition = 80]
```

Note: The word *when* in these lists is optional. The same command could be expressed as follows:

```
stop [boyposition = 80]
```

In either case, the trip would stop when the boy's position is 80.

Here's another type of *when* instruction:

```
stop [when girlposition =
boyposition]
```

This trip would stop when the girl's position is equal to the boy's position. Note that this will be interesting only if the boy and girl do *not* start at the same position. Otherwise, they'll never get started. You could use a command like one of these to remedy that situation:

```
startboy [when girlposition = 10]
startboy [time = 20]
```

Either of these *when* instructions gets the boy started later than the girl.

To change the step size of the girl to 2 when the girl is at the same position as the boy, use this command:

```
changeboystepto 2 [when
girlposition = boyposition]
```

To increase the step size of the girl constantly, one change at every step, use the following:

```
changegirlstepby 1 [always]
```

Trips Messages

The boy and girl on the screen respond to commands as if they were robots. If they do not understand a command, a dialog box may appear with one of the following messages. Read the message, click on [OK] or press <Return> or <Enter> on the keyboard, and correct the situation as needed.

I don't know this command *name*.

> Program does not recognize the *name* command as written. Perhaps it is misspelled. Choose **Vocabulary** from the **Help** menu to check command names.

I don't know what to do with *name*.

> Either you gave too many inputs to a command, or no command at all.

***Name* needs more inputs.**

> Command *name* needs more inputs, such as a number or a condition list. Choose **Vocabulary** from the **Help** menu for more assistance.

Check if you opened square bracket at the beginning of *name*.

> The command may need a square bracket at the beginning of the "*when* list."

Check if you closed square bracket at the end of *name*.

> The command may need a square bracket at the end of the "*when* list."

***Number* is too big [too small].**

> There are limits to the numbers *Trips* can use. Use the numbers in the Trips window as a guide.

Out of space

> There is no free memory left in the computer.
> - Eliminate commands you don't need.
> - Save and start new work.

Other Disk Functions

Saving Work on a Different Disk

For classroom management purposes, you might want to save student work on a disk rather than the hard drive of the computer.

1. Insert the save-to disk into the drive.
2. Choose **Save My Work As...** from the **File** menu.

   Make sure the name of the disk or folder the computer is saving to is displayed in the dialog box.

3. Type a name for your work.
4. Click on [Save].

Deleting Saved Work

When students no longer need previously saved work, you may want to delete their work (called *files*) from the hard drive or a disk. This is most easily accomplished from outside the *Trips* program. Use your computer system's Help feature if you need instructions for deleting files.

Troubleshooting

This section contains answers to frequently asked questions and suggestions for how to troubleshoot problems that users may encounter when using this program. If you find an error that is not addressed here, in the readme file, or elsewhere in this guide, please contact:

Scott Foresman Technical Support
Web Site: http://www.scottforesman.com/
  techsupport
Phone: (800) 882-3030
(8:30 A.M.– 4:30 P.M. CT Monday–Friday)
E-mail: edtech.help@scottforesman.com

If you are new to using a computer, you may want to ask the computer coordinator at your school or an experienced friend for help.

I Can't Find the *Trips* Icon.

- Check that *Trips* has been installed on your computer. If the program hasn't been installed, consult the section How to Install *Trips* on Your Computer on p. 99.

- Macintosh users: Locate the Investigations folder. Double-click on the folder to open it. In this folder, find the Patterns of Change folder. Double-click on the folder to open it. Find the icon for the *Trips* application and double-click on it.

- Windows users: Click Start and go to Programs\Investigations\Patterns of Change\Trips. Some versions of Windows put the Investigations icon at the bottom of the Programs menu and not in alphabetical order.

Nothing Happened After Double-Clicking on the *Trips* Icon.

- If you are sure you double-clicked correctly, wait a bit longer. Depending on the computer you are using, *Trips* may take a while to open or load and you might not see anything new on the screen for a few seconds.

- You may have double-clicked too slowly or moved the mouse between your clicks. In that case, try again.

I'm in the Wrong Setting.

- The *Trips* program has three settings: **1 Boy & Girl Start & Step, 2 Change Step at a Position,** and **3 Change Step Constantly.**

- Select the setting you want in the **Settings** menu.

A Window Closed by Mistake.

- From the **Windows** menu, select the command that will display the window that closed. For example, if the Command window closed, select **Show Command**.

The Graph Was Not Drawn After the Trip. Why?

- After running the trip, you need to click inside the **Graph** window.

- Check the settings that are selected in the **Options** menu. To have the program draw the graph after the boy and girl complete the trip, select **Graph Position** or **Graph Step** in the **Options** menu. Press the **Go** button to run the trip. After the trip, click inside the **Graph** window.

There's a System Error Message.

- Some difficulty with the *Trips* program or your computer caused the computer to stop functioning. If necessary, turn off or restart the computer. Then start *Trips* again. Any work you saved before the error occurred will still be available to open.

I Tried to Print and Nothing Happened.

- Make sure that the printer is "on" and connected, and that there is paper in it.

- When printers are not functioning properly, a system error may occur causing the computer to "freeze." If there is no response from the keyboard when moving or clicking with the mouse, you may have to shut down or restart the computer and start over.

Blackline Masters

_____ , 20 _____

Dear Family,

Our class has begun a new mathematics unit called *Patterns of Change*. We are talking about how changes can be described with tables and graphs. The children first consider tile designs that keep getting bigger in a regular way. They tell the story of each design with a number table and graphs that reflect the changing pattern.

Next we begin talking about changes in speed. The children act out "trips" by walking along a straight track of tape on the floor, changing their speed as they go. Again, the children make tables and graphs to show the changing speeds. In similar work on the computer, the children plan and run "trips" for two walkers. They make changes in the walkers' rate of speed, in their starting position, and in their direction of movement, and they try to predict the outcome as they explore the effects of these changes on "who gets there first."

To learn more about what we're doing, ask your child to tell you about the activities that he or she brings home.

■ Look at your child's drawings of tile patterns, and at the tables and graphs that go with them. Ask your child to explain the patterns to you. How can you tell how the design will continue to grow? With your child, design some other tile patterns that grow in predictable ways.

■ See if you can interpret the diagram your child makes to show how the speed changes during a walk along a straight line. Can you tell the story of the trip? It might be something like this: "Start out walking slowly. Stop halfway for 6 seconds. Then run to the end."

■ Over the next few weeks, help your child look for things that change in different ways and at different speeds. Can you find some things that change faster and faster? Can you find things that change steadily? Can you find anything that changes by gradually slowing down? by gradually shrinking?

■ Look in newspapers and other print material for graphs and tables that show something changing over time. Work with your child to make sense of these.

Making and interpreting tables and graphs that show change over time is an important skill. The understandings that our class gains in this unit will help in their future studies in both math and science.

Sincerely,

Tile Pattern Template

Growing Tile Pattern

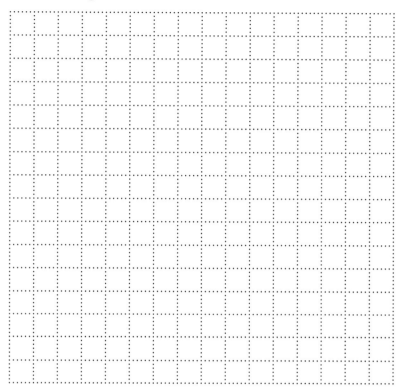

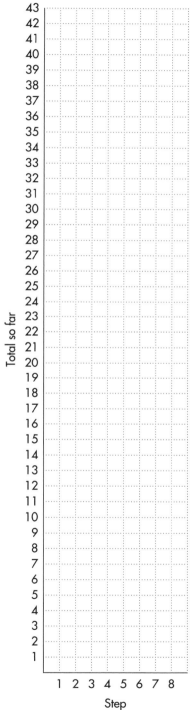

Step number	New tiles (step size)	Total so far
1		
2		
3		
4		
5		
6		
7		
8		

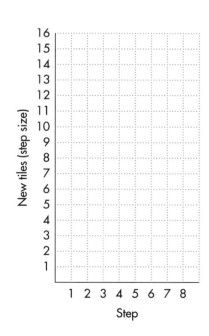

Growing Tile Patterns

Draw a pattern that changes in some regular way. You can color the pattern if you wish. Then fill in the table to show the step size and the total number of tiles in the pattern after each step.

Step number	New tiles (step size)	Total so far
1		
2		
3		
4		
5		
6		
7		
8		

Finally, describe generally how your tile pattern grows:

_____

_____

_____

Growing and Graphing Tile Patterns

Draw one tile pattern, and fill in the table and graphs. You may use any of the tile patterns we discussed in class or one of your own.

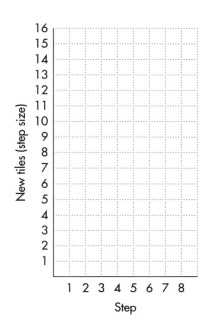

Step number	New tiles (step size)	Total so far
1		
2		
3		
4		
5		
6		
7		
8		

Growing Tile Patterns (page 1 of 4)

Twos Tower

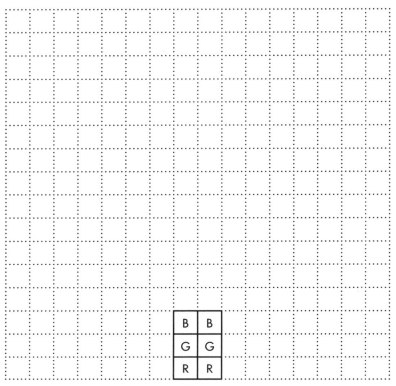

Start

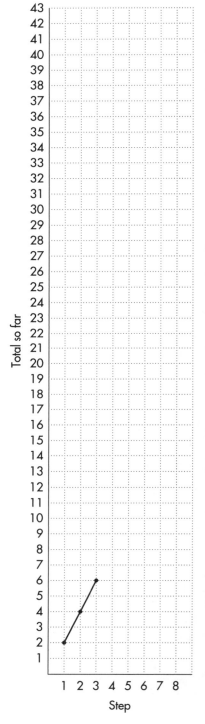

Step number	New tiles (step size)	Total so far
1	2	2
2	2	4
3	2	6
4	2	
5	2	
6		
7		
8		

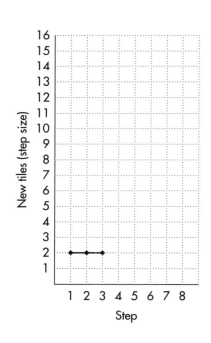

Growing Tile Patterns (page 2 of 4)

Squares

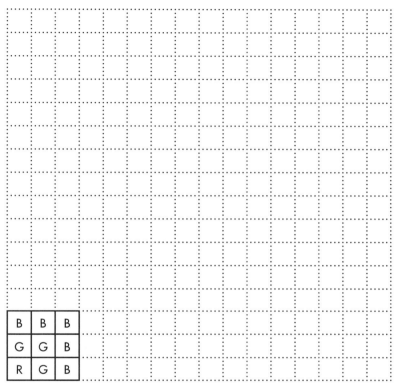

Start

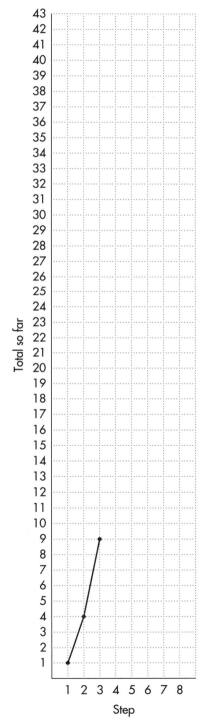

Step number	New tiles (step size)	Total so far
1	1	1
2	3	4
3	5	9
4		
5		
6		
7		
8		
0		

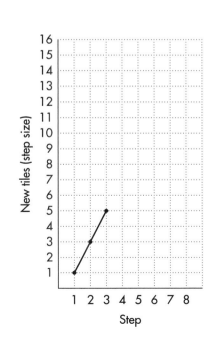

Investigation 1 • Sessions 3–4
Patterns of Change

Growing Tile Patterns (page 3 of 4)

Staircase

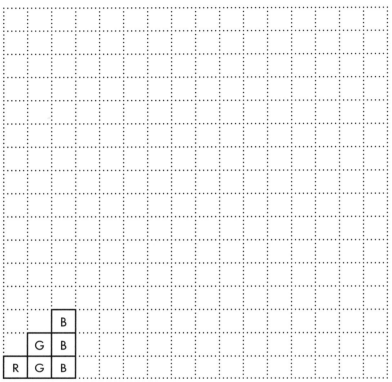

Start

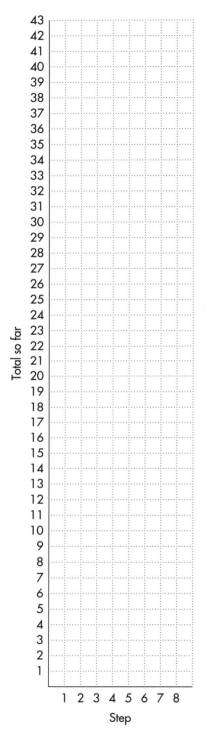

Total so far

Step number	New tiles (step size)	Total so far
1	1	1
2	2	3
3	3	6
4		
5		
6		
7		
8		

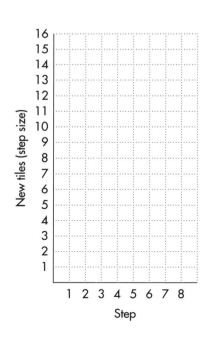

New tiles (step size)

Step

114

Growing Tile Patterns (page 4 of 4)

Doubling

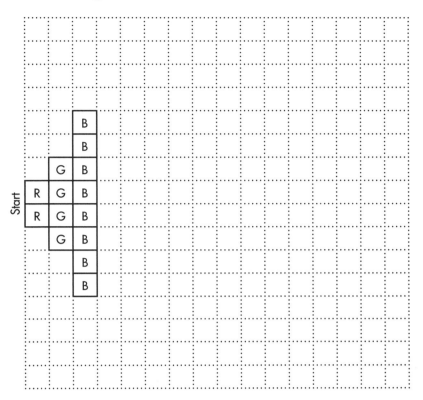

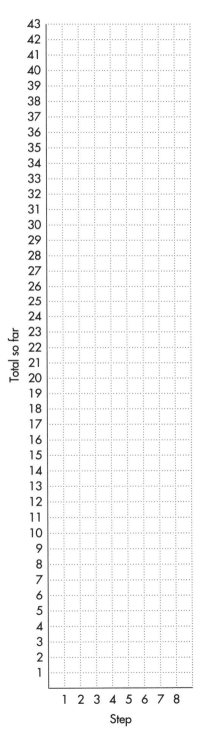

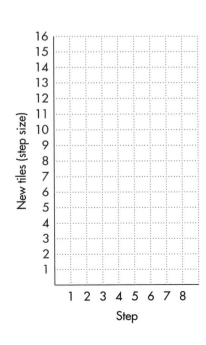

Step number	New tiles (step size)	Total so far
1	2	2
2	4	6
3	8	14
4	16	30
5		
6		
7		
8		

Same Numbers, Different Pattern

Choose a pattern from Student Sheet 4. Draw different
growing patterns that fit the numbers in the table for the
pattern you chose.

I chose: Twos Tower Squares Staircase Doubling

Describe how your tile pattern grows:

_____

_____

_____

_____

Be sure to bring all of Student Sheet 4 back to class for
discussion in the next math class.

Describing a Straight Line Trip

1. Plan a trip along a straight line. Be sure your trip has some changes of speed. Invent a way to show the changing speeds on paper *without words* and *without a key*. You may make a table if you wish.

2. Ask someone at home to act out your trip. Make any changes to your representation that are necessary to make the trip easier for the person to understand and interpret. Ask the person to try again and continue making changes until the person can act out the trip correctly.

3. Write about what the person did and didn't understand, and describe any changes you made to your representation in order to make it clearer.

_____

_____

_____

_____

_____

_____

Template for Tables

Time

Time (seconds)	Total distance so far (meters)
2	
4	
6	
8	
10	
12	
14	

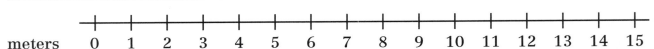

meters

Time (seconds)	Total distance so far (meters)
2	
4	
6	
8	
10	
12	
14	

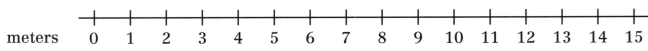

meters

Height of a Girl

This table lists the heights of a girl from age 7 to 17.

Make a graph of her changing height.

Age (years)	Height (inches)	Growth in last year
7	48	
8	50	
9	52	
10	54	
11	56	
12	59	
13	62	
14	65	
15	66	
16	67	
17	67	

Tell the story of the girl's growth. When did she grow fast? When did she grow slowly? What is happening to her growth at the end?

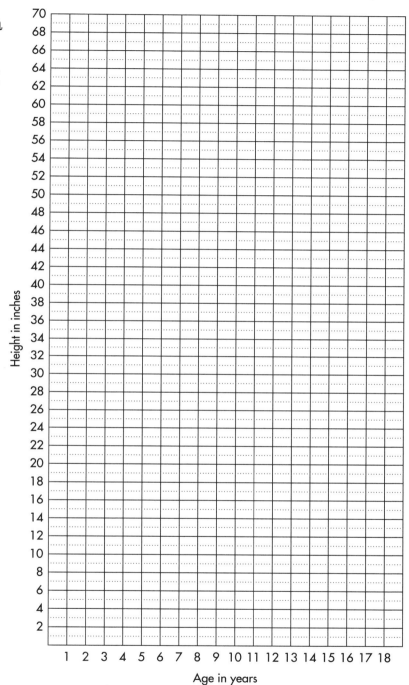

Height in inches

Age in years

Three Motion Stories

Plan a trip for one of the following stories. Make a table showing where the person would be every 2 seconds (that is, where the beanbags would land).

Story A   Run a few steps, stop, run a few steps, stop, then walk to the end.

Story B   Walk very slowly a short way, stop for about 6 seconds, and then walk fast to the end.

Story C   Run about halfway, then go slower and slower until the end.

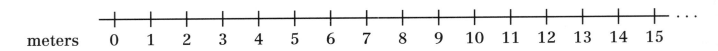

Time (seconds)	Total distance so far (meters)
2	
4	
6	
8	
10	
12	
14	

Graph of a Trip

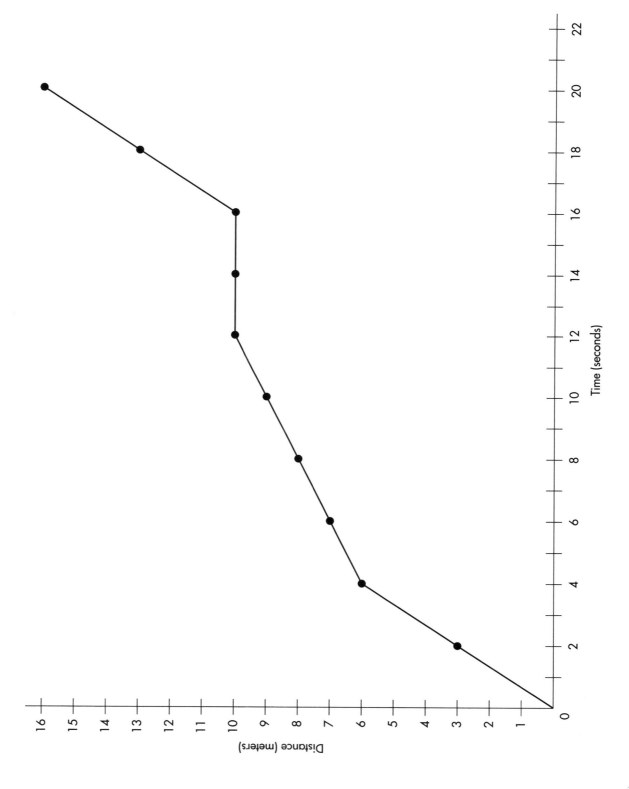

Graph Template

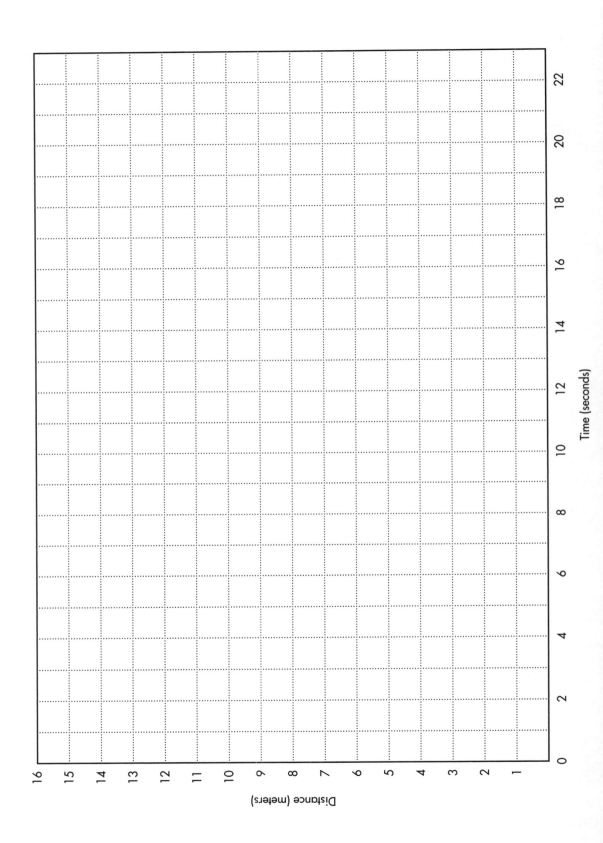

Planning and Graphing a Trip

Plan a story about any sort of trip. It could be a walking or sailing trip, a trip by train or car, or any other idea you may have. Write the story below. Then make a graph to go with it on Student Sheet 13.

Explain how the graph shows the changes of speed that happen in the story. Make the story, graph, and explanation clear enough to be used to teach a fourth grade student how to read the graph. You may want to add a table to make the description of the trip clearer on the back of this sheet.

Another Graph Template

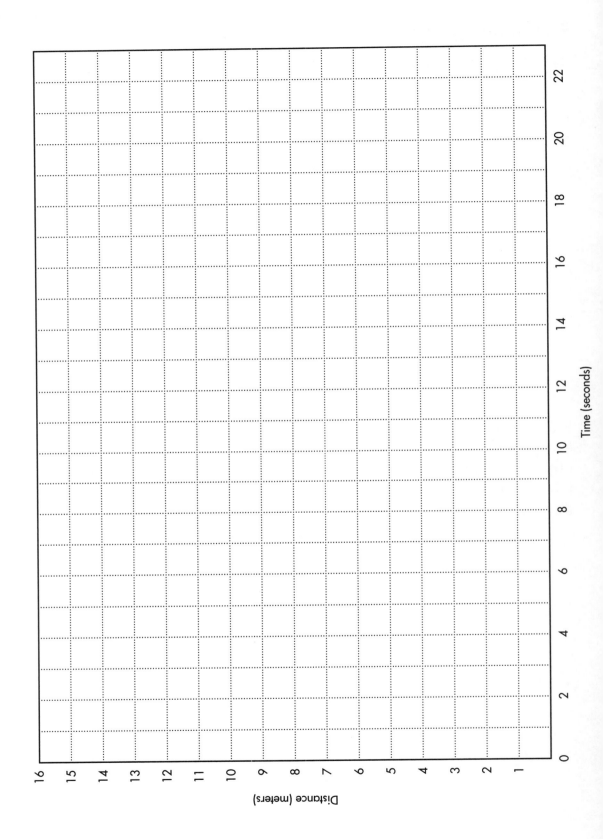

Matching Stories, Tables, and Graphs (page 1 of 2)

Cut apart the stories, the tables, and the graphs.
Which ones match? Group them together.
Finish filling in the tables, and write the missing story.

Story 1 Walk slowly about halfway and then run until the end.

Story 2 Run about halfway, stop for 4 seconds, then walk to the end.

Story 3

Table A

Time (seconds)	Distance in previous 2 seconds (step size)	Total distance (meters)
2	1	1
4	1	2
6	1	3
8		4
10		5
11		8
12		11
14		

Table B

Time (seconds)	Distance in previous 2 seconds (step size)	Total distance (meters)
2	2	2
4	2	4
6	2	6
8		7
10		5
12		3
14		1
16		

Matching Stories, Tables, and Graphs (page 2 of 2)

Table C

Time (seconds)	Distance in previous 2 seconds (step size)	Total distance (meters)
2		
4		
6		
8		
10		
12		
14		

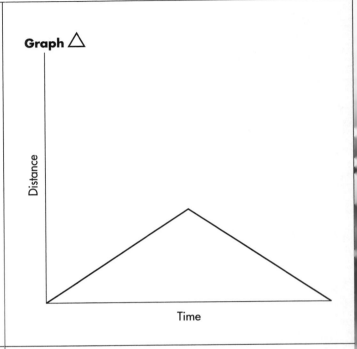

Graph △

Distance / Time

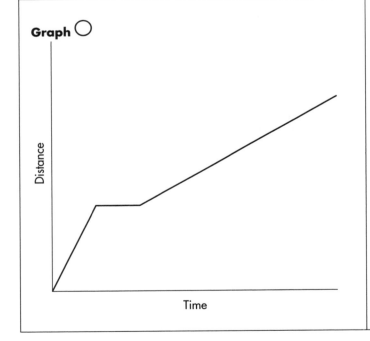

Graph ○

Distance / Time

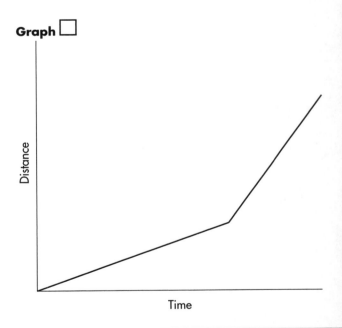

Graph □

Distance / Time

Trips Computer Screen

File   Edit   Font   Windows   Settings   Options   Help

Untitled (1 Boy & Girl Start & Step)

Set   Go   Step

time
50

	pos.	step
Boy	100	2
Girl	60	1

Graph

position

time   50   100   150   200

Command

```
startboyposition 0
startboystep 2
startgirlposition 10
startgirlstep 1
```

Table

Time	Boy	Girl
12	24	22
13	26	23
14	28	24
15	30	25
16	32	26
17	34	27
18	36	28
19	38	29
20	40	30
21	42	31
22	44	32
23	46	33
24	48	34
25	50	35
26	52	36
27	54	37
28	56	38
29	58	39
30	60	40
31	62	41
32	64	42
33	66	43
34	68	44
35	70	45
36	72	46
37	74	47
38	76	48
39	78	49
40	80	50
41	82	51
42	84	52
43	86	53
44	88	54
45	90	55
46	92	56
47	94	57
48	96	58
49	98	59
50	100	60

Trips in Setting **1** (page 1 of 2)

Create a trip for Motion Stories 1, 2, and 3. Use either the meterstick or the computer. In the blanks, write the values for position and step size that you used for each trip.

Note: If you have done a story with the meterstick, check it on the computer if you have time.

Motion Story 1 The girl gets to the tree way ahead of the boy.

startboyposition _____ 		*(The boy is going to start at position __?__)*

startboystep _____ 		*(The boy is going to walk with a step size of __?__)*

startgirlposition _____ 		*(The girl is going to start at position __?__)*

startgirlstep _____ 		*(The girl is going to walk with a step size of __?__)*

Motion Story 2 The girl starts behind the boy, but she passes the boy and gets to the tree first.

startboyposition _____

startboystep _____

startgirlposition _____

startgirlstep _____

Motion Story 3 The boy starts at the tree and the girl starts at the house. The boy gets to the house before the girl gets to the tree.

startboyposition _____

startboystep _____

startgirlposition _____

startgirlstep _____

Choose the trip for one story and use it to fill in the next page. Record here which story you choose: _____

Trips **in Setting 1** (page 2 of 2)

Tell how the trip would look from
the point of view of either the boy
or the girl.

Time	Position of boy	Position of girl
0		

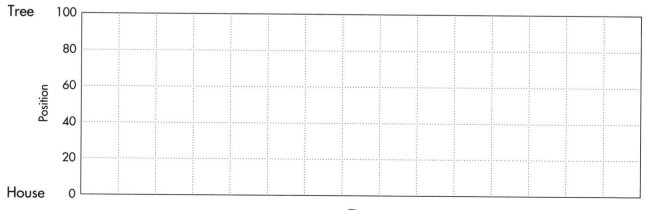

129

Story of a Trip (page 1 of 2)

Story

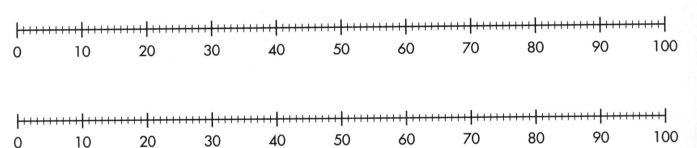

Time (seconds)	Position of boy (meters)		Time (seconds)	Position of girl (meters)

Story of a Trip (page 2 of 2)

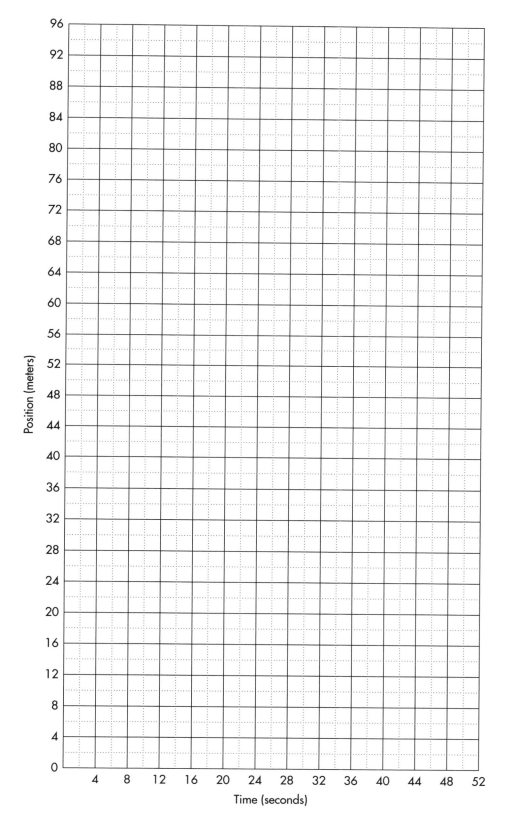

Using the *Trips* Settings

Setting 1

```
startboyposition 50
startboystep -1
startgirlposition 0
startgirlstep 3
```

Time	Boy		Girl	
	Step size	Position	Step size	Position
0	–1	50	3	0
1	–1	49	3	3
2	–1	48	3	6
3		47		9
4				
5				
6				
7				

Setting 2

```
startboyposition 0
startboystep 2
startgirlposition 0
startgirlstep 4
changeboystepto 8
  [when boyposition = 4]
changegirlstepto 6
  [when girlposition = 12]
```

Time	Boy		Girl	
	Step size	Position	Step size	Position
0	2	0	4	0
1	2	2	4	4
2	2	4	4	8
3	8	12	4	12
4	8	20	6	18
5		28		24
6				
7				

Setting 3

```
startboyposition 0
startboystep 0
startgirlposition 0
startgirlstep 10
changeboystepby 1 [always]
changegirlstepby -1
[always]
```

Time	Boy		Girl	
	Step size	Position	Step size	Position
0	0	0	10	0
1	1	0	9	10
2	2	1	8	19
3	3	3		
4	4	6		
5				
6				
7				

Trips in Setting 2 (page 1 of 2)

Create a trip for Motion Stories 1, 2, and 3. In the blanks, write the values for position and step size.

Note: If you have done a story with the meterstick, check it on the computer if you have time.

Motion Story 1 The girl gets to the tree way ahead of the boy.

startboyposition ____   startboystep ____

startgirlposition ____   startgirlstep ____

changeboystepto ____ [when boyposition = ____]

   (The boy changes his step size to __?__ when he reaches position __?__)

changegirlstepto ____ [when girlposition = ____]

   (The girl changes her step size to __?__ when she reaches position __?__)

Motion Story 2 The girl starts behind the boy, but she passes the boy and gets to the tree first.

startboyposition ____   startboystep ____

startgirlposition ____   startgirlstep ____

changeboystepto ____ [when boyposition = ____]

changegirlstepto ____ [when girlposition = ____]

Motion Story 3 The boy starts at the tree and the girl starts at the house. The boy gets to the house *before* the girl gets to the tree.

startboyposition ____   startboystep ____

startgirlposition ____   startgirlstep ____

changeboystepto ____ [when boyposition = ____]

changegirlstepto ____ [when girlposition = ____]

Choose the trip for one story and use it to fill in the next page. Record here which story you choose: _____

Trips in Setting 2 (page 2 of 2)

Tell how the trip would look from the
point of view of either the boy or the girl.

Time	Position of boy	Position of girl
0		

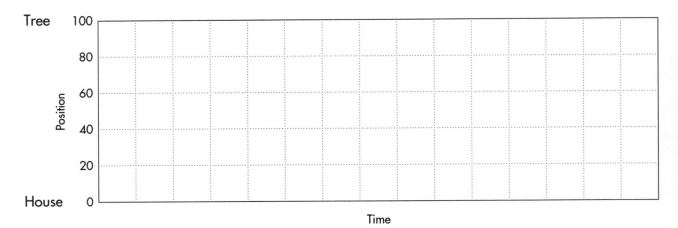

© Pearson Education, Inc.

Investigation 3 • Session 3
Patterns of Change

Trips in Setting 3 (page 1 of 2)

Create a trip for Motion Stories 1, 2, and 3. In the blanks,
write the values for position and step size.

Motion Story 1 The girl gets to the tree way ahead of the boy.

startboyposition ____   startboystep ____

startgirlposition ____   startgirlstep ____

changeboystepby ____ [always]

   (At every step, the boy changes his step size by ?)

changegirlstepto____ [always]

   (At every step, the girl changes her step size by ?)

Motion Story 2 The girl starts behind the boy, but she passes
the boy and gets to the tree first.

startboyposition ____   startboystep ____

startgirlposition ____   startgirlstep ____

changeboystepto ____ [always]

changegirlstepto ____ [always]

Motion Story 3 The boy starts at the tree and the girl starts
at the house. The boy gets to the house before the girl gets
to the tree.

startboyposition ____   startboystep ____

startgirlposition ____   startgirlstep ____

changeboystepto ____ [always]

changegirlstepto ____ [always]

Choose the trip for one story and use it to fill in the next page.
Record here which story you choose: _____

Trips in Setting 3 (page 2 of 2)

Tell how the trip would look from the
point of view of either the boy or the girl.

Time	Position of boy	Position of girl
0		

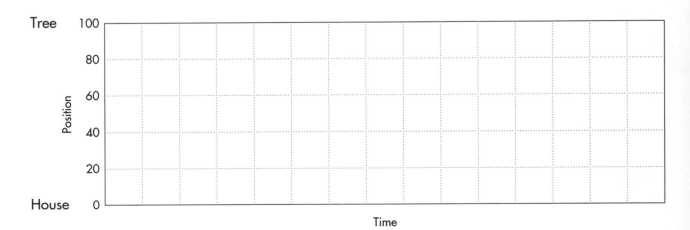

Two Kinds of Graphs (page 1 of 2)

Time (seconds)	Position	Step size

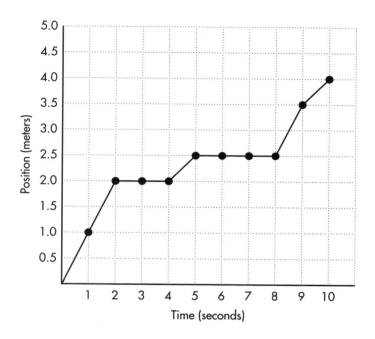

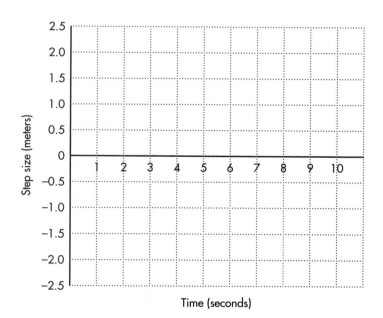

Two Kinds of Graphs (page 2 of 2)

Time (seconds)	Position	Step size

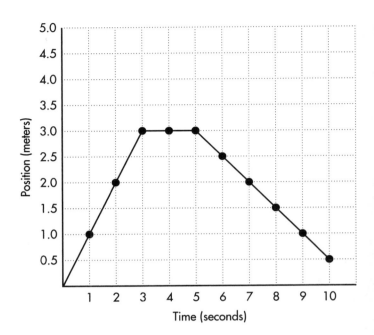

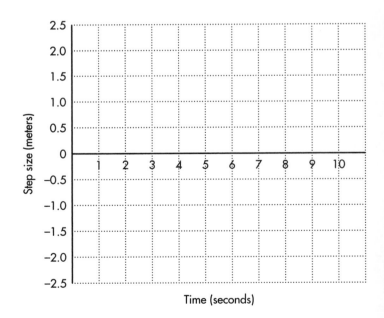

Mystery Walks (page 1 of 2)

1. She walked slowly for 3 seconds. Then she stood still for 4 seconds. Suddenly, during the last 3 seconds, she went quite fast.

2. She ran fast for 3 seconds, then slowly for 4 seconds. Then she went back to the beginning in 5 seconds.

3. He waited for 4 seconds before starting to walk slowly with a step size of 0.5. He walked for a few seconds and then stopped.

4. He walked backward very slowly. After 5 seconds he ran forward for 5 more seconds.

5. She left home running really fast with a step size of 1.5 meters. She went at that rate for 3 seconds, but then she realized that she had forgotten her book. She stopped for a couple of seconds to decide what to do. Then she decided that it would be too late anyway, so she went back home slowly.

6. From his house to the corner store is 10 meters. He ran to the store, spent 1 second looking at the CLOSED sign, and walked slowly back to his house.

7. She decided to cross the park walking slowly at first but going faster and faster each step. It took her 5 seconds to get to the other side.

8. He was going home, not in a rush. As he stepped into the street, he realized that a car was coming. He waited for the car, then ran across the street. As soon as he got to the other side of the street, he walked slowly again.

Mystery Walks (page 2 of 2)

9. At first the old man walked very slowly, as if he was tired. Suddenly, when he was next to us, he started to run amazingly fast. After a few seconds he stopped and walked back to say, "I surprised you, didn't I?"

10. The dog ran off to catch the stick that his owner had thrown. As the dog grabbed the stick, he saw a rabbit. The dog held very still for a moment. Then, instead of running back to his owner, he crept very slowly toward the rabbit. When the dog was close to the rabbit, he jumped forward at great speed.

11. First she went fast, at a steady pace. Then, at around 5 meters, she started to slow down. She went slower and slower until she stopped. She stood still for 4 seconds. Finally she walked slowly and steadily for a while.

12. Trying not to wake anyone up, she walked very slowly with small steps. Once she got to the door, she began to run faster and faster. After 3 seconds of running, she stopped and sat down.

13. Imagine someone walking back and forth two times between the chalkboard and her desk. She always walks fast toward the board and slowly toward the desk. At the end she remains still for 3 seconds.

14. He waited for 4 seconds before starting to run with a step size of 1.5. He ran for a few seconds and then stopped.

15. It is 8 meters between her bedroom and the kitchen. She walked into the kitchen slowly because she was half asleep, and then just stared at the room for a moment. Then she went back to bed very quickly.

Position vs. Time Graph

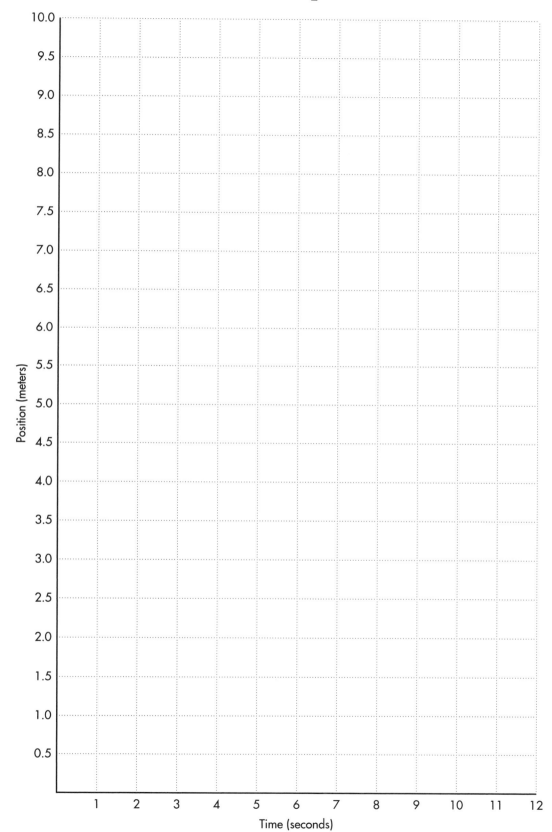

Step Size vs. Time Graph

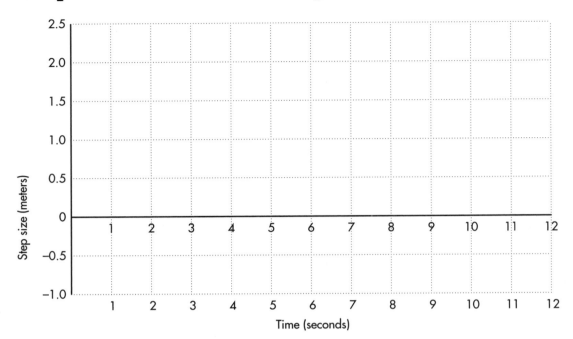

What's the Story? (page 1 of 2)

Cut out these graphs. Match them with the
stories on the next page.

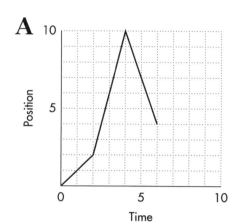

A

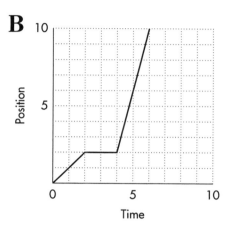

B

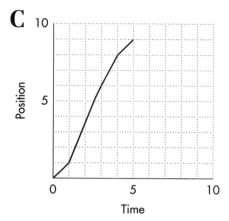

C

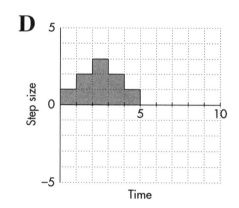

D

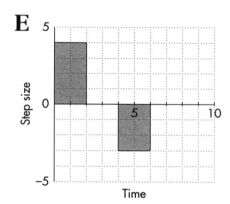

E

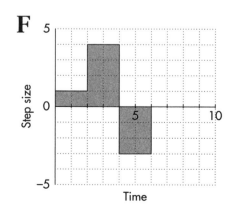

F

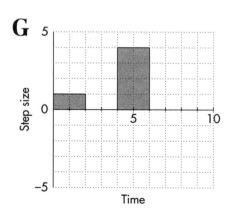

G

What's the Story? (page 2 of 2)

Below each story, paste the two graphs that fit the story. Write how you know *those* graphs go with *that* story.

Story 1 I went very slowly for 2 seconds, then stopped for 2 seconds, then went very fast to the end.

Story 2 I started slowly and went faster and faster. Then I went slower and slower.

Story 3 I went slowly for a while and then fast to the end. Then I turned around and came part of the way back in the other direction.

Graphing a Motion Story

Draw a step size vs. time graph and a position vs. time graph for this motion story:

The lioness was hunting. She walked very slowly for 4 seconds. Then she stood perfectly still for 5 seconds. Suddenly, she pounced, moving very fast for 3 seconds.

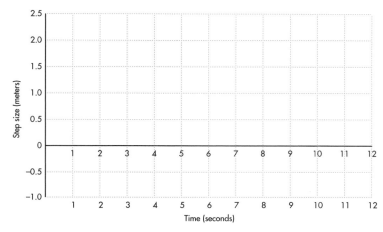

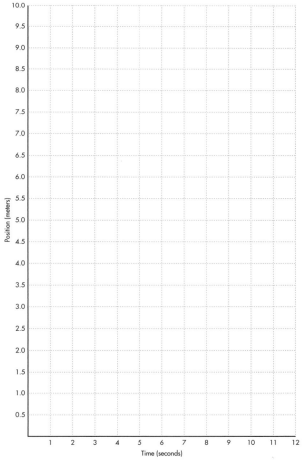

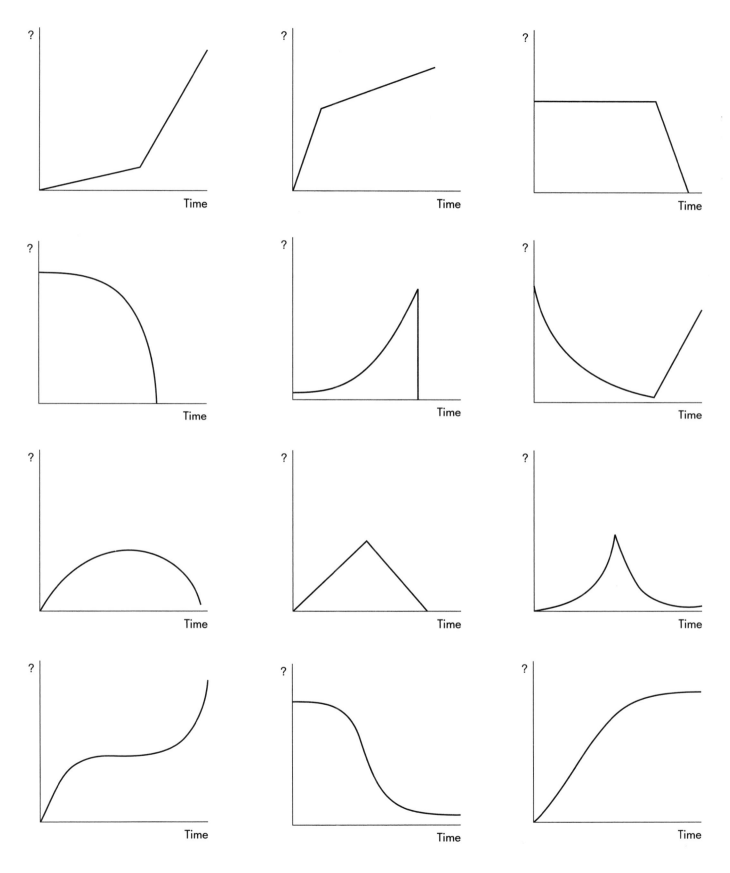

Practice Pages

This optional section provides homework ideas for teachers who want or need to give more homework than is assigned to accompany the activities in this unit. The problems included here provide additional practice in learning about number relationships and in solving computation and number problems. For number units, you may want to use some of these if your students need more work in these areas or if you want to assign daily homework. For other units, you can use these problems so that students can continue to work on developing number and computation sense while they are focusing on other mathematical content in class. We recommend that you introduce activities in class before assigning related problems for homework.

Digits Game   This game is introduced in the unit *Building on Numbers You Know*. If your students are familiar with the game, you can simply send home the directions, score sheet, and Numeral Cards so that students can play at home. If your students have not played this game before, introduce it in class and have students play once or twice before sending it home. In the beginning, ask students to work with 4-digit targets such as 1000, 2500, or 6723. Later, they can try 5-digit targets such as 10,000, 59,500, and 30,000. You might have students do this activity two times for homework in this unit.

Counting Up and Down   In this activity, introduced in the unit *Building on Numbers You Know,* students write the numbers they would say if they counted up or down by a given number. Provided here are three work sheets. Because this activity is included in the curriculum only as homework, it is recommended that you briefly introduce it in class before students work on it at home.

Story Problems   Story problems at various levels of difficulty are used throughout the *Investigations* curriculum. The two story problem sheets provided here help students review and maintain skills that have already been taught. You can make up other problems in this format, using numbers and contexts that are appropriate for your students. Students solve the problems and then record their strategies.

How to Play the Digits Game

Materials: Numeral Cards (with Wild Cards removed)
Digits Game Score Sheet

Players: 2 or 3

How to Play

1. Decide on the target number to use.

   Example: The target is 1000.

2. Deal the Numeral Cards. Deal out one more card than
   there are digits in the target.

   Example: The target has four digits, so you deal out five
   cards: 3, 8, 0, 1, and 5.

3. Players use the numerals on the cards to make a number
   as close as possible to the target.

   Example: You can use 3, 8, 0, 1, and 5 to make 1035, 853,
   or other numbers.

4. Write the target and the number you made on your score
   sheet. Find and record the difference between them.

   Example: 1000 − 853 = 147. The difference is your score.

5. When everyone has finished, compare answers. Which
   number is closest to the target? Is it possible to make a
   number even closer?

   Example: Player A made 853. Player B made 1305. Who
   is closer? Can you make a number with these digits that is
   even closer to 1000?

6. For the next round, mix up all the cards and deal a new
   set.

7. After three rounds, total your scores. Lowest total wins.

Digits Game Score Sheet

For each round you play, record the target number and the closest number you can make with your digits. Put the larger one first. Then find and record the difference between them.

Player A

Game target: _____   Difference

Round 1: _____ – _____ = _____

Round 2: _____ – _____ = _____

Round 3: _____ – _____ = _____

Total score: _____

Player B

Game target: _____   Difference

Round 1: _____ – _____ = _____

Round 2: _____ – _____ = _____

Round 3: _____ – _____ = _____

Total score:

Player C

Game target: _____   Difference

Round 1: _____ – _____ = _____

Round 2: _____ – _____ = _____

Round 3: _____ – _____ = _____

0	0	1	1
0	0	1	1
2	2	3	3
2	2	3	3

152

4	4	5	5
4	4	5	5
<u>6</u>	<u>6</u>	7	7
<u>6</u>	<u>6</u>	7	7

Practice Page
Patterns of Change

8	8	9	9
8	8	9	9
WILD CARD	WILD CARD		
WILD CARD	WILD CARD		

Practice Page
Patterns of Change

Practice Page A

Fill in the numbers you say if you start at 500 and count down by each counting number.

Count down by 25	Count down by 50	Count down by 100	Count down by 125	Count down by _____ (your choice)
500	500	500	500	500
_____	_____	_____	_____	_____
_____	_____	_____	_____	_____
_____	_____	_____	_____	_____
_____	_____	_____	_____	_____
_____	_____	_____	_____	_____
_____	_____	_____	_____	_____
_____	_____	_____	_____	_____
_____	_____	_____	_____	_____
_____	_____	_____	_____	_____
_____	_____	_____	_____	_____
_____	_____	_____	_____	_____

Practice Page B

Fill in the numbers you say if you start at 40 and count up
by each counting number.

Count up by 5	Count up by 10	Count up by 50	Count up by 250	Count up by _____ (your choice)
40	40	40	40	40
____	____	____	____	____
____	____	____	____	____
____	____	____	____	____
____	____	____	____	____
____	____	____	____	____
____	____	____	____	____
____	____	____	____	____
____	____	____	____	____
____	____	____	____	____
____	____	____	____	____
____	____	____	____	____
____	____	____	____	____

Practice Page C

Fill in the numbers you say if you start at 2500 and count down by each counting number.

Count down by 10	Count down by 25	Count down by 50	Count down by 250	Count down by _____ (your choice)
2500	2500	2500	2500	2500
_____	_____	_____	_____	_____
_____	_____	_____	_____	_____
_____	_____	_____	_____	_____
_____	_____	_____	_____	_____
_____	_____	_____	_____	_____
_____	_____	_____	_____	_____
_____	_____	_____	_____	_____
_____	_____	_____	_____	_____
_____	_____	_____	_____	_____
_____	_____	_____	_____	_____
_____	_____	_____	_____	_____

Practice Page
Patterns of Change

Practice Page D

For each problem, show how you found your solution.

Suppose that buttons come in bags of 8.

1. If there are 14 bags of buttons in a drawer, how many buttons are there altogether?

2. If there are 20 bags of buttons in a drawer, how many buttons are there altogether?

3. If there are 34 bags of buttons in a drawer, how many buttons are there altogether?

Practice Page E

For each problem, show how you found your solution.

Suppose that sports cards come in packs of 9.

1. If one box holds 24 packs, how many sports cards are there altogether?

2. If one box holds 50 packs, how many sports cards are there altogether?

3. If one box holds 72 packs, how many sports cards are there altogether?

Contents

chapter six

Writing for the Web   171

chapter seven

Writing for Broadcast   203

chapter eight

Writing Advertising Copy   231

chapter nine

Writing for Public Relations   271

chapter ten

The Writer and the Law   305
by Matthew Bunker

Writing is one thing; writing about writing is another. Like most people, I cannot remember the first word or the first sentence that I wrote. (I am reasonably sure they were not momentous.) I can remember always being encouraged to write, however, by parents and teachers who knew the importance of writing.

I have always enjoyed and admired good writing, and I continue to be in awe of it. How Mark Twain could have created such a wonderful and timeless story as *The Adventures of Tom Sawyer,* how Henry David Thoreau could have distilled his thoughts into the crisp and biting prose of *Walden,* or how Red Smith could have turned out high-quality material for his sports column day after day—all of this is continually amazing to me. I frankly admit that I don't know how they did it.

Yet here I am writing about writing. Why should I be doing this? At least three reasons occur to me immediately. I am fascinated by the process of writing. I write about it so that I can understand it better. For me, it is a process of self-education. I hope that some of the insights I have discovered will rub off on those who read this book.

I am convinced that while great writing might be a gift to a chosen few, good writing is well within the reach of the rest of us. There are things we can do to improve our writing.

I care about the language and the way it is used. Those of us who are fortunate enough to have English as a native language have been given a mighty tool with which to work. It is powerful and dynamic. An underlying purpose of this book is to encourage the intelligent and respectful use of this tool.

This book is the product of many people, some of whom were listed in the first three editions. I particularly want to thank David Davies, who generously contributed many of his exercises and ideas, and Matt Bunker, who wrote the chapter on media and the law despite a very short deadline. Debbie Elliott, once a student at the University of Alabama and now a correspondent for National Public Radio, has an excellent essay on writing for radio that is worth the price of the book.

I would also like to thank LaRae M. Donnellan, Florida A & M University, and Laurence W. Fennelly, Macon State College, who conducted a review of the sixth edition and gave me many helpful suggestions.

My colleagues at Emory and Henry College—Teresa Keller, Tracy Lauder, Herb Thompson, and Paul Blaney—have been especially supportive of this edition of the book.

I also want to thank Pam Doyle, who offered some extremely helpful suggestions on the "Writing for Broadcast" chapter for the third edition, and I continue to use those ideas; and Mark Arnold, who uses the book and has a unique perspective on what belongs in it.

My colleagues on the faculty of the Department of Journalism at the University of Alabama, especially Ed Mullins, Kim Bissell, the late Bailey Thomson, George Daniels, and David Sloan, have always supported me in the efforts that I have put into this book. George Rable, Guy Hubbs, and John Hall—scholars and gentlemen all—gave me more support than they know.

Molly Taylor and Michael Kish at Allyn and Bacon continued with their help and support through yet another manuscript and revision. I also have many friends and former students now in the communication professions who have been kind and generous with their support and ideas.

My wife, Sally, remains my chief critic and always a source of encouragement. My son, Jefferson, as I write this, is in graduate school at Florida State University, making his own contributions to the world of writing.

This book, like the previous editions, is dedicated to my mother, Martha Elizabeth Stovall, who was my first editor.

James Glen Stovall

James Glen Stovall teaches mass communication at Emory and Henry College in Emory, Virginia. From 1978 to 2003 he taught journalism at the University of Alabama. He received his Ph.D. from the University of Tennessee and is a former reporter and editor for several newspapers, including the Chicago *Tribune*. He also has more than five years of public relations experience. He is the author of a number of books, including *Web Journalism: Practice and Promise of a New Medium* (2004), *Journalism: Who, What, When, Where, Why and How* (2005), and *Infographics: A Journalist's Guide* (1997), all published by Allyn and Bacon.

chapter one

Sit Down and Write

I have sworn upon the altar of God, eternal hostility against every form of tyranny over the mind of man. (1800)

Equal and exact justice to all men, of whatever state or persuasion, religious or political; peace, commerce, and honest friendship with all nations, entangling alliance with none . . . Freedom of religion; freedom of the press, and freedom of person under the protection of the habeas corpus, and trial by juries impartially selected. These principles form the bright constellation which has gone before us and guided our steps through an age of revolution and reformation. (1801)

Enlighten the people generally and tyranny and oppressions of the body and mind will vanish like evil spirits at the dawn of day. (1816)

Thomas Jefferson

Ideas carry a society forward. The ideas of freedom, independence, individualism, religion, and social order first existed in the minds of men and women but have been crystallized for us by great writers and thinkers such as Thomas Jefferson.

The written word is one of the most powerful forces available to humans. It has the ability to carry ideas and information, to entertain and distract, and to change the lives of individuals and nations. The person who wants to write rarely realizes the power that is contained in writing. Yet it is there—and available to those who have the information and ideas and who are clever and hardworking enough to learn to write well.

How do you write well? That question defies an easy, quick, or simple answer. Yet all of us have had to consider it. We began that consideration at least by the time we were in the second grade when our teachers made us write in paragraphs. By the fourth grade, we were learning the rules of grammar and punctuation, wondering what in the world these things had to do with good writing. (A lot, as it turns out, although we still may be reluctant to admit it.) Outside the classroom, we were writing in our diaries or writing thank-you letters to relatives and notes to friends.

At some point, we learned that whatever else writing is—fun, exciting, rewarding—it is not easy. Writing is hard work. As Red Smith, a sportswriter for the New York *Times,* once put it, "There's nothing to writing. All you do is sit down at a typewriter and open a vein."

Smith's point is not just that writing is hard but also that it requires us to give of ourselves in ways that other activities, such as reading, do not. Writing demands

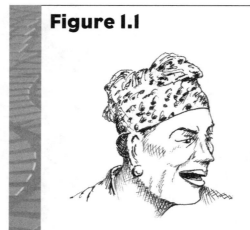

Figure 1.1

Maya Angelou on the untold story

There is no greater agony than bearing an untold story inside you.

total commitment, even if it is just for a few minutes. We can think of nothing else and do nothing else when we are writing. The first step to good writing is recognizing this essential point.

But the question still remains. How do you gather together the words that will convey the information, ideas, or feelings you want to give to the reader? How do you write well?

WHAT IS GOOD WRITING?

Good writing, especially good writing for the mass media, is clear, concise, simple, and to the point. It transmits information, ideas, and feelings to the reader clearly but without overstatement. Good writing is writing that outlines pictures of ideas that readers can fill in with their imagination.

Good writing is efficient. It uses the minimum number of words to make its point. It doesn't waste the reader's time.

Good writing is precise. Good writers use words for their exact meaning; they do not throw words around carelessly.

Good writing is clear. It leaves no doubt or confusion in the reader's mind about its meaning.

Finally, good writing is modest. It does not draw attention to itself. Good writing does not try to show off the writer's intelligence. It lets the content speak for itself, and it allows readers to receive messages directly. Writing should not get in the way of what people need and want to read.

GETTING READY TO WRITE

Those who would write for the mass media must understand the implications of what they do. Part of the prewriting process is developing a sense of what it means to communicate with a mass audience. Writers should understand that they are no longer writing for individuals (an essay for an English teacher, an e-mail to a friend) but for a larger audience.

Nor are they writing for themselves. Much of the writing done in K–12 education is justified as a means of self-expression for students. This kind of writing is a valuable exercise for all individuals, but in the mass media environment, there is relatively little room for self-expression. Audiences are interested in the information and ideas that a writer possesses, not in how the writer feels or in what the writer thinks. This fact drives the spare, unadorned style of writing that the media demand.

Following closely on this deemphasis of self-expression is that in most media environments, writing is a collaborative effort. Writers may work together to produce a single piece of writing. Editors—people whose job it is to read the writing of others—are employed at every level. Writers expect to be edited. Their work is not completely their own. Someone else has the power to alter and, we hope, improve the writing. The editing process is inseparable from the process of writing for the mass media.

Both within their own psyches and in their working environments, writers for the mass media need to develop an active sense of integrity about what they do. This sense of integrity serves as a regulator for their behavior, making them unwilling to accept inaccuracies or imprecision in the writing process and unable to live with less than a very high standard of personal and intellectual honesty. They must understand and assimilate the ethical standards of their profession.

Would-be writers for the mass media should understand enough about the process of writing to know that they can always improve, that they can always do better.

Figure 1.2

Isaac Asimov on thinking and writing clearly

I try only to write clearly, and I have the very good fortune to think clearly so that the writing comes out as I think, in satisfactory shape.

They must view their craft with a generous dose of humility. Every writer, no matter how experienced or talented, begins with a blank page or an empty computer screen. The writer must put the words there, and no amount of experience or talent guarantees success. A good writer should always be willing to do whatever it takes to improve in the craft.

Finally, the would-be writer must do the following four things.

Know the Tools of the Trade

Just as a good carpenter knows hammers and nails, good writers must know and understand the tools with which they work. For writers, knowledge of the rules of grammar and spelling is mandatory. (Not all writers have to be great spellers, but they should know the rules, and they should always work with a dictionary close at hand.) Writers must know the precise meanings of words and how to use words precisely; although they do not have to use every word they know, having a variety available gives the writer extra tools to use if needed. (Most of us have a vocabulary of about 5,000 to 6,000 words; one scholar has estimated that William Shakespeare knew about 30,000 words.)

Writers must not only know the language but must also understand and be genuinely interested in it. English is a marvelous language and a wonderful tool for writers. It also changes constantly. New words are coined, and old ones go out of fashion. Writers for the mass media should take their natural role as caretakers of the language seriously, and they should be unwilling to see English misused and abused.

Know the Subject

Writers must have a clear idea to guide them in their writing. Writers must understand thoroughly what they are writing about, or readers will not understand what they have written. Beginning writers frequently have trouble with this most basic requirement of good writing. They sometimes believe that they can write their way through a subject, that just getting the words down is enough. Even experienced media professionals occasionally fail to understand their topics. For example, some journalists try to write about events without properly researching the background or checking with enough sources. Advertising copywriters may try to compose ads without understanding the product or the audience toward whom the ad is directed. In both cases, the writing is likely to miss the mark and may be confusing and inefficient.

If you are writing about something that you do not understand, stop writing and find out what you need to know. Ask questions of people who do know. Look information up. Or just think the subject through more thoroughly. Writing without understanding or without having your subject firmly in mind is like writing with a broken pencil.

Write It Down

This may be the most basic point of all: You cannot be a writer unless you put words on paper or on a computer screen. People can think, talk, and agonize all night about what they would like to write. They can read and discuss; they can do research and even make notes. But no one is a writer until ideas become words and sentences become paragraphs. At some point, the writer must sit down and write.

Writing is hard work, and few people have the tenacity to stick with it. Anthony Trollope, a nineteenth century English novelist, would begin writing at 5:30 A.M. He would write for two and a half hours, producing at least 250 words every fifteen minutes. Trollope responded to the demands of writing with a strict routine. So did Isaac Asimov, who wrote books on subjects ranging from Shakespeare to the Bible to science fiction. Asimov would wake up every morning at 6:00 and be at his typewriter writing by 7:30 A.M. He would then work until 10 P.M. Asimov wrote more than 500 books in his lifetime.

Writing is physically difficult because it requires the writer to maintain a stationary position and concentrate for a long time. Writing is mentally difficult because of the effort it takes to know a subject well enough and to think clearly enough to put one's thoughts about the subject down on paper. A writer is faced with a thousand ways to say something and has to work out which is best for the information and the context in which he or she is writing.

In addition, writing involves some risk. Writers can never be certain that they will be successful. Something happens to our beautiful thoughts when we try to confine them to complete sentences, and what happens is not always good. Writers always face the chance of failure.

Writers for the mass media have some advantage in overcoming this chance of failure. Their job is to write, and their circumstances force them to write. They must meet deadlines, often on a daily basis. They can sometimes use forms and structures that will help them to produce the writing necessary for their medium. Still, they must produce. They cannot fall victim to what is commonly called *writer's block*.

Edit and Rewrite

Writing is such hard work that most of us want to do it once and forget about it. That's natural, but good writers don't give in to this tendency. Good writers have the discipline to reread, edit, and rewrite.

Rewriting requires that a writer read his or her work critically. Writers cannot go through this process patting themselves on the back for all the fine phrases they have produced. Writers must constantly ask whether the writing can be clearer, more precise, and more readable. And writers should have the courage to say, "This isn't what I wanted to say" or even "This isn't very good."

Figure 1.3   Rewriting and Editing

In this early draft of text from Chapter 1, note how the editing process changed and improved the final copy.

to change and move text, and the proper use of spelling checkers and other utility programs. Writing for the mass media today demands that writers use their time and equipment efficiently.

Writers must

Know your subject. Writers must have a clear idea to guide ~~them in~~ *they* their writing. ~~If you do not~~ *or* understand thoroughly what ~~you are~~ writing *they* about, ~~your~~ readers will not understand what ~~you~~ have written. *they* Beginning writers frequently have trouble with this most basic requirement of good writing. They sometimes believe that they can "write" their ~~way through a subject, that~~ just getting the words down is enough. Even experienced media professionals ~~sometimes~~ *occasionally* fail to understand their topics. For example, some journalists try to write about events without properly researching the background or checking with enough sources. ~~Some~~ *A* advertising copywriters *may* try to compose ads without understanding the product or ~~the audience~~ to whom the ad is directed. In both cases, the writing misses the mark. It is ~~often~~ confusing and inefficient.

If you are writing about something you do not understand, stop writing and find out what you need to know. Ask questions of people who do know. Look ~~things~~ *information* up. Or just think the subject through more thoroughly. Writing without understanding or without having your subject firmly in ~~your own~~ mind is like writing with a broken pencil.

Write it down. This may be the most basic point of all: You cannot be a writer unless you put words on paper or on a computer screen. People can think, talk, and agonize all night about what they would like to write. They can read and discuss; they can do research and even make notes. But no one is a writer until ideas become words, and sentences become paragraphs. At some point, the writer must sit down and write. *people*

Writing is ~~very~~ hard work ~~for most people~~, and few have the tenacity to stick with it. Anthony Trollope, a nineteenth-century English novelist, would begin writing at 5:30 a.m. He would write for two and a half hours, producing at least 250 words every fifteen minutes. Trollope responded to the demands of writing with a strict routine. So did Isaac Asimov, a man who wrote books on subjects ranging from Shakespeare to the Bible to science fiction. Asimov would wake up every morning at 6 a.m. and be at his typewriter writing by 7:30 a.m. He would then work until 10 p.m. He wrote more than 500 books in his lifetime.

Writing is physically difficult because it demands maintaining a stationary position and concentrating for a long time. Writing is mentally

---

Writers for the mass media often work in circumstances that dictate that someone else read what they have written and make judgments about it. Having another person read what you have written and then give you an honest evaluation of it usually makes for better writing. But writers for the mass media are also at a disadvantage because their deadline pressures often prevent thorough rereading and rewriting.

BASIC TECHNIQUES

The suggestions in this section are commonly accepted techniques for improving your writing. Many of them are useful at the rewriting stage of your work, but you should try to keep them in mind as your words are going down on paper or on the computer screen for the first time. Not all of these suggestions fit every piece of writing you will do, so they need not be considered a strict set of rules. They do constitute a good set of habits for a writer to develop, however.

Write Simply

This is a thought you will see repeatedly in this book. The key to clarity is simplicity. A clear, simple writing style is not the exclusive possession of a few gifted writers. Such a style can be achieved by students who are just beginning a writing career. The power of simple writing is immense. The following quotations are famous because they convey powerful messages in clear and simple language:

> These are the times that try men's souls. (Thomas Paine, 1776)

> Rose is a rose is a rose is a rose. (Gertrude Stein, 1913)

> I have a dream. (Martin Luther King, Jr., 1963)

Use Simple Words

"It is a general truth," Henry Fowler wrote in *Modern English Usage,* "that short words are not only handier to use but more powerful in effect; extra syllables reduce, not increase, vigour." Fowler was talking about the modern tendency to use "facilitate" instead of "ease," "numerous" instead of "many," "utilize" instead of "use," and the like. Many people try to use big or complicated words, thinking that these will impress the reader. They don't; they have the opposite effect. Benjamin Franklin once wrote, "To write clearly, not only the most expressive, but the plainest words should be chosen."

Figure 1.4

Mark Twain on using simple words

I never write "metropolis" for seven cents because I can get the same price for "city." I never write "policeman" because I can get the same money for "cop."

Use Simple Sentences

Not every sentence you write should be in the simple sentence format (subject-predicate or subject-verb-object), but the simple sentence is a good tool for cleaning up muddy writing. For example, take the following sentence, which appeared in a large daily newspaper: "She was shot through the right lung after confronting a woman married to her ex-husband inside the Food World store on Bankhead Highway shortly before 1 P.M." The confusion could be lessened by breaking this one sentence into three simple sentences: "She was in the Food World store on Bankhead Highway. Shortly before 1 P.M., she confronted the woman married to her ex-husband. She was shot through the right lung."

Simple, straightforward prose is mandatory for writing for the mass media. It has no substitute, and its absence will not be excused by readers or listeners.

Don't Use One Word More Than Is Necessary

A first cousin to simplicity is brevity. Almost every writer uses too many words on occasion. Even the best writers need to be edited. Go back a couple of paragraphs and look at the Fowler quote; it has at least two unnecessary words: "in effect." If we eliminated those words, the sentence would not lose any information and would increase in power.

Writers should never use one more word than is necessary in their writing. They should be on the lookout for words, phrases, and sentences that do not add substantially to the content of what they are writing. They should also guard against fancy phrases that draw attention to the writing and the writer and take away from the content.

Eliminate Jargon, Clichés, and Bureaucratese

Jargon is the technical language that is used in specialized fields or among a small group of people with a common interest. Scientists, lawyers, sportswriters, and even students have their own jargon. Good writers, especially those who write for the mass media, use words and phrases that are commonly understood by most people rather than the jargon that only a few can understand. It makes no sense to cut readers off from receiving your ideas by using language that they cannot comprehend.

Clichés are overused words, phrases, and clauses. They are groups of words that have ceased to be meaningful and have become trite and tiresome. For example, *dire straits, he's got his act together, it's a small world, par for the course, you don't want to go there,* and *vast wasteland* have been used so often that they have lost their original luster. All of us have our favorite clichés; the trick is not to use them.

Bureaucratese is a general name for a serious misuse of the language. To make themselves or what they write sound more important, many people try to lather their writing with unnecessary and imprecise phrasing. A speechwriter once handed President Franklin Roosevelt a draft of a speech with the following sentence: "We are endeavoring to construct a more inclusive society." Roosevelt changed it to: "We are going to make a country in which no one is left out." Roosevelt's simple words carried far more weight than those of his speechwriter.

Once, a football coach at a major state university was on a recruiting trip and heard over the radio that he had been fired. The next day, the athletic director at the school issued the following statement: "I regret the premature publication of the decision before appropriate notification could be made to all parties involved." The athletic director would not have sounded like such a fool if he had simply said, "I'm sorry we didn't get to tell him before the story got out."

Use Familiar Words Rather Than Unfamiliar Words or Foreign Phrases

William F. Buckley, a conservative newspaper columnist, tries to include in each column at least one or two words that will send his readers scurrying to a dictionary. Readers expect this of Buckley and seem to accept it. Buckley is the exception, however. Most writers cannot get away with this practice. Although there are times when a writer must use a word that is not known by all of a mass audience, those times are rare. Writers should not try to educate their readers by introducing them to new words. Such writing slows the reader down; it makes the reader think about the writing rather than the content; and it eventually drives the reader away.

Foreign phrases often have the same effect. They add little to the content and often irritate the reader. At times they may even be insulting, particularly when the writer does not bother to translate them.

Vary Sentence Type and Length

There are four kinds of sentence structures: simple, complex, compound, and compound-complex. Following are some examples:

Simple: Alex wrote a letter to his friend.

Compound: Alex wrote a letter, and he mailed it the next day.

Complex: Alex wrote a letter that contained his confession to the crime.

Compound-complex: Alex wrote a letter than contained his confession, and he mailed it the next day.

The technical differences among these types of sentences are explained in Chapter 2. The point here is that using only one kind of sentence is boring. A good variety of types and lengths of sentences gives a pleasing pace to writing. It allows the reader's mind to "breathe," to take in ideas and information in small doses.

Such variation also helps the writer. Writers often get so involved in what they are writing that they have trouble expressing their ideas clearly. They try to pack too much into one sentence or one paragraph. Breaking down complex and compound sentences into simple sentences, and then putting these sentences back into a variety of forms, often promotes clarity in writing.

One thing writers should not overuse is the inverted sentence. A good example of this kind of sentence is the previous sentence—as is this sentence. The inverted sentence puts the subject at the end rather than the beginning and is not a good idea for media writing. Writers should convey ideas and information to readers quickly and efficiently.

Pay Attention to Nouns and Verbs

Nouns and verbs are the strongest words in the language. Sentences should be built around nouns and verbs; adjectives and adverbs, when they are used, should support the nouns and verbs. Relying on adjectives and adverbs, particularly in writing for the mass media, produces weak and lifeless writing.

Verbs are the most important words that a writer will use. A good verb denotes action; a better verb denotes action and description. While adjectives and adverbs modify (that is, they limit), verbs expand the writing. A good writer pays close attention to the verbs that he or she uses. They get the reader involved in the writing as no other part of speech does.

Transitions Tie Together What You Have Written

Readers should be able to read through a piece of writing without stops or surprises. Introducing a new idea or piece of information without adequately tying it to other parts of a story is one way to stop a reader cold.

WRITING FOR THE MASS MEDIA

The principles of good writing such as those listed in the previous section apply to any type of writing. The good English theme has much in common with the good news story or the good letter to Mom or the informative label on a bottle of aspirin. These pieces of writing have different purposes and different audiences, and they express different ideas. But good writing is good writing.

Writing for the mass media differs from other forms of writing in several aspects.

Subject Matter

Writers for the mass media must take on a wide variety of subjects and use a variety of formats, including news stories, feature stories, advertisements, letters, and editorials.

Purpose

Writing for the mass media has three major purposes: to inform, entertain, or persuade.

Audience

Mass media writing is often directed at a wide audience, and this fact dictates not only the subject matter but also the way in which something is written.

Circumstances of the Writing

Writing for the mass media often takes place in the presence of others who are doing the same thing. The writing is frequently done under deadline pressure, and many times several people will have a hand in writing and editing a particular item for the mass media.

BECOMING A PROFESSIONAL

Much of what has been discussed in this chapter has revolved around the qualities and skills necessary to be a professional writer. Those who want to make a career of writing in a media environment have to develop these personal and professional qualities and must hone their skills.

One quality that we have not discussed yet is versatility. Rarely do media professionals stay with their first job. Even more rarely does their career involve just one type of writing. Most professionals will have a variety of jobs throughout their career, and they will be called on to write in various forms and structures. Developing a professional agility will be a valuable asset to anyone who pursues a writing career.

This book, in fact, is based on the assumption that all writers need to learn a variety of forms to survive in the mass media. Here students will learn some of the basic principles of good writing—techniques that we have already reviewed in this chapter. Students will read about the importance of using standard English well and the vital role that a stylebook will play in their daily work. They will also be introduced to some of the basic forms of writing.

One of the most important forms is the inverted pyramid structure of news writing. This structure demands that information be presented in order of its importance rather than in chronological order. The writing must also conform to certain journalistic conventions, such as attribution and proper identification of persons mentioned in the story.

Broadcast writing—writing that is written to be read aloud and heard—demands a different structure, dramatic unity, that emphasizes simplicity and efficiency.

Writing advertising copy requires that writers have a facility with the language so that they can use information for persuasive effects.

Writing for public relations calls for wide versatility on the part of practitioners. In most public relations jobs, writers must use the inverted pyramid, good letter-writing structures, and broadcast and advertising techniques.

Writing for the World Wide Web combines all of these structures, techniques, and forms. Still, there is a type of writing on the Web that is almost peculiarly its own. That type of writing has its base in a concept called *hypertext*. Prose writing is linear; that is, the reader begins at the beginning and reads through to the end. Hypertext is nonlinear; the text is broken into bits and structured so that a reader can begin at any number of points and decide which sequence suits his or her purposes. These bits of writing should relate to the whole, but they also need to stand by themselves within the context of the entire article or website. They are generally hierarchical; that is, they go from the general to the specific. But because the Web offers readers the opportunity to move quickly from one item to another, the writer must also look for opportunities to link parts of the writing with other parts to make it easier for the reader to move around. This means that the writer needs to anticipate how a reader might navigate within a website.

Another demand on writers using the hypertext structure is the ability to write headlines, subheads, and summaries. Writing headlines and subheads for the Web is far less restrictive than writing them for newspapers or magazines in terms of making them fit into a certain space. Web writers are likely to have many more options and fewer typographical rules than the headline writer for newspapers. But their ability to summarize, whether in headline, subhead, or summary form, will be severely tested, just as it is in traditional media. Summaries demand precise and concise use of the language. They also demand that the writer understand the material being summarized so well that he or she can do it accurately. Summarizing is a skill that is essential to the web writer. (All of these and other concepts of writing for the Web will be covered in Chapter 6.)

TEXT AND IMAGES

The advent of the World Wide Web has highlighted another phenomenon that writers should understand: the integration of graphics and text. The best publications, broadcasts, and websites are built around strong graphic as well as textual elements. Graphics are a vital part of mass communication, and people who are involved in any mass medium must be fluent in the use of both graphics and text.

The integration of graphics and text is an interesting phenomenon because it simulates in some ways written communication before the printing press was invented around 1455. Writers often freely used both graphics and text to transmit their ideas and information. Leonardo da Vinci, one of the greatest intellects and most talented people in the history of Western civilization, used both text and drawings for his scientific journals. Many of his writings were texts that were built around a variety of pictures (see Figure 1.5).

The advent of the printing press signaled a more distinct delineation of graphics from text. For the printing press, the emphasis was on text. Type could be handled easily and quickly on the press; that was the basis of its profound impact on human beings. But graphics and illustrations were left behind. The press could handle such items, but they were a lot more trouble to produce than simple type.

The development of the technology to produce graphics lagged far behind, and it was not until the late nineteenth century that it began to catch up. During the last half of the nineteenth century, publishers developed techniques that could get illustrations into print along with type. The halftoning process that allows pictures to be printed was part of this technological development.

Still, graphics were not fully integrated with text. This was possibly due to the legacy of 400 years of printing text. As mentioned above, text was most important in the printing press, and graphics were extra. We still live with that legacy today. For example, almost every biography that is published contains pictures, but they are usually grouped onto a few pages in the middle of the book, or in two or three places if the book is long. Technically, a picture can be placed in a part of the book where the text refers to it. But our habit of separating text and graphics lives on.

Figure 1.5   Leonardo da Vinci's Journals

Leonardo da Vinci could observe, write, and draw, and he integrated these skills in his journal entries. He was not bound by columns of type or other restrictions of the printing press.

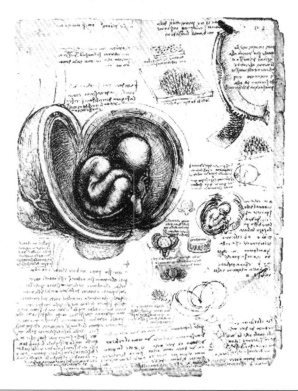

By the last quarter of the twentieth century, news publications were beginning to see the value of graphics and illustrations in presenting content to the reader. Graphics could say what text could not, and they could show what photographs could not. Newspapers such as the Chicago *Tribune* made major investments in producing good graphics and integrating them with text material. The explosion of *USA Today* onto the world of journalism in 1982 took the use of graphics for journalistic purposes to a new level. Journalists began to learn the uses and conventions of presenting data in a graphic format, and they quickly began to see the value of graphics in presenting information quickly and efficiently.

The World Wide Web, ironically, brings us one step closer to the techniques of the fifteenth century writer, who used both text and graphics in a sometimes seamless way. Leonardo da Vinci's wide range of talents—and his willingness to make full use of them—gives us a fitting metaphor for meeting the challenges of communicating in the twenty-first century. Today's writer will have to know more than just how to communicate with text. The writer will need to know the conventions and uses of graphic forms and must constantly be on the alert for better ways to present information and ideas. The twenty-first century writer must have a wide range of understanding about how to communicate and how to use the tools—all of the tools—of communication.

AND FINALLY . . .

With the proper study and practice, anyone can become a better writer. Writing is not simply an inherent talent that some people have and others do not. There are steps that each of us can take to improve our writing, and this book will examine some of those steps and help you put them into practice.

Writing is a process. That is, the rules, techniques, and suggestions in this book must be mixed in with the individual's style, thoughts, and methods, and with the subject and form of the writing. They all should work together to produce writing that is good. The suggestions that are made in this book about achieving good writing are meant to help this process work.

Writing requires discipline. Most people give up writing as soon as they can because it is such hard work. It is physically, mentally, and emotionally demanding. The person who commits to writing must marshal all of his or her resources for the task.

Writing is building. Good writing doesn't happen all at once. It is formed, word by word, sentence by sentence, thought by thought. The writing process is often slow, tedious, and frustrating. But the product of this process—good writing—is well worth the effort.

Finally, reading about good writing is only the first step in learning about good writing. Reading good writing is the next step. If you are interested in learning to write well, in any form, you should read as much as possible—newspapers, magazines, books, and anything else you can get your hands on. Then there is the writing itself. This chapter tells you to "sit down and write." That is the only way to become a good writer.

POINTS FOR CONSIDERATION AND DISCUSSION

1. The author makes several strong points about what is and is not good writing. Did you find anything surprising or unusual about them? Do you agree with what he says about good writing?
2. Many teachers and philosophers believe the following: "Writing is thinking." How do you react to this statement?

3. Do you think that writing is becoming more visual, as the author asserts? Look at the page from the journal of Leonard da Vinci in Figure 1.5. The page includes some notes he made about the engineering of water-lifting equipment. With the advent of the Internet, are we about to embark on an age of writing that looks like this?

4. Take a passage from a book that you have read recently. What characteristics of good writing discussed in this chapter are exemplified in that passage? What characteristics of good writing are not present?

5. In the passage that you selected, make a list of the verbs. How many of them are linking verbs ("to be" verbs, such as *is*, *was*, and *were*)? How many of them are active verbs? How many are passive?

6. The author says, "Good writing is good writing," no matter what form it's in. What does he mean by that? Do you agree?

FURTHER READING

Arnold, G. T. (2003). *Media Writer's Handbook*. New York: McGraw-Hill.

Brooks, B. S., Pinson J., & Wilson, J. G. (2003). *Working with Words* (5th ed.). New York: Bedford/St. Martins.

Clark, R. P., & Campbell, C. C. (Eds.). (2002). *The Value and Craft of American Journalism*. Gainesville: University Press of Florida.

LaRocque, P. (2003). *The Book on Writing: The Ultimate Guide to Writing Well*. Oak Park, IL: Marion Street Press.

Stepp, C. S. (2000). *Writing as Craft and Magic*. New York: McGraw-Hill.

Strunk, W., & White, E. B. (1999). *The Elements of Style* (4th ed.). New York: Macmillan.

Zinsser, W. (2001). *On Writing Well: 25th Anniversary Edition*. New York: Harper Resource.

WEBSITES

American Society of Journalists and Authors: **www.asja.org**

American Society of Newspaper Editors: **www.asne.org**

Power of Words: **www.projo.com/words**

Poynter Online's "Fifty Writing Tools": **www.poynter.org/content/content_view.asp?id=61811**

Writers Write: The Write Resource: **www.writerswrite.com**

EXERCISES

Following is a variety of beginning writing exercises. Try to apply the principles outlined in this chapter as you complete the exercises. Remember that presenting information is more important than telling how you feel about the subject. Also, remember that you should write as simply as possible, using words and phrases that everyone will understand.

1.1 Autobiography 1

Write a 350-word summary of your life. Tell the most important things that have happened to you. Also talk about the things that interest you the most.

1.2 Letter to Mom

Write a letter to your mother, father, or some other close relative. The main part of your letter should be about the course that requires this assignment. Include some information about the professor for the course, what the course is about, the procedures for the class, the grading and attendance policies, and anything else you think is important. You will also want to give the name of your lab instructor. The letter should be at least 250 words long.

1.3 Describe Your Neighbor

Describe the person sitting nearest to you. Be specific. Give the reader a lot of details about the person's physical appearance, including hair and eye color, height, shape of the face, the kind of clothes the person is wearing, and so on. Write at least 200 words.

1.4 An Incident

Write about something that happened to you in the last week. It could be something dramatic, such as being in an automobile accident or meeting a famous person, or something common, such as eating a meal or taking a ride on a bus. You should include some dialogue (quoting someone directly) in the description of this incident. Write 250 words.

1.5 Action

Describe a person or a group of people doing something. It could be something like a couple of carpenters building a part of a house or your roommate trying to type a paper. Be sure to focus on the physical activity and on how people are doing it. Don't try to describe how the people feel or what they may think about what they are doing. Simply write about what you can see and hear. Write 350 words.

1.6 Autobiography 2

Write a 200-word autobiography in the third person; that is, do not use *I, me,* or any other first-person pronoun. Use only simple sentences.

Here's an example of how it might begin:

John Smith was born on April 15, 1983, in Decatur, Illinois. He is the son of Adele and Wayne Smith. John's parents moved to Chicago when he was three years old.

1.7 Autobiography 3

Write a 300-word autobiography, but confine it to a single aspect of your life. As in Exercise 1.6, write in the third person.

Select the aspect of your life that you want to write about. Think about all of the different ways in which that aspect of your life affects you. Think also about how it began and what it means to you now. Construct your essay around the points that you think are the most important.

In your first sentence, let the reader know immediately what you are writing about, and try to use an active, descriptive verb.

Here's an example:

Playing the piano always lifts the spirits of John Smith.

From the first sentence, there should be no doubt about the subject of this essay.

1.8 Biography

Write a 300-word biography of one of your classmates; as in Exercise 1.7, confine it to a single aspect of his or her life.

Everything you write in this essay should be accurate, so you will have to talk with that person.

Make sure you spell that person's name correctly and accurately record all of the details you will include in your essay.

Remember that you are writing about only one aspect of that person's life, not a complete biography. Leave out information that does not pertain directly to the specific subject about which you are writing.

As in the previous exercise, let the reader know immediately what your subject is and try to use a strong, active verb in the first sentence.

1.9 Instructions 1

Tell step by step how to do one of the following things:

- Build a fire.
- Change the oil in a car.
- Apply lipstick.
- Make a sandwich.
- Brush and floss your teeth.
- Change a tire.
- Do a load of laundry.

Use simple terms and simple sentences so that anyone who can read could understand it. Following is an example of such a set of directions.

To drive a nail into a piece of wood, follow the steps below:

1. Lay the wood flat on a solid surface.
2. Check the nail that you are using to make sure it is straight; if it is bent, discard it and choose another.

3. Hold the pointed end of the nail against the wood with the thumb and the first finger.

Etc.

The activity that you describe should have at least seven steps.

1.10 Instructions 2

Describe the procedure for tying a shoelace in 100 or fewer words. You might approach the assignment this way: Write the procedure without regard to how many words you are using. Once you have finished the first draft, edit it to take out as many words as possible but still have it make sense. What does this tell you about the way you write?

1.11 Building

Describe the building in which this class is being held. Don't go outside and look at it, but describe it from what you remember. Write at least 150 words.

1.12 Rewriting

Rewrite the following letter using simpler language. Make sure that you include all of the information that is contained in the original letter.

Dear Stockholder:

In accordance with company policies and the federal law, this letter is to inform you of the general annual meeting of the stockholders of this company which will be held on the 30th day of March of this year. The place of the meeting will be in the ballroom of the Waldorf Hotel, which is located at 323 Lexington Avenue, in New York. The beginning time of the meeting will be at nine o'clock in the morning on the 30th of March.

The agenda for this meeting includes a number of items and actions of great import to the company and its stockholders. The election of officers for the company's board of directors will take place beginning at approximately half past ten o'clock. This election follows the annual reports on the company's activities and financial position which will be presented by the president of the company and the chairman of the board of directors. Other items on the agenda include discussions of the company's operations in the foreign arena and the possibilities for investments in new areas of technology. Time will also be appropriated for discussions of general concerns of stockholders and for the answering of questions from stockholders directed to the company's officers. It is the sincere wish of the company's board of directors and officers that you will be able to attend this most important and hopefully informative meeting. The input of the company's stockholders is an important part of this company's operation and planning for the future.

Sincerely,
The Company President

1.13 Brevity

Edit all unnecessary words from the following expressions:

wore a white goatee on his chin
throughout the length and width of the entire nation
was positively identified
appeared to be ill
a dead body was found
in the city of Los Angeles
cost the sum of ten dollars
broke an existing rule
for the month of May
for a short space of time
an old pioneer
the present incumbent
will draw to a close
at the corner of Sixth and Elm streets
for the purpose of shocking

1.14 Wordiness

The following sentences use too many words. Edit them carefully to reduce the number of words, but do not cut out important information. If necessary, rewrite the sentences completely.

1. There was never any doubt whatsoever that Hannah would one day—and not too far in the distant future—become a famous and internationally known jazz singer who was recognized by jazz fans around the world.

2. Midville is not a large town but rather a fairly small place with a really small town atmosphere that offers a lot of safety and security to its residents and citizens and all who live there, especially to those who are raising families with small children.

3. Ed spent many long and tedious hours drawing the detailed map that charted and traced the growth of the church denomination to which he belonged from its beginnings to the present day.

4. At this point in time, Erin could not see any point at all in continuing to pay tuition to a college where she was absolutely convinced that we was not receiving the best education or her money's worth for the tuition she was spending.

5. Always confused by any kind of mathematical problem, Sally, for no reason that anyone could ever figure out, signed up for one of the hardest and most difficult math courses in the entire curriculum.

1.15 Wordiness

The following sentences use too many words. Edit them carefully to reduce the number of words, but do not cut out important information. If necessary, rewrite the sentences completely.

1. Owing to the fact that the prerequisite courses had not been taken by John, he was having a great deal of difficulty and had to spend a lot of time figuring out his schedule for the semester that is coming up.

2. There is little consideration given by our professors to the very real problem that our textbooks are often extremely costly and expensive.

3. Alex said that the thing to do if he wanted to improve his writing would be to read as many good books as he could possibly read in the time available to him.

4. Baseball has always been thought of as the national pastime, but for all intents and purposes, football has replaced baseball as the favorite sport for many people across this country.

5. During the period of time that included most of February, Laura stayed cooped up in her room and tried to fight off the effects of a very bad and debilitating cold.

6. Basically, I have a disinclination and a disinterest in helping people who are not willing to do some things such as show up for work on time and put forth the effort that it often takes to succeed in this life.

2

Basic Tools of Writing

good writing rests on a solid and working knowledge of the English language. Writers should know the rules of grammar, punctuation, and spelling. Knowledge and application of the rules expand rather than limit creativity.

Those of us who use English have a marvelous tool with which to work. It offers us many possibilities to express the information and ideas we have. But as with any other worker, the writer must know the tools of the trade—their possibilities as well as their limitations. Knowing when these tools can be properly used is vital. The writer who cannot effectively use the English language is like a carpenter who cannot saw a straight line. The products of such a writer or carpenter will not inspire confidence. Nor will they be items that people want to purchase.

Unlike the carpenter's hammer or saw, however, the English language is an extremely complex tool. It has many nuances and subtleties. People spend years mastering English. There are many rules for its usage and many arguments about the propriety of some of these rules.

One thing that makes English so complex is its dynamic nature. English is the closest thing the world has to an international language. It is spoken and understood by more than 300 million people in nearly every part of the globe, but no central authority governs its use. Consequently, the language is always changing. New words and expressions come into use as others fade. Old words take on new meanings. English is mixed with other languages. Spelling rules shift with differing usage. Humans are constantly discovering new phenomena that need description in the language. All this makes English a difficult but exciting tool.

Using a language effectively requires knowing its basic rules and conventions. Writers of English should know thoroughly the eight basic parts of speech (nouns, verbs, adjectives, adverbs, pronouns, conjunctions, interjections, and prepositions) and the basic unit of the English usage (the sentence) and its two parts (subject and predicate). They should have not only an eye for the language but also an ear for it. Writers should know when things that are technically correct sound wrong. Beyond that, they should be able to recognize—and hear—the confusing phrase, the unclear sentence, and the absence of transition. They must be able to spot the confusion and illogic that are the harbingers of misinformation, inaccuracy, and a failure to communicate. Like the carpenter, the writer should use the language to draw a straight line to the reader.

That straight line is one of the chief goals of the writer for the mass media. The writer who does not use English correctly will annoy the reader and call a publication's credibility into question. A misspelled word will not destroy a publication, and an agreement error will not inspire calls for a repeal of the First Amendment, but too many such mistakes will convince the reader that a publication is not worth his or her time and money.

GRAMMAR

Grammar is a system of rules that defines the use of the language. Because English is complex and widely used, its grammar rules are involved, complex, sometimes contradictory, and constantly changing. Yet all of us manage to learn some form of grammar, and we tend to use the language with a consistency that conforms to the rules that we have learned.

English is too dynamic a language to say that the rules of grammar are absolute. The best we can say is that grammar rules are commonly accepted or that they

Figure 2.1   Samuel Johnson

Samuel Johnson (on the right in the picture) was an unlikely candidate to be a leading figure in the development of English, yet he is rated as second only to Shakespeare in his contributions. After nine years of work, Johnson produced the *Dictionary of the English Language* in 1755. It was not the first attempt at compiling, defining, and standardizing the spelling of the words in the English language, but it was to date the most elegant. The dictionary had 43,000 definitions and 114,000 quotations from all of English literature. Johnson's reputation was secured when he met a young Scottish lawyer, James Boswell, who became devoted to him. Boswell had a remarkable memory, and after Johnson died in 1784, Boswell wrote a two-volume biography of him that is still considered one of the greatest biographies in the English language.

JOHNSON AND BOSWELL AT THE MITRE.

are imposed, with varying degrees of effectiveness, by some authority such as an English teacher or a grammar book.

Many writers for the mass media take an active interest in the rules of grammar and language usage. They often join in debates about how a word should be spelled or which syntax is proper, and so they should. Writers need to have an interest in the language and how it is used. But that interest should be secondary to the more important goal of using the language so that it will convey the information and ideas that a writer must convey. Grammar, then, is a tool that allows the writer to communicate with an audience.

The purpose of this section is not to explain all grammar rules but to lay the foundation for an understanding of how the language is commonly used and to point out some problems that often plague those who are beginning to write for the mass media. We begin our look at language with one of its basic units: the sentence.

Sidebar 2.1
Glossary of Grammar Terms

- **Subject:** a noun or noun substitute about which something is asserted or asked in the predicate.

  John is a good student.

  They were happy to hear the news.

- **Verb:** words that denote action, occurrence, or existence.
  Run, jump, did, is, were, etc.

- **Verbals:** verbs used in forms that make them nouns or adjectives; three types of verbals exist:
  Gerund: A verb that ends in "-ing" and functions as a noun.

  Borrowing money is a mistake.

  Drinking before driving is dangerous.

  Participle: A verb form that may function as part of a verb phrase (*was laughing, had finished*) or as a modifier (a *finished* product; the players, *laughing* at their mistakes)

  Infinitive: A verb used primarily as a noun, usually in present tense and usually preceded by the word *to*.

  Hal wanted to *open* the present.

  She failed to *stop* on time.

- **Pronoun:** words that take the place of nouns (*he, she, it, we, they,* etc.).

- **Relative pronoun:** pronoun that refers to a noun elsewhere in the sentence.

  Leslie is the one *who* likes to bowl.

  The board delayed *its* vote.

- **Antecedent:** a word or group of words to which a pronoun refers.
  Like their trainers, *animals* can be polite or rude.
  The *board* approved the project, reversing its earlier decision.

- **Agreement:** correspondence in number or person of a subject and verb.

  A boy asks; boys ask.

  The woman did it herself; the man did it himself.

- **Clause:** A group of related words that contain a subject and a verb.
  Essential or restrictive clause: a phrase or clause that must be present for the sentence to make sense.

  Every drug *that is condemned by doctors* should be removed from the market.

  Nonessential or nonrestrictive clause: a phrase or clause not necessary to the meaning of the sentence and can be omitted.

  My best friend, *John,* understands me.

  The teacher gave extra credit, *which* helped some students.

  Independent clause: a clause that can stand alone in its meaning; an independent clause often functions as the main clause in the sentence.

  I want to go to Tut's Place because I am getting hungry.

  Dependent clause: a clause that serves as an adverb, an adjective or a noun in the sentence; a dependent clause cannot stand alone and maintain its full meaning.

I want to go to Tut's Place *because I am getting hungry.*

- **Inverted sentence:** one in which the usual or expected word order is changed; not recommended for media writing.
  At the head of the class stands the professor.

- **Coordinating conjunction:** a connective word used to connect and relate words and word groups of equal grammatical rank (*and, but, for, or, nor, so, yet*).

- **Modifier:** a word or word group that describes, limits, or modifies another.
  The *blue* sky encouraged us.
  He studied *vigorously* into the room.
  The doorway at the bottom of the stairs was *dark* and *foreboding.*

- **Parallelism:** a grammatical form that uses equal and corresponding words or word groups together in a sentence or paragraph.
  Wrong: *She likes running, cooking and to swim.*
  Correct: *She likes running, cooking and swimming.*

Sentences

A sentence is a group of words that contains a subject and a verb and expresses a complete thought. "John ran to the store" is a complete sentence; it has a subject (John) and a verb (ran), and it expresses a complete thought. "After the rain stopped" is not a complete sentence; it does have a subject and a verb, but it does not express a complete thought. A phrase such as "after the rain stopped" is called a *dependent clause;* it contains a subject and a verb but cannot stand alone. "John ran to the store" is called an *independent clause.*

Structurally, there are four kinds of sentences: simple, complex, compound, and compound-complex. A *simple sentence* is the same as an independent clause and has no dependent clauses, such as the following:

John ran to the store.

A *complex sentence* is one that has an independent clause and a dependent clause.

John ran to the store after the rain had stopped.

| Independent clause | | Dependent clause |

A *compound sentence* contains two independent clauses, and these clauses should be separated by a comma and a coordinating conjunction.

John ran to the store, but he walked back.

| Independent clause | / | Independent clause |

Comma and
coordinating conjunction

The sentence above is a compound sentence because it contains two independent clauses; they are separated by a comma and the coordinating conjunction *but*. Another common coordinating conjunction is *and*. Sometimes a semicolon substitutes for the comma and coordinating conjunction. All of the following sentences have the correct grammar and punctuation:

John ran to the store, and he walked back.

John ran to the store; he walked back.

John ran to the store. He walked back.

John ran to the store—he walked back.

A *compound-complex sentence* is a sentence that contains two independent clauses and a dependent clause. The independent clauses should be separated by a comma and a coordinating conjunction, as in the following sentence:

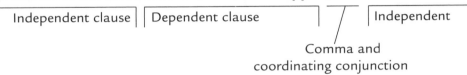

John ran to the store after the rain had stopped, but he walked back.

Independent clause | Dependent clause | Independent

Comma and coordinating conjunction

A good writer will recognize the kind of sentence that he or she is using. More importantly, experienced writers understand that they should be using all of these types of sentences in their writing. A good mixture of these different sentence types introduces a healthy variety to the writing that readers unconsciously appreciate.

In addition to the structural classification, sentences can also be classified by their content as declarative, interrogative, imperative, and exclamatory. A *declarative sentence* is one that makes a statement. This is the most common type of sentence. An *interrogative sentence* is one that asks a question, and it ends with a question mark (?). An *imperative sentence* is a command; it ends with a period, but it may also end with an exclamation mark (!). An *exclamatory sentence* expresses some strong emotion (excitement, joy, fear, etc.), and it usually ends with an exclamation mark.

Sentence Fragments

Earlier, we referred to sentences as groups of words that express a complete thought. Sometimes, someone will write a group of words that does not express a complete thought. That is a sentence fragment. There are some situations in writing in which using a sentence fragment may be appropriate. Generally, writers for the mass media write in complete sentences.

Parts of Speech

English contains eight parts of speech: nouns, pronouns, adjectives, adverbs, verbs, conjunctions, prepositions, and interjections. You should be able to recognize any of those in any sentence.

Nouns are the names of objects or concepts.

Pronouns are substitutes for nouns, and they are among the most confusing parts of speech. There are two ways of looking at pronouns. One way is to decide what "person" they refer to; they may be first-, second-, or third-person pronouns. Another way of looking at pronouns is to examine a pronoun's case: subjective, objective, or possessive. *Subjective case* means that the pronoun can be used as the subject of a sentence; *objective case* means that it can be used as the object of a verb or a preposition; *possessive case* means that the pronoun is used as a modifier for a noun and indicates possession.

Adjectives modify nouns; that is, they describe the noun or define it in some way.

Adverbs modify verbs, but they may also modify adjectives or other adverbs. Many adverbs end in "-ly."

Verbs express action or state of being. We usually refer to verbs as being in a particular tense—or indicating the time of the action. There are three basic tenses: past, present, and future. You should be able to recognize the tense of any verb in any sentence.

Conjunctions connect words, phrases, and clauses. The most commonly used coordinating conjunctions are *and, but, so, or,* and *nor.* Another class of conjunctions is the subordinating conjunction, words such as *although, because, nevertheless,* and *instead.*

Prepositions are words that go with nouns or pronouns to modify other nouns, pronouns, or verbs. Some common prepositions are *in, at, from, to, on,* and *with.*

Interjections are words that express strong emotion (e.g., *wow*!). When they are inserted into sentences, interjections should be set off by commas.

COMMON GRAMMAR PROBLEMS

Most of the time, most people use the language correctly. That includes students who are learning to write for the mass media. However, there are some areas of grammar that continue to give students problems. A few of these are discussed below.

Agreement

Agreement refers to singular or plural references. A singular subject takes a singular verb; plural subjects take plural verbs. In the sentence "The clock strikes on the hour," the subject is *clock.* A singular noun, *clock,* takes the singular verb, *strikes.* However, if the sentence were "The clocks strike on the hour," the plural subject, *clocks,* would take the plural verb, *strike.* All that is fairly simple, but consider a sentence such as this: "The consent of both sets of parents are needed for a juvenile marriage." The subject and verb in this sentence are not in agreement. *Consent* is the subject, not *sets* or *parents.* Consequently, the verb should be *is,* not *are.*

Agreement is also a problem when you are using pronouns to refer to nouns. These nouns are called *antecedents,* and pronouns should always agree with their antecedents. In the sentence "The boys believed they could win," the antecedent *boys* agrees in number with the pronoun *they.* Often, however, the following mistake is made: "The team believed they could win." The antecedent *team* is a singular noun, and its pronoun should also be singular. The sentence should read, "The team believed it could win."

Active and Passive Voice

Learning the active and passive voice is one of the most important grammatical tools a writer for the mass media can learn. Active and passive voice refer to the way in which verbs are used. When a writer uses a verb in the active voice, the emphasis is on the subject as the doer or perpetrator of the action. Passive voice throws the action onto the object and often obscures the perpetrator of the action. It is formed by putting a helping verb such as *is* or *was* in front of the past tense of the verb. Look at the following examples:

Active: John throws the ball.

Passive: The ball is thrown by John.

Active: The president sent the legislation to Congress.

Passive: The legislation was sent to Congress by the president.

Active: The governor decided to veto the bill.

Passive: It was decided by the governor to veto the bill.

Generally, writers for the mass media try to use active rather than passive voice. Active voice is more direct and livelier. It is less cumbersome than passive voice and gets the reader into the action of the words more quickly. When you edit your writing and find that you have written in the passive voice, ask yourself, "Would this sentence be better if the verb were in the active voice?" Very often the answer will be yes.

Sometimes, however, the answer will be no. Changing passive voice verbs to active voice can place the wrong emphasis in the sentence. Consider the following sentence: "The victims were rushed to a hospital by an ambulance." If we used the active voice, that sentence would read, "An ambulance rushed the victims to a hospital." However, the important topic is the victims, not the ambulance, so passive voice is probably preferable.

Take a look at the third set of active-passive examples above ("The governor decided"). In the passive voice sentence, the indefinite pronoun *it* is used with the passive voice verb. This usage is particularly insidious because the use of *it* obscures those who are responsible for an action. This construction—*it* with a passive voice verb—is not acceptable in writing for the mass media.

Dangling Participles

A participle phrase at the beginning of a sentence should modify the sentence's subject and should be separated from it by a comma. One would not write, "After driving from Georgia to Texas, Tom's car finally gave out." The car didn't drive to Texas. Someone drove it—perhaps Tom.

Appositive Phrases and Commas

Appositive phrases follow a noun and rename it. Such phrases are set off by commas in almost all cases. For example, in the sentence "Billy Braun, Tech's newest football star, was admitted to a local hospital yesterday," the phrase "Tech's newest football star" is the appositive to "Billy Braun." It is important to remember to put a second comma at the end of the appositive. This is easy to overlook if the appositive is extremely long. For example, the sentence "Job Thompson, the newly named Will Marcum State Junior College president who succeeded Byron Wilson has accepted the presidency of the Association of Junior College Administrators" needs a comma after "Wilson."

One variation on this rule is that commas should be used to set off nonrestrictive appositives—that is, appositives that are not strictly necessary for the meaning of the sentence. A restrictive appositive—one that is necessary for the meaning of the sentence—requires no commas. The following sentence has both a restrictive and a nonrestrictive appositive: "My sister LuAnn and her husband, Arthur, live in Minneapolis." The author of this sentence has more than one sister, so the name is necessary; LuAnn, however, has only one husband, so his name is not necessary.

That and Which

One of the jobs of these two pronouns is to introduce dependent clauses. The trick is knowing which one to use. *Which* introduces nonessential clauses—clauses that are not necessary to the meaning of the sentence. In the sentence "John wrecked his car, which he bought only last month," the clause "which he bought only last month" is not essential to the meaning of the sentence. "John wrecked his car" could stand alone as an understandable sentence. Nonessential clauses are usually set off from the rest of the sentence by commas.

That introduces an essential clause, one necessary to gain a proper understanding of the sentence. In the sentence "Jane wanted the kind of computer that she had always used," the clause "that she had always used" is essential to understanding the sentence. The sentence would not make sense without it. Essential clauses are not set off by commas. When you are editing your copy, find all of the instances in which you used *which* and determine whether or not you used it properly. In other words, start a "which hunt."

PUNCTUATION

Commas (,), semicolons (;), periods (.), apostrophes ('), and colons (:) are among the most common forms of punctuation.

The *comma* is a mere blip on a page of type. No other punctuation mark, however, gives students more problems, raises so many questions among writers, and causes so much controversy among grammarians. Consequently, we need to give some added attention to the comma.

The comma is an extremely useful tool, and that is part of its problem. It is so useful that its uses are hard to prescribe.

For example, *Harbrace College Handbook* says that a comma should be used to separate items in a series, such as "red, white, and blue," including a comma before the conjunction (in this case, before *and*). Newspaper editors are afraid of using too many commas, so they have set up some rules against their use. Thus, the *Associated Press (AP) Stylebook* advises writers: "Use commas to separate elements in a series, but do not put a comma before the conjunction in a simple series." When this rule is used, the example becomes "red, white and blue."

James J. Kilpatrick, a newspaper columnist and commentator on grammar and usage, has advocated abolishing most rules for using commas, saying that there are too many exceptions for each of the rules to make them useful. A comma, he says, should simply be used whenever a pause is needed. That may be an adequate philosophy for the experienced writer, but for the student who is just learning the rules, the relevant questions are "When should I use a comma?" and "When is it wrong to use a comma?"

While many rules exist for using commas, most of these rules can be reduced to three general instances for including this form of punctuation.

Commas Used to Set Off Items

Commas are sometimes used to set off parenthetical or independent words ("Inside, the building was dark and lonely. Nevertheless, the boys entered."); appositions and

Figure 2.2

Ernest Hemingway on punctuation

My attitude toward punctuation is that it ought to be as conventional as possible. The game of golf would lose a good deal if croquet mallets and billiard cues were allowed on the putting green. You ought to be able to show that you can do it a good deal better than anyone else with the regular tools before you have license to bring in your own improvements.

modifiers ("The man, who was nearly seven feet tall, was arrested. His reaction, silent and calm, was a surprise."); and transitional words ("On the other hand, the brothers held differing views.").

Commas Used to Separate Items

These commas separate introductory clauses or phrases from other parts of the sentence ("After driving all night, they were exhausted."); items in a series ("The flag is red, white and blue"—if we use AP style); and parts of a compound sentence ("The sky is blue, and the grass is green.").

Commas Used Conventionally

Some instances in writing demand commas, such as large figures (28,000), dates, addresses, and inverted names (Smith, John C.). These occasions do not change meaning but often help in the visual presentation of the information.

Students trying to learn when to use commas should remember what the *AP Stylebook* has to say about punctuation in general: "Think of it [punctuation] as a courtesy to your readers, designed to help them understand a story." The comma that helps the reader is correctly placed.

Semicolons are used to separate independent clauses in the same sentence (see above) and to separate items in a series that contains commas ("Attending the dinner were John Smith, mayor of Tuscaloosa; Mary Johnson, president of the League of Women Voters; Joe Jones, vice-president of Jones Steel, Inc.; and Rhonda Jackson, head of the Committee for Better Government").

Colons are often used to introduce a list: "The flag contains the following colors: red, white, and blue." Colons may also be used to separate two sentences when the second explains or clarifies the first ("The winner is clear: Jose is far ahead of everyone else.").

The *period* is most often used to end sentences, but it has other uses, such as ending abbreviations (Mr.). The *question mark* is used to end interrogative sentences, and the *exclamation point* ends sentences and expressions of excitement.

After the comma, the proper use of its cousin, the *apostrophe,* probably gives students more problems than any other form of punctuation. The apostrophe can be used in many ways. First, we use apostrophes to form possessives, as in "Mary's hat" and "Tom's book." If a word ends in *s* or the plural of the noun is formed by adding *s*, the apostrophe generally goes after the final *s*, and no other letter is needed. For example, the possessive of the word *hostess* is *hostess'*. The plural possessive of the word *team* is *teams'*.

Even professionals have problems when the word *it* and an apostrophe come together. Is it *its, it's,* or *its'*? Here are some rules worth memorizing. *Its* (without the apostrophe) is the possessive of the pronoun *it*, as in "its final score." *It's* (with the apostrophe) is a contraction meaning *it is,* as in "it's hard to tell." *Its'* is not a word.

Finally, you should not use an apostrophe to form the possessive of a pronoun. *Hers', yours',* and *theirs'* are incorrect; they should be *hers, yours,* and *theirs.*

Comma splices and run-on sentences. When two independent clauses are contained in a sentence, they must be connected by two things: a comma and a coordinating conjunction. The following sentence lacks that:

I ran down the street, he ran after me.

This sentence is an example of a comma splice or a run-on sentence. The sentence needs a coordinating conjunction to help separate the two independent clauses. The sentence written correctly is "I ran down the street, and he ran after me."

Commas between subject and verbs. Commas should be used to separate phrases and other elements in a sentence, but they should not be used solely to separate a subject from its verb. You would not write, "The boy, sat on the bench," nor should you write, "The moment the train comes in, is when we will see her" or "Having no money, is a difficult thing."

SPELLING

We live in an age of spelling rules. It was not always so. Centuries ago, when English was evolving as a written language, there were practically no rules of spelling. Writers spelled the way they thought words sounded, and that accounted for some wildly differing ways in which some words appeared. As certain spellings were used more and more, they became generally accepted, although not universally so. By the eighteenth century, when the creators of our modern dictionaries began their work, they not only had to decide among diverse spellings for words, but also had to contend with generally accepted spellings that might not be the best or most efficient.

Since that time, movements to simplify the spelling of certain words have sprung up. These movements have targeted words that end in a silent *e*, such as *give, live, have,* and *bake,* and other such silent combinations, such as *-ough* (for example, *thought* would become *thot,* and *through* would become *thru*).

Despite the efforts of many people during the last two centuries, spelling changes have occurred very slowly. People learn to spell most of the words they use before

Sidebar 2.2
Spelling Rules

English does not have many spelling rules, but it does have some general guidelines that can speed the learning process. All of these guidelines have many exceptions, some of which are noted below.

Doubling the Final Consonant

Adding an ending to a word that ends with a consonant often requires that the final consonant be doubled.

> *plan, planned; prefer, preferred; wit, witty; hot, hottest; swim, swimming; stop, stopped; bag, baggage; beg, beggar.*

There are a few exceptions. One illustrates the impact of the accent on certain syllables. *Refer* becomes *reference*, without doubling the *r*, but the accent also changes away from the final syllable when the suffix is added.

There are other exceptions, including words ending in *k, v, w, x,* and *y,* and words such as *benefit, benefited; chagrin, chagrined* (the stress stays on the final syllable of the new word but the end consonant does not double).

Dropping a Final *e*

A final *e* is usually dropped when adding a syllable beginning with a vowel:

> *come, coming; guide, guidance; cure, curable; judge, judging; plume, plumage; force, forcible; use, usage.*

Exceptions: *sale, saleable; mile, mileage; peace, peaceable; dye, dyeing.*

Retaining the Final *e*

A final *e* is usually retained when adding a syllable beginning with a consonant.

> *use, useless; late, lately; hate, hateful; move, movement; safe, safety; white, whiteness; pale, paleness; shame, shameful.*

Exceptions: *judge, judgment; argue, argument.*

Words ending in a double *e* retain both *e*'s before an added syllable.

> *free, freely; see, seeing; agree, agreement, agreeable.*

Retaining Double Consonants

Words ending in a double consonant retain both consonants when one or more syllables are added.

> *ebb, ebbing; enroll, enrollment; full, fullness; dull, dullness; skill, skillful; odd, oddly; will, willful; stiff, stiffness*

Using *all, well,* and *full* as Compounds

Compounds of *all, well,* and *full* drop one *l.*

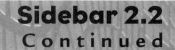
Sidebar 2.2
Continued

always, almost, welfare, welcome, fulfill.

Exceptions: *fullness* and occasions when a word is hyphenated (as with *full-fledged*).

I Before *e*

In words with *ie*, the *i* comes before the *e*, except after a *c*.

receive, deceive, relieve, believe

Exceptions: *neighbor, weigh, foreign, weird, ancient, caffeine*

Changing *y* to *i*

A final *y* preceded by a consonant is usually changed to *i* with the addition of an ending not beginning with *i*.

army, armies; spy, spies; busy, business

Exceptions: *shy, shyness; pity, piteous* (but not *pitiful*). The *ay* endings are usually exceptions: *play, played*.

Using *-ede* or *-eed*

In deciding whether to use *-ede* or *-eed*, use *-eed* for one-syllable words (*deed, need, speed*) and for these two-syllable words: *exceed, indeed, proceed,* and *succeed*. *Supersede* is the only word that ends with *-ede*, while some words use *-ede* as a suffix: *accede, concede, precede, recede*.

Plurals

You will also need to know some of the basic rules for forming plurals. Here are a few:

1. Most plurals for nouns are formed by simply adding *s* to the root word.
2. Nouns ending with *s, z, x, ch,* or *sh* usually require an *es* ending to form the plural: *quiz, quizzes; mess, messes; wish, wishes; fix, fixes.*
3. When a word ends with a consonant and then a *y*, the *y* is changed to *i* and an *es* is added: *army, armies.*
4. When a word ends in a vowel and a *y*, you can simply add an *s* for the plural: *bay, bays.*
5. Compound words without hyphens simply take an *s* on the end (*cupful, cupfuls*), but compound words with a hyphen take the *s* on the significant word (*son-in-law, sons-in-law*).
6. The *AP Stylebook* advises that *'s* should be used only in forming the plural of single letters (*A's, B's*) but not figures (*1920s, 727s*). Never use *'s* to form the plural of a word that is fully spelled out.

they are ten years old, and they are not comfortable in changing what they have learned. It is not up to those in the mass media to lead the fight for more simplified spellings. (Several years ago a number of newspaper editors ran into some trouble on this very point. Thinking that the spelling of a number of words was clumsy and confusing, these editors arbitrarily changed the way these words were spelled in their newspapers. *Through* became *thru, thorough* became *thoro,* and *employee* turned into *employe*. Reader acceptance of these changes was less than complete, and many editors had to beat a hasty retreat.) Rather, people in the mass media should make sure that what they write conforms to the generally accepted rules of spelling and that the spellings they use do not distract or surprise the reader.

Spelling correctly involves three ways of thinking: applying phonics, memorizing some words, and knowing the rules that usually apply to most words. Phonics can be learned, either in one's early years or later. One must memorize those words that are not spelled phonetically or do not follow spelling rules. However, most words can be spelled correctly without memorization because either rules or phonetics apply to the majority of English words. (Some of the rules, with known exceptions, are explained in the sidebar "Spelling Rules.")

Figure 2.3   Spelling Reform

Simplifying the way we spell words has been the dream of many prominent people, not just schoolchildren. One of the leaders of spelling reform was Robert McCormick, who in the 1930s ordered his newspaper, the Chicago *Tribune,* to use shortened forms of words such as *tho, iland, frate, thru,* and *jaz.* These spellings never caught on with the public or with lexicographers, however. In 1975, twenty years after McCormick died, the *Tribune* reverted to using generally accepted spellings. McCormick was not the only person to try. President Theodore Roosevelt and writer Mark Twain were also advocates of simplified spelling rules.

COMPUTER AIDS

When the widespread use of word processors began in the late 1970s and early 1980s, they were little more than electronic typewriters that allowed writers to store documents and change them with ease. The software for these machines has grown increasingly sophisticated, and now they are full-fledged partners in the writing process. Three major types of software are available to the writer: spelling dictionaries, stylebooks, and grammar checkers.

Spelling dictionaries are large lists of words that reside in the computer's memory. In some software programs, they are activated while the document is being written and will check the spelling of words as the document is being created. In other programs, they can be activated whenever the writer wants to use them. They check spelling by matching the words in the document to the words in the list. When a word in the document does not match a word in the dictionary list, it is highlighted. Most spelling programs will then offer a set of alternative words. Writers can also "look up" words while they are writing; they can type a word and then ask the spelling program to determine whether it matches a word in the dictionary list.

The shortcoming of these spelling programs is that they cannot understand the meaning of the words they are matching. Consequently, a writer can use the wrong word, and if it is spelled correctly, the spelling program will not find it. For example, if a writer makes a simple typographical error, as in the sentence "I am coming to you house tonight," the spelling program will not understand that the word *you* should be *your*. Because *you* is spelled correctly and matches a word in its list, the program will skip over that error.

Stylebook programs work in much the same way. (Stylebooks and their importance are discussed in Chapter 3.) Style guide programs can be installed on a computer, and when a writer has a question about a style rule, he or she can call up the program without leaving the document that is being produced. Some programs will automatically check a document for some style errors, but these checkers have some of the same shortcomings as spelling programs. They cannot catch all of the errors of meaning.

Grammar-checking programs are the most sophisticated of all of these kinds of software. They not only check for certain kinds of grammatical and punctuation errors, but also can measure the length of words, the number of syllables in the words, and the number of words in sentences. They will tell writers when words and sentences are overly long according to preset formulas. Some programs have built-in lists of jargon and clichés and will highlight such phrases for the writer. They will also point out the uses of the passive voice, giving writers an opportunity to change it if they wish.

Although these programs have grown in sophistication and are likely to become even more sophisticated, they cannot find all the errors in a document, and they cannot understand meanings or context. Many professionals and instructors argue that these programs should not be used at all because they allow writers to become lazy about checking their own work and dependent on these mechanical devices rather than their own knowledge and understanding of what they are writing. Those criticisms and fears are valid. Beginning writers should understand the very limited capacities of all of this software. No piece of software has been created that comes close to the ability of the mind to understand the subtleties and complexities of the English language.

WORDS, WORDS, WORDS

English works, as any language does, because of a combination of systems that students who seek to use it need to understand. Those systems are lexicon, grammar, semantics, and phonology.

Figure 2.4

Rudyard Kipling on the power of words

Words are, of course, the most powerful drug used by mankind.

A *lexicon* deals with the words that form the building blocks of the language. As society changes, new words must be created to express those changes. Certain rules govern the formation and development of words. We take words from a variety of sources (from ancient Latin to inner-city street talk), but English has developed some rules for using those words. We have prefixes and suffixes, for instance, that allow words to be formed into useful entities. The prefix "anti-" lets a word approach the opposite of its accepted meaning; the suffix "-ed" can be added to many root verbs to form the past tense. Standard dictionaries that we keep on our desks are the chief source of our knowledge of the rules of the lexicon.

Much of this chapter has been devoted to describing the rules of grammar for what we consider standard English. *Grammar* is the way in which we string words together to describe complex thoughts, ideas, or actions. Grammar is also concerned with word order. The English standard order of words in a sentence is subject, verb, predicate. That order is not followed in other languages, however. Because English is widely used, the rules of grammar are studied and evaluated continuously by people who use the language professionally. English is also a democratic language; common usage eventually formalizes many of the rules of grammar.

Semantics refers to the meanings that people assign to words. What a word symbolizes—or means—can change over time. The history of words and phrases, called *etymology*, can be a fascinating study, and many scholars spend productive careers pursuing the origins and derivations of words. Media professionals should pay particular attention to semantics because much of their work depends on a common understanding of the meanings of words.

Phonology is the system by which the language is spoken. A language has far fewer sounds than words; most English speakers get by with about forty sounds, or phonemes. Phonology allows a language to develop a standard way of being spoken so that we can understand one another. (Some would argue that writing constitutes a fifth system of the language because the rules of writing differ from the phonology rules. Not all experts accept that thinking, however.)

The rules of each of these systems are important because they allow us to have a common application of the language. They are "rules" not so much because they are enforced but because they represent the common understanding that we all have about the language. If this common understanding did not exist, the efforts of a writer for the mass media to communicate with an audience would be frustrated or useless. That is why the rules are important. That is why the professional must understand, use, and study the rules. The rules in each of these systems will undoubtedly change within the lifetime of the writer, but there will always be rules.

WRITING WITH CLARITY

All of the rules and systems of the language that have been discussed in this chapter have a single goal: allowing us to use the language with clarity. In writing for the mass media, we are trying to transmit information and ideas to an audience of readers and listeners. Knowing and applying the rules of grammar, spelling, and punctuation help us to achieve that goal.

Good grammar, precise word usage, and correct spelling are a means to an end. That end is communicating with the reader or viewer. Grammar, spelling, and usage are merely tools that a writer uses to convey information and ideas.

Writing is not just fitting words and phrases into a form. If it were, computer software would have been invented long ago to accomplish that tedious task. Writing is much more than mastery of grammar and spelling and even more than mastering the information and ideas about which you are writing. Writing is thinking—the mysterious process of the brain, acting in conjunction with the heart and soul—whereby we form and modify our thoughts and try to communicate and make sense of the world.

POINTS FOR CONSIDERATION AND DISCUSSION

1. What image of grammar and grammarians did you form in grade school or high school?
2. The author makes a strong case for knowing the rules of grammar, but some people do not think that this knowledge is very important. They believe that you can write well without knowing these rules. What do you think?
3. The text says that there are some times when a sentence fragment might be appropriate. When would that be?
4. What do you think are the most important rules for using a comma?
5. Explain the difference between *its, it's,* and *its'*.
6. Make a list of words that you think should be spelled differently than they are.
7. Make a list of words that you often hear people misusing. Why do you think people misuse them?
8. What is the rule of grammar, spelling, or punctuation that you would most like to abolish? Why?

FURTHER READING

Bryson, B. (1990). *The Mother Tongue: English and How It Got That Way.* New York: William Morrow.

Cappon, R. J. (2003). *The Associated Press Guide to Punctuation.* Cambridge, MA: Perseus Publishing.

Hodges, J. C., & Whitten, M. (1999). *Harbrace College Handbook* (13th ed.). Fort Worth, Texas: Harcourt Brace College Publishers.

Kessler, L., & McDonald, D. (2004). *When Words Collide* (6th ed.). Belmont, CA: Wadsworth.

Watkins, F., Dillingham, W., & Martin, E. (1996). *Practical English Handbook.* Boston: Houghton Mifflin.

WEBSITES

Guide to Grammar and Writing: **www.ccc.commnet.edu/grammar**

Language Corner (Columbia Journalism Review): **www.cjr.org/tools/lc**

EXERCISES

The following section contains a variety of exercises that will help you to use the language more precisely. You should follow your instructor's directions in completing them.

2.1 Writing Skills

The following sentences were taken from newspapers and television broadcasts. Correct the errors you find by either copy-editing or rewriting the sentences. Underline your corrections. Some of the sentences are correct, in which case you should write "correct" in the margin.

1. He is one of the greatest choreographers who has ever lived.

2. The general assumed what was then described as dictorial powers.

3. The couple has two children.

4. Inside the box was a man and a woman.

5. Absent from the meeting were the mayor and two councilmen.

6. Every fireman in the city, 250 in all were called out.

7. A total of 650 Eskimos was examined and tested.

8. Only two in four were urgent cases, a group that included cardiacs, asthmatics and those found unconscious.

9. The chairman stated that response to the committee's activities has convinced him that the money for renovation can be raised.

10. Business administration and journalism courses provide the student with good background for work in public relations.

11. Here comes the famous Kilgore College Rangerettes onto the field to perform at halftime.

12. Leading the United States' show of strength were Arthur Ashe and Clarke Graebner.

13. The investigation revealed that none of the team members were involved in illegal endorsements of sports clothing.

14. "There's two knocked out cold on the floor!" the sportscaster shouted.

15. Every one of us have asked that question sometime in our lives.

2.2 Writing Skills

Do whatever is necessary to correct the following sentences.

1. Their rival forces meanwhile prepared to meet Wednesday to patch up peace.

2. Pasadena California is the site of the Rose Bowl.

3. It was O. J. Simpson (who, whom) the coach praised so highly.

4. The tomb of the pharaoh had (laid, lain) buried in the desert for centuries.

5. I heard the train whistle at the crossing that was going to Denver.

6. She borrowed an egg from a neighbor that was rotten.

7. For a year we almost heard nothing from our former neighbors.

8. There was a canary in a cage that never sang.

9. We hope that you will notify us if you can attend the banquet on the enclosed post card.

10. Come here Mary and help us.

11. I know she (swum, swims) the channel regularly in this weather.

12. The children looked forward to celebrating Christmas for several weeks.

13. After setting foot on the uninhabited island of Europe, off Africa, to direct the filming of the sea turtles, a hurricane whirled across the Indian ocean and hit the island.

14. He ran swiftly the dog in front of him and plunged into the forest.

15. The casings had (tore, torn) (loose, lose) from their bearings.

2.3 Punctuation

In the following sentences, insert the correct punctuation.

1. I subscribe to the *New Yorker Harper's Magazine* and the *New Republic*

2. Seven legislators from the southern part of the state changed their votes and with their help the bill was passed.

3. Do you like your steak rare medium or well done?

4. A tape recorder gives very accurate reproduction and it has the great advantage that it can be used at home as well as at the studio.

5. The gun went off and everyone jumped

6. The new cars are certainly more powerful but it is doubtful that they are any safer

7. Light entered the room through cracks in the walls through holes in the roof and through one small window.

8. Hundreds of church bells ringing loudly after years of silence announced the end of the war

9. The book was lying where I left it

10. The advisor who is never in his office makes registration difficult

11. Some years ago I lived in a section of town where almost everyone was a Republican

12. Hearne was still disclaiming with great eloquence but no one in the crowd was listening

13. I bought a large bath towel

14. We were sitting before the fire in the big room at Twins Farms and Lewis had rudely retired behind the newspaper

15. The ranchmen rode with their families into the little town and encouraged their sons to demonstrate their skill with broken horses

2.4 Pronouns and Verbs

In the following sentences, underline the correct pronoun or verb.

 1. He is the player (who, whom) probably will play shortstop.

 2. Is this the person (who, whom) you want?

 3. Each of the three quarterbacks (is, are) good runners.

 4. Both Baylor and Arkansas (has, have) won six games and lost two.

 5. Either of the two players (are, is) eligible.

 6. Each of the members (was, were) in (his, their) seat(s) when the session began.

 7. (Who, Whom), then, would the tax hurt?

 8. Do you know to (who, whom) that notebook belongs?

 9. (Who, Whom) is going with the reporter to get a picture of the crash?

10. He declared that everybody must play (his, their) part.

11. This story is between you and (I, me).

12. No matter how you look at it, it was (she, her) (who, whom) they opposed.

13. Bryan is the kind of man (whom, who) always thinks before he acts.

14. This is the only one of the typewriters that (is, are) working.

15. Everyone was on (their, his or her) best behavior.

2.5 Verbs

In the following sentences, underline the correct form of the verb.

 1. What (lays, lies) in the future for Alaska?

 2. He had been (lain, laid) on a stretcher.

 3. "(Lay, Lie) down and be quiet for an hour," he ordered.

 4. The six-year-old boy was just (setting, sitting) there in the ruins, trying not to cry.

 5. The Ohio State football team (sat, set) back and enjoyed the movie of its game with Michigan.

 6. The men worked all night (raising, rising) a monument in spite of the (raising, rising) tide of the river.

7. After lunch she had (laid, lain) down for a nap.

8. The hard tackling by the Georgia Bulldogs had really (began, begun) to tell.

9. Suddenly a cloud of dust (rises, raises) in the west.

10. Had the tight end simply (fell, fallen) on the ball, he would have (catched, caught) it.

11. Spillane (led, lead) you to believe that the butler was the murderer.

12. Chris Gilbert had (proved, proven) to be the outstanding player.

13. He said that he could (loose, lose) his fortune, but he had (chose, chosen) to gamble all he had.

14. The Smiths (use, used) to live in San Francisco.

15. The man was lucky he wasn't (drown, drowned).

2.6 Clauses

In the following sentences, underline the independent clause and circle the subordinate (dependent) clause.

1. They agreed to open negotiations when both sides ceased fire.

2. If he had known, he would never have said that.

3. Since the current was swift, he could not swim to shore.

4. The horse came up to the first jump, when he stumbled and threw Jean off.

5. This is called the cryptozoite stage, after which the plasmodia break out of the liver cells and float about in the blood stream.

6. An especially big wave rolled in, when I finally managed to get my line unsnagged.

7. While walking past the building, the night watchman noticed the door was unlocked.

8. Harkey's injured knee has failed to heal completely; therefore, he may see little action against Notre Dame on Saturday.

9. The Ace Manufacturing Company, where I used to work, went bankrupt.

10. This last semester, if it has done nothing else, has given me confidence in myself.

Write five correct sentences containing independent and subordinate clauses.

1.

2.

3.

4.

5.

2.7 Punctuation

In the following sentences, insert the correct punctuation.

1. Nobody knows the trouble I've seen nobody knows but Jesus. (This is a line from a Negro spiritual. Punctuate it as if it were in the middle of a paragraph.)

2. The responsible reporter one who is scrupulously honest will still encounter problems.

3. Abraham Lincoln died on April 15 1865 after being shot while attending a play at Fords Theater.

4. My son was born on Nov 15 1980 It was a Saturday so I didnt get to go to the football game

5. Why don't you come over to my place

6. Writing for the mass media takes much skill perseverance and hard work.

7. Wow I couldnt think of any place better to eat myself.

8. According to my professor the world is absolutely positively flat and you should never forget it.

9. Where are the carpenters where are the bricklayers and most of all where are the gardners when we need them the most.

10. I couldnt come to class today Jan said because I had the flu.

11. Joe got a new computer which set his parents back a good bit and hes been dying to tell everybody about it.

12. Help I need somebody the Beatles sang Not just anybody Help I need somebody Help.

2.8 Word Choice

In the following sentences, fill in the blank with one of the words that appear in parentheses.

1. _____ are good reasons why _____ about to sell _____ house. (there, their, they're)

2. _____ not _____ late _____ give the cat milk. (its, it's, to, too)

3. If _____ going home, take _____ books with you. (your, you're)

4. Do you know _____ the _____ is pleasant _____? (whether, weather, there, their, they're)

5. They _____ known for a long time that you would _____ gone if you had heard _____ the game in time. (have, of, 've)

6. Where _____ are many opinions, most people feel justified in holding on to _____ own; and while there are several scientific explanations for stubbornness, _____ be few changes unless we can convince men that they ought to be more open-minded. (there, their, they're, there'll)

7. My _____ objection to the _____ of that school is that he is a man of no _____ . (principal, principle)

8. Not until _____ will you be able to tell whether you have more _____ you need. (than, then)

9. If _____ strap is _____ , you may _____ your books. (lose, loose, you're, your)

10. Not even in the _____ would I _____ the table before eating _____ . (desert, dessert)

11. "_____ going to punch _____ nose?" (whose, who's)

12. We _____ the ruling without protest, although we _____ all those over 45. (except, accept)

13. His speech _____ the audience greatly. (affected, effected)

14. _____ 50,000 people attend the opening game of the World Series. (Over, More than)

15. He was always one to do things _____ . (different, differently)

2.9 Word Choice

In the following sentences, fill in the blank with one of the words that appears in parentheses. The definitions of most of these words can be found in Appendix C.

1. The bomb, which was to _____ havoc on the whole block, killed so many people that their bodies soon began to _____. (reek, wreak)

2. The newsmagazine _____ she subscribed to never seemed to tell her all that she needed to know. (that, which)

3. When he put the book down, he decided that he had just read something very _____. (unique, unusual)

4. The _____ of Queen Victoria was a long and prosperous one. (rein, reign)

5. He decided to _____ his bike down to the town square to see if he could _____ the things that he had made. (peddle, pedal)

6. The priest chose not to _____ the cloths that were spread across the _____. (alter, altar)

7. We visited the _____ building, where we saw the state legislature in session. (Capital, capital, Capitol)

8. All of the fraternities on campus came together to form a voting _____ that could not be overcome by the independent students. (block, bloc)

9. He _____ the poor child's way of speaking. (flouted, flaunted)

10. The professor tried her best to make the grading system more _____. (equal, equitable)

11. I did not make it to the movie last night _____ all the homework I had to do. (due to, because of)

12. She was irritated by the _____ tone he used when he said, "And what have you been doing all week long?" (official, officious)

2.10 Writing Problems

Correct any problems that appear in the following sentences.

1. Gilligan was so charmed by the desert aisle that he decided to marry the movie star.

2. Like that nice Professor said, we should always study for our exams.

3. The cantaloupe-throwing contest was canceled due to averse weather.

4. Rushing to the sight of the crime, the prosecuting attorney was horrified at the grizzly murder scene.

5. The criminal alluded police by hiding under a Toyota Corolla.

6. Faining illness, the President refused to make the trip to Tulsa.

7. Morgan canceled the funeral service after the dead man turned out to be alive.

8. Less than 100 pumpkins were piled in Smith's car.

9. Hurricane Bubba ravaged the Gulf Coast, causing $10 billion in damages.

10. The dancing troupe refused to buy their tights at wholesale.

11. The restaurant owners upped the price of rutabagas by 100 percent whenever Mark Arnold came to town.

12. The journalist's cannon of ethics prohibits taking gifts from sources.

13. Journalists should be guided by one principle: Always be accurate.

2.11 Agreement

Fill in the blank with the correct word.

1. The team, consisting of three boys and three girls, _____ (has, have) a tough schedule this season.

2. None of the candidates _____ (has, have) accepted the invitation to the forum.

3. The faculty _____ (has, have) a meeting scheduled for this afternoon to discuss _____ (its, their) grievances.

4. The drug he took and his lack of sleep _____ (was, were) beginning to have an effect.

5. All of the students in the class tried hard to pass _____ (its, their) final exam.

6. The neighborhood association had certain issues _____ (it, they) wanted to address at the city council meeting.

7. Every journalist should try to write news stories that are as accurate as _____ (they, he or she) can make them.

8. The U.S. Supreme Court normally begins _____ (its, their) annual session on the first Monday of October.

9. Many people in the audience _____ (sees, see) this commercial and _____ (reacts, react) negatively to it.

10. Each parent had _____ (his or her, their) own way of dealing with unruly children.

2.12 Comma Splices and Run-On Sentences

Make sure that each sentence is punctuated correctly. Make whatever changes are necessary to do so. If the punctuation is correct, do not make any marks.

1. I don't know of anyone who went I didn't go myself.

2. The horses came loping into the barn but there was no food for them.

3. There, I said it again, don't do that any more.

4. Many are the times the farmer wished he had bought more land because years ago it was cheap, it was plentiful.

5. The trees in that forest were doomed, they had to be cut down.

6. The St. Louis Cardinals won the National League pennant, while the New York Yankees triumphed in the American league; they will meet in this year's World Series.

7. Where was the truck going, which direction was it heading.

8. He has just finished his seventh mystery novel and he has yet to have one published, he just keeps on trying.

9. John bought a cheap set of watercolors thinking one day he would be a great painter he just wanted to be like Picasso.

10. He has an unusual hobby, he transplants trees, but he says he likes doing it because it gives him a chance to get outside most of the time.

3

Style and the Stylebook

When you write about Frisbees, you should capitalize the word. You should avoid using the word *definitely;* it does not add any information to your sentence. The soft drink Dr Pepper does not have a period after the "Dr" in its name. Some words use hyphens (*point-blank*), while others do not (*postgraduate*).

Who says? Who cares? These are small things, are they not, really unworthy of much consideration? What does it matter?

To writers for the mass media, these points are of enormous importance. Writing accurately, precisely, and consistently is the hallmark of professionalism. Paying attention to the details of writing—and getting those right—means that a writer is likely to be paying attention to facts, context, and meaning. It means that the writer is thinking at various levels, understanding that misplaced commas or errors in capitalization can distract the reader from great ideas or important information. This kind of thinking is the genesis of style.

In media writing, style is the general orientation a writer has toward his or her work. Style is the set of conventions and assumptions underlying the writing and the generally accepted rules of writing and usage for a particular medium. This chapter discusses both the conventions and the rules.

The three most important concepts of media writing are accuracy, brevity, and clarity; the most important is accuracy.

ACCURACY

The chief goal of any writer for the mass media is accuracy. A writer will spend much energy in getting it right. That is, the writer will make every reasonable attempt to ensure that everything in the writing is factually correct and expressed appropriately.

Accuracy is important to the writer for several reasons. First, our society puts much stock in truth and honesty, and most people expect that the mass media will take reasonable steps to present information accurately. There is a great tendency for mass audiences to believe what they see and read in the mass media, and this inclination translates into a responsibility that those who work in the mass media must fulfill.

A very practical reason for an emphasis on accuracy is that people will not watch or subscribe to media they believe to be inaccurate. A newspaper, website, television station, advertising agency, or public relations department that does not tell the truth will not be trusted by the people it is trying to serve and ultimately will not be effective.

The most compelling reason for a strong emphasis on accuracy, however, comes not from the audience but from individuals inside the mass media. Few people, if any, want to be false in what they do or want their life's work to be looked on as a charade. Consequently, they feel a moral need to do the best they can; in the mass media professions, that means trying to produce accurate information and present it honestly.

How can a writer for the mass media be accurate? What are the steps that will ensure that the information presented in the writing is correct? These next two chapters will discuss practical measures for gathering information and writing news.

Writers for the mass media should have an open mind. They should be receptive to new ideas and to various points of view. They should listen to those with whom they may disagree as well as those with whom they agree. They will not put everything they read and hear in their writing, but the more they know, the better judgments they can make about the accuracy of what they write.

Following closely on this characteristic is that writers for the mass media should read widely. Reading, even in the age of video, is still the best way for a person to prepare himself or herself to be a writer.

Writers for the mass media should pay attention to the details of what and how they write. Chapter 2 discussed the importance of using the language correctly. We will continue that discussion in this chapter by focusing on style. Individually, many of the points made in these chapters are small ones, but as a whole, they constitute an important part of the writer's effort to achieve accuracy. Accuracy may be thought of as a large building made up of many small bricks. The writer is the bricklayer and must pay attention to each brick as it is laid.

CLARITY

Clarity must also be one of the chief goals of a writer for the mass media. Facts that are unclearly presented are of little use to the reader. The English language is extremely versatile, but that versatility can lead to confusion when the language is in the hands of amateurs. Writers must be experts in the language and in the proper and clear structuring of a story.

The pursuit of clarity is a state of mind for the writer. Everything the writer does must promote the clarity of the writing. After a piece of copy is written, a writer must look at it with a fresh eye, one that is unencumbered by too much knowledge of the subject. The writer must try to place himself or herself in the position of the reader, approaching the writing as one who was not there and did not see it happen and who has not talked with anyone about it. This approach is doubly difficult for the writer who has followed one of the first rules of good writing: knowing the subject thoroughly. Writing clearly and editing for clarity demand a rare degree of mental discipline on the part of the writer.

Clear writing is an art, but it is also a skill. Expressing thoughts, ideas, and facts in a clear way is one of the most difficult jobs a writer has, even though the product may read as if the clarity were easily accomplished. The mind moves much faster than we can write or even type; thoughts can be easily jumbled, and so can writing.

Figure 3.1

Walt Whitman on writing short

Write short; to the point; stop when you have done. Read it over, abridge, and correct it until you get it into the shortest space possible.

The key to clear writing is understanding the subject. When a writer can express thoughts about a subject in clear terms, then that understanding has been achieved.

The opposite of clarity is confusion. Confusion can infiltrate a story in many ways, and it is the writer's responsibility to eliminate this confusion. The chief source of confusion is often the writer who does not understand his or her subject. Writers who do not understand their subjects are likely to write a story that other people cannot understand.

Following are some tips for helping writers and editors to achieve clarity in their writing.

Keep It Simple

Many people believe that they can demonstrate their intelligence by using complex terms (such as *terminology*). Their language, they feel, will show others that they have mastered a difficult subject or that they speak or write with authority. Consequently, they use big words and complex sentences to express the simplest ideas.

The problem with this attitude is that people forget their original purpose for writing: to communicate ideas. Any writing that draws attention to itself, and thus draws attention away from the content, is ineffective. Writing should be as simple and straightforward as possible. Reporters and editors should use simple terms and sentence structures. They should avoid piling adjectives and phrases on top of one another. They should do this not to talk down to their readers, but to transmit ideas and facts as efficiently as possible.

Avoid All Kinds of Jargon

Jargon is specialized language that almost all groups develop. Students, baseball managers, doctors, and gardeners use words that have special meaning for them and no one else. Journalists are not doing their jobs if they simply record jargon, however accurately, and pass it on to the reader. Journalists must be translators. They must understand the jargon of different groups they cover but must be intelligent enough not to use it in their writing without explaining it for the reader. Writers, too, must watch for the jargon that can slip into stories. Journalists must make phrases like *viable alternative, optimum care,* and *personnel costs* mean something. They cannot simply thrust such language on the reader and believe that they have done their job adequately.

Be Specific

Journalists must set the stage of the story for their readers. They must make sure that their readers understand what is going on, when it is happening, where it is happening, and how it is taking place. Reporters and editors cannot assume that readers know very much about the stories they write and edit. They cannot get by with telling readers that it was a "large crowd" or a "long line" or a "beautiful landscape." Stories are built on facts—little facts and big facts. Sometimes it is the little facts that will make the difference in whether or not a reader understands a story.

Readers who have not seen what reporters have seen will not necessarily know what reporters are talking about. One aspect of this problem occurs with the use of *the,* especially by less experienced reporters. For example, a lead paragraph may begin in the following way: "The city council approved funds for purchasing the new computer system for the finance department at its meeting Tuesday night." A reader is likely to ask, "What new computer system?" (The reader may also ask, "Whose meeting—the city council's or the finance department's?") While covering the meeting, the reporter kept hearing everyone talk about "the new computer system," so that's what appeared in the story. Writers particularly need to watch for this kind of assumption and to make sure that readers are not left behind by the assumptions a writer makes.

Check the Time Sequence

Most news stories will not be written in chronological order, but readers should have some idea of the narrative sequence of the events in a story. When the time sequence is not clear, readers may become confused and misunderstand the content of the story.

Include Transitions

Transitions are necessary for smooth, graceful, and clear writing. Each sentence in a story should logically follow the previous sentence or should relate to it in some way. New information in a story should be connected to information already introduced. Readers who suddenly come upon new information or a new subject in a story without the proper transition will be jolted and confused. The following introductory paragraphs of a story by a beginning writing student about the high costs of weddings illustrates the point about transitions:

> The nervous young man drops to one knee, blushes and asks that all-important question.
>
> What about all the planning involved in a wedding, from reserving the church to choosing the honeymoon site? June and July are the traditional months for making the big decision, according to Milton Jefferson of the Sparkling Jewelry Store.
>
> Jefferson said most engagements last from seven to 16 months.
>
> A woman sometimes receives a ring that has been passed down through her fiancé's family for generations, or maybe her boyfriend has bought an estate ring.

The first paragraph assumes that the reader will know what "that all-important question" is. This assumption might be acceptable if the second paragraph followed the lead properly, but it does not. Instead, it plunges the reader into the subject of planning a wedding; the reader has no indication from the lead that this is coming next—and what happened to "that all-important question"?

In a similar manner, the second sentence of the second paragraph introduces yet another new subject to the reader, again without the proper transition. The reader is taken from a question about planning to the traditionally popular months for weddings, no connection being made between them. In addition, the attribution forces the reader to make another leap. The reader must say, "The man is a jewelry store owner. Jewelry stores sell wedding rings. The jewelry store owner, then, is an authority about when weddings occur."

The third paragraph introduces yet another new subject: the length of engagements. Again, the reader is bombarded by one fact after another with no transitions to help make sense of them.

The fourth paragraph talks about how prospective brides get their engagement rings, or perhaps the wedding rings. What does this information have to do with what has been said? The writer has left it to the reader to figure it all out. The writer has said, "My story is about weddings. Therefore, anything I put in my story about weddings is OK."

Good writers need to develop a mental discipline that prevents this kind of shoddy thinking and writing. They must read their own copy with cold and glaring eyes, never assuming that a reader will take the time and effort to "figure out" what the writer has written. (For more on transitions, see Chapter 5.)

BREVITY

"Brevity is the soul of wit," according to the ill-fated Polonius in Shakespeare's *Hamlet*. Polonius was, in reality, one of Shakespeare's most verbose characters. Words came tumbling out of his mouth. He went on and on. He was not only verbose; he was boring. Polonius was one of those people you try to avoid at parties. He talked too much.

Writers can do the same thing. They can use too many words, piling phrase upon phrase and letting the sentences run on far after their thoughts have run out. They put too many words in the way of what really needs to be said.

Writers need to recognize when they are being long-winded. They should remove the well-turned phrase that is unnecessary and eliminate redundancies. The process can go too far, of course. Accuracy and clarity should never be sacrificed for brevity's sake, but brevity should be another major goal of the writer.

Following are some tips for achieving brevity.

Get to the Point

What is the story about? What does the story need to tell the reader? A writer needs to be able to answer these questions in the simplest terms possible. This is sometimes the hardest part of writing or editing, but once it is done, the writing or editing job can become much easier.

Watch for Redundancies and Repetitions

A redundancy uses too many words to express an idea. Redundancies abound in popular language: *Easter Sunday* (Easter is always on Sunday), *component parts* (parts are components), *advance notice* (what other kind is there?). Redundancies show a lack of disciplined thinking. They slip into writing unnoticed, but their presence can make the most important stories seem silly.

Repetitions repeat words or phrases more than is necessary for the reader to understand what is meant. Repetition is also an indication that the editor was not concentrating on the story. Sometimes facts need to be repeated for clarity's sake, but this is not often the case.

Writers should be confident enough in their use of the language that they can use a variety of words. In particular, writers should avoid repeating a verb from sentence to sentence. (The verb *said* is an exception that we will discuss in later chapters.)

Cut Out Unnecessary Words

There may be words in a story that add nothing to its meaning. These words are hard to pin down, but a sharp-eyed writer can spot them. They are words such as *really, very,* and *actually.* They are phrase-makers, but they do not tell the reader much. (They have much in common with the spoken use of the word *like,* as in "I was going to, like, the grocery story." The word *like* simply fills the air; it does not add anything to the sentence.)

Finally, when you have run out of things to write about, stop.

JOURNALISTIC CONVENTIONS

A strong sense of professionalism has developed in journalism and the mass media during the last 100 years. With this professionalism has come a powerful tradition of conventions in journalistic writing. Like rules of style, these conventions are known to trained writers and used by them to communicate things about their stories to readers. Most readers do not realize what these conventions are when they read the newspaper, hear a news broadcast, or read news on a website. Yet most news consumers expect these conventions to be followed when professionals are making news judgments.

The conventions include both the basic structures of the stories and the individual ordering of facts and even words within sentences that are regularly used in certain types of stories.

Inverted Pyramid

The inverted pyramid is the structure that is most commonly used for the modern American news story for print. For the writer, the inverted pyramid structure means two things. First, information should be presented in the order of its importance, the most important facts coming at the beginning. Second, a story should be written so that if it needs to be cut, it can be cut from the bottom without loss of essential facts or coherence. The inverted pyramid is certainly not the only acceptable structure for the presentation of news, but its use is so widespread that if it is not used, the facts of a story must dictate the alternative form used by the writer. Chapter 5 discusses the technical aspects writing with the inverted structure.

Many people in and out of journalism believe that the inverted pyramid structure has lost its usefulness and that journalists should develop and use other structures. One of the objections to the inverted pyramid is the argument that in the age of instant communication through television and other means, the inverted pyramid is no longer necessary for readers of the written word. They are likely to know what the news is because they have seen it or heard it in some other medium.

Another objection to the inverted pyramid is that it restricts the creativity of the writer and the writer's ability to present information. Many writers argue that stories are more readable and even more accurate if they take some other form, particularly a narrative or chronological form.

Because of its emphasis on presenting information in order from most important to least important, the inverted pyramid structure often prevents writers from putting dramatic endings onto their stories. This characteristic is another reason why many writers and editors object to its use. They argue that the inverted pyramid washes the drama out of a story.

Despite these objections, the inverted pyramid structure has remained a standard form for news writing. It has even gained strength because of its usefulness in writing for the Web (see Chapter 6). Still, as the Web develops as a news medium and as readers grow more sophisticated in using the Web, alternatives to the inverted pyramid structure are likely to grow. Writers for the mass media need to stay flexible in learning the writing structures that a medium demands.

Types of Stories

Commonly accepted news values (discussed in Chapter 4) make it incumbent on reporters and editors to cover and give importance to certain types of stories. These kinds of stories are handled so often that a set of standard practices governing how they are written has been established. For instance, the disaster story must always tell early in the story whether anyone was killed or injured. Newspapers develop their own styles for handling obituaries; some even dictate the form in which the standard obituary is written. For instance, the New York *Times* has a set two-sentence lead for an obituary: "John Smith, a Brooklyn real estate dealer, died at a local hospital yesterday after a short illness. He was 55 years old." Other types of routine stories are those concerning government actions, the courts, crime, holidays, and weather. These stories have standard forms in many newspapers and other publications.

Balance and Fairness

One of the basic tenets of American journalism is fairness. Readers expect journalists to try to give all people involved in a news story a chance to tell their sides and offer their opinions. If a news source makes an accusation about another person, standard journalism practice demands that the accused person be given a chance to answer in the same story. Journalists should not take sides in a controversy and should take care not even to appear to take sides.

Writing and editing a balanced story mean more than just making sure a controversial situation or issue is covered fairly. In a larger sense, balance means that journalists should understand the relative importance of the events they cover and should not write stories that overplay or underplay that importance. Journalists are often charged with blowing things out of proportion, and sometimes the charge is valid. Journalists should make sure that they are not being used by news sources and being put in the position of creating news rather than letting it occur and then covering it.

The concepts of balance and fairness sometimes come under the name of *objectivity,* a term that you are likely to hear often in the world of the mass media. Objectivity means that a news reporter, editor, and publication should report only what they know and can find out. They should be scrupulously "fair" to all sides of a story, although *fair* has many different meanings. In being objective, news people should not inject themselves or their opinions into a report. Objectivity assumes not only that journalists *should* do all of these things but also that they *can* do them.

Many people inside and outside the profession have come to believe that journalists cannot achieve the standards set by the insistence of objectivity and that attempts to do so actually hurt their performance. Objectivity, these people argue, demands that journalists suspend their judgment in ways that would prevent them from fully informing their readers and viewers. Journalists must always decide what stories to cover, whom to use as sources, and what information to include and exclude in their reports. The very fact that these decisions must be made flies in the face of an ideal standard of objectivity.

The Impersonal Reporter

Closely associated with the concepts of balance and fairness is the concept of the impersonal reporter. Reporters should be invisible in their writing. Reporters should not only set aside their own views and opinions but also avoid direct contact with the reader through the use of first-person (*I, we, me, our, my, us*) or second-person (*you, your*) pronouns outside of direct quotes.

Reporters and editors inherently state their opinions about the news in deciding what events they write about, how they write about them, and where they place those stories in the paper. No journalist can claim to be a completely unbiased, objective observer and deliverer of information. Yet stating opinions directly and plainly is generally not an acceptable practice. Even for reporters to identify themselves with readers is not a good idea. For example, the following lead is not acceptable because of its use of a first-person pronoun: "The Chief Justice of the Supreme Court said yesterday that our legal system is in serious trouble." There may be someone reading this story who is not subject to the U.S. legal system, and the reporter should write for that person as well as for all who are.

Journalism in this era is beginning to see cracks in the armor of the impersonal reporter. More personal references are showing up in news stories, and reporters are acknowledging their own involvement in news events. One example of this occurred during the Persian Gulf War in 1991 when Peter Arnett of the Cable News Network (CNN) was allowed to remain in Iraq and to send live reports from there while U.S. bombers were destroying many parts of the country. Arnett's unique position was part of the story itself, and both he and CNN recognized that in their reporting of the war. Readers and viewers often realize that reporters are involved in the stories they cover, and news organizations believe that they should honestly state what that involvement is.

Reliance on Official Sources

Much of the information that is presented in the news media comes from what we might call official sources. These sources are those who are thought to have expertise on the subject, not those who may merely have opinions about the subject. Take, for example, a story about inflation. A journalist writing a story about inflation would probably use information from government reports and the studies and opinions of respected economists and influential politicians. These would be the official sources, and they would have a large amount of credibility with the reader. An unofficial source might be a homemaker, who would certainly have an opinion about the effects, causes, and cures of inflation but who would probably not have information that would be credible in the mass media.

The use of official sources has come under scrutiny and some criticism. Studies of sources used by journalists show that the sources themselves are relatively few in number, thus limiting the range of information and opinion that is presented to the reader. Another objection to the use of official sources is that too few people who are affected by events are quoted. The example of the inflation story in the previous paragraph is a good example. Unofficial sources such as homemakers or hourly wage earners are often ignored. Finally, media critics object to official sources because they are likely to be white and male. Relatively few women and members of other ethnic and racial groups make it into the realms of official sources.

Attribution and Quotations

Journalists should make it clear to readers where information has been obtained. All but the most obvious and commonly known facts in a story should be attributed. Writers should make sure that the attributions are helpful to the reader's understanding of the story and that they do not get in the way of the flow of the story.

Many journalistic conventions have grown up around the use of indirect and direct quotations. First, except in the rarest instances, all quotations must be attributed. The exception is the case in which there is no doubt about the source of the quote. Even then, editors should be careful.

Second, using quotation marks around a word or group of words means that someone has spoken or written those exact words. A writer must not put words inside quotation marks that have not been used by the source. Sometimes a writer is tempted to say, "I know my source said that, but I am sure she meant something else, so I'm going to change the quote to what was meant rather than what was said." This is a dangerous practice. In this situation, the best course for the writer is to get in touch with the source and ask about the quote in question. Most of the time, people's exact words will accurately express their meaning.

Finally, should incorrect grammar, slang, and profane or offensive language appear in a direct quotation? Most publications have policies in place for the use of profane or offensive language. The question of bad grammar plagues journalists. Journalists have a commitment to accuracy, which dictates that they should use the exact words that their sources use. Quoting someone who used bad grammar can make that person appear unnecessarily foolish and can distract from the real meaning of the story. Most professionals believe that if a source is used to being quoted, grammatical mistakes should be included in the statements they make. However, the grammatical mistakes of those who are not used to talking with journalists should be changed. Neither practice should be followed in every instance. Writers and editors should make a decision together when these situations come up.

These conventions are important to observe if journalists are to gain the respect of their readers and colleagues. Conventions should not be looked on as arbitrary rules that must be followed at the expense of accuracy and clarity. Rather, they are a set of sound practices that are extremely useful to journalists in the process of deciding what to write and how to write it.

JOURNALISTIC STYLE

English is an extremely diverse language; it gives the user many ways of saying the same thing. For instance, *8:00, eight o'clock, 8 A.M., eight a.m.,* and *eight in the morning* may all correctly refer to the same thing. A reference may be to *the president, the President, the U.S. president, the president of the United States,* and so on. All of these references are technically correct, but which one should a journalist use? And does it really matter?

The answer to the first question is governed by journalistic style. Style is a special case of English correctness that a publication adopts. It does so to promote consistency among its writers and to reduce confusion among its readers. Once a style is adopted, a writer won't have to wonder about the way to refer to such things as time.

Journalistic style can be divided into two types of style: professional conventions and rules of usage. Professional conventions have evolved during years of journalistic endeavor and are now taught through professional training in universities and professional workshops. The rules of usage have been collected into stylebooks published by wire services, news organizations, syndicates, universities, and individual print and broadcast news operations. Some of these stylebooks have had widespread acceptance and influence. Others have remained relatively local and result in unique style rules that are accepted by reporters and editors working for individual news organizations.

For example, a publication may follow *The Associated Press Stylebook* and *The United Press International Stylebook* and say that AM and PM should be lowercase with periods: a.m. and p.m. The writer will know that a reference to the president of the United States is always simply *president,* in lowercase, except in referring to a specific person, such as President Eisenhower.

Having a logical, consistent style is like fine-tuning a color television. Before the tuning, the colors may be there, and the picture may be visible. Eventually, however, the off-colors and the blurry images will play on the viewer's mind and he or she will become dissatisfied and disinterested. That could cause the viewer to stop watching altogether. In the same way, consistent style harmonizes a publication so that reading it is easier for a reader and offers few distractions from the content.

Beyond that, the question may still remain: Does style really matter? The answer is an emphatic "yes!" Many beginning writers think of consistent style as a repressive force hampering their creativity. It isn't. Style is not a rigid set of rules that have

Sidebar 3.1
Tips on AP Style: Abbreviations

- Spell out—do not abbreviate—names of organizations, firms, agencies, universities and colleges, groups, clubs or governmental bodies the first time the name is used. (i.e., on first reference). But abbreviate such names on second reference, as here:
First reference: Civil Aeronautics Board
Second reference: the board
First reference: National Organization for Women
Second reference: NOW

- Do not use an abbreviation or acronym in parentheses after the first reference of a full name. Wrong: The Radical Underwater First United Sailors (RUFUS) meets tonight. Right: The Radical Underwater First United Sailors meets tonight.

- Avoid unfamiliar acronyms. Wrong: RUFUS was formed in 1923.

- In street addresses abbreviate these:
Street   St.   1234 Goober St.
Avenue   Ave.   3506 Loblolly Ave.
Boulevard   Blvd.   80 Crabtree Blvd.

But the words *road, alley, circle,* and *drive* are never abbreviated.

David R. Davies

been established to restrict the flow of creative juices in the writer. Style imposes a discipline in writing that should run through all the activities of a communicator. It implies that the communicator is precise not only with writing, but also with facts and with thought. Consistent style is the hallmark of a professional.

Adherence to a consistent style is also important to society. As Thomas W. Lippman writes in the preface to *The Washington Post Deskbook on Style,* "A newspaper is part of a society's record of itself. Each day's edition lives on in libraries and electronic archives, to be consulted again and again by the scholars and journalists of the future. The newspaper is thus the repository of the language, and we have a responsibility to treat the language with respect. The rules of grammar, punctuation, capitalization, spelling, and usage set down here are our way of trying to meet that responsibility."

Editors are the governors of the style of a publication. It is their job to see that style rules are applied consistently and reasonably. If exceptions are allowed, they should be for specific and logical reasons and should not be at the whim of a writer. Editors and writers should remember that consistent style is one way of telling readers that everything in the publication is certified as accurate.

STYLEBOOKS

Stylebooks are a fact of life for writers for the mass media. Any area of writing, from newspapers to advertising agencies to public relations firms, will require the use of some form of stylebook. Stylebooks deal primarily with three concepts: consistency, usage, and precision. Promoting consistency in writing is the main reason for the existence of any stylebook. A stylebook establishes the rules of writing for a publication.

These may be arbitrary rules, such as using *a.m.* instead of *AM* to refer to morning times and spelling certain numbers out while using numerals for others. These rules also eliminate inconsistencies in spelling, such as mandating that a certain Southeast Asian country be spelled *Vietnam* rather than *Viet-Nam*. Stylebooks also deal with usage, particularly when dictionaries assign a variety of meanings to a word. A good stylebook will say when a word should be properly and consistently used. Beyond that, a good stylebook helps a writer to find the precise words he or she needs.

This chapter refers mostly to *The Associated Press Stylebook and Libel Manual* because that is the most commonly used reference for writers in the mass media. The first AP stylebook appeared in 1953, growing out of the demands of newspaper editors who subscribed to the Associated Press wire service. Many of these editors wanted to make their local copy consistent with the copy they were receiving and running from the AP. Many of these same newspapers also subscribed to the nation's other major wire service, United Press International, and they wanted the wire services to use a consistent style. Consequently, the AP and UPI got together and produced a common stylebook in 1960. These first stylebooks were simply small handbooks that dealt mainly with the rules of writing. During the next decade, newspaper editors saw the need for a more comprehensive book that would also deal with usage. In 1975, a committee of editors from the AP and UPI again cooperated to compile a comprehensive stylebook that would answer many of the questions that arise daily in newsrooms.

Other publications have produced comprehensive stylebooks. Two of the most influential are *The New York Times Manual of Style* and *The Los Angeles Times Stylebook*. Each contains many local references and has become the major style reference for writers on those publications. Most publications, however, have small stylebooks that deal with local style questions and preferences and rely on a larger reference, such as *The Associated Press Stylebook and Libel Manual,* to answer broader questions.

Any publication, even a college newspaper or yearbook, should have its own stylebook because there are always local questions that a major reference work will not answer. For instance, how should students be identified? One college newspaper stylebook says that students should be identified by class rank and major, as in "Mary Smith, a junior in journalism"; a stylebook for another student newspaper says that students should be identified by major and hometown, as in "Mary Smith, a journalism major from Midville." Style problems such as this one need to be answered by a local stylebook.

Another important style reference is *The Chicago Manual of Style* by the University of Chicago Press. This book is the chief reference for what is known as the "Chicago style," a style that is used by most book publishers. It contains a number of major differences from *The Associated Press Stylebook and Libel Manual*. For instance, Chicago style mandates that numbers one through one hundred be spelled out, whereas AP style says that numbers one through nine should be spelled out. Chicago style began as a single proofreader's sheet in 1891 and was first published for those not working with the University of Chicago Press in 1906. Today, it is more than 500 pages long and deals extensively with footnotes, referencing, and many other style problems that arise when books are produced.

Still another important style reference is the *Style Manual of the U.S. Government Printing Office*. This is the style guide for all government publications and is particularly good in dealing with governmental material and foreign languages.

Stylebooks are an important factor in the life of a media professional. They should be adhered to—but with a note of caution. Roy Copperud, author of *A Dictionary of Usage and Style,* criticizes those who use style rules arbitrarily or who enforce style rules that make no sense. "Meditation and prayer lead to the convic-

Sidebar 3.2
Tips on AP Style: Capitalization

- Capitalize names of holidays, historic events, church feast days, and special events, but not seasons:

Mother's Day	Labor Day	Orientation Week
fall storm	autumn leaves	winter tomatoes

- Do not capitalize points of the compass in usages like these:

an east wind	southern Arkansas
western Canada	southeast Forrest County

- But do capitalize points of the compass when part of the name of a recognized geographic area:

Southern California	Midwest
the South	the West Coast

- Capitalize the proper names of nationalities, peoples, races, and tribes:

Indian	Arab	Caucasian
African-American	Hispanic	

- Capitalize and place quotation marks around the names of books, plays, poems, songs, lectures or speech titles, hymns, movies, TV programs, and the like, when the full name is used.

"The Simpsons"	"The Catcher in the Rye"
"Star Wars"	"Lucy in the Sky With Diamonds"
"Arsenic and Old Lace"	

David R. Davies

tion that the best style is the one which governs least," he writes with wry wit. Style rules should not inhibit creativity or initiative in writing. They should promote readability. Style, as *The United Press International Stylebook* points out, is the "intangible ingredient that distinguishes outstanding writing from mediocrity."

THE ASSOCIATED PRESS STYLEBOOK

The Associated Press Stylebook and Libel Manual (commonly referred to as the *AP Stylebook*) is as much a reference manual today as it is a book of rules for consistent writing. The book has been expanded to explain the differences in words that some are tempted to use interchangeably. It gives valuable information that will help reporters and editors understand a wide variety of topics, such as government and civic organizations. It contains lists of weights and measures, military titles, and sports terms. The book has references on governmental agencies, prominent companies, and private organizations.

The heart of the book is still the rules of writing. Following are some of the AP style rules for problem areas that confront beginning writers.

Capitalization

Unnecessary capitalization, like unnecessary punctuation, should be avoided because it slows reading and makes the sentence look uninviting. Some examples: *Main Street,*

Sidebar 3.3
Tips on AP Style: Numbers

- As a general rule, spell out both cardinal and ordinal numbers from one through nine. Use Arabic figures for 10 and above.

  first day   one woman   10 days
  21st year   nine years   50 more

- Use commas in numbers with four or more digits, except in years and street addresses:

  1,500 eggplants   23,879 students
  7034 Aunt Bea St.   the year 1984

- The words *billion* and *million* may be used with round numbers:

  3 million miles $3 million
  10 billion years $10 billion

- Numbers greater than a million may be rounded off and expressed this way, including sums of money:

  2.75 million rather than 2,752,123
  About $2.35 million rather than $2,349,999

David R. Davies

but *Main and Market streets; Mayor John Smith,* but *John Smith, mayor of Jonesville; Steve Barber, executive director of the State Press Association.* (Note the lowercase title after the name, but uppercase for State Press Association, a formal name and therefore a proper noun.)

Abbreviation

The trend is away from alphabet soup in body copy and in headlines, but some abbreviations help to conserve space and simplify information. For example: West Main Street, but *20 W. Main St.* The only titles for which abbreviations are called for (all before the name) are *Dr., Gov., Lt. Gov., Mr., Mrs., Rep., the Rev., Sen.,* and most military ranks. Standing alone, all of these are spelled out and are lowercased. Check the stylebook for others.

Punctuation

Writers should be familiar with the sections of the stylebook dealing with the comma, hyphen, period, colon and semicolon, dash, ellipsis, restrictive and nonrestrictive elements, apostrophe, and quotation marks.

Numerals

The *AP Stylebook* mandates that in most cases, writers should spell out whole numbers below ten and use numerals for ten and above. This rule applies to numbers used in a series or individually. Writers should avoid beginning sentences with a number ("15 people died in the accident"), but if it is necessary to do this, those numbers should be spelled out ("Fifteen people died in the accident").

Ages

Writers should always use figures for ages: *a 2-month-old baby; he was 80; the youth, 18, and the girl, 6, were rescued.*

Dimensions

Generally, writers should use figures for dimensions: *He is 5 feet 9 inches tall; the 5-foot 9-inch woman; a 7-footer; the car left a skid mark 8 inches wide and 17 feet long; the rug is 10 by 12; the storm brought 1 1/2 inches of rain* (spell out fractions less than one).

Spelling

In journalism, a word has but one spelling. Alternative spellings and variants are incorrect (because of the requirement of style consistency). Make it *adviser,* not *advisor; employee,* not *employe;* **totaled,** not *totalled; traveled,* not *travelled; kidnapped,* not *kidnaped; judgment,* not *judgement; television,* not *TV,* when used as a noun; *under way,* not *underway; percent,* not *per cent; afterward,* not *afterwards* (and the same for *toward, upward,* and *forward*); *vs.,* not *versus* or *vs; vice president,* not *vice-president.* Check the stylebook or a dictionary for others.

Dates

Learn which months must be spelled out and which can be abbreviated. *Feb. 6* (current calendar year), *in February 1978* (no comma), *last February.*

Usage

As we mentioned in previous chapters, those who write professionally need to become experts in the language. As they do, they will come to know items such as the following: *Comprise* means "to contain," not "to make up." *The region comprises five states,* not *five states comprise the region* and not *the region is comprised of five states. Affect* means "to influence," not "to carry out." *Effect* means "a result" when it is a noun and "to carry out" when it is a verb. *Controller* and *comptroller* are both pronounced "con-troller" and mean virtually the same thing, though *comptroller* is generally the more accurate word for denoting government financial officers, and *controller* is better for denoting business financial officers. *Hopefully* does not mean "it is hoped," "we hope," "maybe," or "perhaps." It means "in a hopeful manner." *Hopefully, editors will study the English language* is not an acceptable use of the word *hopefully.*

LANGUAGE SENSITIVITY

Writers must understand that language has the ability to offend and demean. Readers and viewers of the mass media are a broad and diverse group, and those who would communicate with them should be aware of the language sensitivities of some of the people within that group. Although some people have gone to extremes in identifying supposedly offensive language, there are terms and attitudes in writing that should legitimately be questioned and changed. The current state of public discourse demands it.

Writers have not always paid attention to such sensitivities. Phrases such as *all men are created equal* and *these are the times that try men's souls* drew no criticism

Sidebar 3.4
Tips on AP Style: Punctuation

- A colon is used in clock time.
  8:15 a.m.   9:15 p.m.   10 a.m. (not 10:00 a.m.)

  General rules for the hyphen are as follows. (See the hyphen entry in punctuation section at the back of the stylebook for complete guidelines.)

- The hyphen is used in phrasal adjectives:
  a 7-year-old boy   an off-the-cuff opinion
  a little-known man

- But the hyphen is not used in sequences in which the adverb has an "-ly" suffix:
  a gravely ill patient   a relatively weird student

- In combinations of a number plus a noun of measurement, use a hyphen:
  a 3-inch bug   a 6-foot man   a two-man team

- A hyphen is always used with the prefix *ex-*:
  ex-president   ex-chairman

- The comma is omitted before Roman numerals and before Jr. and Sr. in names:
  Adlai Stevenson III   John Elliot Jr.

David R. Davies

for their inherent sexism when they were first published, largely because women were not allowed to be a major part of the public debate. We may accept those phrases now because we understand the context in which they were written, but we would not approve of them if they were written in our age.

Media writers should examine their work closely to make sure that they have treated people fairly and equitably, that they have not lapsed into easy or commonly accepted stereotypes, that they have not used phrases or descriptions that demean, and that they have included everyone in their articles who is germane to the subject. Following are a few areas in which writers should take special care.

Sexist Pronouns

It is no longer acceptable to use the pronoun *he* when the referent may be a man or woman. "A student should always do his homework" should be "A student should always do his or her homework." In some instances, rewriting the sentence using plurals is easier: "Students should always do their homework." Sometimes a sentence can be rewritten so that it does not require any pronoun. "Students should always do homework."

Titles

Many titles that have sexist connotations, such as *mailman* and *fireman* are being phased out of the language, becoming *mail carrier* and *firefighter*. (In these two cases, not only are the terms gender neutral, but they are much more descriptive.) Writers need to be aware, however, that some gender-based titles are still common

---

Sidebar 3.5
Tips on AP Style: Names and Titles

- Generally, identify people in the news by their first name, middle initial, and last name:
  David R. Smoots   Fred L. Rogers
- Use full identification in first reference, but in the second reference, use last name only:
  Richard Cooper (first reference)
  Cooper (second reference)
  Angeline Smoots (first reference)
  Smoots (second reference)
- While proper titles are capitalized and abbreviated when placed before a person's name (except for the word *president*), titles that follow a person's name are generally spelled out and not capitalized.
  Voinovich, governor of Ohio
  Pitts, a state representative
  Wallbanger, director of the Goofus League
- Do not use courtesy titles, such as Mr., Mrs., and Miss—unless not using them would cause confusion. (For example, you might want to use them when both members of a married couple are quoted in a news article: "Mr. Smith was killed in the accident but Mrs. Smith survived.)

David R. Davies

(*congressman*, for instance), and writers should look for more acceptable alternatives (*representative*).

Descriptions

"All people are described equal." That awkward rewrite of Thomas Jefferson's phrasing should be an abiding principle of the modern writer for the mass media. Referring to women's appearance and attire continues to be a problem for media writers. Sometimes such references are important to an article, but often they are not. They are included gratuitously and as such are offensive. For example, in the sentence "Jessica Lynch, the blonde soldier who became the center of a media blitz during the first weeks of the Iraqi war, appeared on a local television station," the word *blonde*, though accurate, is gratuitous. A male soldier would probably not be described as "blonde."

Racial descriptions and references may not be necessary. Richard Arrington was the mayor of Birmingham, Alabama. To describe him as "Richard Arrington, the black mayor of Birmingham" is not necessary unless it is important to the understanding of a story to know his race. The test here is to ask the questions, "What if Richard Arrington were white? Would it be important to know that?"

Stereotypes

Our society abounds in stereotypes, and not all are based on race. We often describe women who stay at home as women who "don't work." We might refer to someone with certain hectoring characteristics as a "Jewish mother," forgetting that not all Jewish women who have children have those characteristics. We might write about "Southern bigots," failing to remember that bigots can live anywhere in the country. An older woman who has never married is often called a "spinster" when she may never have spun anything in her life. We should constantly question these blanket references and phrases—and, more important, our attitudes that give rise to such descriptions.

Illness and Disability

American society is taking steps, by private initiative as well as by law, to open itself to people who have various handicaps, disabilities, or limitations. One of the things that Americans should learn as this happens is that identifying people by these limitations is in itself unfair and inaccurate. To say that a person "has a handicap" is different from saying that a person is "handicapped." The way in which these limitations are referred to can also be disabling. For instance, to describe someone as a "reformed alcoholic" is neither complimentary nor benign; "reformed" implies that the person did something wrong and now the problem is solved. A person who is an alcoholic but who no longer drinks is "recovering." To say that someone has a "defect," such as a "birth defect," is to demean by implication (i.e., the person is defective). It would be better to say that a person "was born with a hearing loss."

These are just a few of the areas in which writers need to maintain great sensitivity and continue close examination of their work. Constantly questioning what you have written and making reasonable changes is not just the mark of a good writer; it is a sign of an intelligent and sensitive person.

Sidebar 3.6
Tips on AP Style: Time

- Time in newspaper usage is always a.m. or p.m. Don't use *tonight* with p.m. or *this morning* with a.m., because it is redundant. Don't use the terms *yesterday* and *tomorrow* to describe when an event occurred. It is acceptable, however, to say *today*.

- In describing when an event happens, use the day of the week if the event occurs in the last week or the next week. But use the calendar date if the event is longer than a week ago or farther than a week off.

- Generally, it's more readable to put the time and then the date when an event will occur:
  Right: The train arrives at 3 p.m. Jan. 3.
  Wrong: The train arrives on Jan. 3 at 3 p.m.

- Avoid putting both the day of the week and the date when an event will occur:
  Right: The fireman's ball will be on Jan. 3.
  Wrong: The fireman's ball will be on Monday, Jan. 3.
  Correct: It's 7 p.m.
  Incorrect: It's 7:00 p.m.

David R. Davies

CONCLUSION

This chapter attempts to introduce you to the concept of style and what it means to those who work in the mass media. Conforming to the rules and conventions of the medium in which you are working is the mark of a true professional. Strict adherence to the details of style shows that you care about what you write.

POINTS FOR CONSIDERATION AND DISCUSSION

1. How has this chapter changed your thinking about the meaning of the term *style* and its use in writing for the mass media?
2. What are some of the reasons why there is such a strong emphasis on accuracy in writing for the mass media? How does adherence to a consistent style contribute to goal of accuracy for a journalist?
3. Find a piece of writing in which you think that writer used big words instead of simple ones. Rewrite it using the simpler language. Now compare the two pieces of writing. Which is better?
4. Some people say that a consistent style restricts creativity; others say that it enhances creativity. What are the arguments on both sides of this question?
5. The concept of objectivity is a controversial one in the field of journalism. Why do you think it causes so much controversy?

FURTHER READING

Arnold, G. T. *Media Writer's Handbook*. (2003). New York: McGraw-Hill.

The Associated Press Stylebook and Libel Manual. New editions are produced on a regular basis, but the essential rules rarely change. Writers should obtain and use the latest edition.

Bernstein, T. M. *Watch Your Language*. (1958). Great Neck, NY: Channel Press.

Bernstein, T. M. (1995). *The Careful Writer: A Modern Guide to English Usage*. New York: Free Press.

Copperud, R. (1982). *A Dictionary of Usage and Style*. New York: Avenel Books.

Lippman, T. W. (1989). *The Washington Post Deskbook on Style*. New York: McGraw-Hill.

Rivers, W. L., & Rodriguez, A. W. (1995). *A Journalist's Guide to Grammar and Style*. Boston: Allyn and Bacon.

Siegal, A. M., & Connolly, W. G. *The New York Times Manual of Style and Usage*. (1999). New York: Times Books.

University of Chicago Press. (2003). *A Manual of Style* (15th ed.). Chicago: Author.

U.S. Government Printing Office Style Manual (29th ed.). (2000). Washington, DC: U.S. Government Printing Office.

Walsh, B. *Lapsing into a Comma*. (2002). New York: McGraw-Hill.

WEBSITES

American Copy Editors Society: **www.copydesk.org**

The Slot: **www.theslot.com**

EXERCISES

3.1 AP Style

For each of the following sets of items, select the one that is correct according to AP style. Answers are at the end of the exercise.

1. **a.** The cats belong to a woman who lives on Fourth Avenue.
   b. The cats belong to a woman who lives on Fourth Ave.
   c. The cats belong to a woman who lives on 4th Avenue.

2. **a.** December 18, 1994
   b. Dec. 18, 1994
   c. Dec. 18th, 1994

3. **a.** Jim Folsom, governor of Alabama, was late to an election meeting today.
   b. Jim Folsom, governor of Ala., was late to an election meeting today.
   c. Jim Folsom, gov. of Alabama, was late to an election meeting today.

4. **a.** The Mardi Gras parade will be on March 4th this year.
   b. The Mardi Gras parade will be on March 4 this year.
   c. The Mardi Gras parade will be on Mar. 4 this year.

5. **a.** One of my least favorite cities is Muskogee, Oklahoma.
   b. One of my least favorite cities is Muskogee, Okla.
   c. One of my least favorite cities is Muskogee, OK.

6. **a.** The 2-year-old child was the flower girl in their wedding.
   b. The two year old child was the flower girl in their wedding.
   c. The two-year-old child was the flower girl in their wedding.

7. **a.** 11 A.M.
   b. 11 a.m.
   c. 11 a.m. this morning

8. **a.** Did they win the 10 million dollar sweepstakes?
   b. Did they win the $10,000,000 sweepstakes?
   c. Did they win the $10 million sweepstakes?

9. **a.** 1990's
   b. the 90s
   c. the '90s

10. **a.** The university claimed that 55 percent of its population was male.
    b. The university claimed that 55% of its population was male.
    c. The university claimed that fifty-five percent of its population was male.

11. **a.** They drove from Nashville, Tennessee, to Fairhope, Alabama, in less than seven hours.
    b. They drove from Nashville, Tenn., to Fairhope, Ala., in less than seven hours.
    c. They drove from Nashville, Tenn. to Fairhope, Ala. in less than seven hours.

12. **a.** Pres. Bill Clinton
    b. president Bill Clinton
    c. President Bill Clinton

13. **a.** 42 students went to the museum.
    b. Forty two students went to the museum.
    c. Forty-two students went to the museum.

14. **a.** 5 pounds
    b. 5 lbs.
    c. five pounds

15. **a.** Mrs. Mandy Finklea
    b. Mrs. Finklea
    c. Mandy Finklea

16. **a.** The moving men took the tables, chairs, beds, and couches.
    b. The moving men took the tables, chairs, beds and couches.
    c. The moving men took the tables; chairs; beds; and couches.

17. **a.** the United States
    b. the U.S.
    c. the united states
    (Assume that this is used as a noun.)

18. **a.** The eight-foot clock was difficult to move.
    b. The 8-ft. clock was difficult to move.
    c. The 8-foot clock was difficult to move.

19. **a.** the College of Communication
    b. the college of communication
    c. the college of Communication

20. **a.** I moved to 1803 4th Ave.
    b. I moved to 1803 Fourth Ave.
    c. I moved to 1803 Fourth Avenue.

Answers: 1., a; 2., b; 3., a; 4., b; 5., b; 6., a; 7., b; 8., c; 9., c; 10., a; 11., b; 12., c; 13., c; 14., a; 15., c; 16., b; 17., a; 18., c; 19., a; 20., b.

3.2 AP Style

For each of the following sets of items, select the one that is correct according to AP style. Answers are at the end of the exercise.

1. **a.** The young man went to the girl's house and encouraged her to go out with him.
   b. The young man went to the girl's house, and encouraged her to go out with him.
   c. The young man went to the girl's house, encouraged her to go out with him.

2. **a.** Fob James, Governor of Alabama, began his term in office this week.
   b. Fob James, governor of Alabama, began his term in office this week.
   c. Fob James, Gov. of Alabama, began his term in office this week.

3. **a.** The three foot tall man was the smallest recorded in history.
   b. The 3-foot tall man was the smallest recorded in history.
   c. The 3 foot tall man was the smallest recorded in history.

4. **a.** The politician is affectionately known as John "Crook" Smith.
   b. The politician is affectionately known as John (Crook) Smith.
   c. The politician is affectionately known as John, Crook, Smith.

5. **a.** Spring graduation is set for Saturday, May 13.
   b. Spring graduation is set for Sat., May 13.
   c. Spring graduation is set for May 13.

6. **a.** I went to the store and bought eggs, milk and bread.
   b. I went to the store and bought: eggs, milk and bread.
   c. I went to the store and bought eggs, milk, and bread.

7. **a.** He always reads "USA Today" to prepare for the news quiz.
   b. He always reads USA Today to prepare for the news quiz.
   c. He always reads *USA Today* to prepare for the news quiz.

8. **a.** The businesss is based in Birmingham.
   b. The business is based in Birmingham, Alabama.
   c. The business is based in Birmingham, Ala.

9. **a.** She gave a large donation to NOW.
   b. She gave a large donation to N.O.W.
   c. She gave a large donation to the National Organization for Women.

(Assume that this the first reference to the organization.)

10. **a.** Smith is the professor for this course.
    b. James Smith is the professor for this course.
    c. James G. Smith is the professor for this course.

(Assume that this is the first reference to the man.)

11. **a.** This lab section begins at 10:00 a.m.
    b. This lab section begins at 10 a.m.
    c. This lab section begins at 10 in the morning.

12. **a.** You are enrolled in the department of journalism in the College of Communication.
    b. You are enrolled in the department of journalism in the college of communication.
    c. You are enrolled in the department of journalism in the department of communication.

13. **a.** *Moby-Dick* was Herman Melville's most famous book.
    b. "Moby-Dick" was Herman Melville's most famous book.
    c. Moby-Dick was Herman Melville's most famous book.

14. **a.** One of my least favorite cities is Galesburg, Illinois.
    b. One of my least favorite cities is Galesburg, Ill.
    c. One of my least favorite cities is Galesburg, IL.

15. **a.** One of my favorite cities is Austin, Texas.
    b. One of my favorite cities is Austin, Tex.
    c. One of my favorite cities is Austin, TX.

16. **a.** The store is located on McFarland Boulevard.
    b. The store is located on McFarland Boulvd.
    c. The store is located on McFarland Blvd.

17. **a.** My husband was born on Nov. 26, 1965.
    b. My husband was born on November 26, 1965.
    c. My husband was born on Mon., November 26, 1965.

18. **a.** Last night, Tuscaloosa experienced its first Winter storm.
    b. Last night, Tuscaloosa experienced its first winter storm.
    c. Last night, Tuscaloosa experienced its first wntr. storm.

19. **a.** The store is located at 1520 McFarland Boulevard.
    b. The store is located at 1520 McFarland Boulvd.
    c. The store is located at 1520 McFarland Blvd.

20. **a.** Democrats are supportive of Pres. Clinton.
    b. Democrats are supportive of president Clinton.
    c. Democrats are supportive of President Clinton.

Answers: 1., a; 2., b; 3., b; 4., a; 5., c; 6., a; 7., c; 8., c; 9., c; 10., c; 11., b; 12., a; 13., b; 14., b; 15., b; 16., a; 17., a; 18., b; 19., c; 20., c.

3.3 Using the Stylebook

The following section contains a variety of style exercises. You should follow your instructor's directions in completing them.

1. He was charged with trafficing in drugs.

2. The Rev. Billy Grahm said God was alive and His will would triumph.

3. The flag, which Francis Scott Key saw, has been preserved.

4. life-like, outfielder, inter-racial, IOU's (plural)

5. Pianoes, nation-wide, P.T.A., Viet-nam War

6. The train will arrive at twelve noon on Tues.

7. The US Census Bureau defines the south as a Seventeen-state region.

8. The judge ruled that because of his oral skills he had entered into a verbal contract.

9. She had an afternoon snack of some Oreo cookies and Coke.

10. harrass, accomodate, weird, likeable

11. Circle the correct form:

    donut, doughnut

    pants suit, pantsuit

    plow, plough

    U.S. Weather Bureau, National Weather Service

3.4 Using the Stylebook

Correct the following items so that they conform to AP style:

1. The defense department is about to propose a new missele system.

2. F.C.C., hitch-hiker, three dollars, 4 million

3. The three most important people in his life are his wife, son, and mother.

4. part-time, 10 year old child, 5 PM, 5300

5. The cardinals won the last game of the world series, 7 to 5.

6. spring (season), fall (season), south (point on compass), south (region)

7. November 15, the last day of Feb., Mar. 16

8. 13 people travelled to Austin, Tex. for the rally.

9. He had ten cents left in his pocket.

10. home-made, well-known, Italian-American, questionnaire

3.5 Using the Stylebook

Correct the following items so that they conform to AP style:

1. The U.S. is sometimes not the best market for U.S. products.

2. Circle the correct form:

   upward, upwards

   British (Labour, Labor) Party

   Riverside (Ave., Avenue)

   cupsful, cupfuls

   eying, eyeing

3. The Republican differed from the democrat many times during the debate.

4. Dr. John Smith and Dr. Mary Wilson performed the operations.

5. Circle the correct form:

   good will, goodwill (noun)

   USS Eisenhower, U.S.S. Eisenhower

   cigaret, cigarette

   midAmerica, mid-America

6. He said he was neither a Communist or a member of the Communist Party.

7. After her surgery, she had to wear a Pacemaker.

8. "What a hair-brained scheme!" she exclaimed.

9. preempt, speed-up (noun), 55 miles per hour, hookey

10. The underworld, or mafia, was responsible for the murder.

3.6 Using the Stylebook

Correct the following items so that they conform to AP style:

1. The first annual rutabaga eating contest was canceled because of averse weather.

2. Its not alright to drink an access of beer before going to the football game.

3. Like Einstein said, all knowledge is relative.

4. The state capital of LA is located at 3722 Dagwood Rd.

5. The Mayor refused to go along with the City Council vote. "I descent," he stated.

6. Madonna certainly has a flare for fashion; she always wears expensive outfits.

7. The bomb totally destroyed Senator Kitsmoot's bird cage.

8. My bright-green Chevrolet which is in the garage needs a new transmission.

9. Knopke's hilarious joke illicited laughter from the Midville city council.

10. Jones laid on the floor waiting for the job interview to begin.

11. Horowitz, an ethics major, vowed never to compromise his principals.

12. At the end of the book report, Haynes sited the World Book as a source.

3.7 Using the Stylebook

Correct the following items so that they conform to AP style:

1. The twenty-five-year-old man wept as he left Hattiesburg, Mississippi.

2. This November 10th will mark our anniversary.

3. Don't park the car on Rodeo Dr. Instead, park it at 12 Davies Street.

4. They spent 130 dollars to buy a new set of nose rings.

5. Smoots moved to the North because the people there are so nice.

6. At 7 p.m. this evening, the rodeo will begin in the Town Square.

7. Yesterday, the Terrorists blew up their home at 123 Melrose St.

8. 22 seamstresses were needed to mend the prom dresses.

9. About 5 percent of the professors have lost their hair.

10. After 2 feet of snow fell at his home in Columbus, Ohio, Jones decided to leave.

11. Miss Smith bet fifty dollars that her brother weighed more than a 1964 Chevy.

12. Guy Reel, the Governor of Calif., set his trailer on fire September 1.

13. A fire began at 3325 McDonald Dr. when an oven full of rutabagas exploded.

14. During the 1970's, everyone wore bell-bottom blue jeans to church.

3.8 Using the Stylebook

Correct the following items so that they conform to AP style:

1. In Aug. 1985, Davies rented a rutabaga stand in Augusta, Georgia.

2. Pomerantz tied the beehive to Senator Gramm's cowboy hat.

3. About 1200 easter rabbits were killed in the explosion at Big Dave's Bunny Warehouse, located at 2525 Hackensack Drive.

4. In the 1980's, Davies left the Midwest and moved to the Loire Valley in France.

5. Smoots brought two cups of coffee to the Governor.

6. About eight percent of the cantaloupes have been stuffed with rutabagas.

7. Jones bet 40 dollars that his roommate had hidden the sandwich.

8. The 3 university professors share a house at 613 25th Avenue.

9. After 2 feet of snow fell at his home in Columbus, Ohio, Davies decided to leave the midwest and move to the South.

10. On December 11th, all classes will been canceled.

11. Yesterday morning, the Mayor skipped her aerobics class.

12. Davies drove 2,000,000 miles in his old Toyota Corolla before it blew up.

13. Doctor Kildare said he had filed a malpractice suit against Marcus Welby.

14. At eight p.m. in the evening, Governor Jim Guy Tucker of Arkansas will give a short speech in front of the Gorgas library.

3.9 Using the Stylebook

Correct the following items so that they conform to AP style:

1. Estalene Smoots dropped her french class the 1st day of school.

2. Sadie Hoots won 3,200,000 dollars on Wheel of Fortune.

3. Frustrated that their professor required them to eat fried rutabagas, the students walked out of class at 9 a.m. this morning.

4. The office manager had twenty-one plants, sixty-two cats and two puppies.

5. President Aubrey Lucas is originally from Compton, California.

6. On October 25th, Ruth Ann Bobetski will turn 41.

7. Goober Hicks lives at 10 West Hardy St. He used to live in a run down shack at 2803 Williamsburg Rd.

8. Abby gave birth to a nine pound baby boy.

9. The President invited me to dinner at the white house, but I could not fit it into my schedule.

10. Senator Davies said his earnings had increased 10% in the 1980's.

11. Barney the dinosaur will be executed on Tuesday, November 2.

12. 25 vagabonds attacked me from behind in front of the hub.

13. Miss Snarkle found a 10 inch bug crawling in her spaghetti. "Great! Now I won't need seconds", she exclaimed.

14. All the men in the R.O.T.C. chapter wore red, white, and blue pantyhose to class in Jan. 1991.

15. The Bay City baseball team lost their final game two to one and climbed dejectedly back onto their bus.

3.10 Using the Stylebook

Using the *AP Stylebook,* answer the questions or correct the following sentences or phrases:

1. What is the acceptable form of abbreviation for miles per hour?

2. What is the difference between civil and criminal cases?

3. Correct this sentence: The eye witness found himself in an eye to eye confrontation.

4. If GMT is used on second reference, what must accompany it?

5. When do you capitalize grand jury?

6. Which is correct: Scene two, Scene 2, scene two, or scene 2?

7. Correct the spelling of "cuetips."

8. Which one of these refers to the building where government resides: capital, Capital or capitol?

9. What use of the term *working class* needs a hyphen?

10. Which term is correct: Christian Science Church or Church of Christ Scientist?

3.11 Using the Stylebook

Using the *AP Stylebook,* answer the questions or correct the following sentences or phrases:

1. The United States (constitutes, composes, comprises) 50 states.

2. How would you write "In the year of the Lord 33"?

3. What is the correct title for Russian leaders before 1914?

4. What is an acceptable abbreviation for the ocean liner Queen Elizabeth II?

5. Which of the following is incorrect: court-martials or cupfuls?

6. What is the long name for the machinists' union?

7. How should the term *NROTC* be used correctly in journalism?

8. Which of the following is not an acceptable term for the journalist to apply to a religious group: evangelical, Pentecostal, or liberal?

9. Which of these words has to do with flowing water: pour or pore?

10. Where are the headquarters for Northwest Airlines?

3.12 Using the Stylebook

Correct the following items so that they conform with AP style:

1. His solution turned out to be the most equal of the two.

2. Ga. Sec. of State George Smith testified at the Congressional hearing.

3. tis, the Gay 1890's, a South America country, 1492 A. D.

4. Write the plurals for the following words: Eskimo, _____;
   chili, _____; memorandum, _____; ski, _____.

5. The ballif opened the court by saying, "Oyes, oyes, oyes!"

6. He spread out his palate and went to sleep.

7. carry-over (adjective), nitty-gritty, nit-picking, know-how

8. What do the following abbreviations stand for?
   USIA _____
   GOP _____
   EST _____
   TVA _____

   Which, if any, of these abbreviations is acceptable for first reference? _____

9. The pan had a teflon surface.

10. He was graduated from a teacher's college in the north.

3.13 Using the Stylebook

Correct the following items so that they conform with AP style:

1. Write the plurals for the following words: referendum, _____; court
   martial, _____; 1920, _____; dead end, _____.

2. Daylight savings time begins on the last Sun. in April.

3. He made the Dean's List after Dean Smith talked to him.

4. The game, that was scheduled for to-night, was rained out.

5. He said the car would go further on premium gas.

6. The movie which starred Sam Jones received an r rating.

7. He had run the gauntlet of criticism and abuse for his views.

8. The woman who the article referred to was a German Jewess.

9. judgement, naval orange, resistible, self-defense

10. He played semi-pro baseball for 3 years.

3.14 Using the Stylebook

Correct the following story so that it conforms to AP style. The story contains other errors besides style errors that you will need to correct. Use the proper editing marks.

Baseball Game

The Bay City Bluebirds rallied from a 3-run defict last night to defeat the Carmel Cardinals 6-3 and win the Western Tri-state division championship.

The bluebirds are now assured a place int eh Tri-state playoffs which begin next week. Their opponent will be determined tonight in a game between the Santa Ana Gnerals and the Redwood Knights.

The cardinals led the bluebirds for most of the game, and they hasa 3-0 lead in the eighth inniny.

In the bluebird hafl of the eighth, Tim Story, the first baseman, walked and stole second. Left fielder Biff Carbosi was walked intensionally, and both runner moved up a base on a wild pitch by cardinal started ronnie Miller. Miller was then relieved by Chuck Nelson.

Bluebird secondbaseman Carbo Garbey lined Nelson's first pitch into deep centefield, scoring both baserunners. Two pitches later, Garbey stole home to tie the game.

Nelson got the next 2 hitters out, but then Carey Clark, the bluebird catcher, homered to put the bluebirds ahead. The bluebirds added two more runs in the ninth to insure their victory.

3.15 Using the Stylebook

Correct the following story so that it conforms to AP style. Use the proper editing marks.

Guilty Verdict

A jury found a Midville man guilty of Second-Degree Manslaughter after an hour's worth of deliberations on Tuesday.

Johnny Gene Garber was convicted at the end of a 3-day trial which featured his mother testifying against him. He was charged in the death of a thirty-nine year old brickmason, Gardner Jackson, of Number Twelve, Ninth Street in Jonesville.

Mr. Garber stood sliently as the jury read the verdict. The Presiding Judge, Jonas T. McMillan, set a sentencing hearing for next Monday at eight o'clock in the morning.

Garber was charged with being druck while driving down highway 69 last March. His car served out of control and ran head on into a car driven by Mr. Jackson, who had been attending services at the Midville Baptist church.

During the trial, the Prosecution Attory, Able Sasson, called Garber's mother, Mrs. Minnie Lee Garber, to testify that her son had been drinking heavily at there home that evening before the accident occured.

Garber could recieve a sentence of two to five years in prison for the crime he committed.

3.16 Using the Stylebook

Correct the following story so that it conforms to AP style. The story contains other errors besides style errors that you will need to correct. Use the proper editing marks.

City Council

The city council passed an ordinance last night requireing people convicted of their second drunk charge to serve a minimum of thirty days in jail and to have their driver's license suspended for six months.

The ordinance was passed by a vote of five to three. Councilman Clarissa Atwell sponsored the change in the law which wil take effect on December 31st of this year.

"I think this new law will save the lives of a lot of people, Miss Atwell said.

The council chamber was filled to overflowing with people interested in the law. Many of the people there were members of Mothers Against Drunk Driving (M.A.D.D.)

One Councilamn who voted against law, Les Honeycutt, said he felt the laws against drunk driving were strong enough and that they needed to be inforced for rigidly. His comments received hoots and jeers from the crowd, and at one point the council president, Harley Sanders, trhreatened to have some of the audience removed and evicted.

3.17 Using the Stylebook

Correct the following story so that it conforms to AP style. Use the proper editing marks.

Power Failure

Power was cut off to nearly a 3rd of the residents of Midville, last night, after a violent storm ripped through the city around six o'clock.

Police chief Robert Dye said that power was restored to most homes within about two hours, but "a substantial number of people," had to go without power for most of the night.

Chief Dye said that many of the city's traffic lights were knocked out by the storm, and traffick problems developed on several of the more busy streets.

Chief dye says that everything should be back to normal today.

A Power company official said that more than 1500 homes were without electricity for some part of the night. They said that crews worked throughout the entire night to get people's power turned on.

The storm dumped over 2 inches of rain on the city in about 30 minutes. The power failure was due to lighting hitting one of the power companys substations in the Western part of the city.

3.18 Writing Problems

Before beginning this exercise, review some of the discussion of writing problems and principles in this chapter. The following sentences contain a variety of problems, such as wordiness, jargon, clichés, and redundancies, as well as errors in AP style. Edit or rewrite them as necessary to deal with these problems.

1. The coach is noted for and has the reputation for welcoming back players, who, he says in his own words, he "didn't want to give up on" and whom just happened to have game breaking talent.

2. Over a year after the zoo bought her for the price of $500,000, Ruby the elephant still cannot be in full physical contact with the two other African elephants that the zoo has acquired.

3. The five officers were fired Monday night after the sheriff and the chief deputy reviewed the preliminary findings of a state investigator's report into the illegal abuse and unjustified incarceration of suspects in a drug raid.

4. Ezer is a parrot of a South Asian variety that the Humane Society is trying to put up for adoption and find a good home for. The society said a man offered to adopt Ezer last week but that he was a long distance truck driver. They did not feel his home would be suitable for Ezer's need because of the strain and confinement.

5. The mayor said the city lacked the necessary monetary resources and revenue to construct a new facility that could house many of the services that it offered to the public. These services include the offices for business license renewals and rezoning petitions.

6. Musick was the second person to plead guilty since an indictment was handed up in the case during the month of March. He is charged with being part of a conspiracy that bought dozens of kilograms of cocaine into the area over the course of a roughly two year period.

7. A traffic department official surmised that the closure of the parkway caused a great deal of inconvenience to local residents and visitors, particularly during the last two months which is the height of the tourist season. He said he was glad all that is behind us.

8. The day after county commissioners received their first form look at the long-term needs study, county officials hashed out jail issues in an effort to reach consensus on what actions the county should take and the direction it should be heading.

9. Smith offered that he had built up his mom-and-pop family business, which originally started as a diner when Binfield Road was unpaved and is now listed as a four-star restaurant, into a thriving business.

10. Better salaries, retirement benefits and educational opportunities are among incentives that might help stem the tide, defense officials said as they met with lawmakers to discuss ways to keep forces who have become so crucial to the war on terror.

chapter four

Writing in the Media Environment

the events on the morning of Tuesday, September 11, 2001, transformed that day from just another weekday into a symbol of the age in which we live. As word spread about the attacks in New York and Washington, D.C., millions of people gathered in front of their televisions sets, tuned in their radios, and visited their favorite news websites. The news was extraordinary and compelling. It was also shocking, but we could not get enough information. Despite an all-day saturation of news on that day, newspapers broke records for sales the next day. Even weekly newsmagazines, which normally do not publish until the weekend, brought out special editions on that Wednesday.

Reading and viewing the news about September 11 were individual acts but also a shared experience. We read and viewed, and then we talked. We may have used the telephone, e-mail, Usenet newsgroups, Internet chat rooms, or Web forums to discuss the events with friends, acquaintances, or even strangers.

Each of us could form our own opinions and interpretations about what happened and what its implications would be. What we shared was the news.

News is one of the elements that holds a society of diverse people together. The fact that a group of individuals share the same current information allows the group to operate as a community. If we were all hermits or if we dealt only with the small group of people with whom we have physical contact, news might not matter so much. September 11 was one of many events that demonstrate that our interests extend far beyond our group of acquaintances. One of the ways in which we establish relationships with those beyond this group is to share the same current information.

This centrality of news makes the news story a fundamental form of writing for the mass media. Those who would write for the mass media in any form—whether for a daily newspaper or a newsletter for a nonprofit organization—must understand the importance of news and should master the news story format.

Writing for the mass media is one of the most important jobs in our society. The people who do this job have a tremendous impact on the shape and direction of the community. They tell us about ourselves. They establish a bond between the individual members of the society and the community and nation as a whole. They must be honest, talented, and dedicated. The job is too important and too difficult for people with lesser qualities.

The writer for the mass media has two jobs. The first is gathering information; the second is putting that information into the appropriate form for the medium in which the writer is working. This chapter explores the environment of writing that is common to most mass media organizations. Although not every such organization deals with the political and cultural information we call news, most media organizations have a news and information function that their audiences expect them to perform.

THE NEWS CULTURE

Anyone involved with the mass media, even if the person does not work for what we normally think of as a news organization, is part of the news culture and must understand the professional standards and demands that this culture imposes.

The news culture arises from the fact that the media deal with information. Media professionals gather and process that information and put it into a form that is distributed to a wide audience for specific purposes. Those purposes can include informing, persuading, or entertaining an audience, but information is always at the core of what any media professional does.

Because of this centrality of information, the media professional is governed by a number of considerations.

The first is *the need for accurate information*. We will discuss the importance of getting good information and presenting it accurately in several parts of this book. Here we should simply say that the quality of information with which the writer must deal is irrevocably tied to the writer's credibility. In fact, more than anything else, accurate information determines how good a professional writer is. Getting accurate information and presenting it accurately, no matter what the purpose of the writing, is the writer's first and foremost duty.

Another consideration of the news culture is *presenting information efficiently*. Many of the forms of writing that we will discuss in this book, whether news, advertising, or public relations, are structured to enhance efficient delivery of information.

Tied to this efficiency is yet another consideration of the news culture: *the economic health of the organization*. In most instances, media professionals work for organizations that are subject to the rules of the marketplace. Their survival depends on their ability to gather the audience, advertisers, and income to pay expenses. Writers must recognize and understand their role in how an organization functions in the marketplace.

Writers in the news culture must also thoroughly understand the processes of the organization. One of the most important parts of this understanding is the concept of *deadlines*. Writers must not only produce good work, but they must also meet the deadlines that the organization establishes. Deadlines enable an organization to operate efficiently.

Finally, *the idea of individual and corporate integrity* must be part of the daily life of the media professional. An individual's commitment to honesty, fairness, and ethical standards should be strong, and the writer's confidence in the corporation's standards should be well placed. An individual professional does not have to agree with every decision that is made at the corporate level, but there should be a degree of confidence in the overall organization that is never violated.

Accuracy, efficiency, processes, deadlines, and ethics are all part of the news culture. Students entering this discipline must understand their importance and the demands that are made on individuals who would work in this environment.

ELEMENTS OF NEWS

What makes an event news? The same thing could happen to two people in two different places, and one would be a news story and the other would not. For instance, if you were involved in a minor automobile accident in which there were no injuries, the incident probably would not appear in your local newspaper. If the president of the United States were involved in that same type of accident, it would probably be the first story on all the nightly newscasts.

The separation of events into "news" and "not news" categories is a function of *news values*. (See Figure 4.1.) These are concepts that help us to decide what a mass media audience is or should be interested in. Millions of events occur in our society every day. Only those few events that editors and news directors select and that have at least one of the following criteria can be classified as news.

Impact

Events that change people's lives are classified as news. The event itself might involve only a few people, but the consequences may be wide-ranging. For example, if

Figure 4.1   News Values

Photographs such as the top one, showing the cleanup of the World Trade Center site in New York City, appeared in newspapers and on news websites around the world. The other picture appeared only in a local daily newspaper. What news values are at work here?
Photo credits: Federal Emergency Management Agency (top); Amy Kilpatrick (bottom).

Congress passes a bill to raise taxes or if a researcher discovers a cure for a form of cancer, both actions will affect large numbers of people. These events have impact, and they would be considered news.

Timeliness

Timeliness is a value common to almost all news stories. It refers to how long ago an event happened. Without the element of timeliness, most events cannot be considered news. For example, a trial that occurred last year is not news; a trial that is going on right now may be news. How much time has to elapse before an event can no longer be considered news? No one answer applies to every case. Most events that are more than a day to a day and a half old are not thought to be news. (Look in today's newspaper or on a news website to see whether can find a news story about an event that occurred two days ago.)

Prominence

Prominent people, sometimes even when they are doing trivial things, make news. The president of the United States is a prime example. Whenever he takes a trip, even for purely personal and private reasons, his movements are covered in great detail by the news media. The president is a prominent and important person. Almost anything he does is likely to have an impact on the country, and people are very interested in his actions. The president is not the only example of a prominent person who often makes news. Movie stars, famous politicians, advocates of social causes—all of these people make news simply because they are very well known and people are interested in what they are doing.

Proximity

Events that occur close to home are more likely to be news than the same events that occur elsewhere. For example, a car wreck killing two people that happens on a road in your home county is more likely to be reported in the local news media than the same kind of wreck that occurs a thousand miles away. We are interested in the things that happen around us. If we know a place where something goes on, we are more likely to have a feeling for it and for the people involved.

Conflict

When people disagree, when they fight, when they have arguments—that's news, particularly if one of the other news values, such as prominence, is involved. Conflict is one of the journalist's favorite news values because it generally ensures that there is an interesting story to write. One of the reasons trial stories are so popular with newspaper readers and television watchers is that the central drama involves conflict: two competing forces, each vying to defeat the other.

The Bizarre or Unusual

A rare event is sometimes considered news. There is an adage in journalism that says "When a dog bites a man, that's not news. When a man bites a dog, now that's news." Unusual events, though they may have relatively little importance or involve obscure people, are interesting to readers and enliven a publication. For example, it's not news when someone's driver's license is revoked (unless that someone is a prominent person); it is news, however, when a state department of transportation revokes the license of a person called "the worst driver in the state" because he had a dozen accidents in the last two years.

Currency

Issues that have current interest often have news value, and events surrounding those issues can sometimes be considered news. In the weeks before the events of September 11, 2001, a major news story that had much currency was about a female intern in Washington, D.C., who was missing and who had been romantically involved with a congressman from California. The case was covered in minute detail and was the subject of many talk shows and commentaries. Once the September 11 attacks occurred, the subject of the missing intern lost its currency. No one was interested anymore. Such is the cycle of many news events and subjects.

News writers and editors must make decisions about events based on these news values. News values are also used in deciding the kind of information needed for a story and in helping the writer to structure the story so that the most important and interesting information gets to the reader in the most efficient manner.

Basic to all writing is having the information necessary for the writing process. Writing for the mass media requires that certain information be gathered at the beginning of the writing process. A journalist gathering information or writing a story tries to answer six basic questions for the reader:

- *Who:* Who are the important people related to the story? Is everyone included so that the story can be accurately and adequately told? Is everyone properly identified?

- *What:* What is the major action or event of the story? What are the actions or events that are of lesser importance? A journalist ought to be able to state the major action of the story in one sentence, and this should be the theme of the story.

- *When:* When did the event occur? Readers of news stories should have a clear idea of when the story takes place. The "when" element is rarely the best way to begin a story because it is not often the most important piece of information a journalist has to tell a reader, but it should come early in the story and should be clearly stated.

- *Where:* Where did the event occur? Journalists cannot assume that readers will know or be able to figure out where an event took place. The location or locations of the event or action should be clearly identified.

- *Why and how:* The reader expects explanations about events. If a story is about something bizarre or unusual, the writer should offer some explanation so that the questions the event raises in the reader's mind are answered. The writer also needs to set the events or actions in a story in the proper context so that the reader can understand the event more fully. Reference should be made to previous events or actions if they help to explain things to the reader.

Acquiring the information needed to write anything for the mass media is an essential part of the writing process. Information is not always self-evident or readily available. The process of reporting—gathering the information—takes considerable skill, creativity, and tenacity. What the writer needs, of course, depends on what he or she is writing about, but essentially, a writer has three fundamental sources of information: people, records (any information that is written or stored so others may find it), and personal observation.

PERSONAL SOURCES

Most information in most news stories comes from personal sources—that is, people. A news reporter is likely to spend most of his or her nonwriting time talking to people either face to face or over the telephone. In fact, many would argue that the more people the reporter talks to, the better a story is likely to be because of the variety of information and views the reporter can obtain.

Here are some examples of paragraphs from news stories in which the information comes from personal sources:

According to Clem Washburn, the festival organizer, the Hayseed Bluegrass Festival drew more than 10,000 for the three-day event.

Rep. Pell Stanley said he disapproved of the amount of money spent on the program.

"I'm against that proposal because it's unfair to the middle class," the senator said.

The first two examples are indirect quotations or paraphrases; the third is a direct quotation. Chapter 5 discusses more fully the handling of direct and indirect quotations.

Interviewing occurs when a reporter talks to a source. All writers who deal with information—whether they are newspaper reporters, magazine writers or public relations practitioners—must master the art of interviewing. A reporter tries to determine what information the source has and would be willing to share. Then the reporter attempts to ask the kinds of questions that would elicit this information. The techniques of interviewing are discussed more fully in the next section of this chapter.

Journalists (and this would include public relations practitioners who have to gather news and information) develop *sources* among the people whom they contact regularly; that is, the reporters will find people who have information and are willing to talk with the reporter about it. Reporters soon realize that many people can provide them with information, and sometimes that information can come from surprising sources. For instance, most reporters who are assigned to a beat—a term in journalism that means a place or topic a reporter must write regularly about—learn that secretaries, rather than their bosses, can be the best sources of information. Secretaries often know what is happening before their bosses do. Consequently, many reporters get to know the secretaries on their beats very well. As reporters and sources deal with each other, they should develop a relationship of mutual understanding. Reporters find out whom they can trust among their sources, and sources come to trust that the information they give to reporters will be used wisely.

One general rule governs the relationships reporters have with their sources: Reporters should always identify themselves clearly to their sources. Sources should know before they talk to reporters that their information could be used in a news story. Sources should have the opportunity not to talk with news reporters if they do not want to.

Attribution is another standard practice of writing for the mass media. Attribution in a news story means telling readers the source of the information so that the readers can judge the credibility of that information. Attribution phrases are those such as *he said, she said,* and *according to officials.* Most of the major information in a news story needs to have some attribution, particularly information that comes from personal sources.

INTERVIEWING

Interviewing ranks at the top of the most important activities a mass media professional can undertake. Talking with people is the chief way we have of gathering current information about almost any topic. Within the daily press, more information is collected through interviews than by any other method.

News stories use two kinds of quoted material: direct quotations and indirect quotations. Direct quotations are the words that the source has used to express an idea; the words should be surrounded by quotation marks.

"I believe the tax some members of the city council want to impose would hurt the economy of the city," the mayor said.

Figure 4.2

Ernest Hemingway on listening

I like to listen. I have learned a great deal from listening carefully. Most people never listen.

Indirect quotations, or paraphrases, express what the source said but use different words from those the source used.

> The mayor said he opposed the tax proposal currently before the city council, saying it would hurt the city's economic recovery.

A paraphrase may use some of the exact words of the source, and the writer may want to put those inside quotation marks.

> The mayor expressed his opposition to the tax proposal currently before the city council, saying it would "hurt the economy of the city."

The qualities of the good interview (from the standpoint of the journalist) mirror the qualities of any good conversation. The participants quickly reach an understanding about why they are talking with one another. They exchange views and information. They learn something about one another. They share nonverbal gestures, such as smiles or frowns.

Yet interviewing for the journalist is not just having a good conversation. The journalist's purpose in an interview is to gain information and material for an article that will be disseminated to others. Therefore, a journalist needs to develop interviewing skills that include not only proper conduct during the face-to-face conversation but also proper preparation and follow-up. The following are some of the steps a journalist should take to have successful interviews.

The first step in interviewing is deciding, sometimes simultaneously, what information is needed and who would be the best source for that information. A journalist should have a clear idea of what information it will take to make a good article. Developing that kind of clear idea takes experience, but it is certainly within the grasp of the beginning reporter. The information that a reporter needs will often dictate who is the best source to provide that information, but the selection of the source may depend on other factors as well. For instance, the best source for certain information might not be available or might be hesitant to talk with a journalist. These are situations in which journalists might have to find other sources of information.

The second step to a successful interview is preparing for the conversation. This preparation may include doing research on the topic of the interview or on the person to be interviewed. In general, the more the journalist knows about both, the more successful the interview is likely to be. In the world of daily journalism, time and deadline pressure may not permit much preparation. In such instances, the journalist must draw on his or her experience and the cooperation of the source.

Another part of the preparation phase of the interview is figuring out what questions to ask. The questions, of course, will depend on the information that is needed, but they will also depend on the willingness of the source to give information. Information that is simple and not necessarily controversial can usually be gained from clear, straightforward, and efficient questions, as in the following exchange:

Reporter: Can you tell me how the wreck occurred?

Police officer: Well, the witnesses said it wasn't raining but the roads were pretty wet from a thunderstorm that had just come through the area. The car traveling in the westbound lane put its brakes on for some reason, and the car skidded out of control and into the eastbound lane.

Reporter: Why did the car brake?

Police officer: We're not sure. Maybe an animal ran across the road. Sometimes at night, especially in wet conditions, you think you see things that aren't there and you hit the brakes.

Reporter: What happened when the car skidded?

Police officer: It skidded about fifty feet and slammed into a car in the eastbound lane. A third car, also traveling eastbound, then crashed into those cars. Fortunately for everyone else, those were the only three cars involved in the wreck.

Reporter: Was anyone hurt?

Police officer: Yeah, two people were hurt pretty bad, and two others were injured. Everyone was alive when we got them to the hospital. You'll have to check with the hospital to see how they are doing.

This short exchange has given the reporter a lot of information (though certainly not everything) that can be included in a story. Chances are that the reporter did not have much time to prepare for this interview. But the reporter understands news values and story construction well enough to ask relevant and productive questions.

Sometimes the information a reporter seeks is much more controversial and the source is not as adept or as willing to give the information. Journalists should be sensitive to and empathetic with their sources, but they should also remember their professional responsibilities.

Interviewers have different methods of asking questions, and they will use these methods when they are appropriate for the situation. Following are some of the various types of questions they can ask.

Closed-Ended Questions

These usually require very short answers, or the question itself may contain a choice of answers from which the respondent will choose. ("How often do you travel out of town?" "Do you feel good or bad about the way things turned out?")

Open-Ended Questions

Sometimes an interviewer will want to give a subject the chance to say anything he or she wants. Open-ended questions allow this to happen. ("What do you think is the most important issue facing the city council now?" "When you think about a person who is homeless, what picture comes into your mind?")

Hypothetical Questions

These are questions that set up a situation or condition and ask the interviewee to respond to it. They are sometimes known as "what if" questions. ("If someone came to you and asked your help in finding a job, what would you tell that person?")

Agree/Disagree Questions

As the name implies, these questions ask respondents to express agreement or disagreement with a statement or action. ("Some people say Congressmen should be prevented from serving more than two terms. Do you agree or disagree with that?")

Probes

These are questions that follow up on something the interviewee has said. They can be neutral ("Can you tell me more about that?"), provocative ("Are you saying you will never do that?"), or challenging ("I think a lot of people will find that difficult to believe."). The purpose of a probe is to get the interviewee to give more information about what he or she has just said.

Personal Questions

These questions have to do with the personal life of a subject. They may be very relevant to the article the journalist must do, but these questions need to be approached carefully. Most experienced interviewers agree that such questions should be left until the middle or end of the interview, giving the respondent a chance to establish some trust in the interviewer.

One of the most important products of planning an interview is for the journalist to have a list of questions that will be asked when the interview takes place. Because interviews are not always predictable, it may not be feasible or necessary to ask every question, and it is likely that unplanned questions will arise, but a journalist should always have some kind of a plan for the interview session.

The next step in the interview process is to establish contact with the source and to set up some mutually agreeable time and place to conduct the interview. When a reporter is working near a daily deadline, he or she may insist that the interview be conducted immediately on the phone. In other instances, however, a source should be told who wants to conduct the interview, for what publication it will be conducted, and what information, in general, the reporter needs. The reporter should be flexible about the time and the place of the interview so that it is as convenient for the source as possible.

During the interview itself, a reporter should keep in mind why the interview is taking place: to obtain certain information but also to remain open to the possibility that other, more interesting or important information may be obtained. If a source decides to offer some new or surprising information, the reporter should be able to evaluate the worth of the information and handle it appropriately. Most of the time, however, a reporter's planning will pay off with an efficient and productive interview. The following are a number of things that an interviewer should keep in mind about an interviewing situation:

- *Control the situation.* Keep the conversation on track by remembering what you came for and what information you need to get from the source. Refer to your notes or questions.

- *Set the tone of the interview early.* Normally, the first few questions will determine how the interview goes, so the reporter should think carefully about how

Sidebar 4.1
Interviewing Tips

1. Think of your audience in preparing questions.
2. Prepare at least twenty questions in advance.
3. Avoid asking yes/no questions.
4. Start with the five Ws and H questions.
5. Don't be afraid to depart from your set of questions if your interview goes off on an interesting or newsworthy tangent.
6. Be on time for the interview. Dress appropriately.
7. First, introduce yourself and state the purpose for your interview.
8. Break the ice with light conversation before beginning your questions.
9. Let your subject do the talking.
10. Listen carefully to your subject's answers and take very good notes. Develop an efficient note-taking system.
11. Get at least three good, insightful direct quotes.
12. Write down exact spellings of names. Double-check them. Then triple-check them.
13. Ask for permission to telephone your source later for more information, if necessary.
14. Know the background of the person you are interviewing.
15. Collect more information than you think you will need.
16. Don't be bashful about asking the person to repeat something important.
17. Be aware of your surroundings during the interview. A few notes about the room and other surroundings may be useful in a feature story to help set the mood of your piece.
18. Leave the most difficult questions for last.

the interview will be structured. If there are difficult questions the reporter needs to ask—questions that would make the source uncomfortable—they are usually not the questions that should be asked first. Those questions will be easier to ask and answer later in the interview when the reporter and source have established some rapport.

- *Take notes.* Do so as unobtrusively as possible, but if you are there as a journalist, the source will expect you to do this. Write down the key words and phrases that the source uses if you cannot get every word. Concentrate on what is being said so that you can reconstruct an accurate quote later. Even during the interview session, you should begin thinking about what information and direct quotations you will use in your article.

- *Make sure you understand what the source says.* If you don't understand what a source has said, ask that the statement be repeated. Read back what you have written to make sure that you have it right. If you don't understand a word or phrase the source has used, ask about it. It is better that you show your ignorance to the source than to thousands of readers or viewers when they read your story.

- *Do not respond to attacks from a source.* If a source attacks or criticizes you, try to absorb it rather than responding defensively. Remember that you are there to get information, not to defend yourself.

- *Use a tape recorder only if you have the permission of the source.* Ask the source's permission before you turn it on. If the source is reluctant, you might say, "This will help me make sure I get everything you say correctly." If the source will not permit the use of the tape recorder, do not use it. Even if you use a tape recorder, always take notes. A tape recorder may not work, or the tape may be bad. Any number of things can happen.

- *Note the surroundings.* Sometime during the interview, take note of something other than what is being said, such as gestures or other physical details of the source, pictures or awards on the wall, or other objects in the room. You may see something you want to ask about or something you will want to use in your article.

- *Always be courteous and professional.*

As soon as possible after the interview, you should go over your notes and listen to your tape recording. Many reporters will listen to a tape and fill in their notes. If there is no tape, it is a good idea to read your notes carefully and fill in parts of the interview you may want to use in your article.

If possible, a reporter should check important information that the source has given with another source to verify it. Many reporters have been taken in by sources who sounded as if they knew exactly what they were talking about. These reporters have looked foolish in print or on the air when they used the information they had obtained.

Finally, a reporter should never hesitate to call a source back for more information or for clarification of information or discrepancies. These callbacks show that a reporter is serious about producing an accurate report, and sources who are honest will not mind helping the reporter in this effort.

OBSERVATION

The second major source of information for the news reporter is observation. Whenever possible, news reporters attend the events they are writing about. They like to see for themselves what happens, even though they rarely write from a first-person point of view. Here are some examples of news reports that have used observational sources:

> The anti-abortion rally drew people from many areas of the Midwest. Cars in the parking lot bore license tags from Missouri to West Virginia.

> Bailey High's Sam Love kicked a 14-yard field goal in the first period, and Mateo Central's Jack Mayo had a 34-yarder in the second period to account for the second-lowest scoring first half in the history of the championship game.

> The packed courtroom listened, in a hushed silence, as the defendant took the witness stand and began to tell her story.

In each of these cases, it is clear that the reporters attended the events they described. One indication of this is the lack of attribution in each of these paragraphs.

Observing is more than just watching an event or being there. Good reporters are active observers. They often enter a situation knowing what they want to watch for and what information they need for an article. They also remain open to bizarre or unusual events so that such events can be included in what they write.

Good observation requires the reporter to develop a sense of what is significant. The fact that two members of a city council confer before a vote is taken and then vote the same way may raise a question in the mind of a reporter—a question that he or she will want to find the answer to after the meeting has occurred. If the reporter had not seen the conference, no question would have been raised, and something significant might have been missed.

Good reporters also put themselves in a position to see what they need to see. Physical positioning is a key part of good reporting. A reporter who wants to do a story on what it is like to be on the sidelines at a football game would not stay in the press box during the game. Visiting a scene before an event takes place, if possible, is a good idea and usually allows a reporter to gain insight about an event.

News reporters are obliged to put what they see into their stories whether or not it makes the people they are writing about look "good" or "bad." Some actions or information may be embarrassing to people, even those in authority. A reporter must not make a judgment about what to include in a news report based on what the source wants. The reporter's obligation is to the readers who are expecting an accurate account of an event.

Generally, reporters do not participate in events. If the event is a demonstration, reporters do not carry signs and march with a group. At a city council meeting where citizens are asking questions or making statements to the council, reporters do not join in by asking their own questions. At the same time, reporters should not leave their humanity behind. If they can prevent injury or help out in an emergency situation, they should certainly do so.

STORED SOURCES OF INFORMATION

"You can look it up!" Casey Stengel used to tell reporters who gathered around him in the manager's office of the New York Yankees baseball team. Stengel, who led the Yankees to a string of World Series championships in the 1940s and 1950s, was known for his long, involved answers to the simplest questions. He would often end his circumlocutions by saying, "You can look it up!"—a challenge to those who might not believe what he had just said.

What Stengel told reporters is what most of us already know: A vast amount of information is available to be looked up. This stored information includes any books, reports, articles, press releases, documents, and computer-stored information to which a reporter has access. Here are some examples of reporters using stored sources:

> Furillo, who died Sunday, played right field for the Brooklyn and Los Angeles Dodgers from 1946 through 1960. He won the NL batting title with a .344 average in 1953, when he missed the last few weeks of the season because of a broken hand he sustained during a fight with manager Leo Durocher.

> A City Social Services Department report estimated that more than 10,000 people were "without permanent or temporary shelter" in the city last year.

> A statement issued by the new administration said that foreign policy problems would be high on the president's agenda.

Stored sources are located in many places: government documents, company records, books, magazines, and so on. A news reporter should be familiar with the holdings of the local public library because that can be a major source of stored information.

The modern journalist has a library as close as the keyboard of his or her computer. That library, of course, is the World Wide Web. Most libraries and many businesses are connected to the Internet, so employees can "look it up" more easily than ever before.

Sidebar 4.2
References

Current Biography. This monthly publication contains excellent biographical pieces on notable personalities. Another source, *Biography Index,* is also useful for finding magazine profiles of individuals.

www.hwwilson.com/currentbio/curbio.html

Encyclopedia of Associations. This publication contains entries for thousands of social, political, medical, religious, labor, legal, cultural, scientific, educational associations, and groups. It also includes fan clubs and hobbyist groups. The companion volumes, *Research Centers Directory, Government Research Directory,* and *International Organizations,* are also useful.

http://library.dialog.com/bluesheets/html/bl0114.html

Facts on File. An indispensable source of news information, *Facts on File* is a weekly publication containing detailed summaries of the past week's stories. There are weekly, annual, and five-year indexes.

www.factsonfile.com/

Official Congressional Directory. This is the official source for basic information on Congress. It includes biographical sketches of members with descriptions of their congressional districts, committee assignments and committee staff, and maps of congressional districts. The name, address, and phone number of foreign ambassadors and consular offices in the United States as well as a list of U.S. ambassadors abroad are also here.

www.gpoaccess.gov/cdirectory/index.html

Readers' Guide to Periodical Literature. This is an index to general interest magazines such as *Time, Life, Newsweek, Business Week, Fortune,* and *Forbes,* and it is a good place to start research on any subject. Another index, called *Public Affairs Information Service (PAIS),* is an index to more specialized sources of information primarily concerning public policy issues.

Statistical Abstract of the United States. The standard summary of U.S. government statistics, the *Statistical Abstract,* has been published annually for more than 100 years. Use it to find data on population, birth, marriage, divorce and death rates, educational statistics such as enrollment figures and graduation rates, crime rates, unemployment rates, gross national product, poverty rates, consumer price indexes, interest rates, housing, business, agriculture, and selected comparative international statistics.

www.census.gov/statab/www/

The United States Government Manual. This is the official handbook of the federal government and provides comprehensive information on judicial, legislative, and executive branch agencies. Use this book to find a particular agency's official name, its mission, when it was founded, how it is organized, and who its key officials are.

www.gpoaccess.gov/gmanual/index.html

Sidebar 4.2
Continued

Who's Who. Just because someone is not in the current edition of *Who's Who in America* does not mean that he or she isn't in another edition. There are many *Who's Who*s (*Who's Who of the South, Who's Who of the East, Who's Who in Science and Engineering,* etc.).

www.whoswho-online.com/

The World Almanac and Book of Facts. This book contains useful features including a chronology of the previous year's major news stories; population; sports; weather; economic statistics; presidential biographies, maps; basic information on cities, states, and nations; U.S. and world history; weights and measurements conversion tables; a perpetual calendar; lists of prize winners; colleges and universities; and a list of noted personalities with their places of birth and birth dates. It also has the text of the Constitution, the Declaration of Independence, and the Gettysburg Address.

www.worldalmanac.com/wab-newsletter.htm

The World Wide Web contains many good general reference sources in addition to those listed above. Among them are the following:

Encyclopedia.com: **www.encyclopedia.com/**
Wikipedia: **http://en.wikipedia.org/wiki/Main_Page**
Columbia Encyclopedia: **www.bartleby.com/65/**
Encarta: **http://encarta.msn.com/Default.aspx**

Akin to the Internet is the stored information that is found in online or electronic information services. Such services provide subscribers with fingertip access to a wide range of information, such as newspapers, magazines, television transcripts, governmental reports, legal opinions, encyclopedias, library card catalogues, and many other sources. These services come through telephone lines from central data banks to personal computers. People who work with information, particularly those in the mass media, are relying more and more heavily on these online databases.

In most cases, information that comes from stored sources—like that which comes from personal sources—should be attributed. In the second and third examples at the beginning of this section, the attribution is clear. Occasionally, as in the first example, the information may either be common knowledge or be available in many references so that telling the reader the source is not that important.

Stored information, whether it comes from a library or from the Internet, presents the reporter with two basic problems. The first problem is management: How do you find what you need? Sometimes, just "looking it up" is not nearly as simple as it sounds, and when you are faced with the enormous amount of information that is available through the Internet, the problem is compounded. Most reporters develop strategies for exploring information sources mainly through experience. The more a reporter uses a library or an Internet search engine, the more he or she will understand what information is available and where it is more likely to reside.

The second problem is that of reliability. Is the information that you get correct? How do you know? Assessing the reliability of information has always been a problem for reporters, but this task, too, has been compounded by the expansion of information that is available. Reporters should consider carefully the source of the information in assessing its reliability. They should also try to find the same information from another source if possible, especially if there is some doubt about the original source. They should remember that just because something is in a book in the library or posted on a Web page does not mean that it is accurate.

THE IMPORTANCE OF ACCURACY

The overriding goal of the writer for the mass media is accuracy. The attempt to be accurate must govern all of the actions of the writer, from the way he or she gathers information to the language that is used to convey that information. Previous chapters have discussed the necessity of using the language precisely and about the attention that a writer must give to the format, style, and usage in writing. These efforts are important because ultimately, they help to increase the accuracy of the writing that is produced.

This attention to precise writing should be preceded by an attention to the details of reporting. Developing good habits in gathering information will pay off for the reporter in many ways. The following are some of the areas of reporting that deserve the reporter's special effort.

Spell Names Correctly

One of the most important possessions a person has is his or her name. Misspelling a name is likely to offend someone more than almost any other mistake. Consequently, reporters should take special care to make sure they have the correct spelling for the names they use in their stories. They should never assume that they can spell a name correctly. For instance, "John Smith" may really be

John Smithe

John Smythe

John Smyth

Jon Smith

The person whose name you are spelling is the best source for the correct spelling, and you should never be afraid or embarrassed to ask. In fact, asking specifically often demonstrates that you are trying to be careful and can increase the confidence that source has in you.

Checking with the person may not always be possible, however. In that case, telephone directories and city directories are generally reliable sources for correctly spelled names. The people who put these directories together are professionals and understand that they are creating a resource that will be checked by others. Police reports, printed programs, and other such material are not reliable sources and should not be used for name checking.

Quote Your Sources Correctly

This chapter has already discussed gathering and using quoted material, and more discussion will follow in Chapter 5. The point here is to make sure you get it right. Many people who are used as sources in news reports complain about being misquoted or quoted out of context. Often that is a way for the source to back away from what he or she said after it has been printed or broadcast. However, news reporters do make mistakes, and it is their responsibility—not that of the source— to make sure they have heard and understood what the source has said. The simplest remedy to not understanding what the source has said is to ask. Make sure you know both the words the source used and the meaning that the source has given to them.

Get Information from More Than One Source If Possible

As a general rule, news stories are better if reporters get information from more than one source. Different people know various things about a situation, or they may have differing viewpoints about it. The more people a reporter talks to about a story and the more records he or she checks, the more likely it is that the reporter will understand the story fully.

Getting information from multiple sources sometimes will saddle the reporter with contradictory information. Where the contradictions are apparent and important, the reporter should attempt to resolve them among the sources; otherwise, the reporter will have to choose which source he or she believes is the most reliable. Either way, the process of resolving contradictions will usually deepen a reporter's understanding of the information.

Do the Math

Make sure that the numbers in a story add up correctly. Numbers do not have to throw journalists, but they often do. For instance, consider this paragraph about a student election that appeared in a college newspaper:

> Officials said a total of 5,865 ballots were cast, representing a 34.2 percent turnout. Smith defeated Jones by receiving 3,077 votes to Jones' 2,385, a margin of 393 votes.

The reporter should have done two things with this paragraph. He or she should have added up to the totals for the two candidates to make sure that total matched the total number of ballots cast and that the stated margin was correct. If the numbers did not match, the reporter should have found out why. Second, the story says that "officials" said there was a 34.2 percent turnout. The reporter should have gotten the figures that these officials used and done his or her own calculations. It may be that the 34.2 figure is correct. It is the reporter's job to make sure.

DEADLINES

The chief enemy of media writers—and occasionally their friend—is time. No matter what the medium, there comes a point when the writing must be finished and put into production. That point is called a deadline, and almost all writers must adhere to some kind of deadline.

Deadlines vary according to the type of medium for which you are writing. Broadcasters have some of the most immediate and intense deadlines. A broadcast writer must finish writing sometime before a newscast is aired; otherwise, the copy will not be used, and the writer will have worked in vain. Reporters for daily newspapers face at least one and sometimes several deadlines each day. Their deadlines are not as rigid as those of broadcasters. Sometimes they can be missed by a few minutes, and the production of the newspaper will still proceed. Still, the deadline pressure is undeniable. (Try observing a newspaper's newsroom 15 or 20 minutes before a deadline. The increased activity—reporters making phone calls, typing on computer terminals, huddling with editors—will be evident.) Many writers are attracted to magazines because the deadline pressures of these publications do not occur as often as with newspapers or broadcast stations. But the deadlines still exist, and when they approach, they, too, exert great pressure on writers. Writers in advertising and public relations positions also face deadlines on a daily basis.

Deadlines for news websites are not so much production-driven as event-driven. A news website that seeks to be an up-to-the-minute medium (MSNBC.com or CNN.com, for instance) places great pressure on its writers and editors to produce stories and updates as quickly as possible. New information can be posted on a website almost as quickly as it is prepared, and visitors to a news website expect to see the latest information on an event whenever they visit one of these sites.

Deadlines can be a blessing because they force writers to produce. Few writers for the mass media experience serious cases of writer's block, the inability to write. Those who work in the mass media simply cannot survive in their job unless they complete their assignments. In fact, the excitement of an approaching deadline can energize a writer, allowing him or her to produce good work in a very short period of time.

Deadlines also enable media organizations to function. They allow production schedules to be set and news broadcasts to be aired. They allow presses to be run at certain times so that newspapers can get their issues to their carriers.

But deadlines have serious drawbacks for the writer. They impose a psychological and sometimes physical pressure on the writer that can be wearing and may ultimately lead a writer to quit the mass media altogether. Deadlines also create or encourage a dependency on formulaic writing. A writer will find it easier to write things as he or she has done it before than to be creative or to let the content of the writing dictate the form. In the news and information business, deadlines sometimes prevent adequate fact-checking and editing of copy, and that has had embarrassing or even legal consequences for the writer and the news organizations. Finally, deadlines shorten the time that a writer has to assimilate the information and ideas that he or she is writing about and to understand their context.

Despite these drawbacks, deadline writing is an irrevocable fact of life for the media writer. No wide-ranging alternatives to deadlines exist, and it is unlikely that any will be developed. The deadline is an integral part of media life and will undoubtedly remain so.

ETHICAL BEHAVIOR

Much has been written about the ethics and ethical dilemmas of people who work in mass communication. Scholars have devoted long years of study to classifying ethical dilemmas and identifying appropriate responses to them. Many journalists, advertisers, and public relations practitioners attend professional conferences at which ethical issues are strongly debated and discussed. Simply put, professional communicators should tell the truth and do as much good as possible, and almost all of the professional associations within mass communication have codes of ethics that admonish their members toward these actions. The following are excerpts from some of those codes:

> "Advertising shall tell the truth, and shall reveal significant facts, the omission of which would mislead the public." Advertising Ethics and Principles, American Advertising Federation.

Figure 4.3

Tom Clancy on interviewing

Every person you meet—and everything you do in life—is an opportunity to learn something. That's important to all of us, but most of all to a writer because as a writer you can use anything. . . . I never even got aboard a nuclear sub until *Red October* was in final editing. On the other hand, I have talked with a lot of people who are or were in this line of work.

"Journalists should be honest, fair and courageous in gathering, reporting and interpreting information." Code of Ethics, Society of Professional Journalists.

"A member shall not knowingly disseminate false or misleading information and shall act promptly to correct erroneous communications for which he or she is responsible." Code of Professional Standards, Public Relations Society of America.

Dishonesty—in the forms of falsification, plagiarism, and misrepresentation—is the deadliest sin of the media professional. Falsifying information includes making up information that is not true or presenting information to an audience so that the audience draws the wrong conclusion about it. Despite the efforts of the vast majority of honest professionals, the mass media are continually plagued by high-profile cases of falsification. Stephen Glass, a writer for the *New Republic* magazine, was caught falsifying information for many of his articles in the late 1990s. That led to his firing, and his story was chronicled in the movie "Shattered Glass." In 2003, the dishonesty of reporter Jayson Blair, who made up much of the information that went into his news reports, brought dishonor and embarrassment to the New York *Times* and led to the resignations of the executive editor and managing editor. The next year, another major newspaper, *USA Today,* found that one of its top reporters had falsified information for more than 700 stories he had written over a ten-year period. The newspaper had to investigate and retract many of those stories. (The reporter, Jack Kelly, was fired, and an editor resigned.)

Plagiarism is using the words and ideas of others without giving appropriate credit or attribution. During his work for the New York *Times,* not only would Blair make things up, but he would also take interviews that had been printed in other newspapers and put them in his stories without telling his editors or the readers where they had originated. The implication was that he had conducted the interviews himself. Plagiarism is not only dishonest, but also a form of theft that media professionals disdain. (Plagiarism, of course, is not confined to the mass media; it occurs often on college campuses, where students get credit for work they have not done. For more about plagiarism, see Exercise 4.1 at the end of this chapter.)

Misrepresentation means that the media professional appears to be something that he or she is not. For instance, most organizations and codes of ethics demand that news reporters identify themselves fully to those who are giving them information. A person who talks to a media professional should be aware that the information and words he or she imparts may be published or broadcast. The concept of misrepresentation also includes the way in which media professionals present themselves to their audiences. A news reporter should not have a relationship with a source or a subject that he or she is covering that would raise questions about the reporter's honesty or objectivity. For instance, reporters should not accept gifts or items of value from the people or organizations they cover.

Despite the famous lapses by some individuals, honesty remains the most important quality of anyone who enters the media professions. The credibility of individuals and organizations rests on the honesty of working professionals, and most people in the media adhere to that standard.

WRITING BY EXAMPLE

The first three chapters of this book attempted to introduce you to some of the characteristics, techniques, and rules of good writing. This chapter has tried to describe some of the aspects of writing in a media environment. As you continue through this text, you will be introduced to some of the forms of writing for the mass media.

The writing that you do from here on will require something more than an application of the rules of writing that we have discussed. Writers for media organizations must assimilate information and ideas as well as understand the demands and expectations of the particular medium for which they are writing. In short, while learning about media forms, they must think and make judgments about the information and ideas they have to present.

One way of doing this is what we might call "writing by example." Writers can learn a form of writing by following examples as closely as possible. Students should recognize that this form of learning is not cheating or bending the rules. What you write—as long as you are not copying it word for word—is still your original work. But if you pattern your writing after a good example, you can learn what it takes to produce a particular form of writing.

The next chapters contain many good examples of writing in various media forms. Study them closely. Try to emulate them and make them your own.

POINTS FOR CONSIDERATION AND DISCUSSION

1. The author says that "writing for the mass media is one of the most important jobs in our society." Do you agree or disagree? Why?
2. Look at three news stories in your local newspaper. What news values are present in each of them?
3. One of the criticisms of the news media that many people make is that journalists emphasize "bad news" rather than "good news." What do you think people mean by that? Do you agree? Do the news values listed in this chapter mean that journalists are more likely to look for "bad news" than "good news"?

4. The author says that secretaries are often good sources of information. What are some other job categories that would make good sources for journalists?

5. Why is it important for a journalist to get information from more than one source?

FURTHER READING

Anderson, D. A., & Itule, B. D. (2002). *News Writing and Reporting for Today's Media* (6th ed.). New York: McGraw-Hill.

Biagi, S. (1992). *Interviews That Work: A Practical Guide for Journalists* (2nd ed.). Belmont, CA: Wadsworth.

Clark, R. P., & Campbell, C. C. (Eds.). (2002). *The Values and Craft of American Journalism.* Gainesville: University Press of Florida.

Downie, L., & Kaiser, R. G. (2002). *The News About the News.* New York: Knopf.

Fedler, F., Bender, J. R., Davenport, L., & Drager, M. (2004). *Reporting for the Media.* New York: Oxford University Press.

Fox, W. (2001). *Writing the News: A Guide for Print Journalists* (3rd ed.). Ames: Iowa State University Press.

Killenberg, G. M., & Anderson, R. (1989). *Before the Story: Interviewing and Communication Skills for Journalists.* New York: St. Martin's Press.

Leiter, K., Harriss, J., & Johnson, S. (2000). *The Complete Reporter* (7th ed.). Boston: Allyn and Bacon.

Mencher, M. (1998) *Basic Media Writing* (6th ed.). New York: McGraw-Hill.

Stein, M. L., & Paterno, S. (2001) *Talk Straight, Listen Carefully: The Art of Interviewing.* Ames: Iowa State University Press.

WEBSITES

American Society of Newspaper Editors: **www.asne.org**

Journalism.org: **www.journalism.org**

Poynter Institute: **www.poynter.org**

Society of Professional Journalists: **www.spj.org**

EXERCISES

4.1 Plagiarism

Write a 250- to 300-word essay on plagiarism. Use as your sources the following websites on plagiarism:

PURDUE UNIVERSITY

Avoiding Plagiarism

Academic writing in American institutions is filled with rules that writers often don't know how to follow. A working knowledge of these rules, however, is critically important; inadvertent mistakes can lead to charges of plagiarism, or the unacknowledged use of somebody else's words or ideas. While other cultures may not insist so heavily on documenting sources, American institutions do. A charge of plagiarism can have severe consequences, including expulsion from the university. **http://owl. english.purdue.edu/handouts/research/r_plagiar.html**

INDIANA UNIVERSITY

Plagiarism: What It Is and How to Recognize and Avoid It
In college courses, we are continually engaged with other people's ideas: we read them in texts, hear them in lecture, discuss them in class, and incorporate them into our own writing. As a result, it is very important that we give credit where it is due. Plagiarism is using others' ideas and words without clearly acknowledging the source of that information. **www.indiana.edu/~wts/wts/plagiarism.html**

DEPAUW UNIVERSITY

Avoiding Plagiarism
Plagiarism is turning in or passing off someone else's work as your own. Sometimes, the line between borrowing and stealing is unclear. In an intellectual community, ideas are passed around freely. Most intellectual inquiry could not take place without borrowing from the work of others. **www.depauw.edu/admin/arc/writing_ center/plagiarism.htm**

Your essay should demonstrate that you understand the major concepts that the articles discuss. The essay will also demonstrate your ability to present information clearly and coherently and to put together information from different sources (without plagiarizing, of course).

You may bring these articles with you to your lab session and use them in writing your essay. If you quote directly from any of the articles, you should put the name of the university and page number of the quoted passage in parentheses immediately after the quotation. You should not quote directly more than two or three times in the essay. This should be in your own words.

Follow your instructor's guidelines for referencing or footnoting for this essay, but you will need to turn in your copies of the articles along with your essay. You may use only these three articles as references for your essay.

The following section contains a variety of public relations writing exercises. You should follow your instructor's directions in completing them.

4.2 News Values

Read the following news stories and answer the questions that follow.

JURY RECOMMENDS DEATH FOR 69-YEAR-OLD GRANDMOTHER

CHILLICOTHE, Mo.—A jury has recommended a 69-year-old woman be sentenced to death for the murders of four transient farm workers whose bodies were found buried in northwestern Missouri last year.

Jurors in Livingston County Circuit Court deliberated more than three hours before making the recommendation Tuesday night in the case of Faye Copeland, whom the jury had convicted Saturday of five counts of first-degree murder.

The jury of eight women and four men recommended Copeland be sentenced to life in prison without parole on the fifth murder conviction.

Circuit Judge E. Richard Webber must decide whether to accept the jury's recommendations or to sentence Copeland to life in prison. He ordered a pre-sentence investigation.

If sentenced to death, Copeland will become the oldest person on Missouri's death row.

Copeland's attorney, public defender David Miller, has said he will file a motion for a new trial. Miller said he would appeal the court's refusal to allow a psychologist to testify about "battered-wife syndrome." Miller had argued that Faye Copeland was dominated by her 74-year-old husband, Ray, who is awaiting trial on the same charges, and had only a minor role in the crimes.

Ray Copeland's trial is scheduled to begin Jan. 24, but the court first must determine whether he is mentally competent to assist in his own defense. His attorneys contend that Ray Copeland suffers from senile dementia, including an organic brain disorder.

The bodies of the victims were found last year in shallow graves in barns or dumped in wells on farms in Livingston County where Ray Copeland had worked. Investigators said the victims had been shot to death. No bodies were found on the couple's farm near Mooresville, about 65 miles northeast of Kansas City.

The Copelands originally were arrested on charges of conspiracy in an alleged fraudulent cattle-buying conspiracy.

Authorities contended that the couple hired the transients to work as cattle buyers, then killed and buried them. Prosecutors said the Copelands netted $32,000 by reselling the cattle. The fraud charges were dismissed after the murder charges were filed.

FBI CONTINUES DIGGING SUSPECTED MOB GRAVE

NEW YORK—Federal agents and state police continued digging up a suspected secret mob grave Monday, where the remains of at least three people were found buried in a garage behind a locksmith shop, officials said.

The owner of the shop, convicted bank robber Richard Joseph Beedle Sr., 58, appeared in U.S. District Court in New Haven and was ordered held without bond, said U.S. Attorney Stanley A. Twardy Jr.

The bones of three and perhaps four people believed to be victims of warfare within the Patriarca organized crime family in the Hartford, Conn.–Springfield, Mass., area were found in a garage behind Beedle's home, Twardy said.

Beedle was charged with being an accessory after the fact of a murder committed in aid of racketeering, which is punishable by up to 10 years in federal prison and a $250,000 fine, Twardy said.

Arrested on the same charge Monday was Salvatore "Butch" D'Aquila Jr. of Middletown, 48, who operates Central News, a newspaper and variety store on Main Street in Middletown, Twardy said.

D'Aquila has past convictions on state gambling and fraud charges, said Twardy.

FBI agents discovered the mass grave in a garage behind Beedle's home in Hamden on Friday after searching for weeks with the cooperation of another suspect convicted on racketeering charges.

Jack Johns, a reputed organized crime figure arrested in March in a roundup of the Providence, R.I.–based Patriarca family, told authorities that bodies had been buried in Hamden, but he could not remember the address, Twardy said.

Johns rode through the New Haven suburb with FBI agents and spotted the house Friday, Twardy said.

Beedle was arrested and federal and state investigators with a search warrant and picks and shovels dug up the remains over the weekend.

Beedle, who operated Dick's Locksmith Shop in Hamden, was convicted in a 1970 bank robbery in Allentown, Pa., and was long associated with organized crime, New Haven police said.

The grave had been disturbed earlier in an apparent attempt to remove the remains and no other fragments were found in the search, which continued Monday, Twardy said.

Twardy said he could not comment on the possible identities of the victims, but a published report said one of those buried in Hamden may be William Grant, an East Hartford restaurant owner who vanished in 1988.

"GOOD GUY" HOLDS TEACHER, STUDENTS HOSTAGE

A teenager described as a "good guy" who "wouldn't hurt anybody" took a teacher and about 15 students hostage at gunpoint Monday in a local high school classroom, gradually releasing his captives until the standoff ended more than eight hours later.

The suspect, Eli Dean, 18, did not fire a shot during the siege at Central High School, and no injuries were reported.

By midafternoon, Dean, who recently was suspended from school for pranks, had released all but five students from a classroom, and early in the evening he released four more hostages, state police Sgt. Martin Jenkins said.

The siege ended about 7:30 P.M. EST when Dean surrendered and released the last student, Jenkins said.

The youth was armed with a pistol, believed to be a .44-caliber revolver taken from his stepfather's room, Jenkins said, but no shots were fired throughout the ordeal.

Dean, twice suspended from the school in the last two weeks for setting off a fire alarm and breaking a window, went to the school to speak to Melody Money, 43, a teacher who had counseled him about previous trouble at the school, the state police sergeant said.

Dean walked into Money's classroom about 11:10 A.M. and brandished the revolver in front of her and about 15 students, Jenkins said.

The suspect was persuaded to release most of his captives soon after the siege began, but state police could not give an exact count of the number of hostages freed.

Dean continued holding six students and Money until about 2 P.M., when a freshman, Stacy Medelli, was allowed to leave, followed soon by the teacher, Jenkins said.

Dean made no demands throughout the standoff.

A fellow student, Amanda Garr, said she believed the young gunman was "upset" at the recent suspensions but expressed astonishment at his reaction.

"Eli, to me, is the best guy anybody could ever ask for," Garr said. "Something got in him and he's gone crazy about it. He's a very good guy. He wouldn't hurt anybody."

Garr said she and other students at first thought there had been a bomb threat when the school was evacuated and a police SWAT team moved into place, but later "we found out it was Eli and everybody started crying."

The youth's parents and stepfather, Rocky Williams, were called to the school to help police negotiators. Williams said he believes Dean took his .44-caliber revolver from their home.

1. What are the news values that are present in each of the stories?
2. List the who, what, when, where, why, and how elements of each story.
3. Which of the three major types of sources of information are used in these stories?
4. List the sources that are specifically mentioned in each story. How do you think that the reporters were able to get this information?

5. On the basis of your limited knowledge about the events, analyze each of the stories for accuracy. Are there points in the story that might not be accurate? If you were the editor, what would you question? What would you want the reporter to double-check?

4.3 Selecting News

You are the editor of your hometown newspaper, and you need to select the stories that will go on the front page for tomorrow's paper. Following are the first two paragraphs of the six news stories from which you must make your selection. Which four of the stories would you select? In what order? Be prepared to justify your answer.

DEARBORN, Mich.—Ford Motor Co. said Monday it is recalling more than 127,000 1987-model Ford Thunderbirds and Mercury Cougar cars with 3.8-liter V6 engines to correct unacceptable emissions levels.

Dealers will be asked to install free of charge a vacuum retard delay valve and change the ignition timing. Cars affected were built for sale in 49 states, with California and Canadian vehicles not affected.

ESCAMBIA, S.C.—A Bay Minette woman was uninjured after a fiery one-car accident on Alabama 225 early Monday morning.

The 1987 Chevrolet driven by Janice Singleton, 28, apparently caught fire in the wreck just north of Baldwin 40, a state trooper spokesman said Monday.

Ms. Singleton was able to escape the car and then abandoned it, the spokesman said. She later notified local police that she was unhurt.

MONTGOMERY, Ala.—An 8-month-old North Carolina boy was reunited with his mother, while the Iowa couple accused of abducting him were expected to be returned next week to North Carolina to face kidnapping charges.

The infant's mother, Susan Tarlton of Greensboro, N.C., offered advice to other parents when Larry Wayne Tarlton arrived at a North Carolina airport. The child was abducted three weeks ago.

CAPE HATTERAS, N.C.—The severed bridge that is the only link between Hatteras Island and the mainland could be repaired within 45 days, state officials say.

Previous estimates indicated that repairs could take at least six months. A dredge battered the bridge during Friday's storm, causing a 370-foot section of the structure to collapse.

BELLEVUE, Wash.—Government health experts Wednesday launched a nationwide, federally funded program to detect hepatitis B among pregnant women and immunize their infants against the serious liver infection.

Doctors from the U.S. Centers for Disease Control and the National Foundation for Infectious Diseases told public health officials at the first of a series of regional conferences that efforts to stop hepatitis B have largely failed despite the availability since 1981 of safe and effective vaccines.

TORONTO, Canada—Union officials representing about 10,000 striking Canadian steelworkers said Monday's tentative settlement with Stelco Inc. that includes full pension indexing was a major victory for its members.

Leo Gerard, the Ontario director of the United Steelworkers of America, said that the union's negotiators had achieved its five major objectives.

4.4 Selecting News

You are the news director of your hometown television station, and you need to select the stories that will go on the local news tonight. Following are the first two paragraphs of the six news stories from which you must make your selection. Which four stories would you select? In what order? Be prepared to justify your answer.

A police officer shot a man during a struggle early Tuesday, then had his weapon turned on him before the suspect fled and was overpowered by two other officers, police said.

Officer David Kelley shot Anthony McQueen, 31, of Duval Street, in the left side as they grappled over Kelley's .357-caliber handgun behind a house in the 1000 block of Cherokee Street shortly after 2 A.M., police said.

A 17-year-old British math prodigy has accepted a one-year post as a visiting lecturer at Local University, becoming one of the youngest people ever to be a faculty member, Local officials said Friday.

Ruth J. Lawrence was taught by her father in their home in Huddersfield, England, and had never been to school before she entered Oxford University at age 11 six years ago.

The liver of a baboon transplanted into a 62-year-old man was functioning satisfactorily Tuesday, surgeons at the University Hospital said.

The man, whose identity was not released, remained in critical condition after the world's second such transplant at Presbyterian University Hospital in a 13-hour operation that ended early Monday. Surgeons said the man was dying from hepatitis B and did not have the option of a human-to-human liver transplant.

Funland, a local amusement park that draws tourists from around the county, will boost its admission prices by $2 for adults and children, a park spokesman said Tuesday.

The new admission prices, which go into effect Nov. 1, are $27.50 for an adult "passport" and $22.50 for children between the ages of 3 and 11, according to spokesman Bob Roth. Children under 3 years old are admitted free.

A local doctor's research says that cigarette smoking may hamper a smoker's ability to feel the chest pains that may be an important early warning sign of heart disease.

Researchers from the University Hospital compared the pain response of 20 male smokers ages 19 to 44 with that of five male nonsmokers in the same age range.

A local art collector, William Chase, has acquired a Van Gogh painting from an auction in New York.

The Van Gogh, "Vase With Cornflowers and Poppies," sold for $8 million. Chase also purchased a rare ink sketch by the Dutch master, "Garden of Flowers," valued at $5 million to $7 million.

4.5 Planning an Interview

INTERVIEW I

Plan an interview with the mayor of your city. First, you will need to decide the central reason why you want the interview. It could be that there is some issue currently facing the city that you will want to build your story around. If no such issue exists, you may want to talk to the mayor about what it is like to be mayor—duties, responsibilities, daily schedule, and so on. Or you may want to do a personality profile on the mayor, asking about family, friends, recreation, and so on.

INTERVIEW 2

Plan an interview with the president of your college or university. Decide the central reason why you want the interview. It could be that there is some issue currently facing the university that you will want to ask about. If no such issue exists, you may want to talk to the president about what it is like to be president—duties, responsibilities, daily schedule, and so on. Or you may want to do a personality profile on the president, asking about family, friends, recreation, and so on.

,Once you have decided what the interview is to be about, what background research will you have to do? How will you go about getting the information you need? Be specific about what information you will need and where you can get it.

Finally, formulate a list of tentative questions that you will want to ask during the interview. This list of questions should be in the approximate order of how you would like to ask the questions. Review pages 91–94 for ideas about the types of questions to ask and the order in which to ask them.

4.6 Paraphrasing

Rewrite the following by paraphrasing the direct quotations. Make what you write no more than half the length of the original quotation. Try to include most of the information that is in the quotation. The first quotation has been paraphrased to give you an example of what is expected.

EXAMPLE

Tom Nelson, president of the citywide Parent Teachers Association: "Our major concern this year will be security in the schools, particularly in the high schools. We will be working with school officials on ways we can help create a safer environment for the education of our children. A number of incidents in the past year have been very disturbing to many parents. We are going to try to provide a way for those parents to make a real difference in their local schools."

PARAPHRASE

Tom Nelson, president of the city Parent Teachers Association, said that the chief concern of the organization this year would be security, particularly in the high schools. Nelson said parents would be working with school officials to make the schools safer.

QUOTATION I

Martin Goldsmith, general manager of the local public radio station: "Our goal in this year's fund-raising effort is to raise $100,000, which will be about 15 percent more than we raised last year. The money we are seeking—this $100,000—will go toward our programming efforts. We spent about $130,000 buying programs each year for the station, and those costs are going up each year. There is a lot that our audience would like to have on the station, and this is the way for them to help pay for it."

QUOTATION 2

Marilyn Wall, president of the Walls Tire Co., a locally owned tire manufacturer: "The current year has been a good one for our company and its employees. Our orders were up about 20 percent over last year, and we were able to recall many of the employees that we had had to lay off during the past three years. In addition, we have expanded our workforce to add about 20 new jobs in various parts of the factory."

QUOTATION 3

Marsha Moss, director of the local symphony orchestra: "The response of the audience to last night's concert was particularly gratifying. They seemed to enjoy everything that we put on the program. I can tell you that playing before an audience like that is a lot more fun than playing to a bunch of critics. It's good to know that people appreciate the many hours of hard work that this orchestra puts into each concert that we do."

QUOTATION 4

Jerry Butts, member of the city council: "Our options were extremely limited this year. We could either grant the police the raise their union requested—one which they deserve, I think, although some might disagree with that—and then raise the property tax to pay for it, or we could have denied the request for a pay raise and kept the tax rates the same as they have been for more than five years. While I think the police do deserve a raise, I am fairly certain that most people would not want them to get it if they thought their taxes would go up to pay for it."

QUOTATION 5

Anita Keller, president of the local chapter of Mothers Against Drunk Driving: "For months now, we have attended meetings of committees of state legislators, and we have tried to make the point over and over again that the laws against drunk driving in this state are too lenient. I do not believe that the legislators have gotten that message yet, or else they are being influenced by money from the alcohol industry, which contributed to many of their campaigns, to keep the laws the way they are. In any event, people are dying every day because of it."

QUOTATION 6

Laura Stewart, president of Stewart Advertising Agency: "The business climate in this city is really quite healthy. That is, we seem to be growing every year. I know that my agency increased its gross revenues by over 20 percent last year over the year before, and that is the third time that has happened. Most of our business comes from local businesses, although some of it—maybe as much as 25 percent—is from out-of-town clients. Anyway, I think things look pretty good for the local economy."

QUOTATION 7

Bruce Hill, organizer of an antique automobile show set for this weekend: "These old cars are really fun and really interesting, too. I have a 1929 Packard that I have had for years, and I've got it running about as good as it was on the day that it was first brought home from the dealership. A lot of people in the show will be driving British cars—old Triumphs, Jaguars, and the like—and some of those old sports cars can really give you a ride. I mean, they can pick up and move. Folks ought to come out and see our show this Saturday and Sunday because I think they would really be interested in it."

4.7 Editing

Edit the following passage. Correct all of the grammar, spelling, and punctuation mistakes you find. If there are any parts that are unclear, rewrite them to make them clearer. Try to find where unnecessary words are used, and eliminate those words or rewrite the sentences to shorten them. Do not eliminate information from the passage, however.

Babe Ruth, through the brilliance of his performance and the force of his personality almost single-handedly transformed the game of baseball. He began his career as a pitcher for the Boston Red Sox and proved to be an excellent hurler. Ruth's hitting was also impressive—especially his power hitting—and the team began to use him to their advantage in the outfield on days that he was not scheduled to pitch.

Ruth discovered that he liked hitting and playing every day. He also enjoyed the cheers of the crowd which came whenever he launched a long one. Those cheers and adulation of the crowd was music to the ears of Ruth the product of a working-class family in Baltimore responded to that adulation with ease. He loved the crowd and never shrank from being the center of attention. Always aware of his fame and the effect that he had on people, Ruth would put on a show. People came to the ball park to see him hit home runs of course but they also came just to see him.

With such a marketable commodity, one wonders why the Red Sox ever traded him to the NY Yankees. The answer is money. Ruth would have helped the financial prospects of any team in the long run, but Harry Frazee, the owner of the Red Sox at the time, had a crying need for some immediate cash. He was a Broadway producer, and his shows were not doing well. Approached by the owners of the New York Yankees, Frazee readily accepted their offer to purchase Ruth's contract in 1919 for $100 thousand and $200,000 more in loans.

Ruth went to New York, and the city, the team, and baseball itself has never been the same.

4.8 Editing

Edit the following passage. Correct all of the grammar, spelling, and punctuation mistakes you find. If there are any parts that are unclear, rewrite them to make them clearer. Try to find where unnecessary words are used, and eliminate those words or rewrite the sentences to shorten them. Do not eliminate information from the passage, however.

Who's likeness should be on the head of a nickel—Thomas Jefferson or James Madison? That question is sometimes posed, not to say that we have honored Thomas Jefferson too much but that we have honored James Madison too little. Of all of those who helped found the U.S. Madison contributed more ideas over a longer period of time than any other person. Yet, when we think of the "Founding Father," Madison's name rarely springs to mind.

Madison was the 4th president, serving two terms early in the 19th century, from 1809 to 1816. He was president when the nation became involved with its first foreign war, the War of 1812 against Great Britain. During that war, the British army invaded Washington, D.C. and burned much of the capital, including the White House.

Madison's greatest contribution came in 1787 with the writing of the constitution. The nation had stumbled along under the Articles of Confederation for 4 years since the end of the Revolutionary War, and the need for a strong, well conceived federal government became more and increasingly evident. Madison became a delegate a new constitutional convention which met in Philadelphia in May. Madison argued that a government should allow for many competing interests so that it would be less likely for a minority to become oppressed by a majority. This and other of Madisons ideas found their way into our constitution.

Madison made one other major contribution to our understanding of the constitution. He kept a daily journal of the proceedings of the convention, and because there was no offical secretary for the convention, his is the only firsthand record we have of what occurred there. This journal alone would have secured for Madison an important and significant place in the nation's history.

chapter five

Writing for Print

Writers for the mass media always work at two tasks: gathering information and putting that information into an acceptable form. Having the proper information—all the relevant facts of a story, the proper identification for the people involved, the times and dates, accurate direct quotations, and so on—is vital to the writing process, but it is only the beginning. There comes a time when the information gathering must cease and the writing must begin.

The ability to write well requires that the writer have a thorough knowledge and understanding of the subject about which he or she is writing. In addition, the writer must understand the basic structure of the news story and the conventions or customs of news writing in order to complete the process.

This chapter focuses on putting information into a form that is appropriate for the print media. Many forms of writing—or writing structures—populate the print media, but the most common are the news story and the feature story. These forms are found in newspapers, magazines, newsletters, and many other publications. Mastering these two forms will give the person who is beginning to write for the mass media a good foundation on which to build while learning to write in other forms and for other media.

CHARACTERISTICS OF NEWS STORIES

All good pieces of writing have one thing in common: a unifying theme. A central idea should govern every book, magazine article, advertisement, or news story that anyone tries to create. The idea of a central theme is important for writers who are learning the different forms of writing for the mass media and particularly those who are learning to write a news story. Faced with a mass of information, facts, ideas, quotations, and the like, the news writer can use the central idea to help sort out what should be included in the article and how the various pieces of information should be presented to the reader.

The central idea will usually be expressed early in the story, normally in the first paragraph. This paragraph, called the *lead,* will set the tone and direction for the story. Lead paragraphs will be examined in more detail later in this chapter, but their

Figure 5.1

Alexis de Tocqueville on the cost of freedom of the press

In order to enjoy the inestimable benefits that the liberty of the press ensures, it is necessary to submit to the inevitable evils that it creates.

importance is noted here. A strong lead that sets forth the central idea of the story will help to unify the writing for the reader.

No two writers will do this is in exactly the same way, so there is no formula that a writer can always use. The information the writer has, the amount of time there is to write the story, and the amount of space available to print the story will be major factors in determining how the story is developed. Still, writers must be aware of the tools and conventions of writing to make the story acceptable for the publication for which they are writing. The following are some of those tools and conventions that writers of news stories must use and observe.

Transitions

The relationship between various pieces of information and the central theme is established with the use of transitions. Transitions are a way of tying the information together and tipping the reader off as to what may come next. Readers should not be surprised by a brand-new subject in the middle of a news story.

Various types of transitions exist for the writer to use in tying a story together. Following are a few of those types.

CONNECTORS. These are simply words that, in a structural way, help unify the writing. For the most part, they are conjunctions such as *and, but, or, thus, however, therefore, meanwhile, on the other hand,* and *likewise.* They do not have great value in terms of the content of the writing, but they are necessary for its flow.

HOOKS. Hooks are words or phrases that are repeated throughout an article to give the reader a sense of unity.

PRONOUNS. One of the best transitional devices, particularly for writing about people, is the pronoun. We use it naturally so that we can avoid repeating the names of people or things.

ASSOCIATIONS. Ideas may be repeated within an article, but the writer may use different words to refer to them. This is called an association. The following example demonstrates this type of transition:

> Arnold came in to pitch in the eighth inning and immediately threw at the head of the first batter he faced. Doing so, he thought, would <u>establish some fear</u> in the minds of the batter.
>
> Johnson, the first batter and the one Arnold threw at, <u>didn't pick up on Arnold's meaning.</u> He lined the next pitch off the left field wall.

The two phrases underlined in that passage represent an association of ideas. Associations are the most subtle of transitional devices, but they can be highly effective in unifying a piece of writing.

CHRONOLOGY. One of the best transitional devices is a word or phrase that refers to a time. Such devices help the reader to establish a sequence for the events that are being written about. Many news stories are not written strictly in chronological order, but references to the time of the events can still be helpful to the reader.

ENUMERATION. Numbering items within your writing is a good way to tie the writing together. A good example of enumeration is in the following paragraph:

> The mayor said there were three reasons why the Pynex Corporation decided to locate the plant in the city. First, the land was available for the plant and possible

expansion. Second, the city has a good education system, and that is important for its employees. Third, the state offered what he called "attractive tax incentives to come to this area."

A news writer must make use of all of these forms of transitions. It is not as important to know the different types of transitions as it is to understand when they can best be used.

Attribution

A major convention of news stories is the use of attribution. Attribution simply means telling readers where the information in a story comes from. Attribution is important because it establishes the news report's credibility. Readers are more likely to believe that the publication is trying to be accurate in its reporting if they know clearly the source of the information. News reports in which the information is properly attributed reflect the professionalism of the publication and its reporters.

Another reason for attributing information in a story is to allow the reader to assess the information by assessing its source. Some sources are more credible than others. By telling the reader where information comes from, the news reporter is letting the reader make up his or her mind whether the information can be believed.

Beginning news writers sometimes have trouble with attribution because it can occasionally be awkward to work into a sentence. In most cases, however, the attribution can be included in a natural or unobtrusive way. Look at these examples:

The mayor said the city is facing a budget crisis.

According to the police report, the car skidded 50 feet before stopping.

The grand jury's report will be announced tomorrow, the prosecutor said.

Most of the major facts in a news story should be attributed to some source (unless they come from an eyewitness account by the reporter), but information that is common knowledge to most readers usually does not have to be attributed. For instance, the attribution is unnecessary in the sentence "A heavy cloud of smog hung over the city today, National Weather Service officials said." As in many other aspects of writing, common sense should prevail. Too much attribution will get in the way of a story; too little attribution will harm the credibility of the story and confuse the reader. The good writer wants neither of these things to happen.

Many writers, particularly beginning journalists, complain that the word *said* is used too much in news stories. It is a colorless word that does not add much to the life of the copy. With this thought in mind, many writers begin the tortuous search for adequate substitutes for *said*. Surely, they think, the English language can come up with at least a few good words to use in its place.

Although English does have many words that can describe the way words are spoken, there is no word that does the job the way *said* does it. *Said* is a neutral word. It simply connotes that words have been spoken; it does not say anything about the way in which they were spoken. Consequently, it is the kind of word that journalists ought to be using. Another point in the word's favor is that *said* is unobtrusive in a news story. Even if used repeatedly, it does not jump out at the reader and get in the way of the information that is being conveyed.

Trying to find substitutes for the word *said* is a dangerous game for the journalist. Although there are many words that might be used in its place, writers should remember that they must use words for their exact meaning, not simply for variety's sake. Too often, writers misuse these substitutes and create erroneous impressions about what was said. Another danger in the search for substitutes for *said* is that

Sidebar 5.1
Verbs of Attribution

Although few verbs are as versatile as *said* for use in attribution, there are occasions when a writer will need to use something different. Following are some of the most commonly used verbs of attribution. These verbs should be used only when they serve the specific purpose of the writer.

- *Said* is a word that connotes only the fact that words were spoken or written. It says nothing about the way the words were spoken, the circumstances of the utterance, or the attitude of the speaker. The word is a modest one, never calling attention to itself. It can be used repeatedly without disrupting the writing. Consequently, there are few real substitutes for *said*. There are words that you can use in its place, however, when it is appropriate for you to do so.

- *Explain* means that more facts are being added to make something more understandable. It can be a neutral synonym for *said,* but it must be used in the right context. It is incorrect to write, " 'Bill Clinton is our current president,' he explained." It would be correct to use *explain* as the verb of attribution for the following sentence: " 'The presidency is the nation's most important office,' he explained."

- *Relate* means to pass along facts. It implies an absence of opinion on the part of the speaker.

- *Point out* means to call attention to a matter of fact. A speaker can point out that grass is green, but a journalist should not write: "The majority leader pointed out that the president was tough in standing up to the communists." That statement is opinion, not fact.

- *State* should be used for formal speeches or announcements such as the State of the Union address in January. It is incorrect to write: "Smith stated that the party would begin at 8 p.m."

- *Declare*, like *state,* implies formality.

- *Add* indicates more facts or comment about the same subject or an afterthought, a comment less important than what has been said before. It is incorrect to write, "She said she was unable to finish her paper. 'My typewriter was broken,' she added."

- *Reveal* and *disclose* are suitable only in referring to something that previously was unknown or concealed.

- *Exclaim* means to cry out in surprise or sudden emotion. It can easily be overused, so writers should be careful. It is usually written with an exclamation point. It is incorrect to use it in the following way: "The meeting will be at 3 P.M.," she exclaimed.

- *Assert* also implies formality but also an intensity on the part of the speaker.

most substitutes are not neutral. If used, they make a statement about how the journalist feels about what was said. For instance, a person who has been accused of a crime may "say" that he is innocent, or he may "claim" that he is innocent. That second verb carries a more negative or doubtful connotation, one that the journalist should not be implying.

Short Sentences, Short Paragraphs

News stories use short sentences and short paragraphs. The news writer tries to get information to the reader as quickly as possible. That is accomplished more easily if the writer uses short sentences. They are easier for the reader to digest.

Unlike other forms of expository writing, the news story does not require that a writer fully develop paragraphs. Instead, paragraph length usually should be kept to three sentences or fewer and to fewer than 100 words. Again, the goal is getting information to readers, not fully developing an idea. Another reason for short paragraphs is that a column of type in a newspaper is so narrow that a long paragraph is difficult and daunting for the reader.

Third Person

News stories are usually written in the third person. That is, a writer does not intrude into a story by using first-person pronouns (unless they are part of a direct quotation from one of the story's sources). Except for unusual cases in which the writer witnesses a dramatic event or is somehow a participant in that event, he or she should not tell the story from the point of view of the first person.

> *Wrong:* From where I was sitting, it looked like the umpire made the wrong call.
> *Right:* The manager protested the call by the umpire.
> *Wrong:* The principal said enrollment at our school has gone down.
> *Right:* The principal said enrollment at Central High has gone down.

By the same token, news stories rarely directly address the reader by using the second-person pronoun *you.* Occasionally, lead paragraphs are questions directed at the reader, but this device can easily be overused, and it is best avoided when you are beginning to learn news writing.

Another aspect of writing in the third person is that the writer's personal opinions—or what journalists call *editorializing*—should be kept out of news stories. News reporters should report only what they see and hear. How they feel about that information is not relevant to the news story. They should present the information and let the readers make up their own minds about it.

An Attitude for Accuracy

Accuracy forms the core of the writing process. Journalists expend much energy in making certain that all of the information they have is correct. Achieving accuracy is not just a matter of techniques of reporting and writing but a state of mind that the journalist should foster. A journalist should never be satisfied with information about which he or she has doubts. The journalist has to make every effort to alleviate those doubts and to clear up any discrepancies.

This attitude extends not only to the major information that a journalist has but also to the smallest details of a story. Making sure that dates and identifications are correct, that numbers in a story add up properly, that locations are correct—all of these things are part of a journalist's job. Journalists should take special care with the names of people to make sure they are spelled correctly.

Journalists strive for accuracy because they realize that their readers and viewers trust them and expect their reports to be accurate. If those reports are not accurate, journalists will lose that trust and eventually lose their readers.

THE INVERTED PYRAMID

Once a writer has gathered the information necessary to begin a story, he or she must decide on the structure of the story. The goal of a proper structure is to get information to the reader quickly and to allow the reader to move through the story easily. The reader must be able to see the relationships between the various pieces of information that the reporter has gathered.

The most common structure for writing news stories is called the inverted pyramid (Figure 5.2). A daily newspaper or news website will contain many news stories. Most stories must be written so that readers can get the most information in the least time. The inverted pyramid structure concentrates the most interesting and important information at the top of the story so that readers can get the information they need or want and then go on to another story if they choose. Headlines and lead paragraphs should be written to describe what the story contains as succinctly and as interestingly as possible.

The *lead*, or first paragraph, is the focal point of the basic news story. It is a simple statement of the point of the entire story. Lead paragraphs are discussed more fully in the next section of this chapter.

Figure 5.2   Inverted Pyramid

Most news stories are structured in the inverted pyramid form; that is, they begin with the most important information, and the information is presented in descending order of importance. To write in this way, the writer must use some judgment about what information is the most important and the most interesting to the reader and what information the reader should have in order to understand the story.

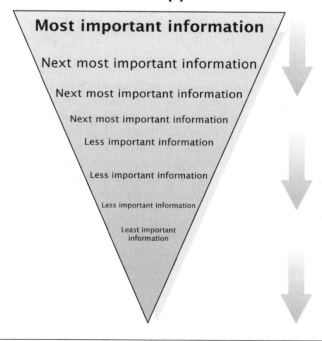

The inverted pyramid

Most important information

Next most important information

Next most important information

Next most important information

Less important information

Less important information

Less important information

Least important
information

The second paragraph is almost as important as the lead. A good second paragraph will take some aspect of the lead and expand it with additional information. By doing this, the second paragraph puts the readers into a story and will give them incentive to read on.

The body of the inverted pyramid story adds detail to information that has been introduced in the lead and the first two or three paragraphs. The body should provide more information, supporting evidence, context, and illumination in the form of more details, direct and indirect quotes, and other description.

The major concept of the inverted pyramid structure is to put the most important and latest information toward the top of the story. As the story continues, the writer should be using information of less importance. There are two reasons for writing a story this way. One is what we have already discussed: Putting the most important information at the top allows a reader to decide quickly whether or not to stick with the story. The inverted pyramid also organizes the information in such a way that the reader can be efficient. Not every reader will read all of every story in a newspaper. In fact, one of the strengths of a newspaper or a news website is that it offers a wide array of information that will appeal to many people. The inverted pyramid structure for news stories allows the readers to get as much of the most important information in that story as quickly as possible; it also allows the readers to stop reading and go on to something else when they have satisfied themselves with that story.

This process would not be possible if all stories were written chronologically. Very often, what happens at or near the end of the chronological story is the most important or interesting thing to the reader. Readers are not accustomed to wading through a lot of less important or less interesting information to get to these parts. Consider a story that begins with the following paragraphs:

> The City Council opened its meeting last night with a prayer from the Rev. Jonathan Fowler, pastor of the Canterbury Episcopal Church.
>
> The minutes of the previous meeting were read and accepted without changes.
>
> Mayor H. L. Johnson then called for a report from the city budget director, Hiram Lewis, who said that property tax collections were running behind what had been expected when the budget was adopted last year.
>
> "If property tax collections continue at this rate, the city will be facing a major deficit," he said.
>
> When Councilmember Fred Greenburg asked what that meant, Lewis replied that the city would have to borrow money or cut back on some of its services.
>
> Johnson then proposed that the council raise the property tax rate by 5 percent for most property owners. The new rates would go into effect next year and would last for only one year, he said. This increase would allow the city to continue operating without any cutbacks in service.
>
> Council member Marge Allen objected to the increase, saying the citizens of her district already had too many taxes to pay. She also said that an increase in the property tax would discourage industries from locating in the city. . . .

Think about the reader of that story who is a property owner in the city. Most likely, that person is asking, "Are my taxes going up?" The reader should not have to read through six or more paragraphs to find out the answer to that question. Instead, the answer should come immediately in the first paragraph:

> The City Council voted against raising property taxes 5 percent last night, despite warning from officials that the city faces a cutback in services unless it gets more money.

Figure 5.3   Inverted Pyramid Example

This story is written in the inverted pyramid style. Compare this one to the stories in Figures 5.5 and 5.6, which are about the same event but written in a bullet structure and eyewitness style.

Violent Storm Crashes City

A violent thunder and wind storm ripped through the city Tuesday afternoon, downing trees and power lines and causing personal injuries and property damage.

The storm hit about 3 p.m. and took approximately 45 minutes to sweep through the city.

While most of the city felt the storm, the most damaging high winds and sheets of rain were confined to the Hillsdale area west of downtown.

Arthur Major, 227 W. Hill St., was struck by a falling limb and taken to Community Hospital during the storm. He suffered severe head injuries and was in serious but stable condition on Tuesday evening.

Hospital officials said five other people were injured in car accidents caused by the storm. All were treated and released by emergency room doctors.

The storm downed power lines throughout the city. West Point Power Co. officials said at one time during the afternoon, about 30,000 city residents were without electricity. They said power was restored to every part of the city except the Hillsdale area by 9 p.m.

"I don't know when we'll get the lights back on in Hillsdale," Brad Jeffries, a spokesman for the power company, said.

Jeffries said all of the traffic lights in the city are operating. At one point on Tuesday afternoon, all of the traffic signals on the west side of town were out.

The storm and high winds damaged a number of cars, houses, and businesses. The home of Mary Golightly, 123 Oakdale Rd., suffered major damage when a large oak tree standing near the house was blown over onto the house.

Golightly was in the house at the time but was not injured when parts of the tree came through the roof and windows.

Martin Best, owner of the Best Hardware Store in the Hillsdale Shopping Center, said his building was among those that were damaged.

"The high winds blew off parts of the roofs of several of the businesses in the shopping center," he said.

Dozens of trees lost large limbs, and that caused some roads to be blocked in the Hillsdale area. City Manager Tom Sprightly said all of the roads are now passable. "It's going to cost the city some time and money to get the Hillsdale area cleaned up," he said.

"It will be a long time before we can drive through Hillsdale and not be reminded of this storm," he said.

Another reason for the inverted pyramid structure is a technical one. When stories are prepared for print publications such as newspapers, they are placed on certain parts of a page. An editor must decide how to fit stories together on a page. Sometimes stories will be longer than the space allotted for them. If this is the case, an editor will try to cut a story from the bottom, knowing that if the story is written properly, none of the essential facts will be lost.

The inverted pyramid structure demands that the writer make judgments about the importance of the information that he or she has gathered—judgments based on the news values discussed in the previous chapter.

The inverted pyramid structure, though it is the most common, is not the only type of story structure that can be used in news writing. There are several others, which are discussed beginning on page 130. These structures are not rigid. If one style alone won't do, a writer should search for combinations of styles that will best fit the information and ideas he or she is trying to organize.

THE LEAD PARAGRAPH

The most important part of the news story is the first, or lead (pronounced "leed"), paragraph. The lead should tell the reader the most important information in the story. It should be written so that the reader will be interested in going further into the story. Let's go back to the example of the city council story in the previous section. A lead on that story might simply say:

> The City Council voted against raising property taxes last night.

This lead gives the most important information in this story, but it should also invite the reader to continue reading. Go back to the lead written for this story in the previous section. That lead tells the reader the following: There was a debate about this matter, and it has some consequences in which you, the reader, might be interested.

An otherwise good story will not be read by many people if the lead is dull or confusing. The lead is the first part of the story with which a reader will come into contact after the headline, and if the lead does not hold the reader's interest and attention, little else will.

In writing the lead, a reporter must make a judgment about what to put in a lead on the basis of the news values discussed in the previous chapter. The writer must get information to the reader quickly—but also accurately and interestingly. Accuracy, speed, and entertainment are finely balanced in a good lead paragraph.

Leads on news stories generally answer four basic questions about a story: who, what, where, and when. A lead paragraph may emphasize any one of these elements, depending on the facts that are available to the reporter, but a lead will contain something about each of these questions. Sometimes the lead will contain or emphasize the why and the how of a story, but such stories are unusual.

Lead paragraphs should say neither too much nor too little. One of the mistakes that beginning news writers often make is that of trying to put too much in a lead. A lead should not be crowded with information; rather, it should tell enough to answer the reader's major questions about a story and to do so in an interesting and efficient way.

Leads can come in a wide variety of forms and styles. While journalistic conventions restrict what writers can do in some ways, there is still plenty of room for creativity. The following types of leads and examples demonstrate some of the ways writers can approach a story.

The *straight news lead* is a "just-the-facts" approach. It delivers information quickly and concisely to the reader and does not try to dress up the information. The following is a straight lead:

> Two people were killed and four were injured today when a truck collided with a passenger car on Interstate 59 near the Cottondale exit.

The straight news approach is the most common type of news lead and lends itself to most of the stories a reporter will have to cover. Because of this, a couple of technical rules have been developed for this kind of story. Such leads should be one sentence long, and they should contain about thirty words (with a maximum of thirty-three words). It is particularly important for the beginning writer to master this one-sentence, thirty-word approach because of the disciplines of thinking and writing that it requires. A writer must learn that words cannot be wasted, particularly at the beginning of the story.

The *summary lead* is one in which there may be more than one major fact to be covered. Again, the one-sentence, thirty-word approach should be used even though such an approach may require even more effort on the part of the writer. The following is a summary lead:

> A tractor-trailer truck carrying dangerous chemicals crashed on Interstate 59 today, killing one person, injuring four others, and forcing the evacuation of several hundred people from their homes.

The emphasis in this kind of lead is on outlining the full story for the readers in a brief paragraph. Writers using summary leads need to take care that they do not crowd their leads with too much detail but also that they do not generalize too much. A balance should be achieved between including enough detail to make the story interesting and enough general material to avoid confusing the reader.

Up to this point, we have been dealing with straight leads for the most part. Straight leads give the *who, what, when,* and *where* elements of the story to the reader in a straightforward, no-frills fashion. Other types of leads exist, however, and the good news writer should be aware of when they can be used most effectively.

The *blind lead* is a lead in which the people in the story are not named. The two previous examples are blind leads. This kind of lead is common when the people in the story are not well known. In the lead paragraph about the accident, we assume that none of the people involved in the accident is well known. If one of the people hurt were the mayor of the city, we would not want to write a blind lead. We would want to mention his or her name in the lead.

The *direct address lead* is one in which the writer speaks directly to the reader. The main characteristic of this lead is the word *you*, present or implied.

> If gardening is your hobby, you'll need to know about Tom Smith.

> If you're a property owner in the city, the City Council is about to take at least $50 more from you each year.

The direct address lead is a good way of getting the reader's attention, but it should be used sparingly. It is also important to follow up a direct address lead quickly in the second and third paragraphs with information about the lead. By implication, the direct address lead promises the reader some immediate information.

The *question lead* attempts to draw the reader into the story by asking a question.

> Do you really want to know how hot dogs are made?

> Why doesn't the president tell Congress how he stands on the pay increase issue?

The question lead has some of the same advantages and disadvantages as the direct address lead. It is a good way of getting the reader's attention. On the other hand, it can easily be overused. It, too, promises to give the reader some immediate information, and the writer should make good on that promise.

The direct address lead and the question lead also imply that the story has some compelling information for the reader. That's why writers should be careful to use them only when that is the case. Otherwise, the reader will likely be disappointed.

The *direct quote lead* uses a direct quotation to introduce the story and to gain the reader's attention. The direct quote, of course, should be something that one of the participants in the story said, and it should be compelling and informative enough to serve as the lead.

"A city that cares!" That's what mayoral candidate George Bramble promised today as he hit the campaign trail in . . .

Any of these leads can be used when a writer believes that the facts of a story warrant their use. Writers should be careful, however, not to use one of these leads simply for the sake of using something different and not to use them when a story does not lend itself to that type of lead.

DEVELOPING THE STORY

The inverted pyramid requires that writers make judgments not only about what should be at the beginning of the story, but also about the relative importance of all the information they present in the story. In other words, writers must decide what the most important information is for the lead, but they must also decide what the second and third most important pieces of information are. Developing the story in a logical and coherent way requires much skill and practice.

If the lead paragraph is the most important part of the news story, the second paragraph is the second most important part of the story. In some ways, it is almost as important as the lead but for different reasons.

A lead paragraph cannot contain all of the information in a news story. If it is written well, it will inform the reader, but it will also raise certain questions in the reader's mind about the story. Chief among the roles of the second (and succeeding) paragraphs is to answer these questions. The writer does this by providing additional information about the story. The writer must decide what information is most important and what will help the reader to understand the story.

One method that writers use to make these judgments is to put themselves in the place of the reader and to ask, "If I were a reader of this story, what would I want to know next?" For instance, a lead might say:

Authorities are searching for a state prison inmate who escaped from a work crew at the Kidder Correctional Facility on Tuesday.

That lead gives some information about the story, but it also raises a number of questions, such as the following:

Who was the inmate?

Why was he in prison?

How long had he been there and how long was his sentence?

How did he escape?

Where is the search for him taking place?

Is the inmate dangerous?

What does he look like?

How have the prison officials explained his escape?

These are just a few of the questions that could be asked about this story. The writer must answer these questions in a logical and coherent manner that will result in a unified and interesting story. The order in which these questions are answered will depend on the specific information that the writer has to work with.

The writer will probably want to give the name of the inmate quickly and the circumstances of the escape. Beyond that, the type of information the writer has will

Figure 5.4   News Story Analysis

Here we have a news story written in a typical inverted pyramid structure. This story demonstrates a number of points that we have made about newswriting in this chapter. Following are some of them. See whether you can find others.

FBI Questions Two about Park Death

The FBI has begun questioning two of its most wanted fugitives about the unsolved death of a Memphis woman in the Great Smoky Mountains National Park.

An FBI spokesman, however, was careful not to declare Howard Williams, 44, or his wife, Sarah, 36, suspects in the death of Gladys Roslyn. Roslyn's skeletal remains were found by hikers in the park more than two years ago.

"At this point, they are being regarded as material witnesses, and that's about all that we can say about the case," Larry Tims, assistant special agent in charge of the local FBI office, said Tuesday.

Clark Summerford, a lawyer for the couple, confirmed that the FBI is seeking information from them about the woman's death, but he, too, emphasized that the FBI was not about to charge them with any additional crimes.

"As far as I know, the FBI has no evidence directly linking the Williamses with this woman's death," Summerford said.

The Williamses were captured last week after more than a decade on the run. They were spotted by a local truck driver who said he had seen them on "America's Most Wanted," a television show that features stories about fugitives from justice. The Williamses escaped from a Massachusetts jail more than 10 years ago, after they had been convicted of armed robbery of a bank in Salem, Mass.

- **The lead** summarizes the story and gives the latest and most important information to the reader.

- **The second paragraph** builds on the lead paragraph with additional information. By the end of the second paragraph, the reader has most of the major information of this story.

- **Note the use of the direct quotes** in the third and fifth paragraphs. They reinforce information that has been presented previously. The direct quotes also add life to the story; they let the readers know that this story is about real people.

- **The last paragraph** gives the reader some background information on this story. We can assume that the information has already been published, but this paragraph informs the readers who haven't heard about this incident and reminds those who have.

- **Note that *FBI* is not spelled out,** even on first reference. According to the *AP Stylebook,* FBI is so well known that it does not need to be spelled out on first reference.

dictate the order in which the questions are answered. For instance, the second paragraph might go something like this:

> Billy Wayne Hodge, 22, who was convicted two years ago for armed robbery, walked away from his work crew Tuesday afternoon at about 3 p.m., according to prison officials. The crew was picking up trash along Highway 69 about four miles from the prison at the time of the escape.

This paragraph answers some of the questions but leaves others unanswered. Even though a second paragraph can be longer than the lead, it still cannot answer all of the questions a lead can raise. Now the writer will have to decide what questions he or she will answer in the third paragraph. Again, those decisions will be based on the kind of information the writer has. The writer might want to say something about the search for the prisoner, such as the following:

> Sheriff Will Harper said Tuesday night that he thought the prisoner was still in the thick woods in the area of the escape. He said deputies would patrol the area tonight and a full-scale search would begin early Wednesday.

Or the writer may expand on the circumstances of the escape:

> "It appears that one of our guards wasn't watching the prisoners as closely as he should have been," Sam Mayer, the prison warden, said. "There were 15 men in the work crew and only two guards."

Either choice may be appropriate, depending on the circumstances of the story and the writer's preference. The writer has not answered all of the questions raised by the lead, but the story is becoming more complete.

Following is another example of the way in which a story can be developed. Suppose this situation took place: *An automobile accident occurs on a busy street in your city. Three cars are involved. The driver of one of the cars is arrested for drinking and driving. One person is killed, and another is seriously injured. The accident occurred during the afternoon rush and tied up traffic for more than an hour.*

A reporter covering that accident would get all of the information listed above plus other details. Of all of these facts, however, which one would you say is the most important? Which would rank as the second most important fact? The third?

Death and personal injury are usually considered the most important facts in a story such as this one. The fact that one person was killed and another was seriously injured would be the most important things that the reporter would have to tell the readers.

The reporter would then have to decide what the second most important fact is. It could be the arrest of one of the drivers, especially because drinking and driving are always items of great interest. Or the reporter may think that traffic being tied up for so long on a busy street was the second most important fact; a lot of people (many of them readers of the publication) would have been affected by the traffic jam.

If the fact that one person was killed and another was seriously injured is the most important fact, the reporter would want to use that fact to start the lead. But what else would be in the lead? Think about the *what, when,* and *where* or the story. If we put all those things together in one sentence, it might come out like this:

> One person was killed and another seriously injured in a three-car accident Tuesday afternoon during rush hour on Chester Street.

What do you think? Is this the best lead that could be written for a story like this one, or can you think of a better approach to this story? (One of the most noticeable problems about the way it is written is that it uses the passive voice—something we try to avoid in writing for the mass media.)

The paragraph above is a serviceable lead, but there may be more that can be done with it. Adding a few more details, such as more identification of the person who was killed, might make it more interesting for the reader. Then we might have the following lead:

A Centerville man is dead and another person seriously injured after a rush hour collision on Chester Street on Tuesday afternoon.

Or if we wanted to take a different tack and try to work in the fact that one of the drivers was arrested, the lead might read like this:

One person is dead and another seriously injured after a three-car accident on Chester Street on Tuesday, and police have arrested one of the drivers involved in the collision.

As you can tell from this one example, there are many approaches to even the simplest story. Note some things about each of these examples, however. All of them begin with the most important information—the fact that one person was killed and another was injured. All of these are one sentence long and contain thirty words or fewer, and all use simple, straightforward language to give the reader information. The writer does not try to bowl the reader over with fancy words or phrasing but rather tries to keep the language as simple as possible.

Now for the second and third paragraphs of the story: The reporter would want to give the name and identification of the accident victims and would want to relate a few more details about the events surrounding the accident. A second or third paragraph for this story might read this way:

George Smith, 2629 Silver St., was killed when the car he was driving crashed into a telephone pole after being hit by another car. His wife, Sylvia Smith, was also injured in the accident and is in serious condition at General Hospital, according to hospital officials.

Police said they arrested Sam Johnson, 30 Pine Ave., and charged him with driving under the influence of alcohol in connection with the accident.

Sgt. Roland Langley, the officer who investigated the accident, said the car Johnson was driving swerved across the road and hit the Smiths' vehicle, driving it into a telephone pole. A third car was also hit, but no one in that car was injured.

At this point, the writer may want to make the story even more interesting by adding some direct quotations from the news sources:

"A number of witnesses said they saw Johnson's vehicle swerving all over the road, and it appears that he was going pretty fast, too," Langley said.

The police measured 60-foot skid marks made by Johnson's vehicle, Langley added.

A spokesman for the City Jail said Johnson was being held pending other charges that might be lodged against him. A bail hearing for Johnson was set for today.

So far, the story has concentrated on the accident. Now, however, the writer might return to the victims and give more details about them:

Hospital officials said Smith suffered head injuries, and he died shortly after he arrived at the hospital. Mrs. Smith also suffered injuries to her head and neck and has three broken ribs and a broken arm.

The third car in the accident was driven by Lester Matson, 406 Altus Drive. Matson said Johnson's car smashed into his after it had hit the Smiths' car.

"There was simply nothing I could do to get out of the way," he said. "I saw this car up ahead, swerving all around the road, but there were cars all around me, and I couldn't go anywhere." Matson was not hurt, but he said his car was damaged in the accident.

The examples in this section should give you some idea of how a news story is developed. That development is based on a series of decisions that the writer must make about the information he or she has. Even with simple stories, these decisions are rarely simple. They require that the writer understand the news story structure as well as the facts of a particular story.

How should a news story end? A writer should stop writing when all of the logical questions have been answered and when all of the interesting information has been presented in the story. A writer should not be concerned with concluding or summarizing a story, particularly when he or she is beginning to learn how to write news. Instead, the writer should make sure that the reader can understand and be satisfied with what is written.

USING QUOTATIONS

One of the most important parts of any news story is the material that writers quote directly or indirectly from their sources. Learning proper news writing form means understanding how to use quoted material. A good news story usually has a mixture of direct and indirect quotations, and a news writer must have a good sense of when to use a direct or an indirect quotation.

A *direct quotation* is one that uses the speaker's exact words, and those words are contained within quotation marks. An *indirect quotation* may contain one or a few of the words that a speaker has used but will also have words that the speaker did not use. No quotation marks are used with an indirect quotation. Most news stories will use more indirect quotations than direct quotations.

Indirect quotations should maintain the meaning of what the speaker has said but use fewer words than the speaker has used. Competent writers quickly learn that most people use more words than are necessary to say what they have to say. They can paraphrase what people say and be more efficient than the speakers themselves. And as a news writer, you will find that you can get more information into your story if you use indirect quotes.

If that is the case, why worry about using direct quotations at all? Why not just use indirect quotations all the time?

Direct quotations can be used by the skillful writer to bring a story to life, to show that the people in the story are real, and to enhance the story's readability. Occasionally, people will say something in a memorable or colorful way, and the writer should preserve that. Think about some of the famous direct quotations in American history:

"Give me liberty or give me death." (Patrick Henry)

"Read my lips. No new taxes." (George Bush)

"We have nothing to fear but fear itself." (Franklin Roosevelt)

"Four score and seven years ago . . ." (Abraham Lincoln)

Another reason for using a direct quotation is that some quotations simply cannot be paraphrased. They are too vivid and colorful, and they capture a feeling better than a writer could. For instance, when Heisman Trophy winner Bo Jackson was playing college football for Auburn in the 1980s, he was once stopped from making what would have been a game-winning touchdown near the end of the game.

The opposing linebacker who made the hit on Jackson was asked about the play after the game. Still high from his accomplishment, he said, "I waxed the dude!" That quotation would be impossible to paraphrase.

If you are going to use direct quotations in your stories—and you should—you should follow some basic rules.

Use the Speaker's Exact Words

Anything that is within quotation marks should be the words the speaker said in the order in which he or she said them. The words should be the speaker's, not the writer's.

Use Direct Quotations Sparingly

Good writers will let people speak, but they won't let them ramble on. Most news writers avoid putting one direct quote after another in a story. You should never pile one direct quote onto another in paragraph after paragraph of a story. The writer who does that is not a writer but a stenographer.

Use Direct Quotations to Supplement and Clarify the Information Presented in the Indirect Quotes

In a news story, a direct quote is rarely used to present new or important information to the reader. It is most commonly used to follow up information that has already been presented.

Knowing how to deal with direct and indirect quotations is one of the most important skills that a news writer can acquire. It takes some practice to paraphrase accurately and to select the direct quotations that should be used in a story. The key to both is to listen—listen carefully so that you understand what the speaker is saying and so that you remember the exact words that the speaker has used.

The correct sequence for a direct quote and its attribution is DIRECT QUOTE, SPEAKER, VERB. This sequence is generally used in news stories because it follows the inverted pyramid philosophy of putting the most important information first. Usually, what has been said is the most important element a journalist has; who said it, assuming that the person has already been identified in the story, is the second most important element; the fact that it was said is the third most important element. (Some editors allow an exception to this sequence when a source has to be identified within the attribution, as in the following: "I hope the bill is enacted," said Nathan Lightfoot, the third district representative.)

One of the common faults among many writers is the inverted attribution: putting the verb ahead of the subject.

"I do not choose to run," said the president.

There is no good reason for writing this way, and it violates one of the basic structures of English sentence: Subjects precede verbs. Remember, one of the major goals of the journalist is to make the writing of a story unobtrusive and the content of the story dominant. Sticking with basic English forms is one of the ways the journalist can do this.

One additional note: Use the past tense of verbs in news stories unless the action is continuing at the time of publication or unless it will happen in the future. Writing

"I do not choose to run," the president says.

is inaccurate unless the president goes around continually saying it. Chances are that it was said only once. It happened in the past, and that's the way it should be written.

Although you would probably be able to find many examples of the use of the present tense in many publications, it is inaccurate when it is referring to things that have happened and to action that has been completed.

OTHER STORY STRUCTURES

The inverted pyramid story structure is not the only form that writers of news and information can use. Sometimes the facts, the publication, or the situation will dictate that a different form be used to present ideas and information. Beginning news writers should first master the inverted pyramid form, but they should also be able to use a different story structure when the situation calls for it. The following is a brief summary of some of the various story structures that are used in writing for print.

Narrative

As the name suggests, this form uses traditional storytelling techniques, particularly a chronological approach. Instead of a summary lead paragraph, the story begins at the beginning. Events are then related in the order in which they occurred.

The narrative structure demands a strong, interesting lead paragraph to draw the readers into the story, just as the inverted pyramid structure does. It also requires the writer to relate everything to a central theme and to weave the events together so that they have a unity for the reader. Finally, readers must come away from a narrative story with a strong sense of the sequence in which events occurred and an understanding of why this sequence is important.

Bullet

This structure is useful when several things happen at an event that are not closely related to one another but the event itself needs to be covered in one story. It uses a summary lead to tell the reader what the story is about in general and then a series of short paragraphs called bullets—hence the name—summarizing the different events or points that the story will cover. This establishes the structure of the story (see Figure 5.5). Each bullet is then expanded with several paragraphs of explanation. In this structure, the news writer does not have to be closely concerned with transitions or with trying to tie the different parts of the story together for the reader.

Eyewitness Accounts

This approach to news writing can occur in two ways. One is when the reporter is present at the event. This type of eyewitness report requires that the reporter get away from the impersonal approach with which most news is written. It opens up possibilities for the reporter to describe sights, sounds, and smells that might be left out of news stories (see Figure 5.6).

Another type of eyewitness account is for a reporter to collaborate with an eyewitness to an event to produce an on-the-scene story about the event. This approach requires more than just interviewing an eyewitness. It means that the reporter should talk with the subject long enough to understand not only what the subject saw and heard, but also how the subject felt about the event. Before this approach is used, the reporter and the subject should agree on their collaboration. Normally, a reporter will draft an account of the event using the words of the eyewitness as much as possible and writing from that person's point of view. The eyewitness will then review the draft and suggest changes. This process of drafting and reviewing will continue

Figure 5.5   Bullet Structure

This story is written in the bullet style. The story begins with a summary lead paragraph and then quickly summarizes several pieces of information in the next few paragraphs. Compare this one to the stories in Figures 5.9 and 5.10, which are about the same event but written in inverted pyramid and eyewitness styles.

30,000 Residents without Power

VIOLENT STORM CRASHES CITY

A violent thunder and wind storm ripped through the city Tuesday afternoon, downing trees and power lines and causing personal injuries and property damage.

The storm caused the following injuries, disruptions and damage:

- One man was seriously injured when a tree limb hit him on the head; five others received minor injuries because of car accidents caused by the storm.
- Some 30,000 West Point Power Co. customers were without electricity for part of the evening Tuesday; power has been restored in most areas.
- Several homes and businesses in the Hillsdale area were seriously damaged by the strong winds.
- Traffic signals were out in much of the western part of the city immediately after the storm, but all have been restored.

Arthur Major, 227 W. Hill St., was struck by a falling limb and taken to Community Hospital during the storm. He suffered severe head injuries and was in serious but stable condition on Tuesday evening.

Hospital officials said five other people were injured in car accidents caused by the storm. All were treated and released by emergency room doctors.

The storm downed power lines throughout the city. West Point Power Co. officials said at one time during the afternoon about 30,000 city residents were without electricity. They said power was restored to ever part of the city except the Hillsdale area by 9 p.m.

"I don't know when we'll get the lights back on in Hillsdale," Brad Jeffries, a spokesman for the power company, said.

until the article is ready for publication. An eyewitness should always see the final draft before it is published.

Micro-Macro

This structure, used most prominently by the *Wall Street Journal* in its lead articles on page 1 each day, works well when the topic of the story is a large event that affects many people. It begins by focusing on some person or situation that has been affected by the event. This "micro" beginning reflects or demonstrates the larger issue or problem. After describing the person or situation, the story then expands to the larger problem (the "macro") with a transition paragraph that explains what the story is about. This transition paragraph often uses facts and figures that summarize the issue. The subsequent paragraphs continue to discuss the larger issue, although they may refer

Figure 5.6   First-Person Account

This story is written as an first-person account. Here the writer focuses on himself and his experiences. Compare this to the stories in Figures 5.9 and 5.11, which are about the same event but written in inverted pyramid and narrative styles.

One Man's Story

VIOLENT STORM CRASHES CITY

By Guy Hibbs

I have lived in this city for nearly 20 years, and I've never seen anything like it.

The storm that blew through this city yesterday was the noisiest, most violent roaring of Mother Nature in my memory. Others who have lived here longer than I have have told me the same thing.

Normally, I'm in the office of the *Daily News* at 3 p.m., usually putting the finishing touches on the day's work and thinking about the evening at home.

But yesterday, when the storm hit, I happened to be driving back to the office from an interview that I conducted for a Sunday feature story.

As I was driving by the Hillsdale shopping center—later to be one of the hardest-hit areas—I looked at the sky and noticed a line of thick, dark clouds marching from east to west across the sky. The wind was picking up.

A bad storm, I thought, but nothing too unusual.

Within minutes, I knew I had misjudged the elements . . .

to the situation presented at the beginning. The story will return to the beginning situation for some type of resolution or ending. These stories take time to develop because the reporter must become familiar enough with the large problem and the small situation to write about both accurately. A lead story in the *Wall Street Journal* can take as long as three or four months to research and write.

These are just a few of the different approaches that news writers can take to their stories. All of these structures demand that writers adhere to the basic characteristics of good news writing: a goal of accuracy, a knowledge of the language, and an adherence to the rules of style.

TYPES OF NEWS STORIES

Despite the inherent creativity associated with all writing, news writing has some routine aspects that make its production easier and more efficient for news organizations and for the journalists themselves. One such aspect is the types of stories that appear in newspapers and on news broadcasts and news websites. Looking at these over just a short period of time, a reader will recognize that certain types of stories recur. They involve different characters and describe different events and situations, but they fall into some general categories that are easy to classify.

Just as beginning writers need to learn news values (discussed in the previous chapter), they also need to learn about these types of stories and the kind of information they demand. These categories are not confined to daily journalism; they occur in all types of media writing, especially when public relations practitioners are asked to produce various types of informational publications such as customer and employee newsletters.

Following are some basic types of stories and some of the expectations journalists and readers have developed for them.

Meetings

Governmental and quasi-governmental bodies that make decisions that affect the public are often required to do so in public. The form this decision-making process takes is the public meeting, such as a meeting of the city council or the local school board. Such meetings take place on a regularly scheduled basis, involve those who have been elected or appointed to serve on the council or board, and follow some kind of agenda. Often, too, they will have some time set aside for interaction with the public.

Journalists who write about these meetings must attend them, but they also need to do some preparation so that they will understand what they are seeing and hearing. For many such meetings, agendas are available well before the meeting occurs, and a reporter can obtain an agenda and begin inquiries about what will be discussed. Reporters should know the members of a board or council and what their jobs are.

News stories about meetings should emphasize the most important actions that the board or council takes. This will likely be a decision that involves the most people—a tax increase, for instance—but it could also be something dramatic or unexpected, such as the firing of a school principal. Conflicts that arise about the member of a board, particularly if they come out in open debate, are interesting items to include in a news story about a meeting. A reporter may also want to note, and sometimes emphasize, the public's interaction with the officials during a meeting.

Speeches

News stories about speeches are a staple of journalistic routine, but they take some skill on the part of the reporter if they are to be written correctly and interestingly (see Figure 5.7). A person may speak to an audience for five or forty-five minutes; the news story about the speech has to reflect accurately what the person said in both an interesting and coherent way.

In writing a speech story, the writer has to make a decision about the most interesting and important thing the speaker has said and has to put that in the lead paragraph. The writer should go beyond just identifying the speaker and stating the fact that he or she spoke. For instance, consider the following lead paragraph:

> Sen. John Warner (R-Va.), chairman of the Senate Armed Services Committee, delivered the commencement address to the graduating class of Emory and Henry College on Saturday.

Such a lead does not give the reader any information about what the speaker said. The following is much better:

> Sen. John Warner (R-Va.), chairman of the Senate Armed Services Committee, told the graduating class of Emory and Henry College on Saturday that the U.S. involvement in Iraq is likely to be "long and painful."

A good speech story is a mixture of direct and indirect quotes from the speaker. The writer will want to summarize or paraphrase much of what the speaker has said because that is the most efficient way to tell the readers about the speech. But the writer will also want to use direct quotations for emphasis and to give the reader some of the flavor of the speaker's manner of speaking. The story should also contain information about the setting of the speech (where it occurred, how many people were there, audience reaction, etc.) and some background information about the speaker.

Figure 5.7   Speech Story

This story is a good example of the speech story that journalists are called on to write every day. Pay attention to how the story is structured, as pointed out in the notes.

A former official of the National Aeronautics and Space Administration told a campus audience Wednesday that it was time for America to "turn its head back toward the earth" and abandon manned space flight.

Jack Cotter, who recently retired after working for more than 30 years at the space agency, said the manned space program was too costly and Americans are not getting any benefits from it.

"I would like to think otherwise," he said to an audience of more than 150 students, faculty and members of the community. "After all, I spent most of my career helping us get into space."

Cotter was the third speaker in this semester's "Science in Daily Life" series. Joseph Edison, professor of biology at Spring Hill University in Dayton, Tenn., will conclude the series on Monday at 7:30 p.m. in the Board of Visitors room of the Van Dyke Center.

Cotter pointed to the *Challenger* accident of 1986 and the *Columbia* accident of 2003 as evidence that the manned space program has become too costly. "Space is a very dangerous place," he said. "The folks at NASA don't really want to talk about that because they do not want people questioning what they do."

Cotter, who was an assistant program director on the NASA team that put the first man on the moon in 1969, said America got into the space program largely because the Russians were already there.

"It was a race, pure and simple," he said. "We had to beat the Russians."

He described how President John F. Kennedy pledged to America that it would land the first man on the moon in 1961. "Kennedy said that would happen before the decade was out," Cotter said. "Then it became our job to make it happen."

- **The lead paragraph** gives the *who, what, when,* and *where* of the speech but also includes something specific the speaker said.

- **The second paragraph** follows up with more information about the quotation in the first paragraph.

- **The third paragraph** has a full direct quotation as well as some more information about the setting of the speech.

- **The fourth paragraph** has information that puts the speech in a local context. Note that it has information that would not have been in the speech itself.

- **The remaining paragraphs** alternate between paraphrasing and direct quotations. Much of the information is contained in the paraphrases, and they are followed up by relevant quotations.

Figure 5.7   Continued

Cotter joined NASA in 1966 after a tour of duty in Vietnam. He had earned a degree in mechanical engineering from the University of Fargo before going to Vietnam.

"Those were exciting times," he said. "Just about everybody supported us, and we could get just about anything we wanted from Congress. Remember, we had to beat the Russians, and it was during the Cold War."

Cotter called what developed inside the agency a "cowboy atmosphere" where the tendency was to take undue chances with people's lives. That is when he began to have his doubts about the wisdom what the agency was doing.

"I stayed with the agency because I believed that if we did it right, it would be worth doing," he said. "I believed that a lot of people would benefit from it."

Cotter said the *Challenger* and *Columbia* accidents convinced him that it was simply too dangerous.

"We got to the moon," he said, "but we are never going to get to Mars. It's just too far away."

If possible, the reporter should obtain any prepared text that a speaker has—before the speech is made, if possible, or afterward. A prepared text makes taking notes about the speech much easier and helps to ensure that the writer quotes the speaker correctly.

Obituary

The death of a person is a significant event not only to those who knew that person but also to the community itself. Newspapers once emphasized the journalistic aspects of this event. Today, most newspapers have given the obituary over to the classified advertising section, and most obituaries are composed by funeral directors rather than journalists.

Despite this sad trend, when prominent or interesting people in a community die, reporters are called on to write a death story or, in journalistic jargon, an *obit*. Such a story is not routine. Reporters must often speak with grieving or distraught friends and family members and must conduct themselves with great courtesy, patience, and sympathy.

Many publications have a standard form for an obituary that begins with a lead paragraph such as the following:

Mary Marple, a long-time resident of the Coldwater community, died on Wednesday after a long illness. She was 87 years old.

A good obituary will list the accomplishments of a person during his or her lifetime and will include contributions that the person has made to the community. It will also try to give some of the personal characteristics or interests of the person, such as "She was a life-long St. Louis Cardinals fan and even went to Florida regularly to watch the Cardinals during spring training."

Information that might reflect badly on the person should not be ignored, particularly if such information is generally known. In this kind of story, however, the reporter and editor may choose not to emphasize it. Stating the cause of death, too, may be a matter of editorial judgment; some families object to listing certain causes of death, such as AIDS or alcoholism.

A typical obituary will list family members, the time and place of the funeral or memorial service, and information about sending flowers or making memorial contributions to honor the deceased person.

Weather

The weather is something that we all share, that we are interested in, and that is important to our daily lives. Most news organizations pay some attention to the weather, and broadcasters have found that weather information and forecasts help them to draw in large audiences. They are often willing to spend significant amounts of money for people and equipment to bring good weather information to their viewers.

When weather becomes unusual—particularly when it causes deaths, injuries, or property damage—reporters must pay special attention. Journalists are often called on to write about significant weather events, such as a tornado, a violent rainstorm, or a snowfall. Such events generally take place over a short period of time. In writing about them, the emphasis should be first on any deaths or injuries they have caused and then on any property damage that has occurred.

In covering specific weather events, more long-term and significant weather-related stories are sometimes ignored. For instance, in the last two decades of the twentieth century, more than 8,000 people died because of excessive heat—more than the number of deaths from hurricanes, tornadoes, floods, earthquakes, and lightning combined. Reporters should pay attention to the effects that even "routine" weather is having.

Crime and Courts

The news media have often been criticized for giving too much emphasis to crime and legal battles, but these types of stories continue to be of high interest to readers and of significant value to the public. Crime, of course, can be a matter life and death to the people who are involved, and it is certainly an important issue for any community.

Most news organizations rely on the news values of conflict, impact, and unusualness in deciding how to cover crime. Information about crime must be obtained from law enforcement officials—often the police officers involved—and they must be treated with a good deal of respect. As in weather stories, death, injury, and property damage are the most important aspects of any crime. Amounts of money that are involved in a crime also need attention.

The legal system, especially trials, provides an unending series of interesting subjects for the news media. A trial has a built-in conflict that plays directly to one of the basic news values. To write well about a trial, a journalist must understand the issues that are in question and must also know about legal procedures and the legal system. A trial is the culmination of much work and activity on the part of everyone involved, and trials can be extremely time-consuming and tedious (far more so than is depicted on television shows). Reporters who cover trials must be alert for the key moments and must be able to anticipate when those moments will occur.

Periodicals and Anniversaries

Some news stories are as predictable as the calendar. In fact, they are tied directly to the calendar. As with weather stories, these are articles about events that we all share: the beginning and ending of the school year; the approach of April 15, the deadline for filing income tax returns; the anniversary of the bombing of Pearl Harbor (December 7) and D-Day (June 6); the holiday seasons, particularly Thanksgiving, Christmas, and Easter; Valentine's Day, Mother's Day, Father's Day; and so on.

News organizations pay attention to all of these events because they are predictable, because they have activities that surround them, and because readers and viewers expect information about them. Because these events and anniversaries occur regularly, journalists must work to provide fresh information about them and look for creative ways to tell their audiences about them.

These are just a few of the types of stories that make up the daily fare that is news. The fact that the news media cover many of the same types of stories reflects the routine functioning of society and the predictability of the world in which we all live. These stories play an important role in helping news organizations to operate and in giving them some basic on which to plan their activities.

In addition, news helps individuals to make decisions about their lives and gives them a world view in which to put their lives in context. Paying attention to the news is a grave individual responsibility. People who do not read newspapers or news websites or do not watch television news programs or listen to radio news broadcasts are not fulfilling their responsibilities both to themselves and as citizens of a larger society.

More broadly, routine news such as that described in this section has an important societal role by informing people about how the society functions and by giving people a common pool of information and common points of reference. Without such commonalities, we would be unable to function as a society and to solve problems collectively. Even the routine work that journalists do helps to move a society forward.

EDITING AND REWRITING

Benjamin Franklin would tell the following story: John Thompson, a hatter, was about to open his first shop. He made a sign to put in front of his business that read, "John Thompson, hatter, makes and sells hats for ready money." He was proud of his sign and showed it to his friends. One friend said it was a fine sign, but the word "hatter" was unnecessary because the sign also said "makes and sells hats." Another friend said "makes and" could be dropped. Yet another friend said the phrase "for ready money" could be eliminated because it could be assumed that people would pay money for the hats. The word "sells" could also be dropped, another friend pointed out, because it could also be assumed. With all these suggestions, Thompson remade the sign to read, "John Thompson, hatter." Then a

Figure 5.8

Lillian Hellman on rewriting

Nothing you write, if you hope to be any good, will ever come out as you first hope.

friend suggested that a picture of a hat could replace the word, "hatter." The sign was redone again, hung outside the shop, and Thompson had a long-lasting and prosperous business.

The point is this: All writers need an editor, even if those editors are your neighbors. The nature of writing is that first drafts are rarely satisfactory. They do not often accomplish what the authors intend.

Editing and rewriting are integral parts of the writing process. A writer who finishes an initial draft has the responsibility to try to improve it, and most writers readily recognize this necessity.

In writing for the mass media, editing and rewriting in some form are usually part of the production process. News organizations employ people to edit copy just as they employ reporters to write it. These copy editors, many of whom have experience as news reporters, develop an expertise in the techniques of editing. They can edit under deadline pressure, just as writers must learn to write under those same pressures.

The first responsibility for editing lies with the writer. A writer should develop a good understanding of the purpose and techniques of copy editing. The writer should also acquire good editing habits that, when put to use, will improve what has been written.

Two general types of editing can occur: copy-editing and rewriting. Copy-editing involves various techniques and operations that change and improve copy but do not alter its basic structure and approach. Rewriting, just as its name implies, means rewording large portions of the copy and reexamining its structure. Rewriting produces a different piece of copy, and its purpose is to make the copy more suitable for the medium in which it is to be used (see Figure 5.9). Both copy-editing and rewriting should be done when the copy demands it, but the amount of time available for these activities will often dictate how much can be done.

Given that time is not often available to rewrite every piece of copy completely, the following are some of the things that writers should look for first in articles they have drafted.

Spelling, Grammar, and Style Mistakes

No mistakes are more embarrassing or more harmful to the writer than spelling and grammar mistakes. Such mistakes tag the writer as unprofessional or ignorant of the basic tools of the language. These are the mistakes that a writer should look for first. Writers should look up any words they are not sure about, and they should use every means possible to verify that the proper names in their stories are spelled correctly.

Style mistakes can also be painfully embarrassing to a writer. Ignorance of style rules for a particular medium will signal to other professionals that the writer does not understand the importance of consistency in writing and does not care to learn.

Verbs

The quickest way to improve writing is to improve the verbs. If possible, verbs should be active and descriptive. A writer should look at every instance where he or she has used the passive voice (see Chapter 2) and consider whether or not the passage should be changed to the active voice.

Writing that is laden with linking verbs is probably not going to sound very interesting. These verbs (*is, seems, feels,* etc.) are useful and necessary at times, but they lack the power that active, descriptive verbs have. Changing linking verbs to action verbs will inject life into a piece of writing. For instance, consider this sentence: "Smith is the leader of the winning team." Changing from a linking to a

Figure 5.9   Rewriting

The lead paragraph is the most important part of a news story. It should present the reader with the most important information in the story. It should be long enough to give the reader a good idea about what is in the story but short enough to let the reader get through it quickly. In other words, leads are not easy to write. Quite often, it takes more than one try to write a good lead. Here are some lead paragraphs as they appeared in print. The writers and editors who produced them did not have the time or make the effort to rewrite them. Below each lead are rewritten versions that are considerable improvements over the first efforts.

- A new law that gives prosecutors additional power to halt the distribution of movies they believe are obscene prompted videotape rental stories in Decatur to pull nearly 2,000 adult films off their shelves.

  REWRITE:
  Owners of videotape rental stores in Decatur have pulled nearly 2,000 tapes off the shelves because of a new law that gives prosecutors more power to halt the sale of obscene materials.

- Several steps are being taken to prevent a repeat of the error that caused an ambulance answering a heart attack call to be sent to the wrong street last week, the Emergency 911 board of directors was told Tuesday.

  REWRITE:
  Emergency 911 is taking several steps to make sure that ambulances are sent to the correct addresses, according to testimony before the E-911 board.

- Civilian unemployment, rising at the fastest clip in more than three years, jumped to 5.3 percent last month, the government said Friday in a report that was taken as the strongest evidence yet of an economic slowdown.

  REWRITE:
  Unemployment is up to 5.3 percent, the steepest rise in three years, according to a government report, and many economists believe that is the strongest sign yet of an economic slowdown.

action verb makes this a more powerful and interesting sentence: "Smith led his team to victory."

Wordiness

Some writers delight in finding passages in their own writing that use too many words. They recognize that wordiness—using too many words to say something—is one of the major and consistent problems in writing. Like the man in Benjamin Franklin's story, every writer could use friends who are good editors to improve copy.

In examining your writing, look at the parts that were difficult for you to write initially. You may have gotten something down to express the idea or information, but chances are you could improve it on a second reading. This improvement will usually involve cutting down on the number of words it takes to express the thought.

Answering All the Questions

Writing for the mass media will raise questions in the readers' minds. Writers must make sure that they answer all of the logical and relevant questions that their articles create. For example, an article may say that three people were hurt in an automobile accident and may give the name of the person who was hurt seriously enough to remain in the hospital. A natural question from this information would be "Who are the other two people?" Or an article may mention that a coastal storm is the second worst such storm in the history of the state. What was the worst storm? The article should tell the reader at some point.

An article that does not answer all of the logical questions often means that a reporter has not done a complete job in gathering information about the subject. It is not unusual for a reporter to discover in the editing process that he or she must find out more if the article is to be complete.

Internal Consistency

An article should make sense for the reasonable and sensible reader. Figures should add up properly, and times and dates should be logical. Even though most news stories are not written chronologically, a reader should have a good idea of the time sequence of a story. Confusion in the writing often indicates confusion on the part of the writer, and it almost guarantees confusion for the reader.

Looking for the writing problems listed above constitutes the beginning of good copy-editing. Given enough time, writers should not stop with these problems. They should judge their copy on its emphasis, tone, and structure. All of these factors need to be correct for writing to be at its best. The best writers avoid falling in love with their copy. In fact, the best writers are among their own harshest critics. Good writers are always trying to improve their writing, using whatever means are necessary. A willingness to copy-edit and rewrite are two such means from which writers should never shy away.

WRITING FEATURE STORIES

Differentiating feature stories from news stories is misleading. The two actually have a great deal in common. The difference is in emphasis. The styles that are commonly used for feature stories assume that the reader has more time to read. They still require a central theme. The writer must be able to summarize the point of the story. But the writing may require that the reader go further to fully understand the point of the story. Of course, that means that the writer must sustain interest for a longer period of time.

Feature writing is a way for both readers and writers to get away from the "relevant facts only" approach of most news stories. Feature stories generally contain more detail and description. They go beyond most news stories by trying to discover the interesting or important side of an event that may not be covered by the six basic news values.

Feature stories are also a way of humanizing the news, of breathing life into a publication. Most feature articles center on people and their activities and interests. A good way for a feature writer to approach the job is to believe that every person is worth at least one good feature story.

Feature stories vary not only in content, but also in structure. Following is a brief discussion of some of the structures a feature writer may use. Feature stories have no single structure that is used most of the time. Feature writers are freer to adapt whatever structure is suitable to the story they are trying to tell.

Figure 5.10 Feature Styles

Below are the beginnings of two feature articles. Take a close look at each of them. Any feature story can be approached and written in a variety of ways. Note the approach of each. What are the attention-getting devices? What are the sources of information in each article? Would you suggest any changes for either of these articles?

She spends most of her day in her six-by-ten-foot cell, reading her Bible, writing a letter occasionally, and walking back and forth a little. She rarely speaks to other inmates at the Miranda State Women's Prison even when she has the chance. She prefers to keep to herself.

"All my life I've been around other people. I never had any privacy," she says. "That's the one good thing about being in this place all alone."

"This place" for Wendy Hoffman is Death Row, an isolated corner of the third floor of one of Miranda's cellblocks. She's "all alone" because she is currently the only woman in the state living under a death sentence.

Hoffman has been there for six months now, ever since the end of her celebrated trial in Molene. There she was convicted of shooting 13-year-old Chrissy Staten on the orders of her husband. The trial generated a barrage of international publicity for everyone involved, including Dax Hoffman, who is also living under a death sentence at the Norton Jones State Prison, about 100 miles away.

Norma Sasser is determined that next Wednesday will be like any other day has been for the last 45 years. She'll walk into her first-grade classroom at Rockwood Elementary, give her students their final report cards, and wish them a happy summer.

The problem is that however much "Miss Norma" follows her routine, it won't be the same. It will be her last day of teaching kids to read, write, count, and be still.

She knows that, and even though she dreads the last day, she's looking forward to what comes after that: lots of travel, time to read and gardening, she says.

The day might be more normal if all she had to do was meet with this year's students. But soon after they've received their grades, a day-long celebration will begin at the school, all in her honor. More than 1,000 of her former students will be there, some of whom will travel from distant parts of the country.

"That's the part I dread—not leaving the classroom for the last time," she said . . .

Anecdotal Features

This style usually begins with a story of some kind and usually follows with a statement of facts to support the point of the story. Quotations, anecdotes, and facts then are interwoven throughout the story. The trick is to keep the quotes and anecdotes relevant to the point of focus and to keep the story interesting without making it trite.

Suspended Interest Features

This style is often used for producing some special effect. It is usually used for a short story with a punch line, but sometimes it is drawn out into a much longer story. In either case, the style requires the writer to lead readers through a series of paragraphs that may raise questions in the readers' minds while keeping readers interested in solving the puzzle. At the end, the story is resolved in an unexpected way.

Profiles

A profile feature story centers on a single person. One approach to a profile is to write a general description of the person's life, past and present. Usually, this is narrative that begins with the birth of the person and ends with the present. Another approach is to zero in on a specific aspect of the person's life and weave a story around that particular item. In doing this, the writer can include biographical and background information about the person but can stay focused on the chosen subject.

Question and Answer

This is a simple style that is used for a specific effect. An explanatory paragraph usually starts the story. Then the interviewer's questions are followed by the interviewee's answers, word for word. Using this style requires articulate participants in the interview. Sometimes, however, it makes clear how inarticulate an interviewee is about a topic. In any case, it is effective for showing the reader an unfiltered view of the interviewee's use of language.

CHARACTERISTICS OF FEATURE WRITING

To the reader, the feature story seems to have a more relaxed style of writing than a news story. It may be easier to read than a news story, and because of its content, it may be more entertaining. Feature writers, however, work just as hard and are just as disciplined as news writers. They may work under a slightly different set of rules than news writers, but the goals of a feature writer are essentially the same ones that a news writer has: to tell a story accurately and to write well.

The main thing that sets feature stories apart from news stories is the greater amount of detail and description features contain. This difference is the backbone of a good feature story. Whereas the news story writer wishes to transmit a basic set of facts to the reader as quickly as possible, the feature writer tries to enhance those facts with details and description so that the reader will be able to see a more complete picture of an event or a person. For instance, while the news writer might refer to "a desk" in a news story, the feature writer will want to go beyond that simple reference by telling the reader something more—"a mahogany desk" or "a dark mahogany desk." Better yet, the writer might rely on verbs to enhance the descriptions of the subject: "A large, soft executive chair enveloped him as he sat behind a dark mahogany desk."

The three major kinds of descriptions that should be contained in a feature story are description of actions, description of people, and description of places. All of these are important to a good feature story, but the description that makes for the strongest writing is generally the description of action. Telling about events, telling what has happened, telling what people are doing—these things make compelling reading. Descriptions of this type help readers to see a story, not just read about it. In addition, feature writers should make sure that readers see the people in their stories, just as the writers themselves have seen the people. Feature writers also need to describe adequately the places where the stories occur. Readers need an idea of the surroundings of a story to draw a complete picture of the story in their minds.

A couple of tips will help writers to attain more vivid descriptions in their stories. One is the reliance on nouns and verbs. Beginning writers sometimes believe that they should use as many adjectives and adverbs as possible to enhance their writing, and in doing so, they rely on dull and overused nouns and verbs. That approach is a wrong turn on the road to producing lively, descriptive writing. A second tip for writers is to remember the five senses. Often writers simply describe the way things look, and they forget about the way things sound, feel, taste, or smell. Incorporating the five senses into a story will help make a description come alive for a reader.

Feature stories often contain more quotations and even dialogue than news stories. News writers use direct quotations to enhance and illuminate the facts they are trying to present. Feature writers go beyond this by using quotations to say something about the people who are in their stories. Quoted material is generally used much more freely in feature stories, although, as in news stories, dumping a load of quotes on a reader without a break often puts too heavy a burden on the reader. Dialogue and dialect are other devices a feature writer may use if the story calls for them.

One of the charms of feature writing for many writers is that the writer can put more of himself or herself into a story. Whereas in news stories, writers stay out of sight as much as they can, feature writers are somewhat freer to inject themselves and their opinions into a story. Although feature writers do have more latitude in this regard, they must use this latitude wisely and make sure that a feature story does not become a story about themselves rather than about the subject they are trying to cover.

PARTS OF A FEATURE STORY

Feature stories generally have four parts: a lead, an engine paragraph, a body, and an ending. Each needs special handling by the writer.

As in a news story, the lead of a feature story is its most important part. Feature writers are not bound by the one-sentence, thirty-word lead paragraph structure that news writers must often follow. A lead in a feature story may be several sentences or paragraphs long. From the beginning sentence, however, the feature writer must capture the reader's attention and give the reader some information of substance—or at least promise some information of substance. A news writer can depend on the story's subject to compel the reader's interest. A feature writer must sell the reader on the subject in the first few words or sentences.

A good lead uses the first words or sentences of a story to build interest in the story's subject, but the reader must soon discover some benefit for reading the story. That's why the writer should build a lead toward some initial point that the story is to make, something that will hook the reader for the rest of the story.

The *engine paragraph* (also called the *fat paragraph,* the *snapper,* or the *why paragraph*) gives the reader this payoff and sets the stage for the rest of the story. It puts the story in some context for the reader and tells the reader why the rest of the story should be read.

The body of the feature story is the middle of the story that expands and details the subjects introduced in the lead. The body should answer every question that was raised in the lead, and it should fulfill every expectation that the lead raised within the reader. Unfortunately, like products bought in a store, features often promise more than they deliver. They tell the reader in the lead that the information they contain will be of interest or help to the reader, and they turn out to be neither interesting nor helpful. The body should contain the substance of the article, and it should be what the reader has been led to expect.

News writers using the inverted pyramid generally do not have to worry about the ending of their stories. Feature writers need to take care how a story ends. The ending of a story may be used to put the story in some perspective, to answer any lingering questions that a reader may have, or to make a final point about the story's subject. The major point about an ending is that a writer should not allow a story to go on too long. Like any other writer, the feature writer should stop writing when there is nothing of substance left to say.

THE CHALLENGE OF WRITING

Writing for print encapsulates most of the challenges that a media writer will face: gathering information, learning the appropriate structures and writing conventions, and understanding the graphic devices that may enhance the writing. The type of writing that we have discussed in this chapter occurs every day in newspapers, magazines, newsletters, websites, and many other forms of media. The professional writer is always faced with the same task: to present information accurately, completely, precisely and efficiently. Learning to do this takes reading, analysis, study and practice.

POINTS FOR CONSIDERATION AND DISCUSSION

1. Some critics argue that newspapers should abandon the inverted pyramid news story structure. They say that television and radio deliver news much faster than newspapers; therefore, newspapers should not be as concerned with getting information to readers quickly as with getting more complete and accurate information. What do you think?
2. Chapter 3 discussed journalistic style and the conventions of journalism. How does what you learned in that chapter fit in with the principles presented in this chapter?
3. The author says that you shouldn't go out of your way to find substitutes for the verb *said*. Do you think that is good advice? Why or why not?
4. The author says that a direct quote "should be the exact words of the speaker." Can you think of any circumstances in which this would not be true?
5. The author describes some routine types of news stories (meetings, speeches, weather, etc.). What other types of stories can you think of that the author did not include?

FURTHER READING

Johnson, C. (2005). *21st Century Feature Writing*. Boston: Allyn and Bacon.

The Missouri Group. (2004). *Telling the Story: The Convergence of Print, Broadcast, and Online Media* (2nd ed.). New York: Bedford/St. Martin's.

Mitchell, C. C., & West, M. D. (1996). *The News Formula*. New York: St. Martin's Press.

Yopp, J. J., & Haller, B. (2005). *An Introduction to News Reporting: A Beginning Journalist's Guide*. Boston: Allyn and Bacon.

WEBSITES

National Scholastic Press Association: **www.studentpress.org**

Poynter Institute: **www.poynter.org**

Society of Professional Journalists: **www.spj.org.**

EXERCISES

A Note to Students: The following section contains a variety of exercises for news and feature writing. You should follow your instructor's directions in completing them. Some of the exercises are written in sentence fragments; others are written in complete sentences, often in narrative form. If you are assigned to write news stories from the exercises in this section, you should use the information but not the exact wording contained in the exercises (except for the direct quotes). Many of the exercises are badly written on purpose. It will be your job to rewrite the information you have so that it is better written than the exercise material.

5.1 Writing Leads

Write a lead paragraph from each set of facts.

CRASH

- Happened today at noon.
- Killed: Rufus N. Hebernowski, an Air Force major.
- Happened at the Super Shopping Mall, a huge new mall on the western edge of town.
- The jet aircraft he was piloting crashed.
- Fortunately, no one on the ground was injured or killed.
- 15 cars were destroyed in the mall's northern parking lot when the aircraft crashed into them.
- Hebernowski had no known connections locally. He was killed.
- He was stationed at Little Rock Air Force Base.

CITY COUNCIL

- City council met this morning.
- 10 percent increase in city property taxes.
- Increase will cause average taxes to go up by about $50 yearly.
- Higher rate takes effect at the first of next month.
- Tax will be used to pay for doubling the size of the city park.

UNIVERSITY RAISES

- Harold R. Drazsnzak, university vice president for finance.
- Made an announcement at a press conference on the front steps of the university Administration Building.
- He said that all faculty and staff will get 15 percent pay raises.
- Will take effect this fall.
- Said the raise is possible because of increased revenues from the state.
- "Without a doubt, our faculty is long overdue to get a raise," he said.
- First raise for the faculty in two years.

JOURNALISM STUDENTS MEET

- Journalism Student Association met today at noon. About 200 students attended.
- Meeting began with Pledge of Allegiance, followed by a group song: "America the Beautiful."
- Journalism Student Association treasurer Rufus L. McSnorkel reported that the organization has a balance in its bank account of $725.35.
- Members voted to hold their next regular meeting two weeks from today.

- Members decided to organize a boycott of all journalism classes tomorrow to protest university tuition increase. Tuition is supposed to go up by 10 percent beginning in the fall semester.
- David S. Kuykendall, Journalism Student Association president, said: "We are confident that all journalism students will boycott all classes."

Hint: Do not try to put all of the available information into the lead. Be selective. Use proper style and copy-editing symbols. Double-check facts and spelling of proper names before turning your story in. Copy-editing symbols can be found in Appendix A.

5.2 Writing Leads

Write a lead paragraph from each set of facts.

PLANT ACCIDENT

- Duane LaChance, 53, of Petal, a pipe fitter employed by Gross Engineers.
- Company based in Petal, Miss.
- LaChance suffered third-degree burns and was listed in serious condition tonight in the intensive care unit at Methodist Hospital.
- Happened 3 P.M. today at Petal Municipal Power Plant, 222 Power Drive.
- LaChance installing new pipes on the roof of the plant when he accidentally touched a power line carrying 15,000 volts with a wrench.
- Source for this information is Henry Rosen, project manager for Gross Engineers.

MCCARTNEY ILLNESS

- Peter McCartney, famous rock singer.
- Entered Riverside Hospital for exploratory throat surgery today.
- Voice had been reduced to a whisper following Bennett Auditorium performance in front of capacity crowd of 1,000 fans tonight.
- Checked in the hospital late tonight; surgery is scheduled tomorrow.

PEROT WORLD

- Press conference held at University Administration Building.
- Ross Perot, Texas billionaire, held the press conference. Press conference held in third-floor conference room.
- Announced plans to buy local City Park and convert it into a theme park.
- Park will be called Perot World.

BOE MEETING

- Hattiesburg Board of Education met this morning. All members were present.
- Assistant Superintendent Max Hoemmeldorfer reported that enrollment this school year dropped by 200 students to 1,050.
- "This is the third year we've lost enrollment. The future looks bleak," Hoemmeldorfer said.
- Board accepted report and then passed a group of new rules proposed by the administration.

- New rules will prohibit female students from wearing miniskirts and will prohibit all students from wearing blue jeans. Male students will not be allowed to wear their hair below their ears.
- Board then accepted a low bid from Farmer's Dairy to provide milk to the schools at one-half cent a pint.

Hint: Do not try to put all of the available information into the lead. Be selective. Use proper style and copy-editing symbols. Double-check facts and spelling of proper names before turning your story in. Copy-editing symbols can be found in Appendix A.

5.3 Writing Leads

Write a lead paragraph from each set of facts.

FACULTY IN PLANE CRASH

- Associate Professor of Rural Sociology John Dumont and associate professor of English George Johnson, both from Backwater State University.
- Were returning Thursday night from separate conferences in New York City.
- Were aboard the same TWA jet.
- Crashed on takeoff at Kennedy International Airport.
- 45 passengers and crew members aboard. Five persons were killed.
- Two from Backwater escaped injury.

You are a reporter for the Backwater State student newspaper, *The Backwash*.

MAILER SPEAKS

- Noted author Norman Mailer, winner of the Pulitzer Prize.
- Spoke at 4:30 P.M. in Room 111 of the William Oxley Thomson Memorial Library Sunday.
- Told his audience of 67, mostly English students:
- "You can't be a great writer by imitating the styles of prize-winning authors. You've got to get out and sample life, learn how other people live, and then let your inner feelings pour out. These parodies they assign in college English courses are a bunch of hogwash."

PROFESSOR WINS AWARD

- The Freedoms Foundation at Valley Forge announced its annual George Washington Honor Medal winners.
- At ceremony in Pennsylvania last week.
- Among the 32 winners was Clement Crabtree, a professor of horticulture.
- Crabtree was cited for his essay called "Plan for Peace," in which he urged distribution of free packets of red, white, and blue flower seeds in foreign nations.

Hint: Do not try to put all of the available information into the lead. Be selective. Use proper style and copy-editing symbols. Double-check facts and spelling of proper names before turning your story in. Copy-editing symbols can be found in Appendix A.

5.4 Leads, Second Paragraphs

Write a lead and second paragraph for each of the following sets of information.

CURRICULUM CHANGES

- Recent study showed only 15 percent of students took a foreign language course and only 20 percent took a math course while at the University.
- University president announces changes in requirements for graduation.
- Students entering next fall must take one math, computer science, and foreign language course.
- President: "We feel that these new course requirements will allow us to turn out better-educated persons."
- President's name is French English.

ARREST

- Cathy Bensen, 22-year-old senior.
- Daughter of locally prominent attorney Jim Bensen, 211 Green Grove Drive.
- Mother, Sharon Bensen, lives in Canada.
- Arrested for driving under the influence of alcohol for third time in six months last night.
- Cathy was this year's Homecoming Queen; has been cheerleader; straight-A student.
- Going to Vanderbilt University for graduate studies in biology.

RECORD WEATHER

- It is warm.
- Students keep talking about the unseasonable weather. Your editor tells you to find out what the temperature is and to write a story about the weather.
- You call the Port Columbus weather office and learn that the high yesterday was 82 degrees at 3:30 P.M.
- It was the hottest temperature for this date since 1888.

5.5 Leads, Second Paragraphs

Write a lead and a second paragraph for each of the following sets of information.

PROTEST

- Group of citizens angry because University biology class is teaching evolution.
- Group led by Wilbur Straking, pastor of the Ever-Faithful Church of the Living Water.
- Straking: "I plan to lead a group of 25 dedicated Christians to the state capital next Monday to speak with legislators about this problem. We believe the teaching of evolution is against the principles of this Christian country, and we want to put a stop to it."
- Class they're objecting to is taught by Laura Cliff, associate professor of biology; she wouldn't comment on the group's charges.
- Neither would University president.

LAWSUIT

- Suit filed in Circuit Court today; for $100,000.
- Against Amburn's Produce Market.
- By Ellie Maston, 313 Journey Road.
- Charges market with negligence; suit says green beans left on floor of market; she walked through them and slipped and broke her hip.
- Suit says she "suffered permanent bodily and mental injuries, incurred medical expenses and lost income."
- Accident happened April 1 this year.

AGREEMENT ANNOUNCED

- Clyde Parris, president of Ambrose Steel Company, and Charles Pointer, president of United Steelworkers Local 923, make joint announcement.
- Company and union have reached collective bargaining agreement.
- Strike set for midnight tonight has been called off.
- Strike would have stopped production at Ambrose and put 457 steelworkers off the job.
- Terms of agreement will be read tonight to a meeting of the union, Pointer says.
- Parris says contract includes "substantial wage agreement" but won't say how much; that will be announced tonight.
- Union will vote on contract next week.
- Pointer says contract "the best we can get out of the company."

5.6 Leads, Second Paragraphs

Write a lead and a second paragraph for each of the following sets of information.

MALPRACTICE SUIT

- Two doctors being sued for malpractice; Barney Olive and Stephen Rogers, both of whom practice at Riverside Hospital.
- William Hamilton, lawyer for plaintiff, Bertie McNicholls, 623 Leanto Road.
- Hamilton, beginning final arguments in case, has heart attack.
- Quick work of Olive and Rogers save his life.
- Hamilton, 73, now recovering at Riverside Hospital.
- Trial to resume next week.

ALUMNI FESTIVAL

- University Alumni Association planning spring festival for April.
- Games, contests will be held on football field.
- Barbeque lunch and exhibition baseball game.
- All proceeds to go to school library, plus alumni hoping to raise more money through pledges.
- Date depends on whether or not baseball team makes it to playoffs this year.
- Alumni president Bobby Don Willis: "This kind of activity is one of the positive things we can do to make this university a better educational institution."

WEBSITE POLICY

- Lots of people at Backwater University are building websites.
- University says 50 to 100 people using University connection to establish websites.
- University has looked at these websites and found that many contain pornographic pictures and other material.
- University announcing policy to inspect and approve websites before they are put up using the University's web connection.
- Sperling Sprinter, University public relations officer: "This type of stuff isn't good for Backwater University. We had to put a stop to it."
- Art Waddell, associate professor in the art department.
- Waddell is planning to sue University if it tries to enforce the policy.

5.7 Writing News Stories

Write a three- or four-paragraph news story based on the following information.
   An accident report gives the following information:

- Incident: Two-car accident on Hwy 14 and Gilmore Ave.
- Time and date: 2:45 AM, Oct. 8
- Involved: Carol Gleson, 19, Saint Mary's College Student
- Home town: Minneapolis, MN.
- Driving a 1983 Toyota Tercel; Northbound on Hwy 14.
- Minor injuries: Treated and released from Winona Hospital.
- Involved: Candy Floss, 17, Daughter of Daryl and Stacy Floss, 1352 Broadway, Winona, MN. Driving a 1990 Chevrolet Camaro; Westbound on Gilmore Avenue. Drugs were recovered from the Floss car. Did not require hospitalization. Released to parents at police station.

In an interview with State Police Trooper William Troutner at the scene of the accident, the officer says, "Y'know the girl who walked away was the daughter of the president of the local school board? She just pulled right out in front of the kid from Saint Mary's. I'll tell you one thing that's just a shame, she had more drugs in her car than you could sell in a month. You don't use my name. You media ghouls are all alike."

5.8 Writing News Stories

Write a news story from the following set of facts.

CHICKEN TRUCK CAUSES PILE-UP

25 people got hurt. A pile-up happened on McFarland Blvd. at about 6 in the evening. It was yesterday.
   It happened at the corner of McFarland and 15th. Police say eleven cars were involved. Sergeant John Jones tells you that a semi-truck carrying chickens (laying hens) made an illegal left turn causing the accident.
   The chicken truck driver got hurt. His name—Jeff Johnson. He's 45. Ambulance transported him to DCH. He had bruises and a possible broken ankle. He lives in Alberta City with his wife, three children. Jones reports this.

The chickens, police say, may be as many as 300, also suffered. The truck turned on its side making a sharp turn. At least 30 are dead. Many others trapped in the vehicle until firemen arrived. Several, as many as 40, remain at large.

Jones also notes that Sarah Bernell was hurt. She, at age 63, is a retired local kindergarten teacher. Miss Bernell was riding in the car driven by her nephew, Mike Kenyon. She was taken to the hospital.

The animals are the property of the chicken company, Alabama Poultry, Inc., and should be returned if found, Jones stresses.

Clarence DiMotta reports Johnson is in good condition. Clarence is the hospital spokesperson. Also, the teacher has a slight concussion and is also in good condition.

Jones says "It was the biggest pile-up I've ever seen. Lots and lots of smashed bumpers but the worst part was the screams of the chickens. Those things sure do make a lotta noise, you know."

The chickens were on the way to one of the company's new farms near Gadsden.

Only other injuries to the 23 others in the cars were bruises. None admitted.

The chicken company pres. Carlton Fitzsimmons reports the dead and missing chickens are worth over 700 dollars. Each chicken was insured for 10 bucks. His company's chickens—the farm holds about 20,000—supply eggs to IGA stores across the south.

Other damages to the 12 cars in the accident were minor, police report said.

Several smashed eggs were also found in the wreckage of the truck. "It was so hot out there I thought we might have fried eggs for dinner" Jones adds.

5.9 Writing News Stories

Write a news story from the following set of facts.

PROSPER

Prosper is a mining town of 909 people in the northeast corner of Crocker County. Since the deep-shaft coal mine was opened in 1901, it has provided a major source of employment for the town's people, and in the last 18 years has brought more than 800 people from other towns to work every day at the mine, United Coal Company's Mine No. 3, known locally as Hellpit. The company announced yesterday that the mine will close in two weeks for an indefinite period. Since 1980, when Prosper was incorporated and became eligible for coal tax revenue, its budget has risen from $40,000 to $300,000 ($125,000 in coal severance tax monies, $125,000 in federal matching money for capital improvements). Mayor Lester Jenkins tells you that "With the mine closed, our revenue is just about gone." Some tax money will continue to dribble in as stockpiles of coal are depleted, but Wilma Foster, the city clerk, foresees a cutback for the fiscal year, which starts in 30 days, to $60,000. "That will cover essential services like police protection and utilities at city hall and at the new ball park," she adds. Councilman Ed Barnes tells you that most of the coal money went into building projects. "And we've got the city hall and the park paid for, so at least we're not in debt." The town council will talk about a new budget at its meeting tomorrow night. The mine employed 1,000 people. The shaft is a quarter mile deep, the deepest in the state. Company officials cannot be reached by phone, but a statement delivered to you gives the reason for the closing as a severe cutback in demand for coal because of a shutdown in manufacturing nationwide. It quotes Wilson Standridge, company president: "We hope to see an increase in demand, but until we do, the mine will remain sealed."

5.10 Writing Meeting Stories

Write a news story from the following set of facts.

- City school board met last night; big issue on their agenda was to select a new principle for Haraway High School.

- Board did some other things like approve some tenure applications for about a dozen teachers.

- Most of the debate centered on the two finals for the Haraway job: Juli McCorvey, who is currently the assistant principal at Haraway and has held that job for six years; Mike Coleman, the principle of a high school in Louisiana.

- Over 40 people applied for the job; search committee of the school board narrowed the choices down to these two.

- Harley Duncan: "We have two fine candidates here. I find it very difficult to choose between them. Both of them have accomplished a lot during their careers, and I believe they each would do a good job for us at Haraway." Harley is a member of the board, weighs 270 pounds and speaks very slowly.

- Crowd of 200 people there; some supporters of McCorvey, some not. McCorvey and Coleman were not in the room; they were waiting in another room in the city board offices while the debate was going on.

- Alex McCreless, 1615 Ireland Dr.: "I have a child who is about to graduate from Haraway, and while I have nothing against Ms. McCorvey, I think it high time we got some new blood into our school system. We need some fresh thinking and new ideas. I think we need a change." Alex is a housewife with two other children in elementary school.

- Taylor Whitson: "I have a daughter in the 10th grade at Haraway, and we have been helped a great deal by Mrs. McCorvey. Haraway is a good school, and I don't see . . . I mean, like I think that's because Mrs. McCorvey has worked so hard. I think she deserves this chance to be in charge and that she will do a good job." Taylor has a daughter in the 10th grade at Haraway and lives at 2121 Blackoak Drive. He works for the local Alcoa Aluminum plant.

- Darren McGarity: "Let me tell you something. My son done real well because of the extra time and attention that Mrs. McCorvey give him. He was having some problems in the 9th grade, and she was able to figure out what help he need and got him that help. He's going to graduate in June, and its because of her. She deserves that job." He was real excited and talked real fast. McGarity is the owner of McGarity Lawn Service.

- About a dozen other people spoke, three of them in favor of Coleman and the rest in favor of McCorvey, thus proving where the crowd stood; board voted after an hour of debate and discussion to hire Coleman; vote was 5 to 4.

- Coleman was born and grew up and has lived most of his life in Louisiana and has a bachelor's and master's degrees from Backwater State University in Tennessee. He is the principal of Sandy Bar High School in Sandy Bar, LA. He's done that for about 10 years.

5.11 Writing Meeting Stories

Write a news story from the following set of facts.

CITY COUNCIL

Here's what happened at the city council meeting last night.

The meeting started about five minutes late because city council member Harvey Haddix couldn't find a place to park. He came rushing in and made a comment about how the city police were going to have to crack down on illegal parkers. That brought a laugh from the overflow crowd of over two hundred people there. Mayor Ray Sadecki called the meeting to order, and Wilber Mizell, the minister of the Vinegar Bend Baptist Church, started the meeting with prayer. The minutes of the last meeting of the council were read, and no one had any additions or corrections to them.

The first item of business was a report from the Metropolitan Zoning Commission. Bobby Thompson, who is the chairman of the Zoning Commission, said the commission had met two days ago to consider a request by a local developer to move a cemetery so that he can build a supermarket. The developer's name is Carl Erskine. The cemetery is located in the 2800 block of Forbes Street, much of which is zoned for commercial purposes now. Erskine told the council that he will pay all the costs of having the graves relocated in Peaceful Rest Cemetery, which is located about a mile away from the present site. "I think rezoning will be good for the neighborhood and good for the city," Erskine said. "There's not another supermarket for at least a mile and a half in any direction." Thompson said: "We've studied the traffic patterns along Forbes Street, and we don't believe the supermarket will cause any problems." After several more questions by various council members, the mayor asked for any questions or comments from those in the audience. About twenty people spoke, and all but two of them were against the rezoning. It took about an hour. Here are some of the comments:

Early Wynn, 122 Forbes Street: "This thing is going to destroy our neighborhood. It's pretty quiet there now, but if you get this thing in there, it's going to turn noisy."

Dick Groat, 1811 Polo Grounds Road: "Nobody on my street wants the supermarket. We have plenty of places to go to shop. We don't need this. Besides, some of those graves are pretty old, and I don't think it would be the same if you moved them."

Sarah Yawkey, 555 Bosox Drive: "I just can't believe you'd do this. Anybody who'd do this would steal the dimes off a dead man's eyes."

Walt Dropo, 611 Forbes Street and president of the Forbes Street Residents Association: "We've been fighting this thing for two years now. All the zoning commission did was study the traffic patterns. They didn't consider what it would do to the neighborhood. Besides, that cemetery has some of the oldest graves in the city in it— some of those people helped found this city. I'm sure that if you tried to move some of those stones, they would crumble in your hands. I can promise you that we will mount a campaign to recall any council member who votes for this thing." (That comment drew lots of applause from the people who were there.)

Harry Walker, 610 Forbes Street: "I'm afraid Walt's gone overboard on this one, like he usually does. I think our neighborhood needs a supermarket. We've got lots of people who have trouble getting around. Walt's one of these people who's against anything that is progress. He just wants to get some publicity for himself."

When the speakers were done, the council voted 5–2 against the rezoning petition. At that the crowd cheered, and most of them filed out, leaving a small audience of only about 35 or 40 people.

The next item of business was a one-cent sales tax proposed by councilwoman Wilma Rudolph. "The city desperately needs this money," said Rudolph, "or there is a chance that we'll have to start laying off workers next year." Mr. Joe Black, the city treasurer, agreed, saying the city's financial condition was pretty bad. A one-cent sales tax would raise about $400,000 for the city next year, and not only would that mean there would be no layoffs, but it's possible that the city could expand some services, such as having garbage pick-ups twice a week instead of just once a week, he said. "Besides, we figure that such a tax will only cost the average family in the city about $75 a year," Black pointed out. Mayor Sadecki is against the tax. He said, "I believe the people are taxed too heavily now. I don't believe they want this. I think they want to look at our budget and see where we can cut back." But the majority of the council didn't agree with the mayor, and they voted for the tax 5–2. Those voting for the tax were Rudolph, Haddix, Sam Jones, Eddie Matthews, and Lew Burdette; those against were Sadecki and Bill Mazeroski.

The last item of business was a proposal from councilman Mazeroski to license morticians in the city. "The state gives us the power to do this, and I think we should take advantage of it," he said. He said his proposal would assess an annual license fee that morticians would have to pay every year. Mazeroski said, "We've got more than 30 mortuaries in the city now, and assessing a fee from them would bring in a considerable amount of revenue." His bill calls for a $150 fee per mortuary per year. Several morticians were in the audience and spoke against Mazeroski's proposals. Don Blasingame, who owns Blasingame Mortuary and who is president of the city's Mortician Society, said: "We don't believe Mr. Mazeroski is correct when he says the state gives the city the power to do this. The state licenses morticians and gives the city the power to enforce this licensing procedure if it chooses to do so. Otherwise, the state enforces the licensing. I believe that if the city did this, it would just have to turn the money over to the state." Harold Reece, the city attorney, said there is some question about this in the law, and he has asked the state attorney general to give an opinion on it. Mazeroski said, "I don't believe we should wait for the opinion. I think we should go ahead and do it." Burdette made a motion to table the proposal, and that passed by a vote of six to one.

With that, Mayor Sadecki adjourned the meeting.

You find out later that when councilman Haddix got to his car after the meeting, there was a parking ticket on it.

Hint: Make a list of the things that happened during the meeting. Which do you think is the most important one? Why? The thing you think is the most important is what you should put in the lead paragraph.

5.12 Writing Speech Stories

Write a speech story from the following information.

- Graduation ceremonies at Barnaby College; 275 students graduated this year, Barnaby's second-highest total in their history. Barnaby College is a liberal arts college founded in 1921 and is affiliated with the Presbyterian Church USA. Number of students enrolled this year was 1,133.

- Graduation speaker: Kay McDavid. She is an alumna of Barnaby College, having graduated in 1985. She was a business major at Barnaby while she was there. Has an MBA from Harvard.

- McDavid is president of Flyover Airlines. This is a small air carrier based in Minot, South Dakota, that serves more than 30 cities in the upper Midwest. The airline flies mostly small planes, the largest holding 25 passengers. Recently, Flyover has begun a new service: air rides on demand, or what they call AirTaxi. Using small, extremely efficient new jets, the airline will fly someone immediately to a destination for about 20 percent more than the regularly scheduled fare. The new service got Flyover named as the Small Airliner of the Year by International Airlines Magazine last year. McDavid was named as the Airline Executive of the year.

- The following are excerpts from her speech:

  "Congratulations, graduates. It's a great feeling. Believe me, I know. Not too long ago, although longer than I would like to admit, I was sitting right there—right there where you are. I was proud of what I had accomplished after four years at Barnaby."

  "But I was scared, too. Scared that I was going to walk off this campus and nobody would notice. Nobody would pay attention to what I had to offer. You know something—I was right. Practically nobody did. I couldn't understand why I didn't get the job I wanted, why I wasn't living where I wanted to live, why I couldn't get people to pay attention."

  "I soon realized that it was mostly my fault. I made the mistake of thinking the rest of the world should be like the campus of Barnaby where people cared about you no matter what you did or who you were. It took me about six months to realize the world was very different—that you had to have something the world wanted. Only then would you get noticed. I had to change my plans."

  "For me the change was graduate school and trying to see the world differently. For you it might be something different, but I predict that if you are serious about contributing something to your community and making something out of your life, your plans—whatever they are—will change in the next two years, too."

  "The key to our success at Flyover is that we tried to think differently and figure out what people really wanted. Strange as it seems, that's not the way most people do things in the airline industry. While most of the rest of the world has changed, the airline system is still the same system of hubs that we had 30 or 40 years ago. In the South, they say if you want to go to heaven, you have to connect through Atlanta. But if someone wants to fly from Tampa to Mobile, why send them to Atlanta? And why tell them they have to wait until this afternoon to do it? That used to make economic sense, but in this day of increasing technology and decreasing costs, it doesn't. Consequently, at Flyover, we worked with developers to manufacture small, extremely efficient planes that we could fly at the lowest possible cost. Then we used those plans to offer a service that we believe can revolutionize the industry. Just as the Internet has revolutionized communication by putting it back into the hands of consumers, we want to put the airline industry back into the hands of the customers."

"Will we be successful? Frankly, I don't know. Check with us in two or three or five years. We're still tinkering with the right business formula, but we're doing something else, too. We're having fun. We're shaking things up. We keep getting told by the big airline executives that our idea is a bad one, and it's bound to take us under. That scared me at first, but now, I realize I'm not the one that should be scared. They're defending an outdated system, and they know it."

"We're building something new, and that's the fun part. If you get a chance to do that in your life, count yourself as blessed—truly blessed."

"So, graduates, be creative, have fun—and above all, let this day be yours. If you do that, all the others will follow."

5.13 Writing Obituaries

Write an obituary story from the following information.

- Velda Elizabeth Fletcher.
- Noted local dietitian and church and community volunteer.
- Graveside services Saturday at two o'clock.
- Survived by her parents, Gina and Vandergriff Fletcher; brother and sister-in-law, Vandergriff and Davida Fletcher; sister Vonda Fletcher Reed; and various nieces and nephews.
- Burial at Forest Cemetery off Lexington Road in Midville.
- In lieu of flowers, the family requests that memorials be made to Mission of Mercy.
- Miss Fletcher, 47, died Tuesday night at Park West Hospital after a medical emergency situation.
- Member of Little Springs Methodist since she was 11 years old, in the Adult Choir and throughout the years participated in numerous missions projects. At one time, she served as a Sunday school department director in the singles program.
- Devoted volunteer with Mission of Mercy, a Midville-based nonprofit group that collects and distributes school supplies and Christmas gifts to children in the area. She had worked with the ministry since it was launched in 1996.
- Longtime cast member in the Midville Nativity Pageant.
- Gave her time to many charitable activities, especially Interfaith Health Clinic, and was a member of the Junior League.
- Worked as a clinical dietitian and diabetes educator at Dialysis Clinic Inc. in South Midville.
- Spent many years in management in the dieticians department at the University of West State Medical Center and also had worked in private practice.
- Belonged to national, regional, and local dieticians and diabetes-educator professional organizations.
- Graduated in 1980 from Midville High School.
- Earned her bachelor of science degree in 1979 and her master of science degree in 1985 from the University of West State.
- Active in Alpha Chi Omega and at the Wesley Center.
- An enthusiastic supporter of all UT sports.

Interview with her sister: "Velda always had time for anyone. She devoted herself to her work and her family and her church. My children always felt like she was their second mother—sometimes their first (laughs). She just never said no to anything or anyone that she thought was worthwhile. We are going to miss her very, very much."

5.14 Writing Crime News

Write an inverted pyramid news story based on the following information.

An arrest report gives the following information:

- Incident: An assault and battery at Watter's Hall.
- Time and date: 2:45 A.M., February 26, 1991.
- Involved: Sharron Peters, 19, Saint Mary's College Student.
- Home town: Minneapolis, MN. Daughter of Wm. Peters, SMC Vice-President of Student Life.
- Minor injuries: Treated and released from Winona Hospital.
- Involved: Thomas Harnell 21, Son of Sherman and Tricia Harnell, 1352 Broadway, Winona, MN. Reported driving a 1990 Chevrolet Camaro. Arrested on Gilmore Avenue at 2:50 A.M. and charged with assault and battery.

As police led Harnell away, he shouted, "She owed me money, man! Those Saint Mary's brats think they own us."

In an interview with State Police Trooper William Troutner at the scene of the arrest, the officer says, "Y'know the girl who got attacked was the daughter of the vice-president of Saint Mary's? I'll tell you one thing that's just a shame, she had more drugs in her purse than you could sell in a month. Because we were on private property, we couldn't make an arrest. You don't use my name. You media ghouls are all alike."

5.15 Writing Crime News

Write a news story from the following set of facts.

MURDER

Francie Franklin, proprietor of a small bakery in Pleasant Grove, was killed during the night. Police Chief Wilburn Cole tells you over the phone that Miss Franklin did not deliver a wedding cake as expected this morning, and when the bride's mother went to the bake shop in Miss Franklin's home to check, she found the front door open and a display case smashed. "She didn't go no further," Cole says. "When we got there we found Miss Francie in the kitchen. She was shot dead." The little shop is in a shambles when you go by to check, and you note the contrast to the neat, clean operation the woman normally kept. You can't find the chief, but the radio dispatcher reads this memo to you: "Francie's body was taken to Smith's Funeral Parlor where they'll do an autopsy. It must have happened before midnight because her television set was still on, and she always turns it off after the late movie. She was shot once in the chest, and her pistol is missing from the drawer under the cash register. Money was scattered around, but they probably got away with some." Kenton County Homicide Investigator Kelton Kelly says she was shot with a .22 caliber bullet and that they didn't find any fingerprints. However, a strange, unidentified red wool ski cap was found under the body. Kenton County Coroner Ransom Cranwell tells you that death was from a single gunshot wound and that there were no other injuries. "It was crazy the way they messed up the place though," he adds. "She was always so proud of it. She was just an old maid who loved everyone and everyone loved her." Arrangements are pending. No known survivors. Age 68. Address, 504 Ash St. She started the business 20 years ago under the name Francie's Fancies. She recently expanded by building a small service area at the front of the house.

5.16 Writing Crime Stories

Write a news story from the following set of facts.

IN THE COUNTY COURT OF FORREST COUNTY, MISSISSIPPI

CAUSE NO. 37,733

VICTORIA FULTON VICUNA,   VERSUS   MILTON JEROME FINE,
      PLAINTIFF   DEFENDANT

COMPLAINT

Plaintiff, Victoria Fulton Vicuna, sues the Defendant, Milton Jerome Fine, on the following grounds:

1. Plaintiff is an adult resident citizen of United States of America, presently domiciled in New York City, New York.
2. Defendant, Milton Jerome Fine, is an adult resident citizen of Forrest County, Mississippi, residing at 113 South 22nd Avenue, Hattiesburg, Mississippi.
3. That on or about the first part of May, 1989, the Plaintiff left her dog, one Chinese Shar-Pei male dog (named Ming-Ming-Jai) in the care and custody of the Defendant. The dog was left with the Defendant on a temporary basis and at no time was the dog intended to be given to the Defendant.
4. But since the above referenced date, the Plaintiff has repeated demands for said dog, has offered to pay reasonable boarding expenses, and has agreed to reimburse the Defendant for any veterinarian medicine and expenses which he has incurred.
5. That Plaintiff claims that she is the rightful owner of aforementioned dog pursuant to the Certificate of Pedigree which is attached hereto and marked as Exhibit A.
6. Plaintiff is entitled to immediate possession of the above referenced dog, yet the Defendant unlawfully withholds possession of the dog from the Plaintiff within the jurisdiction of this Court.
7. Plaintiff tenders herein a surety bond in the amount of $4,000.00 which amount is equal to double the value of the dog.

WHEREFORE, Plaintiff prays that this Court will examine the allegations of this Complaint and all documentary evidence exhibited with this Complaint, will satisfy itself that Plaintiff has a prima facie claim to possession of the dog described in the Complaint and will order the immediate issuance of a Writ of Replevin conditioned upon Plaintiff's posting of the Security Bond described above, and will further schedule a hearing to determine the rights of the parties to the possession of the described dog within the time and manner provided by law.

Respectfully submitted,
Victoria Fulton Vicuna

5.17 Writing Courtroom Stories

Write a story for tomorrow morning's newspaper.

RUSSEL

Last New Year's Eve, John Page was found shot to death in his home. At first, the police and the coroner ruled the death a suicide, but that changed when they later found that Page had withdrawn a large amount of money from his bank account on the day that he died. Page was the owner of Page Auto Parts Store. He was also a real estate developer, a deacon in the First Baptist Church, a city councilman, and generally thought to be one of the wealthiest citizens in town. The amount of money Page withdrew from the bank that day was $10,000. Page's wife told the police that he had been depressed for some weeks before his death, but she didn't believe that he committed suicide.

Page's death and all of the subsequent events, including the police investigation and the trial, received a great amount of publicity from the city's newspapers and television stations.

A month after Page's death, the police arrested William Russel and charged him with first-degree murder. William Russel is owner of Russel Realty, and even though they were competitors in business, Page and Russel were known to be good friends. They grew up together, and their families had been friends. Police said that several clues pointed to Russel as the murderer. Russel had been seen leaving the Page home late New Year's Eve by a neighbor who had been walking his dog. The bank provided the police with serial numbers of the money it had given to Page, and most of that money was found in Russel's house.

During the trial, which began a month ago, it came out that Russel had been having an affair with Page's wife, Genevieve. The district attorney, Hix Bradfield, tried to paint Russel as a desperate man whose business was failing and who was blackmailing Page. The key witness in his case was Page's wife, who said that Russel had threatened Page by saying he would "tell everybody in town about your slutty little wife" if he wouldn't pay. She said Page was worried that his reputation in the community would be damaged and it would mean the end to his political career. She said he had been planning to run for Congress next year.

Russel took the stand in his own defense and denied killing Page, and he denied having an affair with Page's wife. He said Page had asked him to keep the money because of a business deal he was about to make, but he didn't know any of the details. He said Page had been despondent because he had found out that his wife had been having affairs with other men. "I felt sorry for John," he said. "He married a little slut. I suspect that she was blackmailing him." Russel said he went to talk with Page on New Year's Eve but found him too depressed to talk. When he left, Russel said, Page was drinking heavily. Russel said he didn't tell the police about the visit or the money because "I got scared. It was a stupid thing to do."

Yesterday, after three days of deliberating, the jury found Russel guilty. Russel broke down and cried when he heard the verdict.

This morning, Judge Cecil Andrews sentenced Russel to death by lethal injection. In handing out the sentence, Andrews said, "This was a heinous crime—one that merits swift and severe retribution. The victim was a leading citizen in the community, a man who had made many contributions. In a cold-blooded way, the defendant ended his life while posing as his good friend. He has shown no remorse for his deed and has, in fact, lied about it. He showed no mercy to his victim, and I, in turn, can show no mercy to him." Russel, who looked pale and puffy-eyed when he came into the courtroom, had to be helped out.

Outside the court, Regina Wright, Russel's lawyer, said she would file an immediate appeal of both the verdict and the sentence. "Mr. Russel didn't get a fair trial.

The massive amount of pretrial publicity surrounding this case prevented that. Early on, we asked for a change of venue, but that motion was denied. There was just no way that a person accused of killing a popular man like John Page was going to get a fair trial in this town." Asked about the sentence, Wright said, "I just can't believe he was given the death penalty. I believe Judge Andrews had it in for my client. He should have disqualified himself because he was a friend of John Page. He should have granted our change-of-venue motion. He did neither, and then he winds up sentencing my client to death."

After the sentencing, Bradfield said, "The sentence was a harsh one—not the one we would have recommended. We would have preferred a life-without-parole sentence, but I'll go along with what the judge said. It was an awful crime, and John Page was one of our leading citizens."

You try to get a comment from Mrs. Page, but her attorney, Frank Story, tells you she left immediately after the sentencing for New York to discuss writing a book about the trial and her experiences.

5.18 Writing Courtroom Stories

Write a news story from the following set of facts.

ATHLETE LAWSUIT

Several months ago, last fall, the local newspaper printed a story about your university's basketball team. The story was written by the sports editor, William Sonoma, and it said that five members of the team were being investigated in a cheating and grade-fixing scheme and might not be returning to the team.

Here's what part of the story said:

> Sources within the university said the players conspired with the registrars at their high schools and junior colleges to have their transcripts reflect that they took courses they did not take and that in some of the courses they did take, they made passing rather than failing grades.
>
> A spokesperson for the athletic department would have no comment on the investigation.
>
> "The policy of the university is that student records are a private matter," John Balk of the athletic department said. "We can neither confirm nor deny any of the details about this story."

The story made quite a splash. Newspapers and television stations all over the state carried it, and even ESPN's SportsCenter ran a couple of stories.

The newspaper continued to run stories about the matter for several days, but the names of the students under investigation were never revealed.

A month later, the athletic department announced that two players would not be returning to the team this year. They were Tad Rankin and André Johnson, two stars who had been recruited from a large high school in the state's largest city. The announcement that they would not return did not say why they would not return. Reporters asked whether this had anything to do with the cheating investigation, but the athletic department people would not comment on that. All of the details of the investigation was dredged up again by the newspaper.

Right after the first of the year, three members of the basketball team—Pettus Ford, Joseph Garfield, and Marcus Van Buren—sued the newspaper for invasion of privacy. The suit asked for an apology by the paper, and it asked that the university be ordered to state the names of the players who were being investigated. It also asked for $100,000 in damages from the papers.

Here's what Pettus Ford said at the time the suit was filed: "We were treated very unfairly by the newspaper when it talked about five basketball players. There are only fourteen of us on the team, and we had to spend the next few months telling people that we were not one of those who was being investigated. The university did not give us much help either. We think our reputations have been tarnished and our privacy has been invaded by these stories, and we want the newspaper and the court to set things right. We want people to know that we were not the ones being investigated."

The players' attorney, O'Banin Dirsky, said at the time that precedents in the law provided for suits such as this one. He cited the part of privacy law that deals with embarrassing private facts. "A member of a small group who has been unfairly tarnished by something that was said about the group has some recourse in the court," he said.

Today, a judge granted a motion for summary judgment, dismissing the case against the newspaper. Summary judgment occurs when a judge finds that no facts are in dispute and there is nothing to litigate. In a short opinion that the judge read in court, he said: "While the facts show that the plaintiffs were embarrassed by the newspaper stories, there is simply no legal basis for a suit against the newspaper, and the law offers them no relief. Life sometimes is not fair, and there is nothing the law can do about it." The judge's name is Sheila Latham.

Dirsky: "My clients are very disappointed with this ruling. I believe that they had a legitimate case that should have been tried on its merits. Unfortunately, the judge did not think so."

Sonoma: "This is exactly what we had been hoping for. This thing has taken up a lot more time than it should have and so far has cost the newspaper about $10,000 in legal fees. I'm glad the judge put an end to it."

Ford: "None of us believe the judge gave this case a fair hearing. We still have this thing hanging over our heads, and we want to clear our names. We're going to talk with our lawyer about an appeal."

Randall Flowers, a friend of Ford who appeared outside the courtroom with him: "This is a travesty. To me, the judge's opinion showed her to be senile and in the pocket of the university. They didn't want any of this to come out so they can protect their precious image. They don't care about the players, just how they look."

5.19 Writing Weather Stories

Write a news story from the following set of facts.

SNOWSTORM

This is what you know by 6 p.m. on March 5:

Major late season snowstorm; 8" fell between midnight and 3 a.m.; unexpected, caught city by surprise; most forecasts evening before predicted some rain and sleet.

Art Carrie, meteorologist at local National Weather Service center: "We had been saying there was a slight possibility of snow, but the upper atmospheric temperature must have dropped more suddenly than we figured." Sounded slightly embarrassed and somewhat defensive.

Felicity Ryan, mayor: "I got a call from the police about 2 this morning telling me about the snow. We tried to get some plows and salting trucks out on the streets as soon as possible, but we weren't very successful. Some of our equipment was in for repairs. We figured it was safe to start doing that since it rarely, if ever, snows this late in the season. In fact, I can't recall a March snowstorm for many years."

Mayor is right; worst March snowstorm in 50 years; last one occurred in 1980 but accumulation only 1"; 1954 saw 12" fall on Mar. 1; this storm is historical record snowfall for city for this date; source of this info in National Weather Service center.

Wayne Tisdale, chief of police: "It's been a mess all day long. This city doesn't do well trafficwise when it snows anyway, and this one really caught us all off guard. Lots of people were on the road for no good reason. All of the roads in the city were officially closed until about 2 p.m. today. When that happens people shouldn't try to get out. For one thing, many auto insurance policies will not pay off when a driver has an accident on a road that has been officially closed. I'm afraid a lot of people are going to find that out the hard way today." Police reports indicate 119 accidents reported between midnight and 3 p.m.; dispatcher says on a clear day there are about twenty to thirty; tells you about Elmer, the guardian angel with the tow truck. "He really helped us and a lot of other people out today."

School superintendent Buddy McMartin says schools shut down today and tomorrow; decision about shutting down the rest of the week will be made tomorrow; if temperatures stay around freezing as predicted, that's probably what will happen. Local university also shut its doors; first time in 20 years that that has happened. You drove through the campus today and can describe what you saw.

National Association of City Planners national convention meeting in downtown Sheraton Inn; more than 800 city planners from around the country; today was last day of three-day national convention; many stuck here for extra day because airport closed. Melodie Goldstein, executive director of the association: "This has been a disappointment. Most of us were ready to go home, but even if we had been able to get to the airport, it would have been hard to make connections." Much of this part of the country is affected by this storm, and most airports experienced flight delays. You asked Goldstein how she thought the city responded to the storm, and she said, "Not very well. People around here don't seem to know how to handle it."

City Central Hospital emergency room spokesperson: "dramatic increase" in number of broken bones treated; 70 to 80 people treated for this by midday. "Usually we only have two or three at the most." Seven people treated for heart attacks or chest pains contracted while shoveling snow. One of these seven died, and two are in critical condition; hospital won't release names. Dr. Sandra Smith, local cardiologist, had this to say about shoveling snow: "Shoveling snow is one of the most strenuous activities you can undertake and under some of the worst conditions imaginable. You shouldn't try it unless you are used to doing that type of thing."

Delores Bunker estimates that fewer than half of the city's workforce made it to work today. She is executive director of the Chamber of Commerce. A spot check of some of the city's businesses is what she bases her estimate on. She says storm will mean substantial losses for many businesses, but usually such losses are made up by increased business when the storm is over. "We think people ought not to try to get out unless it's safe."

Elmer's Garage tow truck seen around the city streets today, pulling people out who had gotten themselves stuck. One woman who had been helped called you. "I was driving down 15th Street trying to get to work this morning. There was no one on the street. I hit my brakes and skidded into a ditch. The wheels just kept spinning. I sat there for a few minutes wondering how I was going to get out and whether or not I was going to freeze to death. Then I heard this truck coming along. Elmer pulled me out and had me back on the road in just a few minutes. And, you know, he wouldn't let me pay him anything." You talk with Elmer Burton, owner of Elmer's Garage. He estimates that he pulled out "fifty or sixty" cars from being stuck between about 6 a.m. and 1 p.m. You ask him what he charged for doing this and say he must have made a lot of money. "Naw, I didn't charge nuthin'. I just enjoyed helping people out. Besides, maybe next time when people need a tow, they'll remember old Elmer." He adds that one person he helped called him a "guardian angel." Has he done this before when it snows? "No, this is the first time. You don't get too many chances around here. But I'll probably do it again next time."

5.20 Writing Weather Stories

Write a news story from the following set of facts.

TORNADO

Yesterday afternoon was unseasonably warm for this time of year. Early in the afternoon, the temperature reached 70 degrees, and the people at the weather bureau became concerned. There was a lot of moisture in the air, and the conditions seemed just right for a tornado. At two o'clock, the bureau issued a tornado warning because of some buildup of moisture west of here.

At three P.M., after receiving several reports of funnel clouds, Lee Harper, chief meteorologist at the weather bureau, issued a tornado warning. Funnel clouds had been sighted just south of Midville, and there was one report that a barn had been damaged and some cows had been killed. The tornado watch was to stay in effect for one hour.

At 3:33 P.M., a tornado touched down on Cleveland Street, a street with a lot of businesses and homes on it. The tornado damaged the following businesses: the Cleveland Street branch of the Trust National Bank; Red Cedar's used car lot; the Jiffy-Kwik 24-hour food store; and the Big Bank Sound Record Shop, which is located in the same building as the food store. Also, several homes were damaged, including that of Robert T. Mellon, the mayor. The bank was being housed in a mobile home while a permanent structure was built. There was no damage to the building site, which was located nearby. The mobile home was lifted completely off its foundation, however, and was totally destroyed. Clyde Plenty, vice president of the Trust National Bank said the following: "Thank goodness the tornado hit when it did. We had closed up about three o'clock, and nobody was in the building." Some of the records housed in the building were destroyed, but Clyde said nothing of importance had been lost permanently, and all the records could be duplicated. There was also no money in the building to speak of.

The people at Jiffy-Kwik and the record shop weren't so lucky. At least four people had to go to the hospital to be treated for injuries due to flying debris and broken glass, according to hospital officials. Mr. and Mrs. George Jones—his wife's name is Thelma—were treated for minor cuts and lacerations and then released at Good Hope Hospital, and Irving Smalley was being kept overnight because of more serious cuts. He's listed in good condition. He lives at 123 Urban Street. The Joneses live at 1311 13th Avenue. Anna Patton had major injuries after being buried by an aisle of canned goods; she had just come out of surgery at 8 o'clock last night and was listed in critical condition. She lives at 12 Pinto Avenue. Killed was Evelyn Morrison as she was coming out of the record shop and getting into her car. She was a teller who worked at the Trust Bank, the same one that had been damaged by the tornado. She was on her way home. She lived at 67 Kent Street. She was dead on arrival at the hospital, and her body was taken to Green Acres Chapel. None of the funeral arrangements have been set.

Holbert Morrison, manager of the Jiffy-Kwik, said his store was not a total loss, but the damage was several thousand dollars' worth. "The worst thing was the looters," he said. "I just couldn't believe that some people would steal from us after something like this had happened." Police Chief Robert Sykes said they had arrested several youths for looting after the tornado hit, but they weren't going to release their names yet. Bill Belson, the manager of the record store and a noted area record collector, also said the damage to his shop would go into thousands of dollars. "Fortunately, none of my most valuable records were damaged."

Red Cedar said that one of his cars was damaged when some limbs fell on it, but otherwise nothing was hurt. Three homes in the next block of Cleveland Street were damaged, including that of Mayor Mellon. The roof was torn off of his home. "We were lucky because no one was home. I just feel awful about Miss Morrison, though. She was an old friend and a life-long resident of the town. Lots of people knew her, and I think it's tragic. You know, she used to be a teacher—was a teacher at Elmwood Elementary School about ten years ago. She taught there for about 20 years before retiring and going to work for the bank. She didn't have much family, but everybody in town knew her." The roofs of the other homes on Cleveland Street were damaged by flying limbs, but none of the owners reported serious damage.

The police chief said the total amount of damage done by the tornado would come to about $150,000. "That part of Cleveland Street looks like a bomb has been dropped on it. It's going to take us several days to get it all cleared. It's amazing that all this damage was done in less than two minutes. I feel awfully bad about Miss Morrison, but we were lucky that more people weren't hurt. There were quite a few people in the area at the time." One of the people who was in the record store at the time said the noise right before the tornado hit was the "scariest thing." He was Josh Gibson. "It was like the loudest drum roll I ever heard. Then there was sounds of glass breaking and things crashing around you."

That night Dan Rather devotes about 30 seconds to the tornado. Your editor tells you that it is the first time the town has ever been mentioned on a network newscast.

Harper said this tornado was the only one that did any damage. At least three others were sighted during the afternoon.

5.21 Features

Write a short feature story on each of the following sets of information.

BANK ROBBERY
- Man named Jesse James tried to rob First Fidelity Bank this morning.
- Caught by passing policeman as he backed out the door.
- Had $20,000.
- Same bank had been robbed nearly 100 years ago by real Jesse James and his brother Frank; they too had been caught. Suspect says: "Jesse James was my great-great uncle. I was just trying to finish the job he started."
- Police Chief Weldon Freeman: "This man has no sense of history."

NOISE ABATEMENT
- City Civil Court this morning.
- Judge Jan Sommerfelt.
- Suit involved Lakeshore subdivision residents suing Weatherford Construction Co.
- Company was building a road near subdivision.
- Residents complained that noise the construction company was making violated city ordinances against loud noises.

- Judge ruled in favor of the residents but refused to stop the construction; said construction company would have to give earplugs to anyone who complained about the noise.

STUDENT SIT-UP

- Local high school student Bobby Lott, junior at City Central, now sitting in tree in front of school.
- Will sit there until Friday's football game with County Central, City's arch-rival; winner of the game goes to state championship.
- Climbed into tree at 9 A.M.
- Principal Dick Barrett says Lott is a good student, "has his parents' permission to do this," and "I won't make him come down. I don't think he'll get behind in his school work." Friends taking class notes for him, handing him food.
- Lott says this is his way of showing support for the team; he won't come down except to go to the bathroom; says he won't stay in the tree if there's a lightning storm. "I may be crazy, but I'm not stupid."

5.22 Writing Feature Stories

Write feature stories based on the following sets of information.

TENNIS PLAYER

Bucky Haskiell is a tennis pro who graduated from your college two years ago. While in college, he led the team to the conference championship during his senior year and was named the conference's best player. When he graduated, he turned pro.

During this year's Wimbledon tennis tournament in London, England, Haskiell held the limelight briefly when he had to play John McElroy, the eventual champion, during the first round. Haskiell lost to McElroy, but only after he and the champion had played five full sets. The match was also highlighted by one of the fiercest temper tantrums McElroy had ever thrown. At one point during the match, McElroy stormed around the court cursing the officials and nearly got himself eliminated.

Haskiell has returned to the college for an exhibition tournament to raise money for the college tennis team's travel expenses. You are sent to interview him and here's how the interview goes:

What was it like playing John McElroy during the first round at Wimbledon?
Very hard (he says, laughing). In some ways McElroy is much like any other tennis player—only he's very, very good. When he concentrates on tennis alone, there aren't many people who can beat him. When he gets distracted, he tends to let down. But even then, he's hard to beat. I guess I found that out.

Was it the first time you had played him?
No, I had played him once before in a tournament in South Carolina. I beat him the first two sets, but he came back and won the last three to take the match.

Did he throw any tantrums that day?
No, he was pretty calm.

Do you think that the fit he threw at Wimbledon hurt your game that day?
I'm not sure. I've thought about that a lot. I don't think I played as well after he had finished his argument with the line judge as I had been playing. But I don't know if

I was tired or what. I didn't really think about it at the time. I was trying to concentrate on my game.

Do you know McElroy personally?
Yes, I've been with him on several occasions. He's really a nice guy off the court and doesn't deserve his "bad boy" image. Once he even gave me some pointers about how I was serving that really helped my game.

What was Wimbledon like? Everybody says it's a great place to be.
Well (laughing), I really wasn't there that long. As a player, it's not a great tournament because of the grass courts, which most of us aren't used to, and the accommodations aren't as good as some we've had at other tournaments. But the atmosphere at Wimbledon is hard to beat. There's so much tradition there—it makes you feel good just having a chance to play. Of course, next year I would like to win a match or two.

Do you expect to be invited back to Wimbledon next year?
I hope so. I'm having a pretty good year. I've won one tournament and have finished in the semifinals in at least four others. My ranking with the tennis association is better than last year, so maybe I'll get back there.

What's it like having been a tennis pro for two years?
I really enjoy it, but it's not what people think. Tennis pros aren't pampered people. All of us have to work very hard just to maintain our forms. And we're required to travel a lot—it's not like being a tourist either. It's just one hotel or motel after another. The time you might spend seeing the sights is time you should spend practicing—and you do if you want to be any good. For instance, I saw relatively little of London when I was there for Wimbledon. I'd like to go back sometime when there's not a tournament.

OLDEST TREE

A plaque marking the oldest tree on campus will be dedicated today. Ceremonies for the dedication will take place under the tree at 10 A.M., and the event will also be used to announce a fund-raising drive by the alumni association for the school. A news story has already been written about this event. Your job is to write a feature story about the tree that will be used as a sidebar (a journalistic term for a secondary story) with the news story. You gather the following information about the tree:

The tree is a water oak and is thought to be about 100 years old. University records show that the tree was probably planted by students who had been hired to do some work on the campus. One record says that during the same spring 50 trees were planted in that area of the campus.

Marcus Maxwell, professor of history and University historian: "The University used to hire students to do odd jobs around the campus, so we think students planted this tree. There is no exact record of what was planted and by whom, so we're not sure about it.

"A number of buildings have been built in the area of the tree, but none has come so close to it that the tree had to be destroyed. The tree has some significance in university history. The first troop of soldiers that gathered at the University to fight in World War I assembled under that tree right before they left by train to report to their army base. A crowd of people gathered, a band played, and some politicians made speeches. It was a pretty festive occasion.

"Likewise, when the first of the University's reserve units was activated right after the beginning of World War II, they also gathered under the tree for a send off. I understand that it wasn't such a festive occasion then."

Elmer Hinton, a retired bicycle repairman in the town, was among the soldiers who started for World War I at the tree. He tells you: "It was hot as blazes that day, even though it was April. Fortunately, we got to stand in the shade, and I remember being thankful of that. I enjoyed the music the band played, but I coulda done without the speeches. Lots of people thought this war was going to be a lark—that all we had to do was show up and the Germans would fade away. It turned out not to be like that at all. The part of World War I I saw was pretty rough."

A number of legends exist about the tree. One is that a man was lynched on the tree around the turn of the century. He had killed the family of the mayor of the town, and one night an angry crowd broke into the jail, took him out and hung him. Newspaper accounts say that a man named Josiah Lindy was hung by an angry crowd in 1901; he was accused of killing the family of Mayor Tyree Jones—Jones's wife and two daughters—after the wife had let him in the house and given him something to eat. The news account doesn't say exactly where the lynching took place. Nor does it say whether Mayor Jones was part of the crowd.

Another legend that was once popular with students is that the girl who walked under the lowest branch of the tree on the night of the full moon before the homecoming queen election would win that election. That legend became so popular in the 1920s and 1930s that students had a ritual of requiring all homecoming queen candidates to walk under the tree on the night before the election. That ritual died out during World War II.

Flora Handle, a professor in the biology department, says: "The tree is a good example of one of the major types of trees of this area. It is in remarkably good shape for a tree of its age. Usually a tree that old will have too many limbs and not enough foliage to support the whole system. That's not the case with this one. If something doesn't happen—if the tree isn't struck by a disease or by lightning—it should live another 50 or 75 years. It must be trimmed properly."

Your story should include a description of the tree and its location. (For that, you may pick any large tree on your campus.)

HIKER

A local high school teacher, Will Henderson, was lost for four days last week while hiking in the Great Smoky Mountains National Park. Henderson had been hiking along the Appalachian Trail and had gotten off the trail near a place known as Gregory Bald. After a couple of hours of walking off the trail, Henderson tried to cross a stream when he slipped and broke his leg.

Henderson is an experienced hiker. He is a member of the National Hiking Association. He had plenty of food with him at the time. He had been hiking for about 10 days before the accident. He had started in Georgia and was in Tennessee at the time of the accident.

After his fall, Henderson used some sticks and string to make a splint for his leg. He then began four days of crawling, pushing his 40-pound hiking pack in front of him. He crawled through a lot of thick underbrush. Finally, he made it back to the main part of the Appalachian Trail and was soon found by two other hikers.

The Appalachian Trail is nearly 3,000 miles long, stretching from Georgia to Maine. It is one of the most popular hiking trails in the country.

Henderson teaches biology at Jefferson High School. He is 39 and has been hiking since he was a boy of 10.

Henderson was hospitalized for several days in Knoxville, during which time a number of stories were written about his ordeal. Now he is back home, recuperating in a local hospital, and your newspaper sends you to interview him. Here's some of what he tells you:

"I never doubted that I would be found. I got discouraged sometimes, but I figured that I had plenty of food and thought that if I could get back to a trail—particularly the main Appalachian Trail because it's so busy—somebody would come along before long.

"I'll tell you though, I sure was happy when I heard those first footsteps coming up behind me. Those guys thought I was some kind of animal at first. I guess I looked pretty rough. They kind of hesitated in approaching me, but when I said, 'Help' a couple of times, they came running.

"One of the guys stayed with me while the other went for help. They kept telling me not to go to sleep, and I didn't. I was so happy then that I probably couldn't have, even if I had wanted to. I'll never forget the feeling I had when they found me, not if I live to be a hundred. Those guys are going to get mentioned in my will.

"The hardest thing about being lost was thinking that other people might be worrying about me. I was supposed to meet some friends in Gatlinburg a couple of days after I got lost. As it turned out, they weren't worried but said if I had been gone another day, they would have contacted the park rangers and started a search.

"After a day or so of crawling, I had to discard most of my clothes and most of the other things in my pack. They had gotten too wet and heavy for me to push. Of course, I kept all of the food I had. It was mostly dry stuff—crackers, fruit, peanut butter, things like that.

"The mountain foliage was like a jungle. There had been a lot of rain up there this year, and it was really thick. If I had stayed where I was when I fell, I probably would still be there. At least, that's what one of the park rangers said. I think I knew that instinctively when I fell, so I never thought about staying put. I knew that I had better get somewhere where people could find me.

"Besides food, I did manage to keep a few small things with me. I had several pictures of my wife and two little girls. I looked at them a lot, especially when I got discouraged. I would spend a little time looking at those pictures, and then I would crawl a little bit more.

"I broke the first rule of hiking, of course. I hiked alone. If you're on the Appalachian Trail, it doesn't matter because you're not really alone. There are so many people on that trail. But when you get off the beaten track—that's when you need to be with somebody. I learned my lesson about that. My goal is still to hike the entire trail, but I guess I'll have to wait until I get my leg in shape."

5.23 Magazine Writing

TRAVEL ARTICLE

A travel magazine is running a series of short pieces on several cities in your area. The series is geared toward college students and is trying to tell them things they would want to know if they visited these cities. Write about 300 words about the city where your college or university is located. Include some basic information about the city and the colleges and universities located there; also tell about places which are popular with students; finally, include something about places in the city that any tourist would want to visit.

STUDENT BUDGET

Write a short article (about 300 words) on how to live on a limited budget during your first year in college. This article is for a magazine that goes to high school students. You should talk about some of the unexpected expenses a new college student encounters as well as giving some advice on how to save money on books, food, or other expenses.

A STORY WITH A MORAL

Write a short story, possibly based on some incident in your life, that has a moral to it. The story, which should be about 300 words long, is for a religious publication that is geared to teenagers. The story should not be heavily theological, but it should contain some moral message. The story can be completely fictional or based totally on a real incident.

PROFESSOR

The alumni magazine of your college or university wants stories on file about the professors who have been selected as the school's outstanding teachers: you have been asked to write one of them. (You will have to select the professor about whom you do the story.) There are four professors who have been awarded the Outstanding Teacher Award, and the editor wants a 400-word article on each of them. Be sure to include information about the teacher's background, research, personal activities, and interests and what makes this teacher outstanding.

"MY MOST UNFORGETTABLE CHARACTER"

Reader's Digest runs a regular feature article called "My Most Unforgettable Character." It is a character sketch about the author's encounter with an unusual and interesting character. Write a 400-word article on your most unforgettable character. What was your relationship with the person? What makes the person unforgettable?

5.24 Writing a Profile Story

Write a profile story about someone on your campus.

A good profile story is not a biography. Rather, it takes an aspect of the person's life—one that the writer finds interesting—and emphasizes that. For instance, a student may work on Habitat for Humanity houses in the summer, or a faculty member may have an interesting hobby that does not have anything to do with what he or she teaches. The profile story takes that part of a person's life and tells something about that person through that interest or characteristic.

The profile story should include the following:

- A lead paragraph that talks about the part of the subject's life the story is emphasizing.
- Background information about the person that gives the reader a good idea about how he or she got to this point in life.
- Information from an interview with the person, along with direct quotations.
- Interviews with at least two people who know the person well and who can talk about the aspect of that person's life that you are emphasizing in the story.

chapter six

Writing for the Web

the singular news event of this generation occurred on September 11, 2001, when terrorists struck decisively and dramatically at the United States. What began as a normal fall day played out in front of us in horrible and shocking fashion. Millions watched as the two towers of the World Trade Center collapsed, killing thousands of people, and as one side of the Pentagon near Washington, D.C., burned. Later, we learned, another airplane, hijacked by the same terrorist group, crashed in western Pennsylvania. The news reports came swiftly, brought to us instantly by live television, as had so many other news events during the previous half century.

During those earlier years, as dramatic news events unfolded, we had only television and radio to rely on. Print publications—newspapers and magazines—were simply too slow in their production and distribution process to be of much help in the first hours of a dramatic news event.

But on September 11, 2001, we had something else: the Internet, or, more specifically, the World Wide Web. And we had news organizations that were willing to provide us with up-to-the-minute information. Consequently, we had far more information about this breaking news event than we had ever had before and much more than television alone could provide.

Even as people were riveted by the awful pictures on their television sets, they were logging onto their favorite news websites by the millions. In the first hours after the planes hit the World Trade Center, CNN.com got an average of 9 million hits an hour. (That average rose to 19 million hits an hour the next day; at the time CNN.com was typically averaging about 14 million hits a day.) The web portal Yahoo.com had forty times its normal amount of traffic in the first hour after the attack. MSNBC.com doubled its normal number of site viewers. Many websites had such heavy traffic loads on that day that they stripped off all of their ads and graphics to make loading their sites easier.

What viewers found when they got to these websites were some pictures, audio, and video. But mostly they found words—thousands and thousands of words. Many of these words were written by journalists at the locations of those events and elsewhere who were gathering information to help us know and understand what was happening. Many of the words were from experts on terrorism who offered their opinions and insights, and many were from people who simply needed to react.

In the early part of the twentieth century, radio had allowed us to hear the sounds of news events as they were occurring. (CBS correspondent Edward R. Murrow made a number of famous broadcasts from a rooftop in London in 1940 as German airplanes were bombing the city.) By the 1960s, television was giving us live pictures and sounds of news events such as the funeral of President John F. Kennedy. By the end of the century, the Web was letting us read about those events as they were happening, and it was giving us a chance to respond immediately.

CHARACTERISTICS OF THE WEB

The World Wide Web continues to grow and change—and to have a profound influence on our lives. More websites go online every day, and more people use the medium. The U.S. government, along with many states, has set as its goal the wiring of every school building to the Web so the vast educational advantages of this medium can be available to all children. The Web has altered the way we trade stocks, the way we do our banking, the way people shop, the way many people get their music, and even the way some people listen to baseball games.

Figure 6.1   Elements of a Website

This illustration shows many of the elements that are contained in a typical news website. Most important to the reader are the headlines and summaries, which will change often on an active site. Even though they are brief, they must be written quickly and with both clarity and accuracy. This requires talent and practice.

THE DAILY NEWS *ONLINE*

Good morning, 8:10 a.m., August 12

NEWS
SPORTS
BUSINESS
FEATURES
OBITUARIES
CLASSIFIEDS
FEATURED ADS

ABOUT DN
STAFF
CONTACT US
PRIVACY

News

Plant strike enters third day

Workers at the Second Edition plant stayed away from work for the third day today while executives and union leaders grappled with several tough issues. *More*

Workers at the Second Edition plant continued their strike for the third day this morning. Photo by John Ray.

Sports

Eagles take second straight

The Midville Eagles have a modest two-game winning streak going after winning last night's game against the Bay City Bluebirds. *More*

Business

No news yet on new store

The new shopping center at Exit 7 has yet to announce its main store, despite the fact that owners said the announcement would come during the first week of August. *More*

NEWS | SPORTS | BUSINESS | FEATURES | OBITUARIES | CLASSIFIEDS | FEATURED ADS
ABOUT DN | STAFF | CONTACT US | PRIVACY POLICY

Morton's Morturary
Serving you in your time of need (Click here for more information)

So what is it about the Web that it is having this impact? Isn't it like broadcasting because you see all this stuff on your computer screen? Or isn't it like newspapers and magazines because you can read all the copy and look at the pictures?

The answer to those last two questions is both yes and no. The Web is like broadcasting and newspapers, but it is also something quite different. Although it shares many of the characteristics of other media, it has qualities that make it unique. Those qualities are immediacy, flexibility, permanency, capacity, and interactivity.

Immediacy

It is much easier and less time-consuming to "broadcast" or "publish" on the Web than in the traditional broadcasting or print media. Certainly, broadcasters can go on the air quickly when news occurs. But what they broadcast may have little substance, or they may be reduced to showing live camera shots in which nothing is happening. In less frenetic times, broadcasters spent a great deal of time and effort in preparing material for their shows.

The publishing process for the print media involves several unavoidable steps. Whatever is being published must be in printable form, it must be duplicated by some machine (a photocopier, printer, or printing press), and then it must be distributed to an audience.

With the Web, once information is available in some form, it can be loaded onto a website within a few seconds. The president could go on television to declare war, and before the statement was finished, it would be on the Web, and reaction to it could be coming in. The Web does not require the personnel or equipment that broadcasting needs, and it does not have the distribution problems of print.

Flexibility

The Web can handle a wide variety of formats for presenting information. It can simulate print with words, sentences, and paragraphs. It can show still pictures and video. It can play sound recordings. The Web journalist works in a multimedia environment and, along with other decisions he or she must make, has to choose the format that is best suited for the information.

In addition, the Web is fostering new forms of information presentation. The audio photo gallery is one simple example. This format marries a series of pictures to an audio recording of commentary from the photographer. Such a format was not possible in the world of print, but it is now being used extensively by some news organizations such as the New York *Times*.

Permanency

Unless we turn our videotape recorders on every time we turn on the television, there is little about broadcasting that is permanent for the user. We certainly cannot (unless we happen to be taping) go back to watch again a story by Dan Rather or part of a *Friends* episode. Once these are broadcast, they are gone.

Although we can reread stories in newspapers and magazines, we are unlikely to save every print publication we get. Lack of storage space would quickly overwhelm us if we tried (not to mention the tag of "eccentric" that our neighbors would hang on us). Printed materials are certainly more lasting than broadcasting, but their life and usefulness are limited.

With the Web, however, material can remain in place and accessible as long as the Web server and electronic storage space exist. Although many websites, particularly news websites, change their content every day, the previous day's stories, pictures, graphics, video, and sound can remain available as long as the webmaster wishes. Even when the server ceases to exist, material can be stored in a variety of ways so that it can be accessible to users.

Capacity

Most news organizations produce more than they can show or print. Broadcasting is limited by time. Print media are limited by space. The Web races past these problems with its ability to keep and show huge amounts of text and image material.

Not only can a news website present a story about an event, but it can also offer pictures, video, audio, graphics, and ancillary text. It can even set up a forum so that visitors can react to the event, see the reactions of others, and carry out discussions about these reactions. Professional communicators are now faced with the problem of figuring out the best way to present the material they have—a problem that we will discuss later in this chapter—rather than to choose what material to present.

Then there is storage. We have already alluded to what your neighbors might say if you kept too many newspapers and magazines around your place. This is a problem of capacity. You are probably running out of room in your house, apartment, or dorm room. So is the Library of Congress and almost every other library in the world. No one has enough physical space to store copies of all of the books, magazines, newspapers, videotapes, audiotapes, pictures, and other material that are being produced.

The Web and other technological advances have alleviated the space problem by enhancing our ability to store more in smaller spaces and by centralizing information so that it is available from one location to people anywhere in the world. You no longer have to keep a copy of Shakespeare's plays and poems on your bookshelf. You can access them from any number of websites in just a few seconds.

Interactivity

Broadcasting in its traditional forms has a low level of interactivity with its listeners and viewers. People can change television or radio stations and the sound volume with the ease of using a dial or a button, but they have no control over what they receive from those stations. Nor is there any mechanism to offer feedback to the stations.

Newspapers, magazines, and other printed media are highly interactive in at least one sense. Readers can select what they will read and look at and what they won't. Choosing, however, can be slow and cumbersome. And in doing so, readers do not communicate directly with the media they are using or with the people who have produced the material.

The technology of the Web offers a level of interactivity between producers and consumers that goes far beyond what other media are capable of. The wide variety of material on a site can offer visitors many more choices than they would get if they were reading a magazine or a newspaper. Linking to other material on other sites is another way in which visitors can interact with what they are seeing.

Visitors can choose the parts of the website they want to see, and producers can track those choices. Software can record "hits" for various pages within a site, and they can show site managers the sequence of those hits and the amount of time visitors spend on a page.

Visitors can communicate directly through e-mail or other means set up by the producers. They can send producers their money, as many commercial sites hope they will do. And they can communicate with other visitors to share thoughts and reactions about what is on the site.

With all of these characteristics and differences, the Web remains a medium of words, images and sounds—especially words. The Web requires people who understand the language and are skilled in using it.

DEMANDS OF THE AUDIENCE

The audience for the Web has grown exponentially since the mid-1990s, and it continues to expand. Once the preserve of the young and the geek, the Web has become a major information provider for almost all demographic groups. A study by the *Wall Street Journal* in 2004 found that senior business executives considered the Web a chief source of business news and were spending 12 percent more time with the Web than they had four years before. And as they were doing this, they were spending less time with other media.

Most websites are developed to satisfy a particular audience, usually an audience that shares a common interest and a limited set of demographics. News websites—those devoted to showing the latest in news, information, and sports—seek a broader audience, just as general interest newspapers and magazines try to satisfy many demographic categories.

Whether the audience is broad or narrow, the single thing that people of all demographic categories expect from the sites that they visit is information. (A secondary and overlapping expectation is entertainment, but the focus of this chapter will be on information.) People visit websites because they want to know certain things. They often want this information for a particular purpose—to further investigate some news item they heard about, to help them solve a problem, to buy something, and so on.

That leads to another characteristic of Web users: They often know the type of information they are seeking. A user might visit a website to see whether it sells a certain product or contains a set of instructions or has the latest information about a celebrity. It is important that website developers and writers understand that many visitors come to a site committed to finding something specific. The task of developers and writers is to figure out what visitors are seeking and how to give it to them in the best way.

Web surfers, in a relatively short time, have come to agree on a common set of expectations for almost all websites. Those expectations include the following.

Speed

Websites are thought to be bad or amateurish if they do not load quickly and if their links do not respond instantly. The desire for speed is often a technical and a design problem. But the whole concept of speed has great implications for the work of the writer. Pictures and graphics decrease the loading speed of a website, but they may be necessary for the proper presentation of news and information and for the visual appeal of the site.

Visual Logic

A visitor should be able to figure out a website quickly and easily. What the website is about should be clear at first glance; so should what it contains and who produced it. While this expectation, too, is a designer's problem, some responsibility for the visual logic of the site and its appearance rests with the writer, as we shall see later in this chapter.

Simple Organization and Navigation

A well-organized website is one where the visitor has a good idea about where to find information from the very beginning of the visit. Good organization means that the site takes advantage of the concept of layering information. Layering information is the presentation of more and more specific information as the user goes more deeply into the website. Information must be presented in logical layers and in such a way that the user can quickly understand how to access those layers.

Depth

Websites that are speedy, visually attractive and logical, and easy to navigate will be incomplete and often die from lack of visitors because they simply do not contain enough information. The hard part about website development and maintenance is not the design or navigation. It is the continuous gathering of the information necessary to sustain the site and organizing and presenting the information in a way that allows visitors to access and use it.

News

Not every website is a news site, but almost all sites need to present new and updated information. A static website—one that changes so little that visitors see the same things when they return—will not hold or increase its audience. The people who produce the news, the new information for websites, not the people who design the site, are the ones who do the heavy lifting for the site.

CHARACTERISTICS OF WEB WRITING

All of the characteristics of good writing that we have discussed in this book—accuracy, clarity, efficiency, and precision—come into play in writing for the Web. Despite its seemingly infinite capacity for information, the Web is not a medium in which words can be taken lightly or wasted. Users are often in a hurry, and websites seek to achieve maximum speed in serving them. That said, the following are some of the characteristics of writing for the Web that have emerged as important within the medium.

Efficiency

Students who are new to writing for the mass media probably struggle more with one of its major characteristics—efficiency—than with any other. To write efficiently, using the fewest words to present the most information, is not the type of writing that most students have been taught in English grammar and literature classes. To write less and say more is a difficult skill to develop. Writing efficiently is time consuming because it involves editing and rewriting. Most of us use too many words when we put together our first drafts (as we discussed in Chapter 1), and those drafts need to be edited and rewritten.

The Web demands efficient writing, but it goes further because of the forms and structures of writing that are most common to the Web. (Those forms are discussed in the next section.) Writers should remember that readers do not want to waste time—and will not waste time. The Web offers many points at which information can be obtained. Readers will gravitate to those points where information can be gained most efficiently.

Simplicity

Reading a computer screen is usually more difficult than reading something in a printed form. It requires a different posture and more intensive focusing of the eyes. A writer cannot alleviate these physical demands, but he or she can make it easier on the reader by writing that uses the simplest, most straightforward language possible.

Writing simply is one of the continuing themes of good writing for the mass media that has been raised repeatedly in this book. Writers need to get past their

English-theme habits and mentality and work toward producing the simplest, most unadorned prose possible. The task is not easy. Figuring out simple language takes a great deal of thought and effort. On the Web, that effort is a particular necessity.

Tone

Writers should write in a tone that is appropriate for their information and the context of their writing and one that meets readers' expectations. The Web requires writing that is formal at certain times and informal at other times. A straightforward news story will have a formal tone because the writer is trying to present information, and readers expect to receive it without the opinions or attitudes of the writer.

Some forms of writing for the Web invite a more casual tone. Some websites allow writers to take such a tone in writing summaries (see the next section) because the opinions and attitudes of the writer can be entertaining and can help to sell a story to the readers. Weblogs may also be casual in tone, as if the writer were talking one-on-one with the reader. Still, with most audiences, the Web is not a place where anything goes and any language is appropriate. A writer needs to understand when more informality is appropriate and expected and what the limits of that informality are.

Visual Aspects

Many people who write for print do so without understanding or caring about the visual aspects of their medium. They simply expect the words to appear without their having to think about the visual context of those words. The writer for the Web has to understand and pay attention to the visual aspects of writing, because those are an inherent part of the content and the medium itself. The following paragraphs discuss a few of those visual aspects (see Figure 6.2).

Figure 6.2   Visual Aspects of Web Writing

These examples illustrate ways in which a writer can make copy more legible for a reader of a news website. These techniques create space around the words so that they are easier for the reader to scan.

Links

The **Webster Wire Company,** an international producer of screen products, announced today it would be locating its new plant in Ticonderoga County near the community of **Binfield.**

Paragraph spacing

The new plant will hire about 100 people when it opens in May.

Officials expect more than 200 people to be working there when it is in full production. That should occur by May, they said.

Job applications are being accepted now, they said.

Indentions

Harvey Baker, president of the company, had this to say about the plant's location:

> We are very pleased about the chance to work with the people of Ticonderoga County. We think our partnership will be a good one.

Baker did not say when construction would begin.

Bulleted lists

Officials said the company is accepting applications in the following job categories:

- Plumbers
- Electricians
- Carpenters
- Draftsmen
- Secretary and clerical

The application process will be open for another two weeks, they said.

Links constitute one of the most important characteristics of the Web. In fact, the very nature of the Web is tied to the fact that links exist at all. The Web was built for a hypertext system, in which readers can jump from one point to another and do not have to follow the lines that are set up by the producer of the website.

Links are those words or groups of words that lead a reader to more information on a topic on a separate Web page. Links can be handled or presented in a variety of ways. They may be words within the text that are underlined, are shown in a different color, or both.

The Mercedes Widget Company manufactures a complete line of <u>widgets</u> that will meet every widget need.

Or links may be placed at the end of the article text or beside it, clearly indicating that the reader can find out more information if he or she chooses.

As much as any other aspect of writing, links demonstrate the power of the Web as a medium for news. Properly formatted and presented, links enable users to make their own way through a package of information rather than following the path set up for them by the writer and editor. Links allow the user to select what information the user believes is important and interesting.

Web writers need to know the minimum amount of hypertext mark-up language (HTML) to be able to establish links in their copy. HTML is a series of tags that tell Web browsers what to do with the items they encounter on a website. If the writer wants to set up a link within a sentence, such as the one above, he or she would have to know the URL (uniform resource locator) address of the Web page to which the reference would be linked and would have to type the following into the copy:

The Mercedes Widget Company manufactures a complete line of **<a href=http://www.widgetsgalore.com>**widgets**</a>** that will meet every widget need.

The material inside the brackets before the word *widgets* is called the opening tag. The "</a>" after *widgets* is the closing tag. The (imaginary) URL, www.widgets galore.com, indicates that more information about widgets can be found at this Web page. The "a href=" at the beginning of the tag is a reference command that makes this tag into a link. (There are many websites that explain the basics of HTML tags in case you are interested in knowing more; some of those sites are listed at the end of the chapter.)

The technical aspects of setting up links are relatively easy to learn. What is more important in this discussion is for the writer to understand when links should be established and how they should appear to the reader. A writer should try to anticipate when readers might want more information about a topic and should set up links to where that information is easily available. At the same time, a link might be available but unnecessary, confusing, or distracting; on those occasions, the writer should avoid using links.

Links should be as transparent as possible; that is, readers should have a good idea about what they are going to find if they follow the link. That is not always an easy thing to do. Look at the following sentence:

Abraham Lincoln delivered the <u>Gettysburg Address</u> on Nov. 19, 1863.

The words *Gettysburg Address* are set up as a link, but it is not clear what the reader will get by clicking on that link. It could be the text of the speech, more information about it, a picture of Lincoln's handwritten text, or any number of other items. The small addition in the following sentence clears that up:

Abraham Lincoln delivered the Gettysburg Address (<u>text</u>) on Nov. 19, 1863.

A writer should not overload the copy with links, something that is relatively easy to do with many topics. If the writer has found a number of links that are helpful to the reader, a list of those links at the end of the story or in a sidebar may be more appropriate than trying to embed them in the copy.

Short paragraphs and paragraph spacing are other ways of visually enhancing Web writing. Short paragraphs are visible enticements for the reader to read. A paragraph that has a line of white space above and below it can be especially easy for the reader to digest.

Short paragraphs make for easier reading, but they demand disciplined thinking on the part of the writer. Information must be broken into bits that the writer can put together in small portions but also in a manner that is logical and effective.

With this type of writing, transitions are particularly important (see Chapter 4). The writing must tie together the information tightly so that the readers can easily follow it. A new paragraph should be introduced in a way that follows from the previous paragraph; new paragraphs should not surprise or confuse the reader.

Indentions can be used to present material that can be set off from the main text, such as a block quotation. The indention must be logical, however. That is, it should be readily apparent to the reader why the material is set off and that it actually fits together.

Bulleted and numbered lists are other ways of introducing white space and enhancing the readability of text on a screen. The bulleted list is one step beyond the indention. Bulleted lists are indented and use black dots in front of individual items on the list. A bulleted list implies that there is no particular order for the items on the list. Such a list is relatively easy to set up in HTML.

A numbered list is much like a bulleted list but uses numbers instead of dots. The numbered list implies an order for the items on the list and that the number of items itself may have some importance.

All of the devices mentioned here will help writers to conform to some of the demands of writing for the Web. These forms also help writers to deal with large blocks of prose that can be daunting, particularly if the prose appears in small type on a screen. These devices aid the reader in scanning information and in deciding what information is relevant to their needs. They should be used only when appropriate, however, because the form should support content, not control it.

FORMS OF WRITING

If the chief purpose of websites is to offer information and the chief form of that information is text, then it is writing—not design and not flashy programming—that becomes the all-important activity in producing a website. In some quarters, this is known as *creating content*—not a very satisfying term but one that is useful in that it helps us distinguish writing from design. (Some, such as Web writing guru Jakob Nielsen, have gone so far as to distinguish "macrocontent" from "microcontent," the former being large blocks of text, such as a full news article, and the latter being shorter pieces of text, such as labels, headlines, and summaries.)

Whatever the content is called, writers must understand that they are writing for an audience, just as newspaper and magazine writers write for an audience. They must have credibility, and they must master the language. Their writing has to display the characteristics of all good media writing: accuracy, completeness, precision, and efficiency.

The forms of writing for the Web, however, are somewhat different from what we have learned so far in writing for print. (They are quite different in writing for broadcast, writing for advertising, and writing for public relations, as we will see in

Figure 6.3   Labels, Headlines, and Summaries

A label is a one- or two-word designation that gives the reader a general idea of what a story is about. As they are used in this illustration, they indicate what section of the website the stories are located in. This illustration also contains an example of each of the three types of summaries discussed in the chapter. Can you tell which is which? (Answers below.)

News

100-year-old plant set to close next month

Workers have known for some time the Marvel Textile plant in Binfield was going to close. The reason is now clear: foreign competition. *More*

Sports

Loyalty lacking in NBA

Seattle Supersonics guard Alvin Spenser gave his word to owner Mort Mocha that he would be back next year. Spenser's word turned out to not mean very much -- as is the case with many other NBA stars these days. *More*

Business

Target to anchor new shopping center

Officials of the new Binfield Meadows shopping center con-firmed an open secret today saying that Target would be the fourth anchor store in the mall, which is set to open next month. *More*

Top: analytical. Middle: provocative. Bottom: informational.

subsequent chapters of this book.) Because of the physical nature of a website and the varied expectations of website visitors, writers must present their information in different ways. Not all of the forms are different, however. One form that has translated easily from print to the Web is the inverted pyramid.

Inverted Pyramid

Presenting the most important information first, without introduction and without much verbal baggage, satisfies the Web's demand for speed and efficiency. In Chapter 5, we discussed the inverted pyramid structure as a good way to present news, but its essential element—ordering information from most important to least important—is applicable to many other writing tasks. (See Chapter 5 for a detailed introduction to this structure.)

Take, for instance, the problem of writing an introductory statement about a company or organization for its website. The writer must decide what is the most important thing the visitor needs to know about the company:

> The Mercedes Widget Company is the oldest and largest widget company in America.

Or

> The Mercedes Widget Company manufactures a complete line of widgets that will meet every widget need.

Or

> The quality of the widgets produced by the Mercedes Widget Company has been unsurpassed for more than 150 years.

Each of these sentences presents information that is likely to be of value to the website visitor. What the writer has to balance is the company's desire to present information about itself and the needs and expectations of the visitor for a particular type of information.

As with news stories, the writer has the job of ordering the information and putting it together in a simple prose form that is interesting and readable. This kind of writing also requires another characteristic that most other media writing also demands: impersonality. The writer should use simple, clear language that is unadorned with personal opinions or personal writing style. As with news stories, the reader is interested in getting the information, not the writer's point of view.

In addition to the standard demands of the inverted pyramid structure, the writer should try to incorporate some of the visual aspects of the Web that were discussed in the previous section into the construction of the news story. Short paragraphs and paragraph spacing are standard aspects of inverted pyramid news stories on websites. Writers should also look for appropriate ways to incorporate links, lists, and indentions into a story.

Labels

A label is the one- or two-word moniker that indicates the overall organization of the website. Because of their brevity, labels do not contain much specific information for the reader. Rather, they are general guidelines that tell the reader where he or she is or is going in the site.

Still, labels must be accurate and as specific as possible. Writers must understand the widely accepted meanings and implications of words, not just their strict dictionary definitions. Writers should understand that within some contexts, words that may seem the same carry different connotations. One example of such a pair of words is *story* and *article*. Within the confines of some parts of journalism, a *story* is likely to refer to something in a newspaper while an *article* is a magazine piece. The word "electronic" might mean broadcasting is some contexts of media discussion and Internet-related in others.

Applying the correct labels to website content and categories is an important task and sometimes more difficult than it first appears.

Headlines

A headline is one of the most important devices that a news website has for delivering information to its readers. A headline that is clear and specific will tell the reader what a story is about and allow the reader to decide whether or not to delve more deeply into the site. A general or vague headline will confuse the reader and may end up wasting his or her time. Good headlines are not easy to write. They take a great deal of skill, understanding, and practice on the part of the writer.

Most of us are familiar with headlines as they appear in newspapers, magazines, and newsletters. They are cryptic summaries of information that indicate the content of a longer piece of prose. News websites have developed two main types of headlines: the label headline and the sentence headline.

Label headlines range from two to four words and do not try to express a complete thought. They simply give the reader some indication as to the topic of the information they head. The following are some examples:

Campaigning Democrats

Babes in Paradise

Summer Reading Choices

Sentence headlines are more common for news websites and are more like the headlines that are found in newspapers. These headlines take the form of a complete sentence with a subject and a verb, but they leave out words that are not essential to understanding them. For example:

President Threatens Veto of New Tax Bill

Smith Throws One-Hitter as Tigers Get Key Win

Sometimes a verb or part of a verb form is understood but not explicitly stated:

Midville Man Charged with Larceny

Jones on Team's Final Roster

(In each of those headlines, the verb *is* is missing.)

Notice a couple of things about these examples and the ones you see in the illustrations. First, the headlines are written with present tense verbs. Second, articles (*a, an, the*) are missing. The third characteristic is specificity; even though just a few words are used, the headline contains specific, meaningful information.

Though brief, headlines are a challenge to write. They first require that the writer understand thoroughly the article that the headline is for, which requires reading the article carefully, of course. Headlines should not mimic the beginning or lead paragraph of the article, so if the writer wants to use the idea in the lead for the headline, he or she needs to find different words to express it. Many journalists consider the headline to be a sales pitch for a story. The headline should be interesting enough to engage a reader and help him or her decide to read a story. For that, the headline needs specific information and concrete wording. Vague or abstract words do not help to build interest.

Most websites will develop a style and set of requirements for headlines. The New York *Times* news site (www.nytimes.com) requires its headline writers to meet the same standards that print headlines meet; other newspaper sites are not as restrictive and demanding.

Headlines are increasingly important to websites because of the growing use of RSS (which variously stands for "rich site summary" or "really simple syndication"). Many news websites offer RSS feeds; that is, they allow the latest headlines and summaries on the site to be picked up by software programs that will feed those headlines into an individual's computer or hand-held device. Thus, a person can read a site's headlines and story summaries (see below) without actually going to the site. The reader who wants to read the entire article can click on the headline, which comes in as a link, and the page with the article will open up. Many Web experts view RSS feeds as a way of drawing people onto a website, but to do so, the headlines must be informative and interesting. Vague or confusing headlines are unlikely to attract readers.

Summaries

The summary has developed into one of the major forms of writing on the Web. A concise, well-written summary allows the reader to gain information and understanding that is found more deeply in the site. Summaries are commonly located on the front page or the section front pages of a site, but they may also be located on the article page itself.

Some news websites use the first paragraph of an article as the summary, but even with inverted pyramid news stories, this is rarely a good idea. A summary is a shorter version of the entire story and needs to give the reader a broad view of the story. Using the first paragraph as a summary can also be irritatingly repetitive for the reader who will likely expect something different if he or she goes to the article page. Finally, using the first paragraph as a summary shows that the news organization does not take its website seriously enough to create original content for it.

Summaries fall into three general categories: informational, analytical, and provocative.

Informational summaries simply try to give readers an overview of a longer story. A summary can be as long as two or three sentences, so the writer has the opportunity to give the readers more information than is normally found in a lead paragraph of an inverted pyramid news story. The summary does not have to isolate or emphasize the most important information about a story, as a lead paragraph for an inverted pyramid news story would. Rather, it can deal more generally with all of the information a story may contain. An example of an information summary follows:

FIGHTING WASPS LOSE TO DARTFORD, 65–62

The Fighting Wasps stayed close through the entire game on Saturday night, but in the end the Dartford Dogs proved too much for the Pearl College basketballers. The loss puts the Wasps' tournament seed in doubt just a week before the end of the season.

Analytical summaries give the reader some interpretation of the information in the story. They emphasize the *how* or *why* of a story rather than the *who, what, when,* or *where.* The writer of an analytical summary must be thoroughly familiar with the story itself and must have a good understanding of the general topic. For example:

FIGHTING WASPS LOSE TO DARTFORD, 65–62

The Fighting Wasps lost to Dartford Saturday night, but not because the Dogs proved they were the better team during the bulk of the game. Instead, it came down to free throws in the final three minutes. The Dogs hit theirs, and the Wasps didn't.

Provocative summaries try to pique the interest of the reader not only by presenting information about the story, but also by expressing some opinion or displaying some attitude. The writer may use humor, sarcasm, irony, or some other device to get the reader thinking about the information. The point of doing that is to entertain the reader and induce him or her to read the story. Many nonnews, magazine websites, such as Slate and Salon, use provocative summaries to increase readership of articles.

FIGHTING WASPS LOSE TO DARTFORD, 65–62
Chances are Coach Lou Wackman will have his Fighting Wasps spend some quality time at the free throw line during practice this week. If he had done that last week, the outcome of Saturday night's game might have been different.

As the Web continues to grow and develop, individual websites will formulate their requirements and styles for summaries. Generally, since the beginning of the decade, summaries have been growing shorter. Where once a writer had two or three sentences to work with, the writer may now have only one sentence. That trend may change as websites get a better handle on who constitutes their readership and as readers understand the value of a good summary. Meanwhile, writers must master the form and develop the skills to execute it as quickly as the Web requires.

Subheads

A subhead is a line of type within the body copy of an article that informs the reader what is coming up next within the copy. Subheads also break up the copy, introducing more white space and making articles easier to read.

Subheads are best used at natural breaks within the article rather than being arbitrarily inserted every few paragraphs. They should help the reader through the article rather than interrupting the flow of the prose.

Like all forms of concision, subheads can be difficult to write. They require that the writer or the editor read the copy closely enough to capture the essence or the most important idea of the paragraphs to which the subheads refer. Then the writer must state that idea in just a few words—usually no more than three or four.

Weblogs

The weblog began in the late 1990s as a form of writing that could be done only on the Web. In essence, a weblog is a personal diary or journal that a writer posts onto a website (see Figure 6.4). The journal is updated at the pleasure of the writer, sometimes once a week (or less) or possibly even several times a day. The weblog is available to anyone who wants to read it, and over time, it may build an audience of people who are interested in what the writer has to say.

Occasionally, those audiences can be huge. Glenn Reynolds, a law professor at the University of Tennessee, adds to his weblog, http://Instapundit.com, several times a day with amazing consistency and energy. His weblog attracts about 100,000 hits per day. (A *hit*, simply put, is when someone calls up the site on his or her browser.) That number is greater than the number of subscribers to most daily newspapers in the United States. Andrew Sullivan (http://andrewsullivan.com), a former editor-in-chief of the *New Republic* magazine, has a weblog that draws more than 10,000 visitors a day—far fewer than Reynolds but still an impressive number.

Figure 6.4   Weblogs

Weblogs began as one-person operations. Someone would have an interest in a topic or would just want to post writings and comments on a website, and weblog software would give him or her an easy way to do that. The weblog here is an illustration of what the one-person weblog can be like. Many news organizations have begun to commission weblogs because they tend to draw a lot of readers.

ALLCARDSALLTHETIME.COM

A weblog devoted to the Binfield Cardinals minor league baseball team -- the best club in the St. Louis Cardinals farm system

ABOUT ACATT
ABOUT ME
CONTACT
PRIVACY

SPONSORSHIPS
AND AD
OPPORTUNITIES

HOW MANY ARE
SHOWING UP?

Season nears completion and the Cards are one game out

Just two weeks left to go, and the Cards are on a hot streak. They're about catch the first place Bay City Bluebirds, who are stumbling as they near the season's finish line. Last night lefty Biff Risher pitched the Cards to a 6-2 win over the Jefferson City Reds. It was Biff's best performance of the year. He needs better defense behind him when he pitches in the future. That's been the big weakness for the Cards all year long. ***Posted Aug. 15***

Bluebird takes umbrage

Apparently a Bay City fan took umbrage at **what I wrote** last week about the Bluebird's star hurler, Ronnie Reecer, who really isn't a star and who certainly is not ready for prime time. Here's **what he said,** in case you're interested. My advice to our Bay city friend: Get over it. ***Posted Aug. 15***

Whither Ralph?

Everyone agrees that Ralph Kinser, the Cards manager, deserves his shot at a big league managing job. That just might come next year, as several managers have their **heads on the chopping block**, according to ESPN's Peter Gammons. ***Posted Aug. 14***

Who will get the call?

You never like to see guys hurt, but the disabled list might be kind to one of the locals. The Cards had to put utility infielder Ray Chapman on the disabled list today, and it could be a Binfield player who gets the call to replace him. Speculation now centers on Hernando Lopez. ***Posted Aug. 13***

Southhaven League
Western Division
Today's standings

	W	L	Gms
Bay City	25	20	--
Binfield	24	21	1
Royda	20	20	2.5
Jeff City	19	20	3
Trinity	15	30	10
Pennfield	14	31	11

Tonight's game:
vs. Jeff City at 7 p.m. at the Binfield Ballfield.

Weblogs, or *blogs,* as they are often called, contain the opinions and comments of the writer. Occasionally, a writer may do some original research as a reporter for a news organization would, but the majority of the content of many weblogs consists of comments about topics that interest the writer, responses to e-mails or other communications the writer has received from readers, and links to material elsewhere on the Web that interests the writer. Consequently, many media professionals do not consider weblogs to be journalism in the sense that people gather and disseminate information. Another reason they are not considered real journalism is that they do not go through the normal editing process of journalism. This process not only corrects errors but also holds journalists accountable to others in their profession.

Yet other professionals argue that weblogs are a new kind of journalism and that the profession should pay attention. A weblog allows anyone to express his or her opinions without the support of a media organization. If those opinions are interesting and appealing, that person can gather an audience. The audience—depending on the inclinations of the writer—can participate in the weblog by sending comments to the writer, who may publish them or comment about them. Who is to say, many argue, that this is *not* journalism?

Some media organizations, recognizing the potential popularity of weblogs, have adopted the form in a number of ways. Some have simply hired people to write weblogs that are posted on the organization's website. Others have invited citizens (in some cases political candidates) to start their own weblogs on the organization's site. Some have even encouraged reporters who cover beats on a regular basis to maintain a weblog on popular topics. The last idea has caught on in many sports departments that cover college or professional sports in which the audiences are large and avid.

Weblogs thrive on good writing—writing that adheres to the practices and principles discussed in various parts of this book. Content that attracts an audience is not only substantive but also clear and precise. The current most common characteristics of weblogs are the following:

- Individual entries in weblogs are relatively short. Writing short pieces is often difficult because the writer has to have the discipline and skill to gather thoughts and information into a few well-chosen words. But most popular weblogs present short pieces because they are easy and entertaining for the reader.

- Weblogs are written for the highly interested audience. Weblog writers do not feel that they have to write for everyone. They can safely assume that readers will understand what they are talking about without a lot of background information. They can also assume that readers have a high degree of knowledge about their topic.

- Links are an essential part of weblogs. The weblog writer has to know how to set up links and use them to enhance the writing and the experience for readers.

- Popular weblogs pay attention to their audience. Many weblog writers will post comments from their readers and will often respond to them. The understanding between a weblog writer and the audience is that the individual reader will not be ignored.

- The writing in a weblog may be formal or casual depending on the voice that the writer wants to use. Many of the most popular weblogs are written in an informal style that speaks directly to the reader. Still, the standard grammar, spelling, and punctuation rules are observed, and if the writer has journalistic training or experience, he or she is likely to observe most of the style rules of the *AP Stylebook.*

Weblogs are not a fad, as many media professionals thought when they first began to appear. Instead, they have attracted many participants and readers, and they are likely to continue to do so as the Web develops as a mass medium.

E-Mail

The Web has fostered one of the most important submedia forms of mass communication: e-mail. Sending and receiving e-mail are the most popular individual activities on the Web. The importance of e-mail is increasing as people discover its speed and efficiency and as technical advances continue to open up more possibilities for its use. E-mail, once viewed as a personal convenience, has become a tool of mass communication.

As such, professional writers are finding that the informal, grammarless style with which they might have begun using e-mail needs to be set aside for a more formal, disciplined approach to the writing. As with any writing, e-mails should be clear in their context and their structure. Writers of e-mail messages should consider the reader—what does the reader need to know about the message to respond appropriately to it? Cryptic, ungrammatical messages without context may be fine for communicating between friends or even in chat room settings, but they simply won't do in a professional environment.

E-mail newsletters are an increasingly popular form of keeping those with a common interest informed. Many news websites have established e-mail headline services that inform readers about new and interesting features on the site. Usually, these newsletters take the form of headlines and summaries, along with links that allow receivers to go directly to articles and pages being referred to. Other e-mail newsletters, such as A. Word. A. Day (www.wordsmith.org/), present a single new item each day and are short enough to be read easily and quickly. As Web guru Jakob Nielson (http://useit.com) has written,

> Newsletters need to be smooth and easy: they must be seen to reduce the burdens of modern life. Even if free, the cost in e-mail clutter must be paid for by being helpful and relevant to users—and by communicating these benefits in a few characters in the subject line.

All of these forms of writing require a great deal from a writer: full understanding of what the writer is writing about, skill at using the language efficiently, the ability to edit and rewrite, and a willingness to spend the time it takes to write succinctly.

LATERAL REPORTING

As a medium, the Web allows us to go beyond the few forms of information presentation that confine other media. We are not limited to prose, whether it is in the inverted pyramid or some other structure. The Web lets us think laterally about what information a reader might need or want and what form that information should take. Editors and writers for the Web, if they are to take full advantage of their medium and if they want to attract and hold a large audience, must consider these forms and must tailor their reporting, writing, and editing efforts to produce them when necessary.

Just what forms are we talking about? The following is a partial list of forms, some of which are very much part of other media (pictures in printed media and

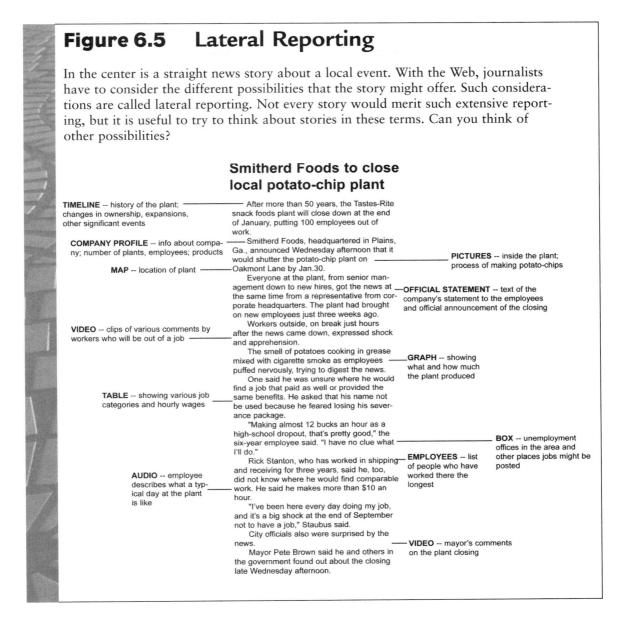

Figure 6.5   Lateral Reporting

In the center is a straight news story about a local event. With the Web, journalists have to consider the different possibilities that the story might offer. Such considerations are called lateral reporting. Not every story would merit such extensive reporting, but it is useful to try to think about stories in these terms. Can you think of other possibilities?

Smitherd Foods to close local potato-chip plant

After more than 50 years, the Tastes-Rite snack foods plant will close down at the end of January, putting 100 employees out of work.

Smitherd Foods, headquartered in Plains, Ga., announced Wednesday afternoon that it would shutter the potato-chip plant on Oakmont Lane by Jan.30.

Everyone at the plant, from senior management down to new hires, got the news at the same time from a representative from corporate headquarters. The plant had brought on new employees just three weeks ago.

Workers outside, on break just hours after the news came down, expressed shock and apprehension.

The smell of potatoes cooking in grease mixed with cigarette smoke as employees puffed nervously, trying to digest the news.

One said he was unsure where he would find a job that paid as well or provided the same benefits. He asked that his name not be used because he feared losing his severance package.

"Making almost 12 bucks an hour as a high-school dropout, that's pretty good," the six-year employee said. "I have no clue what I'll do."

Rick Stanton, who has worked in shipping and receiving for three years, said he, too, did not know where he would find comparable work. He said he makes more than $10 an hour.

"I've been here every day doing my job, and it's a big shock at the end of September not to have a job," Staubus said.

City officials also were surprised by the news.

Mayor Pete Brown said he and others in the government found out about the closing late Wednesday afternoon.

TIMELINE -- history of the plant; changes in ownership, expansions, other significant events

COMPANY PROFILE -- info about company; number of plants, employees; products

MAP -- location of plant

VIDEO -- clips of various comments by workers who will be out of a job

TABLE -- showing various job categories and hourly wages

AUDIO -- employee describes what a typical day at the plant is like

PICTURES -- inside the plant; process of making potato-chips

OFFICIAL STATEMENT -- text of the company's statement to the employees and official announcement of the closing

GRAPH -- showing what and how much the plant produced

BOX -- unemployment offices in the area and other places jobs might be posted

EMPLOYEES -- list of people who have worked there the longest

VIDEO -- mayor's comments on the plant closing

video in broadcast, for instance) and some of which are particularly applicable to the Web.

Background, Details, and Lists

Most reporters have far more information than they can appropriately put in their inverted pyramid stories. This kind of information includes names, addresses, telephone numbers, and e-mail and website addresses of people and organizations that are involved in the news. A reporter who had covered previous events that have led up to a story may not be able to put all of that in a straight inverted pyramid structure but could build a timeline. The possibilities for this kind of information are many and vary from situation to situation. What a reporter or writer should do is to consider what would be useful to the website's visitors.

Pictures

Photographs allow readers to visualize the subjects of a story. They are popular in the print media and are just as effective on a website. In addition, a website is not confined by the same space considerations that newspapers, magazines, and newsletters have, so pictures can be used much more extensively. More and more, the profession of journalism is demanding that the reporter report not just with words but also with a camera.

Graphics

Some information is better suited to a graphic form than to a text paragraph. Graphics help readers to visualize information. Graphics are particularly suitable for presenting numerical information. They can also illustrate events, processes, and procedures that cannot be photographed.

Maps

Location is an important concept for many people in understanding information. We like to know where things are and where events occur. Providing maps, either geographic or illustrative, can give a reader a greater sense of understanding about a story.

Documents

A reporter who covers a speech for a newspaper is generally confined to writing an inverted pyramid–style story about that speech. If there is space in the paper, an editor may run a photograph along with the story. But what if the reader reads the story and then wants to read the full text of the speech? A newspaper generally does not have the space to do that, but it can be put on a website.

Court opinions, laws, policy statements, organizational reports—all of these can be included with a news report. Some book review sections are including the full text of the first chapter of books they review. (This must be done with the permission of the publisher, of course, but many publishers consent because they believe that this will help to sell copies of the book.) A set of instructions on how to use, assemble, or build a product referred to in a story is another type of document that might be included on a site.

Previous Stories

One of the easiest things to produce is a list of previous stories that a website has published about an event. This list, appropriately linked, gives the reader some background and context without a great deal of effort on the part of the writer or editor.

Audio and Video Clips

The Web allows a true merger of broadcast and print journalism by letting reporters and editors include audio and video with their stories. Thus, a reporter covering a city council meeting can write a full story on the meeting and include a clip of some of the debate on the most important issues. Currently, the practice is to keep these clips relatively brief—usually less than two minutes—because of their size (they can take up a lot of room of a server) and because readers may not have computers that allow them to download and view large audio or video packages.

Links to Other Websites

A good website on a particular topic can provide a great deal of information for the reader, but editors and writers should be careful about linking to other sites for the following reasons: First, links can take readers out of the news website, and they might not return. This tendency can be limited somewhat with pop-up windows and frames, but sometimes these devices are irritating to readers. Second, another website may not be as substantial as it appears. You do not want to promise the reader something and then not deliver it.

Figuring out where to put links is another issue in placing links on a page. Some people prefer that links be within the text so that the reader can have instant access to them. Others maintain that a list of links at the side of an article is less distracting and just as useful. Still other editors and writers prefer a list of related links at the end of the story so that once a reader finishes reading the entire piece, he or she can go somewhere else.

Wherever they are, links are an essential part of Web journalism. They take advantage of one of the Web's strengths, and they allow the user to participate in choosing the information that he or she wants to see. A good set of links with any story shows that the writers and editors of a site have taken the time and effort to provide the reader with a wide range of information.

E-Polls

An e-poll or online survey offers readers a question and a set of responses. The reader can click on a response and submit that to the site. Readers can also see how others have responded to the same question. E-polls are not scientific samplings of general public opinion or even the opinions of those who have visited the site, but they are highly popular items for many news sites because they are a quick and easy way of allowing readers to respond to what they read.

Discussion Forums

These, too, are popular interactive devices for readers, and many news sites are finding ways to take advantage of them. A discussion forum allows readers to respond to an event, issue, or topic of current debate. Those responses are posted on a part of the website where everyone can see them and add their own responses. The responses may be monitored by an editor (although not always), and inappropriate or irrelevant responses should not be allowed.

A chat room allows users to enter into an e-mail-type discussion with others who are interested in the topic at hand. The chat room is usually conducted on a real-time basis. That is, statements and responses can be seen immediately, and the discussion can be ongoing.

A variation on the discussion forum is the question-and-answer forum that a site may conduct. This involves a reporter or someone familiar with an event or topic who can answer questions about that subject. Discussions can be viewed live (that is, text can be read as it is created), giving viewers an added sense of participation. The text can then be preserved so that it can be read later.

Setting up the forms of information and presentation that we have discussed in this section is not particularly difficult technically. The hard work is thinking about what information might be helpful to a visitor, gathering that information, and putting it into a form that would be useful. News sites find themselves limited not by the technology it takes to present information, but by the personnel and brainpower that are required to gather, organize, and prepare it.

Figure 6.6   Web Package

If some of the suggestions of lateral reporting in Figure 6.5 had been followed, a Web package might look like this. Take note of the three-paragraph introduction. Rather than using the first three paragraphs of the main story, the editors have written a different introduction for the entire package. Now look over the entire page. Are there other aspects of the story that the news organization might have covered?

THE DAILY NEWS ONLINE

Good morning, 8:10 a.m., Dec. 1

NEWS
SPORTS
BUSINESS
FEATURES
OBITUARIES
CLASSIFIEDS
FEATURED ADS

ABOUT DN
STAFF
CONTACT US
PRIVACY

Smitherd to close local potato-chip plant

More than 100 will be out of a job by next February unless Smithherd Foods reconsiders its decision to close the Oakmont Lane potato-chip plant. The plant made Tastes-Rite potato chips.

Employees, who found out about the closing yesterday were stunned. So was Mayor Pete Brown, who said he had not clue that this was coming.

Check out the links on this page as the Daily News Online gives you full coverage of this important story. *Main story*

John Berringer, plant manager, makes the announcement that the plant will close. Photo by John Ray.

Resources

The area has a number of offices and agencies to help the unemployed get hired. The Daily News has put together a list. *More*

Timeline
Plant has 50-year history

The Oakmont Lane plant opened more than 50 years ago and has been through many changes and expansions. *Timeline*

Photo gallery
How do you make a potato chip?

Go inside the plant with Daily News photojournalist Tim Hudson and see what it's like to make a potato chip. *Photo gallery*

Employee Laurie Leland says she doesn't know what she's going to do for a job when the plant closes. Photo by John Ray.

Tell us your story

Have you recently lost a job but found another one? Tell us how you did it. Your story may help an Oakmont Lane plant worker. *More*

Company profile
Smithherd worldwide company

The company that owns the Oakmont Lane plant is based in Plains, Ga., but it has a reach that is global.
Company profile
GRAPH: What the plant produced
OFFICIAL STATEMENTS on closings

Employees
Afternoon of sadness

Employees had no idea they would be losing their jobs when they came to work yesterday morning. Find out how they feel about it -- and what they may do,
AUDIO: Rick Stanton speaks
VIDEO: Donnie Graves on a day at work

Do you have a job for a good employee?
Post a free notice *here.*

See Mayor Pete Brown's comments about the closing on our exclusive *VIDEO.*

NEWS | SPORTS | BUSINESS | FEATURES | OBITUARIES | CLASSIFIEDS | FEATURED ADS
ABOUT DN | STAFF | CONTACT US | PRIVACY POLICY

WANTED FOR THE WEB: WRITERS AND EDITORS

In one major sense, the World Wide Web is no different from any other mass medium: It uses words and images to convey information. Words are its chief tool. Words—not images and not increasingly sophisticated technology—are the way in which websites convey information, ideas, and meaning.

The Web is voracious in its appetite for words and information. Every website becomes a beast, and it is imperative for the producers of the site to "feed the beast." Many people who begin websites do not understand this dynamic, believing that once a site is up, it can be left alone and will continue to gain an audience. What these people discover is that information can quickly become stale or perishable. New information must constantly be prepared.

That is why the Web is being inherited by people who can gather information, make sense of it, and present it to an audience in a satisfying way. The Web will always need writers and good writing.

POINTS FOR CONSIDERATION AND DISCUSSION

1. Which websites do you regularly visit? Why?
2. Do you use the Web to find specific material or just to surf and see what's there?
3. Do you have an idea for a website that no one else has done? What kind of information would that site contain? How would it be written and reported?
4. Some people say that loading time—the time it takes for a site to appear fully on a computer screen—is critical to a site's retaining visitors. Others argue that loading time is not nearly as critical as some believe. What do you think? How patient are you in letting sites load onto your computer?

FURTHER READING

Blood, R. (2000). "Weblogs: A History and Perspective." *Rebecca's Pocket,* September 7, 2000, http://www.rebeccablood.net/essays/weblog_history.html

Kramer, S. (2004). "RSS Feeds Can Build Web Traffic, but Fence Sitters Note Problems." *Online Journalism Review,* June 4, 2004, http://ojr.org/ojr/technology/1086293132.php

Lasica, J. D. (2004). "Surf's Down as More Netizens Turn to RSS for Browsing." *Online Journalism Review,* May 5, 2004, http://ojr.org/ojr/workplace/1083806402.php

Nielsen Norman Group Report (Jakob Nielsen). (n.d.). "Email Newsletter Usability," http://www.nngroup.com/reports/newsletters/summary.html

Stovall, J. G. (2004). *Web Journalism: Practice and Promise of a New Medium.* Boston: Allyn and Bacon.

WEBSITES

Cyberjournalist.net: **www.cyberjournalist.net**

Online Journalism Review: **www.ojr.org**

Poynter Institute: **www.poynter.org**

World Wide Web Consortium: **www.w3.org**

(an excellent place to find out about HTML and many other things about the Web)

EXERCISES

6.1 Writing for the Web

Take the following information and write a short inverted pyramid news story for a local news website. Before you begin, think about the concepts and principles discussed in this chapter. How would a story for the Web be different from one that you would write for print? Do you need more information than what is given here? Include a headline and a summary for your story, and follow the directions and advice of your instructor.

- Bridge over Roaring Creek; washed out by a flood last year. Bridge was more than 75 years old.

- County has been working on getting it fixed ever since then.

- Roland Lively: "The bridge was not in great shape when it was destroyed. We already had some money in the county budget for repairs. Problem was, we didn't have enough to replace the bridge. We were just going to repair it. Fortunately, some state and federal money was available, and we were able to do it a lot quicker than we had expected." Lively is the department head of the County Department of Transportation.

- Bridge cost $700,000 to replace.

- County paid $100,000 of the cost; state paid $200,000; U.S. Department of Transportation funds were $400,000.

- Bridge is a 33-foot span over Roaring Creek along Roaring Creek Road.

- When the bridge went out, it created a bad hardship for the Oak Grove neighborhood, just north of Roaring Creek off Roaring Creek Road, because when the bridge was passable, the neighborhood was only about a mile away from Highway 19, a main route into Midville, where lots of people in the Oak Grove neighborhood work. With the bridge out, residents had to drive a lot farther, north up Roaring Creek Road to Highway 111, east to Rice Mine Road and then south to where it runs into Highway 19—a total of more than 9 miles.

- Oak Grove resident Josh Spiva: "Traveling all that way has made it very inconvenient for a lot of people. We've had to use a lot of time and gasoline just to make what otherwise would be very short trips. Having this bridge erected so quickly is a blessing." Spiva is an attorney in Midville.

- Official opening ceremonies: this morning at 11. Attending: Midville Mayor Seth Montana. There'll also be U.S. Congressman Nancy Draughorn, a Democrat, and United States Senator Warren Johns, a Republican.

- Bridge has actually been open for a couple of weeks. Residents say they're happy.

6.2 Linking

Read through the story below and select at least three things that could be made into links where readers could get additional information. Rewrite the sentences where you have chosen to put links so that they include the HTML tags. For instance, the first sentence with a link for the Civil War might be the following:

Matthew Brady is the chief source of the images we have of the <a href=http://www.civilwar.com/>American Civil War,</a> and according a local historian, he is the chief source of the way in which we look at ourselves.

(Refer to the part of the chapter that discusses this if necessary.) You may need to use a search engine such as Google or Yahoo to find the appropriate links. Follow the directions of your instructor in completing this exercise.

Matthew Brady is the chief source of the images we have of the American Civil War, and according a local historian, he is the chief source of the way in which we look at ourselves.

The citizens of Ticonderoga County will have a marvelous chance to take a look into that mirror beginning today with a major exhibit of Brady photographs. The exhibit includes more than 150 unretouched images that Brady took during his more than 30 years of photography in the last half of the 19th century. They include some of the famous photographs that we have seen many times, such as portraits of Abraham Lincoln and a variety of Civil War leaders from both the north and the South.

They also include some rarely seen battlefield images that recorded for history the horror and devastation of the war.

"Brady took an unblinking and unromantic look at the civil conflict that erupted in our nation in the 1860s," David Sloan, a history professor at Ticonderoga College, said. Sloan is the chief consultant for the Hyatt Museum in putting the exhibit together.

"Brady gave us an image of ourselves and that image is not very attractive," Sloan said.

Sloan gives much of the credit for the photographs we have to Brady's assistant, Alexander Gardner, who made many dangerous trips near the battle lines to take the photographs in the Brady collection.

"We have forgotten about Gardner," Sloan said, "but we really shouldn't. He took as many photographs as Brady.

The reason we remember Brady, Sloan said, is because of the studio photos of practically every famous person of the day.

"When you were in New York in the 1850s, the 'in' thing to do was to visit Brady's studio and have your picture taken," Sloan said. "Everyone did it, from the not-so-famous to the very famous. Even European royalty knew to drop by."

The exhibit hours are 9 a.m. to 5 p.m. Monday through Saturday, and 1 p.m. to 5 p.m. on Sunday. A reception to open the exhibit will be held at the museum Thursday night. Admission to the exhibit is free.

6.3 Headlines and Summaries

The following stories have label headlines. Write sentence headlines and summaries for each. Follow the directions of your instructor as to the type of summary (or summaries) that you should write.

DWINDLING FAMILY FARMS

Family farms in Ticonderoga County have been dwindling steadily for more than 40 years now, and agricultural officials say there is no comeback in sight.

"Our image is that the family farm is the backbone of America, the ultimate expression of American values," Jeff Mackey, professor of sociology at Ticonderoga College, said.

"Unfortunately, the family farm is becoming as rare as the dinosaur," he said.

That is certainly the case in Ticonderoga County, where in 1955 the U.S. Department of Agriculture said there were more than 800 working farms. A farm is defined by the department as land on which $1,000 worth of farm produce was made or could have been made during the year.

NEW HOTEL REFERENDUM

Residents of Elizabeth City will be asked in June whether they approve of using public funds for a new downtown hotel and convention center, even though there is no specific recommendation for such a project.

In a technical compliance with a recommendation from the state Department of Elections, the Ticonderoga County Election Commission on Thursday voted to put the referendum on the ballot.

It will be on the June 5 ballot, and only city residents will be able to vote on the question. It will simply ask for a yes or no vote on whether public funds should be used for such a project.

Although City Commission members approved an ordinance to prohibit any public funding for a hotel and convention center shortly after the petition was certified, state Coordinator of Elections Bailey Throckton said the referendum still must be held.

"Putting this on the ballot is appropriate," Ticonderoga County Commissioner of Elections McKenzie Martin said at Thursday's meeting of the commission.

TEN COMMANDMENTS LEGAL BATTLE

Officials seeking to keep the Ten Commandments mounted in the Ticonderoga County Courthouse lost the first round of a federal legal battle over the display Thursday.

Attorneys representing the County sought unsuccessfully to convince U.S. District Judge Verdie Johnston that Midville attorney John O'Kelly had no standing to sue over the display because he isn't a Ticonderoga County resident or a regular user of the courthouse there.

Manford Mabley, an attorney with the Religion and Justice Institute and co-counsel for Ticonderoga County, said O'Kelly shouldn't be allowed to sue because he had only visited the courthouse once before the American Civil Liberties Union filed the suit on his behalf.

Mabley argued that O'Kelly didn't have "frequent, direct contact" with the display and therefore had suffered no specific injury.

BASEBALL COACH CHANGE

Rickey Rust is trying to look at the bright side after being "forced to resign" as baseball coach at Ticonderoga County High School.

"I've already had one offer to be an assistant and there's no doubt in my mind I'll end up somewhere," he said. "Everything happens for a reason and this will end up being a positive for me."

Rust was head coach at County for 12 years.

During that stretch, the Beavers won either regular-season district titles or district tournaments six times.

Ticonderoga won 177 games during the Rust tenure, an average of nearly 15 per season.

6.4 Headlines and Summaries

The following stories have label headlines. Write sentence headlines and summaries for each. Follow the directions of your instructor as to the type of summary (or summaries) that you should write.

ACCIDENT AT SUBWAY CENTRAL

A restaurant patron died of a heart attack today after an automobile crashed through the front window of the restaurant where he was dining.

John Barker, 59, a resident of the Roaring Creek Community, died at Memorial Hospital. Barker was sitting in the Subway Central Restaurant shortly after noon today when a car crashed through the large plate glass window.

The car was driven by Annie Coulter, 82, of Midville. Police said Coulter reported that the brakes on her car failed as she swerved to avoid a pedestrian. Coulter was hurt in the accident.

Barker was not hit by the car but did receive minor cuts from flying glass. Moments after the accident, however, Barker complained about pains in his chest. He was then taken to Memorial Hospital.

No other injuries were reported.

SCHOOL SYSTEM RESTAURANT

After a decade of running The Eatery on State Street, the Ticonderoga County school system has decided to get out of the restaurant business.

The restaurant, where special-education students came during the school day to work and learn about the food-service industry, will close at the end of this school year.

The move will save the school system $20,000 to $50,000 a year, according to school spokesman Randall Styles, whose office in the downtown Franklin Pierce Building is just upstairs from the restaurant.

"It will certainly save us money to close The Eatery," said Styles, who ate lunch at the conveniently located restaurant almost daily for the past three years. "But it's something that is not needed anymore because we can provide the same level of instruction at other facilities."

The school system has relationships with some 80 other Midville-area restaurants, where special-education students can get experience preparing food and waiting on customers, according to Ray Coward, who runs the school program.

TICKET FOR DOG BITING

Police ticketed a dog owner Thursday after his pet bit a 6-year-old child around the ear and neck.

Midville Police Department officers and an animal control officer found the child about 7:30 p.m. at an apartment at 1240 Victor Ave., said MPD spokesman Darnell Wright. The child was treated at Children's Hospital for minor injuries.

Gordy Jamison was issued a citation for having a vicious dog, Wright said.

This is the second time Jamison's dog, a mixed Chow, has bitten a small child, Wright said.

The first incident occurred last year. Jamison was cited for a leash law violation, and the dog was quarantined for 10 days, Wright said. After that, Jamison obtained tags for the dog and got its shots up to date.

6.5 Writing for Web Packages

Take a look at Figure 6.6 earlier in the chapter. It shows how a news story has been turned into a Web package that offers readers a variety of items related to the subject. This is an example of lateral reporting. One of the most important parts of the package is the introduction, which must be carefully written to reflect the substance of the package. Another such package is shown on the following page, though—as you can see—it does not have an introduction. The main story of the package is also given here. Your assignment is to look at the different items the package contains, read the main story, and then write a three-paragraph introduction to the package. Use the introduction in the illustration for Figure 6.6 as a model.

Main Story

SOCCER ASSOCIATION "KICKS GRASS" TO OPEN SEASON

Soccer—a kick in the grass.

That's this year's motto for the upcoming season of the Upper East Tennessee Soccer Association, which begins this weekend.

Here in Ticonderoga County, the Ticonderoga County Soccer Association, an affiliate of the UETSA, will also begin its schedule of league play this weekend.

Milo Schmitt, the president of the local association, said that more people will be playing soccer this year than at any time during the association's 15-year history.

"Right now, we have more than 500 kids signed up to play on all of our teams," he said. "That number could grow because a few teams still have some open spots."

Schmitt said that those who are interested in playing should contact the local YMCA, which handles most of the administration of the soccer league.

Schmitt said the association is sponsoring six leagues this year, and there are at least four teams in each league. Overall, there are some 27 teams. The leagues are divided by age.

Schmitt said that girls and boys play together until they are 12 years old. After that, they play in separate leagues. The soccer association has one league for girls who range from 12 to 14 years in age.

"All of our coaches have been to at least one coaching clinic, and several of them have been coaching soccer for a number of years," Schmitt said. "I believe the caliber of playing and coaching in our leagues will be better than ever."

Last year, teams from Ticonderoga County won regional championships in the 8-year-old and 12-year-old divisions. The 12-year-old all-star team went on to win the Tri-State Championship.

"We are awfully proud of that team," Schmitt said.

But, he emphasized, the program is designed to teach kids to play soccer and to let them have fun. Winning, he said, is secondary.

"We like to focus on skills," he said. "The better a kid can play, the more fun he or she will have. We let winning or losing take care of itself.

THE DAILY NEWS *ONLINE*

Good morning, 8:10 a.m., Sept. 1

NEWS
SPORTS
BUSINESS
FEATURES
OBITUARIES
CLASSIFIEDS
FEATURED ADS

ABOUT DN
STAFF
CONTACT US
PRIVACY

Resources

Want to know more about the game of soccer? The Daily News provides you with dozens of links to finding out more about the game. *More*

Join the forum

Passionate about soccer? Got an opinion on how the game should be played. Express your opinion and read those of others at the Daily News forum, online, right now. *More*

Soccer gear
Best stuff
Best prices
Give us a look

headline
headline

Copy

VIDEO: View last year's UETSA championship game from the archives of the Daily News archives.

Web extra
UETSA: Who's in charge

The Upper East Tennessee Soccer Association: Who's in charge? Who are the coaches? The Referees? The Daily news has all the people in charge. **Click here.**

Photo gallery
Playing the game

The Daily News has compiled the best photos from last year's UETSA soccer season. Take a look and catch the soccer fever. **Photo gallery**

Rules of the game
How to play soccer

Whether you're playing or just watching, you need to know what's going on. Become an expert.
Official rules
GRAPH: How teams line up
GRAPH: What's offsides.

Schedule
When and where they will play

Get a complete practice and game schedule for the upcoming season.
TABLE: Soccer schedule

Last year's season had some exciting moments and Daily News photographer John Ray captured many of them. Photo by John Ray. Click here for audio.

Schmitt said he has been gratified at the increased interest in the game of soccer during the last five years. In 1990, he said, the association had barely 100 kids playing in all its leagues.

"The big thing that sparked interest in the game was the World Cup that took place in the United States in 1994," he said. "Lots of people looked at that and decided that soccer could be fun to watch and fun to play."

Schmitt pointed out that soccer is a simple and inexpensive game to learn and play. Most parents spend less than $100 per season for their child to play soccer. That includes the league dues, he said.

6.6 Lateral Reporting

Review the section in this chapter on lateral reporting. Then read the story below. How would you apply lateral reporting to this story to make it the centerpiece for a Web package? What other information would you include? Where would that information come from? Make a list of the items you would include and sources of information. Be as specific as possible. You might even want to sketch out how you think the package should look. After that, write an introduction for the package along the lines of the one found in the illustration in Figure 6.6.

CABLE RATES SET TO RISE—AGAIN

MacGlobal Communications, the major cable television provider for Midville and Ticonderoga County, announced today that it would be increasing rates for most of its cable services—the third such increase in the last five years.

MacGlobal will increase its rate for its basic cable service $1.50, according to Mindy McDermott, assistant manager of the company. The rates will take effect in two months.

"Many of our costs have gone up during the last six months," Woody Wilson, assistant director for communication at MacGlobal, said in making the announcement about the new rates.

Several premium cable channels such as ESPN, Cable News Network, Arts and Entertainment, and the Shopping Channel have increased their costs to the cable operators, Wilson said.

"We have absorbed many of those costs, but we can no longer do so and continue to provide the premium service that our customers have come to expect," Wilson said.

The new rates will go into effect in three months.

Customers now paying $37.50 for the basic cable packages—70 channels but no premium channels—will be paying $39. Other cable packages will also be increasing. For instance, the Basic Plus service—the basic package plus two premium movie channels—will increase from $49 to $52.

Wilson said the rate that MacGlobal charges for its high-speed Internet service will not change.

The announcement from MacGlobal provoked a storm of criticism from several quarters, including Bryce McFee, Fourth District city councilman and candidate for mayor of Midville.

"The cable customer in this city simply cannot stand another increase—particularly when there is no competition among cable providers," McFee said.

McFee blamed the increase on Mayor Ernest Trotman, his opponent in the election who has accepted campaign donations from MacGlobal. "Obviously, with the money it has given to the mayor's campaign, MacGlobal feels as if it has the go-ahead to lay these increases on the consumer," McFee said.

McFee said his campaign was filing a motion in the county circuit court for an injunction against the cable company to stop the increase until the city council can investigate the company.

The mayor's office had no comment on the fee increase or McFee's charges.

6.7 Weblogs

Select a topic that you are particularly interested in and knowledgeable about. It could be a hobby, your college's sports program, your professional interest, fashion, food, exercise, or any number of other subjects. Pretend that you have a weblog on that topic. Go on the Web and find out all you can about the topic, particularly the latest information.

Over about a three-day period (or however long your instructor designates), write at least five weblog entries on that topic. The entries should contain comments about the topic and any new information you have picked up. They should also contain links to websites that you refer to or to sites where readers can get additional information.

Each entry should be less than 100 words long. It should be written with all the characteristics of media writing in mind: accuracy, precision, clarity, and efficiency. But you should not hesitate to express your point of view about the information you are presenting.

If necessary, go over the section on weblogs in this chapter, review the example in Figure 6.4, and look at some of the weblogs referred to in the chapter.

7

Writing for Broadcast

broadcasting is the world's most pervasive medium of mass communication. It is not unusual for the American home to receive fifty or more television channels via its cable system or satellite dish. A wide variety of radio stations has been available to anyone with a receiver since the early days of the medium. Underdeveloped areas that cannot get access to even a newspaper will usually have a transistor radio to link it with the rest of the world. Satellite broadcasting has drawn the world closer together (although not always with positive results) by ensuring that we have instant, live coverage of major news events from almost anywhere in the world and even beyond. Consider the following:

- When Americans first landed on the moon in 1969, a television camera was positioned outside the lunar lander to record the event.
- When Prince Charles, heir to the throne of England, married Lady Diana Spencer in 1981, television cameras were at every part of the event.
- In late 1992, when U.S. Marines invaded Somalia, their landing was met not by hostile forces but by American, European, and Asian television crews who broadcast live pictures of the event all around the world. (The Marines, in fact, complained that the television lights made them more vulnerable to hostile fire.)
- The automobile accident in Paris that took the life of Princess Diana in 1997 was not recorded, of course, but her funeral a week later was watched by people in almost every part of the world.
- The collapse of the World Trade Center towers on Sept. 11, 2001, had an audience of millions because television cameras focused on the scene from the first moments of the attack.

In the United States, broadcasting delivers information with immediacy and impact. Most Americans get their news from a variety of sources, and it would be a mistake to believe that broadcasting is always the dominant medium in this regard. Newspapers, news magazines, and websites deliver a large amount of information to the American public and will continue to do so, but broadcasting is often perceived as dominant. More than 6,000 local radio and television stations in the United States (and thousands more shortwave radio operators) are broadcasting, in contrast to 1,700 daily newspapers.

A person who wants to succeed in the field of broadcasting needs to have intelligence, diligence, dependability—and the ability to write. Even though broadcasting is an audiovisual medium, almost everything you hear or see in the way of news or entertainment has been written down. The occasions for ad libbing before the cameras are relatively rare, and even the "spontaneous" lines that some broadcasters deliver are written and rehearsed. Broadcasters consider air time too valuable to leave to chance. Even reporters doing live news spots often work from notes and have a good understanding of the forms of writing for the medium.

Broadcasters look for the same qualities in writers that have been discussed in other parts of this book. They want people who know the language and its rules of usage; who are willing to research their subjects thoroughly and understand them well enough to report on them with clarity; who do not mind working hard; and who are willing to rewrite their work and have it rewritten by others. In addition, they are particularly interested in people who can write under pressure and can meet deadlines.

Writing for broadcasting is similar in many ways to writing for the print media, but there are some important differences. Those differences concern the way in which news is selected for broadcast, the characteristics of writing and story structure, and the style with which the information is presented.

SELECTION OF NEWS

Most of the same news values that we discussed in Chapter 4 apply to news selection for broadcasting. Broadcast journalists are interested in events that have a wide impact, people in the news, current issues, events that happen close to home, and conflicts or unusual happenings. Because of the opportunities and limitations of their medium, however, broadcasters are likely to view such events in different ways than their counterparts in print or web journalism. Following are some of the factors that broadcasters use to select news.

Timeliness

Because of the nature of their medium, broadcasters often consider timeliness the most important news value. Broadcasters work on hourly, or less than hourly, cycles. A news broadcaster may go on the air several times a day. The news must be up-to-the-minute. News that is more than an hour or two old may be too stale for the broadcaster. When you listen to a news report about a breaking news story, you expect to hear the very latest news—what happened just a few minutes before.

Information, Not Explanation

Broadcasters look for stories that do not need a lot of explanation for listeners or viewers to understand them. They prefer stories that are simple and can be told in a straightforward manner. The maximum length for almost any story on a television newscast is two minutes; the more normal length is twenty to thirty seconds. In some larger markets, radio reporters are being told to reduce their story lengths to ten seconds and actualities (using the actual voice of the source) to five seconds. That amount of time is not enough to explain a complex story. It is only enough time to give the listener or viewer a few pertinent facts. Of course, some stories are both complex and important, and explanation cannot be avoided. Still, even with complex and important stories, the broadcast writer must wrestle with condensing these stories to their essence.

Audio or Visual Impact

Broadcasters want stories that their audience can hear or see. Playing part of the president's state of the union address is more dramatic than a news reporter talking about it; pictures of a flood are more likely to be watched than an anchor's description of it. Broadcasters often choose stories for their newscasts because they have sound or pictures, even though the stories themselves might not merit such attention otherwise. This is one of the major criticisms of broadcast news, but audio or visual impact remains one of the chief factors in news story selection.

CHARACTERISTICS OF WRITING

A 1960s edition of the *UPI Broadcast Stylebook* says that while print journalism has the five Ws, broadcast journalism has the Four Cs: correctness, clarity, conciseness, and color. These four Cs still serve as the basis for broadcast writing and form a good framework for talking about broadcast writing styles.

The first commitment of the broadcast journalist is to correctness, or accuracy. Everything a broadcast journalist does must contribute to the telling of an accurate story. Even though the broadcast journalist must observe some strict rules about how stories are written, these rules should contribute to, not prevent, an accurate account of an event.

One of the most admirable characteristics of good broadcast writing is its clarity. Good broadcast writers employ clear, precise language that contains no ambiguity. Clarity is an absolute requirement for broadcast writing. Listeners and viewers cannot go back and rehear a news broadcast as they might be able to read a newspaper account more than once. They must understand what is said the first time. Broadcast writers achieve this kind of clarity by using simple sentences and familiar words, by avoiding the use of pronouns and repeating proper nouns if necessary, and by keeping the subject close to the verb in their sentences. Most of all, however, they achieve clarity by thoroughly knowing and understanding their subject.

Another important characteristic of writing for broadcast is its conversational style. Even the clearest, simplest newspaper style tends to sound stilted when it is read aloud. Broadcast writing must sound more conversational because people will be reading it aloud. Broadcast news should be written for the ear, not the eye. The writer should keep in mind that someone is going to say the words and others will listen to them.

This casual or conversational style, however, does not give the writer freedom to break the rules of grammar, to use slang or off-color phrasing, or to use language that might be offensive to listeners. As with all writing, the broadcast writer should try to focus attention on the content of the writing and not the writing itself. Nor is casual-sounding prose particularly easy to produce. It takes a finely tuned ear for the language and a conciseness that we do not normally apply to writing.

Another characteristic of writing for broadcast is the emphasis on the immediate. Although past tense verbs are preferred in the print media, broadcasters use the present tense as much as possible. A newspaper or website story might begin something like this:

> The president said Tuesday that he will support some limited tax increase proposals when Congress reconvenes this week.

A broadcast news story might begin with this:

> The president says he's for higher taxes.

Another way of emphasizing the immediate is to omit the time element in the news story and assume that everything has happened close to the time of the broadcast. In the example above, the broadcast version has no time element, since it would probably be heard on the day the president made that statement. The elimination of the time element cannot occur in every story. Sometimes the time element is important and must be mentioned.

The tight phrasing that characterizes broadcast writing is one of its chief assets and one of the most difficult qualities for a beginning writer to achieve. Because time is so short, the broadcaster cannot waste words. The broadcaster must work constantly to simplify and condense. There are a number of techniques for achieving this conciseness. One technique is the elimination of all but the most necessary adjectives and adverbs. Broadcasters know that their stories are built on nouns and verbs, the strongest words in the language. They avoid using the passive voice. Instead, they rely on strong, active verbs that will allow the listener to form a picture of the story.

Another technique of broadcast writing is the use of short, simple sentences. Broadcasters do not need the variety of length and types of sentences that print journalists need to make their copy interesting. Broadcasters can more readily fire information at their readers like bullets in short, simple sentences.

The fourth C of the UPI Stylebook—color—refers to writing that allows the listener to paint a picture of the story or event being reported. This picture can be achieved

Figure 7.1

Thomas Jefferson on writing

The most valuable of all talents is that of never using two words when one will do.

in a variety of ways, such as the inclusion of pertinent and insightful details in the story or allowing the personality of the writer or news reader to come through in a story. The nature of the broadcast medium allows for humor and human interest to inject itself into many stories.

A final characteristic of broadcast writing is its almost complete subjugation to deadlines. Broadcast copy is often written in an atmosphere in which a deadline is imminent. Broadcast writers have to learn to produce in a highly pressurized atmosphere. Unless broadcast writers are able to meet deadlines, their compact, understandable prose will never be heard.

STORY STRUCTURE

The most common structure for broadcast news is called dramatic unity. This structure has three parts: climax, cause, and effect. The climax of the story gives the listener the point of the story in about the same way that the lead of a print news story does; it tells the listener what happened. The cause portion of the story tells why it happened—the circumstances surrounding the event. The effect portion of the story gives the listener the context of the story and possibly some insight into what the story means. The following examples will show how dramatic unity works (note, too, some difference in style rules from print):

> Taxpayers in the state will be paying an average of 15 dollars more in income taxes next year.
>
> The state senate defeated several delaying amendments this afternoon and passed the governor's controversial revenue-raising bill by a 15 to 14 vote. The bill had been the subject of intense debate for more than a week.
>
> The bill now goes to the governor for his signature. Estimates are that the measure will raise about 40 million dollars in new revenue for the state next year. Elementary and secondary education will get most of that money. Passage of the bill is a major victory for the governor and his education program.

Many children in the city school system will begin their classes at least a half hour later next year.

The City School Board last night voted to rearrange the school bus schedule for next year as a cost-cutting measure.

The new schedule will require most elementary school children to begin school one half hour later than they do now. Most high school students will begin one half hour earlier.

Broadcast journalists think of their stories as completed circles rather than inverted pyramids. While the pyramid may be cut without losing the essential facts, the broadcast story, if written in this unified fashion, cannot be cut from the bottom or anywhere else. It stands as a unit. Broadcast journalists and their editors are not concerned with cutting stories after they have been written to make the stories fit into a news broadcast. Rather, stories should be written to fit into an amount of time designated by the editor or news director. For instance, an editor may allot twenty-five seconds for a story. The writer will know this and will write a story that can be read in twenty-five seconds. If the story is longer than it should be, the editor will ask that it be rewritten.

Because they are so brief, broadcast news stories must gain the listeners' attention from the beginning. The first words in the story are extremely important. Getting the listeners' attention is sometimes more important than summarizing the story or giving the most important facts of the story. The broadcast news lead may be short on facts, but if it captures the listener's attention, it has served its purpose. Here is an example:

The lame duck keeps limping along.

Congress met for the third day of its lame-duck session today and again failed to act on the president's gas tax proposals.

The first sentence has very little in the way of facts, but it gets the listener into the story. This sort of story structure is appropriate only for certain stories, however. If the facts of the story are strong enough to gain the listener's attention, they should be used to open the story. For example:

The five-cents-a-gallon gas tax is law.

The governor signed the bill authorizing the tax today while vacationing in Florida.

In both of these examples, the writer has not attempted to tell the whole story in the first sentence. Rather, the stories have attention-getting leads and are then supported by facts and details in subsequent sentences. This structure for broadcast news writing is a common one that should be mastered by the beginning student. Here are some more examples of newspaper stories and the attention-getting leads that could be written for broadcast:

Americans overwhelmingly oppose the taxation of employee benefits, and congressmen who tamper with such tax-free worker benefits may face trouble at the polls, two Roper Organization surveys say.

Keep your hands off employee benefits.

That's what Americans are willing to tell congressmen who want to tax things like retirement payments and educational allowances.

The United States is turning out inferior products that are too costly for foreign customers, and the problems go beyond a strong dollar, high wages, and high taxes, a presidential commission reports.

Many American products aren't worth what we are asking for them.

A lone juror, a city sanitation department supervisor, forced a hung jury and a mistrial of Midville Mayor Reggie Holder's trial on perjury and conspiracy charges involving alleged illegal campaign contributions.

One man has made the difference in the perjury and conspiracy trial of Midville Mayor Reggie Holder.

Stories are measured in time—minutes and seconds. Whereas a newspaper can devote 300 words to a story, a broadcaster may have only twenty to thirty seconds for it. The broadcast writer must keep this time factor in mind during every stage of the writing and editing process. Broadcast news stories cannot go into the detail and explanation that print or web stories can. The broadcast writer has to omit certain facts and explanations if the story is to fit into the time allowed.

BROADCAST WRITING STYLE

The style and customs of broadcast writing differ somewhat from those you have learned for print and Web journalism. Although the *AP Stylebook* is still consulted for many usage questions, broadcast writing has some conventions of its own. Following are some of those conventions.

Sidebar 7.1
Losing the Drawl, the Clip, the Twisted *R*

Henry Higgins was right.

Higgins, the professor in the play and movie *My Fair Lady,* is out to rid Eliza Doolittle of her Cockney accent. Higgins knows that the way she pronounces words would mark her as someone that people in high London society would look down on.

Change the accent, change the person—or at least the attitude that people have toward her.

In practical terms, particularly in today's broadcast media, Higgins was right. His advice to Eliza Doolittle could be given to anyone who is interested in being on the air in broadcast news: Lose the accent.

The nation is filled with many distinctive regional variations in the way we speak. People recognize the Southern drawl, the Brooklyn "thirty" that becomes "toity," the Boston "ah" that turns "ask" to "ahh-sk," the Texas twang, and the Midwestern clip. In certain parts of life, these accents are interesting and fun.

But this is not the case in broadcasting, where the important thing is not how the broadcaster sounds but what he or she says. If a broadcaster's accent distracts from the information he or she is trying to present, the broadcaster is less effective as a journalist and, chances are, will not be able to advance from a regional station where the accent is not noticed. Instead, broadcasters should learn standard American speech so that the accent will not be an issue.

Losing an accent is no small task. We grow up speaking and hearing certain sounds and patterns, and most of us never think about them. In addition, the process of losing an accent can sometimes cause ill feelings among family and friends.

Many people entering the field of broadcast news hire speech coaches and spend many hours practicing new words and new patterns—just like Eliza Doolittle.

Titles usually come before names. Just as in print stories, most people who are mentioned in broadcast stories need to be identified. In broadcast news writing, however, titles almost always precede a name. Consequently, whereas a print story might have "James Baker, former secretary of state," the broadcast journalist would say, "former Secretary of State James Baker."

Avoid abbreviations, even on second reference. Only the most commonly known abbreviations should be used in broadcast writing. The FBI and the UN are two examples. FTC, however, should be spelled out as the Federal Trade Commission.

Avoid direct quotations if possible. Broadcast writers prefer paraphrasing rather than using direct quotations. Direct quotations are hard to handle in broadcast copy because signaling the listener that the statement is a direct quotation is difficult.

Sometimes a direct quotation is essential and should be used. When that is the case, the writer needs to tip the listener off to the fact that a direct quotation is being used. The use of the phrase *quote . . . unquote* is awkward and should be avoided. Instead, use phrases such as *in the words of the speaker, in his own words, used these words,* and *as she put it.*

Attribution should come before a quotation, not after it. The sequence of direct quote–speaker–verb that is the standard in print journalism is not useful for the broadcast writer. Tagging an attribution onto the end of a direct or paraphrased quote is confusing to the listener. The listener should know where the quotation is coming from before hearing the quote.

Use as little punctuation as possible but enough to help the newscaster through the copy. Remember that broadcast news copy will be read by only one person: the news reader. That person should be able to read through the copy as easily as possible. The excessive use of commas, dashes, and semicolons will not help the newscaster.

Numbers and statistics should be rounded off. Whereas a print journalist will want to use an exact figure, a broadcast journalist will be satisfied with a more general figure. Consequently, $4,101,696 in print becomes "more than four million dollars" in broadcast copy.

Numbers themselves are handled somewhat differently than the *AP Stylebook* dictates for print journalists. Here are a few rules about handling numbers in broadcast copy: Numbers one through nine should be spelled out; numbers 10 through 999 should be written as numerals; write out hundred, thousand, million, billion, and use a combination of numerals with these numbers where appropriate (for example, 15-hundred, 10-billion); don't write "a million" or "a billion," but rather use the word *one* (*a* sounds like *eight*).

Personalize the news when possible and appropriate. In the example on page 208 the lead sentence could read, "Gas is going to cost you five cents more a gallon." Where possible and appropriate, broadcast stories should draw the listeners into the story by telling how the story might affect them.

Avoid extended description. "President and chief executive officer of International Widgets John Smith said today . . ." would become "International Widgets President John Smith says . . ."

Avoid using symbols when you write. The dollar sign should never be used, nor should the percent sign. Spell these words out so that there will be no mistake on the part of the news reader.

Use phonetic spelling for unfamiliar and hard-to-pronounce names and words. Again, you are trying to be helpful to the newscaster. Writing "former California governor George Deukmejian (Dook-MAY-gen) . . ." helps the newscaster to get a difficult name over. Notice that the syllable that is emphasized in pronunciation is written in capital letters. Difficult place names also need phonetic spellings. "A car bomb exploded in downtown Caracas (ka-RAH-kus) today . . ." Writers should also be knowledgeable about local pronunciations of place names. For instance, most people know that Louisville, Kentucky, is pronounced LU-ee-vil, but most people do not know that residents of Louisville, Tennessee, and Louisville, Colorado, pronounce the name of their communities as LU-iss-vil. Pronunciation to the broadcast writer is like spelling to the print journalist. It should always be checked if there is any doubt.

Avoid pronouns, and when you have to use them, make sure the referents are clear to the listener. Putting too many pronouns in a story can be an obstacle to the kind of clarity a broadcaster must achieve. For instance, in the following sentences, it is unclear to whom the pronoun is referring: "The president and the chief foreign affairs advisor met yesterday. They discussed his recent trip to the Mideast."

Avoid apposition. An apposition is a word or set of words that renames a noun. In "Tom Smith, mayor of Midville, said today . . . ," the phrase *mayor of Midville* is an appositional phrase. These phrases are deadly in broadcast writing. They slow the newscaster down and confuse the listener. Appositions, when they are found in the middle of sentences, are surrounded by commas. Listeners to broadcast stories do not have the advantage of those commas, however. Consequently, they may hear the example above as ". . . Midville said today . . ." Broadcast writers should keep subjects and verbs as close together as possible.

Use the present tense when it is appropriate. Using the present tense ("the president says" rather than "the president said") is one way in which broadcast writers can bring immediacy to their writing. Care should be taken, however, that using the present tense does not make the broadcaster sound foolish. For instance, if the president made a statement yesterday, a broadcast news story probably should not have the attribution in the present tense. The past tense would be more appropriate. The present tense should be used for action that is very recent or that is continuing.

Avoid dependent clauses at the beginning of sentences. Dependent clauses are troublesome to the broadcast writer because they are confusing and tend to hide the subject of the sentence. For instance, "Stopping on the first leg of his European tour today, the president said he . . ." gives the listener too much to digest before getting to the main point of the story. The broadcast writer should always remember that the simple sentence—subject, verb, object—is the best format to use.

BROADCAST COPY PREPARATION

Copy is prepared for one person: the announcer. The copy should be presented in a way to make the announcer's job as easy as possible (see Figure 7.2). Different stations and news organizations will have rules about how to prepare copy. The following list should give you an idea of the kinds of rules the station will employ:

- Type only one story on a page. A story should have some ending mark, such as "—30—", at the end.

- Use caps and lowercase. An old style of broadcast writing (and the one that you can see in some of the examples in this chapter) was to capitalize everything. That is changing. The all-caps style is hard to read.

- Don't carry a paragraph over to another page. If a story is more than a page long, end the page at the end of a paragraph, and begin the next page with a new paragraph.

- Don't hyphenate at the end of a line.

- Broadcasters often want to work tapes (either audio or video) of interviews into their stories. The following example shows you how to indicate this on your copy.

Figure 7.2   Broadcast Copy

This is the script sheet for the beginning of a local news broadcast. The directions on the left indicate that videotape or film is being shown while the announcer is speaking.

Slug Williams lands	Page _____ 1 _____
Directions	**Script**

Directions	Script	
TWO SHOT	(2 shot) (s) Good evening, I'm Richard Scott. (H) and I'm Hallie Jones.	1

ON JONES/ FF
SHUTTLE
LANDING
	*****
	    Latrell Williams, welcome home.
	    That's what Mercury College said today to its one-time All-American linebacker and newly hired football coach.	

ROLLCSS--VO----
Mercury Fliers
football clip;
Williams greeted
by athletic
department staff
	Williams was hired last January after longtime Coach Harold Reynolds retired. Williams has been an assistant coach at Cotter College in Cotter, Michigan.
	    He arrived on campus today as permanent resident of the city, moved into his office and met with his assistant coaches.
	    Williams was met by the Mercury College athletic staff. He told them his goal was to make them part of a QUOTE "championship team."	

ON JONES/CU	Williams played for Mercury from 1992 to 1995. (2 shot)	

People who want to buy a Chevrolet next year are going to have to pay more. That's what company spokesman John Smith said today in Detroit. The new cars will cost about seven percent more than last year's cars. Smith blamed the increase on the new contract recently negotiated with the United Auto Workers.

ROLL TAPE: The workers are getting more . . .

END TAPE: . . . really no way of avoiding this.

[:15]

Labor leaders disputed this reasoning, however. Local auto workers president Stanley Porter said Chevrolet was raising its prices just to make the union look bad. At a separate news conference in Detroit, he called on Chevrolet to roll back its prices.

ROLL TAPE: The union gave up a lot . . .

END TAPE: . . . without good reason. [:18]

The number in each of the sets of parentheses indicates the number of seconds of each tape.

Sidebar 7.2
Writing for the Ear

Working in radio is unique. You have only one shot at reaching your listener. Print journalism offers the option to refer back or reread information that might have been overlooked the first time around. Television can use pictures to get the point across. But in radio, every word has to count the first time and help the listener create a picture in his or her mind. Your writing must be clear and engaging.

The best way to connect with radio listeners is to have a conversation with them. Think about how you might tell a story. For example, explain to your Mom what it was like attending your first college class. Or tell your best friend from home about your first campus party. What kind of language would you use? Would you be formal or casual? How would you describe the people you met? What would you say about the places you've been? That's the style you should strive for when writing for radio.

Always keep it conversational—using common, easy-to-understand language. Don't talk down to your listeners in a false, authoritative tone. And never fall into the trap of using the "lingo" of what you're writing about. Consider the following two sentences:

The sick smoker sued for a million dollars.

The plaintiff filed a smoking and health claim for a million dollars in compensatory damages.

The first is simple, clear, and to the point. The second is dull and wordy and could be a major tune-out.

Choose your words carefully. And never use something that you wouldn't say in everyday conversation, even if it does look good on paper. Remember, you're writing for the ear, not the eye.

Debbie Elliott is a correspondent with National Public Radio. She covers the Gulf South region and tobacco litigation for NPR News. She is a graduate of the University of Alabama.

Debbie Elliott

PUTTING TOGETHER A NEWSCAST

Broadcast journalists work with and against time. They use time to measure their stories, but they are also always working against time in the form of tight deadlines. Their stories must be completed for the next newscast. People who work in radio feel this pressure keenly because of the hourly news shows that many radio stations produce. Many local television stations are also producing such hourly newscasts. For the broadcast journalist, the clock is always ticking toward a deadline, and the deadline cannot be delayed.

Many broadcast journalists—even those who are fairly new to the business—must worry not only about writing their stories but also about putting together a newscast. Producing such a newscast, whether it is a forty-five-second news brief or a half-hour telecast, involves many of the skills they learned as news writers.

The first such skill is that of exercising good judgment about what to include in the newscast. Writers must use traditional news values in deciding what events constitute news. Editors and producers use those same values in deciding what goes into a newscast. The key element in putting together newscasts is the timeliness of the stories. A newscast producer looks at the stories that are available and often decides which ones to run on the basis of how recent the stories are. Because broadcasting is a medium that can emphasize the immediate, news producers often take advantage of this quality by telling listeners and viewers what happened only minutes before a newscast.

Timeliness is not the only news value used in these decisions. A story that is the most recent one available will not necessarily be the first one used in a newscast. Stories that have more impact or involve more prominent people may take precedence. All of the other news values come into play in putting together a newscast.

Another element that news producers use in deciding what to put into a newscast is the availability of audiotapes, slides, film, and videotapes. One of the criticisms of broadcast journalism is that decisions about what to run and what not to run are based on the availability of such aids. It is true that often such decisions are made, but broadcast journalists—especially television journalists—feel that they must take advantage of their medium to show a story rather than just tell it. Pictures compel viewers to watch, and the feeling of many people in television is that the "talking head," the news announcer with no visual aid, is not as compelling to the viewer as the talking head with a picture or slide.

Time is the pervasive fact in putting together a newscast. Not only must stories be timely in themselves, but they must also be written to fill a certain amount of air time. The producer or news director is generally the one who assigns the amount of time for a story to fill. The writer must then write a story that can be read in that time. The producer, of course, must have enough copy to fill up the time allotted for the newscast. Sometimes, however, even with the most careful planning, a newscast producer will come up a few seconds short. The producer should always give the announcer more stories than he or she will need in order to fill any extra time.

A news director for radio or television has a variety of formats from which to choose in putting together a newscast. The following is a brief description of some of those formats for radio. Generally, each of these formats, except the minidocumentary, runs for less than a minute.

Written Copy/Voicers

This format is a story without actualities or sound bites.

Sound Bite or Actuality

When possible and appropriate, a radio news writer will want to include some sort of sound effects from the event that is being covered. This actuality may be someone speaking, or it may be some other identifiable sound, such as gunshots or crowd noise, that will give the listeners an added dimension to the story. News anchors introduce the sound bite with the copy they read.

Wrap-Around

In this format, a news anchor briefly introduces a story and the reporter. The reporter then gives the story and includes a sound bite. The sound bite is followed by the reporter giving a conclusion or "tag line."

Minidocumentary

This format allows a story to run for more than a minute, and some run for as much as fifteen minutes. They may include several sound bites with a variety of sources or sounds, such as interviews, noise from events, or even music. A reporter will weave in and out of the minidocumentary, guiding it along for the listener. A news anchor usually introduces a minidocumentary with a short lead-in that sets up what the listener is about to hear. This format is most commonly used on public radio news broadcasts.

Television newscasts can use any of the following formats.

Reader Copy

This format is a story read by an anchor or reporter without visual or audio aid. It may have a slide or graphic in the background.

Voiceovers

A videotape of an event is shown with the sound of the event turned down. An anchor or reporter speaks over the tape to talk about what the viewer is seeing.

Voiceover to Soundbite

An anchor or reporter speaks over a videotape that includes someone talking. The news copy is timed so that when the reporter stops, the sound on the tape is turned up and the person on the tape is heard speaking.

Package Stories

An anchor, using what is called a *lead-in,* introduces a story and the reporter. The prerecorded piece then includes a mix of video, sound bites, voiceovers, and a "stand-up" from the reporter who explains some element of the story or summarizes the entire story. These packages may run for as long as two and a half minutes.

Live Shots

An anchor will introduce a reporter who is shown live at the scene of some news event. The reporter can then do one of several things: present a simple stand-up, interview

Figure 7.3

Edward R. Murrow on the use of television

This instrument [television] can teach, it can illuminate; yes, it can even inspire. But it can do so only to the extent that humans are determined to use it to those ends. Otherwise, it is merely wires and lights in a box. There is a great and perhaps decisive battle to be fought against ignorance, intolerance, and indifference. This weapon of television could be useful. . . .

someone, introduce and voiceover a videotape, or answer questions from the anchor. Satellite technology now allows even local news departments to use such live shots frequently.

CONCLUSION

The nature of broadcast news is changing dramatically, and the technology that is developing for broadcasters is placing new demands on broadcast journalists. Computer editing stations, allowing the reporter to do all of the editing of both videotape and copy on a single workstation, will give reporters more direct control in producing their stories. These systems will also allow reporters to call up file footage—videotapes that may have run in previous stories—for use or reference. Those entering the field of broadcast news must be increasingly computer-oriented.

Another development is the increased use of satellite technology to produce live shots from the scene of news events. This means that reporters will be called on to do more stand-ups and that they must develop the ability to think on their feet, outline stories quickly, and read unobtrusively from their notes. Reporters must understand the forms and formats of broadcast news to be able to put these shots together. Even though the writing may occur in a different form, the ability to write clearly and concisely will continue to be a must for the broadcast news reporter.

Still another development is the merging of broadcast and print news under a single roof. The Chicago *Tribune* has a broadcast news studio built into its newsroom; it owns CLTV, a twenty-four-hour news channel that is carried by many Chicago area cable systems, as well as WGN radio and television stations. News reporters for the *Tribune* often wear two hats. They write their copy for print, and then they do a stand-up spot for broadcast outlets. The *Tribune* is one of many newspaper/broadcast combinations that are developing throughout the nation. Increasingly, writers will have to know how to construct news in both print and broadcast forms.

All of these characteristics of broadcast writing place a heavy burden on the writer of broadcast copy. Producing such copy is no easy task. The person who can do it consistently and well, however, is likely to have a large audience for his or her work.

POINTS FOR CONSIDERATION AND DISCUSSION

1. The author begins the chapter by saying that many people believe that the broadcast medium is the most important medium of mass communication. Do you agree or disagree?
2. List the major differences between writing news for broadcast and writing news for print. Which of these differences makes writing for broadcast more difficult than writing for print? Which makes it easier?
3. Take a story from the front page of your local newspaper. Read it through completely. Now list, as briefly as possible, the three major facts of that story. That's the kind of thing a broadcast journalist must do. Try to write a thirty-second story using the three facts that you have listed.
4. Look at the lead paragraph of the story in Figure 7.2 (page 212). What device did the reporter use in writing this lead? Do you consider this lead a good one?
5. Make a list of names of local personalities that might be hard for broadcasters to pronounce. Then write their phonetic spellings.

FURTHER READING

Bliss, E. (1991). *Now the News: The Story of Broadcast Journalism*. New York: Columbia University Press.

Hausman, C. (1992). *Crafting News for Electronic Media*. Belmont, CA: Wadsworth.

Hilliard, R. L. (2000). *Writing for Television, Radio and New Media* (7th ed.). Belmont, CA: Wadsworth-Thomson Learning.

Keller, T., & Hawkins, S. A. (2005). *Television News: A Handbook for Writing, Reporting, Shooting and Editing*. Scottsdale, AZ: Holcomb Hathaway.

Mayeux, P. E. (1994). *Writing for the Broadcast Media*. Madison: Brown and Benchmark.

Rosenbaum, M. D., & Dinges, J. (Eds.). (1992). *Sound Reporting: The National Public Radio Guide to Radio Journalism and Production*. Dubuque, IA: Kendall-Hunt.

Shook, F., Lattimore, D., & Redmond, J. (2001). *The Broadcast News Process* (6th ed.). Englewood, CO: Morton.

Stephens, M. (1993). *Broadcast News* (3rd ed.). New York: Harcourt Brace Jovanovich.

Tuggle, C. A., Carr, F., & Huffman, S. (2003). *Broadcast News Handbook*. New York: McGraw-Hill.

WEBSITES

National Association of Broadcasters: **www.nab.org**

Radio and Television News Directors Association: **www.rtnda.org**

EXERCISES

The following section contains a variety of broadcast writing exercises. You should follow your instructor's directions in completing them.

7.1 Writing Broadcast Stories

Write a thirty-second broadcast news story based on the following sets of information.

WRECK

- Two trucks collided on I-59 last night.
- Caused a traffic jam; the road was blocked both ways for about 45 minutes.
- Fuel from both trucks spilled onto the highway and caused a big oil slick.
- One truck was refrigerated, and most of the contents thawed, causing a loss of an estimated $10,000 worth of goods.
- Accident happened on a part of I-59 undergoing repairs, so it was two lanes at that point; the trucks collided head on.

HONOR SOCIETY

- Alpha Alpha, university honor society, to hold inductions next Friday.
- 5 sophomores, 20 juniors, 10 seniors will be named.
- Names will be kept secret until ceremony.
- Ceremony will be at 10 A.M. at Student Center.

NEW COURSE

- Political science department announces new course, "Communism and Social-ism," to begin next semester.
- Open to juniors and seniors who have had the freshman-level beginning politi-cal science course.
- Taught by Jerald Wiseman, associate professor.
- Wiseman: "These two political theories have been major forces in helping develop our 21st century political world."

POLL

- Local polling firm, City Research Associates.
- Poll of more than 500 city residents.
- Completed last week.
- Showed 65 percent of citizens "satisfied" or "very satisfied" with the quality of life in the city; showed 75 percent of those with school-age children "satisfied" or "very satisfied" with city school system.
- Poll sponsored by Chamber of Commerce.

7.2 Writing Broadcast Stories

Write a thirty-second broadcast news story based on the following sets of information.

FACULTY DEATH

- Education professor Elizabeth Billson, dead at age 58.
- Had taught here for 36 years.
- Estimated to have taught 10,000 future teachers during her years.
- Awarded University's "Outstanding Professor" award last year.
- Had suffered from cancer for 10 years.

BASEBALL STAR

- Junior baseball star drafted by St. Louis Cardinals.
- Willie Ames says he won't turn pro this year but will stay in school.
- Ames says Mom advised him to stay in school: "She was never able to finish high school. It's important to her for me to get my education. I can play baseball later."
- Ames was reportedly offered a signing bonus of $15,000 by the Cardinals.

COMPUTER DONATION

- Mike McCracken, president of Computer Corporation of America, headquartered in the city, made this announcement this morning.
- His company donating 10 computers to local high school; donation worth more than $30,000.
- Schools Superintendent Harvey Butterworth says computers will be used to teach word processing and business programs.
- Computers should be in use by the fall term.

DRINKING BILL

- State legislature just finished marathon debate; 30 straight hours in the senate and then 30 hours in the house.
- Bill would raise drinking age in state from 19 to 21.
- Bill passed by house, 55–40, early today; passed by senate, 18–12, yesterday.
- Bill sponsored by local legislator, Representative Tom Hartley.

7.3 Writing Broadcast Stories

Write a thirty-second broadcast news story based on the following sets of information.

WATER ALERT

- Brownsville, twenty miles south of your city.
- Last week placed on a "water alert" by state health commission because of "parasitic contamination."
- Alert lifted by commission.
- Jones Lamson, head of commission, says testing by commission shows the danger has passed.
- Residents had been boiling their water since the alert began.

THEFT INVESTIGATION

- Police chief Clayton Wheat, at press conference this morning.
- Talks about department's continuing investigation into auto theft ring.
- Says ring responsible for 200 to 300 auto thefts in city last year.
- Says investigation has been expanded into surrounding counties.
- Says most cars were disassembled and sold for parts.

INDUSTRY RETURNING

- Local group of investors, lead by First Trust Bank president Joe E. Jamison.
- Announcement made this morning.
- Buying abandoned Lochs Papermill plant.
- Investor to team up with Textron Corp. to start a machine tool plant. Refurbishing the plant will take about a year.
- When machine tool plant is opened, it will employ about 200 people.

FOOTBALL GAME

- School's football team defeats archrival, 2–0.
- Final game of the season.
- Only score, safety, comes with 5 seconds left on the clock.
- Breaks three-game losing streak.
- Archrival unbeaten this season until this game.

7.4 Writing Broadcast Stories

Write a thirty-second broadcast story for each of the following sets of information.

FCC OFFICIAL

- James Graybeard, congressional liaison for Federal Communications Commission.
- Speaking to meeting of state broadcasters, meeting in town today.
- "We are on a brink of new era in communication . . . new technology is not all that new—what's different is that costs are lower. Many more people can now use technology because the prices are going down and because equipment is easier to operate. Every day, engineers are making technology more accessible. Direct broadcast satellites (DBS) will soon be available to everyone in the U.S. for the price of a television set."

CAR TELEPHONES

- Survey by local telephone company.
- Number car telephones in area doubled last year.
- 948 last year; 2110 this year.
- Survey shows mostly used by businesses for business purposes; personal use of car telephone limited but growing.

HOMECOMING

- Pep rally on Friday right before Saturday's homecoming football game.
- Begins at 7:30 P.M.

- Featuring bonfire and music by pep band.
- For the first time this year, a fireworks show, produced by fireworks artist Larry Lain, who designs fireworks for world's fairs.
- Fireworks to begin about 9 P.M.

COUNTRY MUSIC SONGWRITER

- Bill Gillespie, country music songwriter; resident of Nashville; spoke to university music appreciation class today.
- Told students to "write if you feel like it; don't write if you don't."
- Gillespie has written hit songs for Dolly Parton, Buck Owens, Charlie Pride.
- Most recent hit: "Sell Your Soul to the Devil."

HOUSE FIRE

- House valued at $150,783 burned completely this morning.
- Address: 716 Ruppert Street, in Woodland Lake subdivision.
- Owner: George Mason, vice president of the First Trust Bank.
- No one at home at the time of the fire.
- Three engines fought the fire for more than an hour.
- Don Kerlinger, photographer for local paper, hurt by falling timbers as he tried to take pictures of the blaze; in satisfactory condition at local hospital with minor burns and bruises.

HISTORIC DOCUMENT

- Letter signed by Robert E. Lee found by local woman this morning.
- Mattie Harrington, 718 Donald Avenue.
- She was going through some papers in a trunk in her attic.
- Says letter was written to her great-grandfather after the battle of Gettysburg.
- Says Lee talked about the battle, saying he had made some mistakes during the battle but still expressed optimism about the outcome of the war.
- Letter dated August 17, 1863.
- Letter now in the custody of the university history department.
- Dr. Robert Weir checking its authenticity.

ABSENCE POLICY

- New absence policy being considered by university.
- More than four absences from class during the semester will result in automatic failing grade.
- Neil Hendron, president of the Student Government Association, said today the policy is "unreasonable" and "outrageous." "I don't think it can or will be enforced."
- Faculty senate last week passed a resolution endorsing the policy.

7.5 Writing a Newscast

Construct a two-minute newscast based on the following items.

CAPSIZE

A fifteen-foot boat capsized in rough waters off Point Lookout yesterday evening. Two men—Terry Reston, twenty-three, and Will Bendix, twenty-five—were in the boat. The men said offshore winds increased wave heights and capsized their boat. The men were picked up by a Coast Guard boat after an hour in the water. Both were hospitalized for observation, but the hospital lists their condition today as good. The men say they were hunting sharks about 200 yards offshore.

BASKETBALL DEATH

A fifteen-year-old freshman basketball player died this morning during practice at Central High School. The freshman, Todd White, collapsed while running during a practice game. White had not had any known illness, according to trainer Mike Way. White was pronounced dead at Central Valley Memorial Hospital after all efforts to revive him failed. An autopsy will be performed by the county coroner today.

ENERGY PLAN

The Secretary of the Interior announced a new $800 million energy plan while traveling through the western United States on a busy three-day tour. The Secretary of the Interior announced his plan at a Western Governor's Conference meeting in Salt Lake City. The plan calls for a five-year program to ease strains brought on by strip mining and other energy ventures.

ABUSE ACQUITTAL

A fourth-grade school teacher in Midville has been acquitted of child abuse for allegedly spanking a ten-year-old girl with a wooden paddle after the girl lied about having gum in her mouth. The District Court jury returned a verdict of not guilty after deliberating three hours. Lynda Kristle had been charged with child abuse after parents noted bruises on the child's buttocks.

HOTEL OPENING

The world's largest casino-hotel opened yesterday in Reno, Nevada. The MGM Grand is on a 145-acre site and will accommodate more than 1,500 people. It has nineteen bars. Prices for rooms range from fifty dollars to $250 per day.

7.6 Writing a Newscast

Construct a two-minute newscast based on the following items.

RETIREMENT

The speaker of the state House of Representatives, Milton Bradford, has announced that he will not seek reelection. He has served in the state house for twenty-seven years and has been speaker for the past ten years. He is a Democrat from Logansville. He has always been closely aligned with the state's education lobby and has recently worked for substantial pay raises for the state's elementary and secondary school teachers.

NEW RUNWAY

The Airport Authority has announced that a new runway will be built some time next year. The airport now has three runways, and this fourth one will increase the airport's capacity. The new runway is being built to meet increased demands from airlines that want to schedule more flights into the city. The costs of construction for the new runway will be about $3 million, but Sam Peck, chairman of the Airport Authority, says the airport should recover the costs within about three and a half years.

STRIKE

Machinists Union Local 333 has called for an indefinite walkout of all local members against the city's General Motors plant. The walkout was called because the contract that GM has with the machinists expired last Friday. Since then, workers have been working without a contract, and Barney Olive, president of the union, said this situation cannot continue. "We have bargained in good faith, but we can see no evidence that General Motors is doing the same thing." General Motors spokesmen refused to comment about the walkout but said the plant will maintain its operation. The plant manufactures hubcaps for GM cars.

CONCERT

The City Community Orchestra and the City Chorus will combine forces this Sunday and present a joint concert that will feature the last movement of Beethoven's Ninth Symphony. Lister Banks and Quenton Hill are leaders of the orchestra and chorus, respectively. Banks said this is the first time the two organizations have performed jointly. In addition to the Beethoven symphony, the chorus will perform works by Bach, and the symphony will play works by Brahms. The concert will be at the City Auditorium at 3 P.M. Sunday. Admission is two dollars for adults and one dollar for students.

CUSTODY BATTLE

Bobby Ray Hacks, a native of the city and now a famous songwriter in Nashville, has said he will try to disprove a child-molesting charge and regain custody of his twelve-year-old son. In a Nashville courtroom, Hacks vowed to fight the charges brought against him by his former wife. They were divorced last year. He was convicted of child molestation last week, and his sentence hearing was today. He received a six-month suspended sentence but was also told that he had to give up custody of his son.

7.7 Writing a Newscast

Construct a two-minute newscast using the following information.

BANK ROBBERY

The city hasn't had a bank robbery for six months. That changed this morning when two men, both wearing ski masks, entered the downtown branch of the Fidelity Federal Bank just after it opened this morning. Police Chief Arthur Shultz said the men must have been waiting for the bank to open. They took $22,000 in cash and an undetermined amount in checks and securities, according to the bank's manager Jack Sherry. The men came into the bank brandishing shotguns, and one of them fired a couple of shots into the air. They made all the people in the bank lie down on the floor except for Sherry. "Fortunately, we hadn't taken all of the money we would have out of the vault, and they seemed interested only in the money they could see." Both men were tall and wearing leather jackets. They ran out of the bank and jumped into a red, four-door Chevrolet with a New York license plate. The county sheriff, Pat Gibson, said that roadblocks have been set up on all main roads leading out of the western part of the county. That's all you have right now. A reporter from your station is working on the story.

DONATIONS

The county's United Way drive has been going on for three months. Today it was officially brought to a close by this year's chairman, Sara Morris, a local attorney. She said that a record had been set. The county United Way raised $455,789.03. More than a hundred thousand people contributed. That's a record, too, according to Morris. "We couldn't be happier with the progress that we have made in this year's fund drive. The people of this city and county have responded far beyond our expectations." Last year's drive netted just over $400,000, and the goal this year was $400,000 again. United Way helps various community charitable and service organizations. Morris said the United Way board will meet soon to decide on how the money will be allocated.

REACTIONS

Don Seigel, the press secretary to the mayor, says that the mayor's office has received "literally hundreds" of phone calls this morning. Most of the people calling are mad because of the increase in property tax the city council voted last night. The council voted to increase the property tax 10 percent across the board. That means everyone who owns property in the city will have to pay 10 percent more in taxes. "Actually, a 10 percent increase isn't that much because our property tax base is so low now," Seigel said. Mayor Lyle Fester proposed the tax, and after a heated debate, it passed 5–2. A number of people have called the radio station this morning complaining about the tax. It will go into effect next July 1. One citizen's group, the Taxpayer's Union, has announced that it is planning a recall movement against the mayor because of the part he played in proposing the tax. Seigel says, "We knew people would be upset. It was a tough decision, but it was the right thing to do. Most of this new money will go the the city school system, and they need it bad."

BOOKS GIFT

Stanley Minion taught journalism at the local university for more than 30 years. He retired last year. Yesterday, the university announced that he had donated his entire collection of books and newspapers to the library. Minion was a noted collector of newspaper front pages, and his collection includes many pre-Revolutionary War newspapers. Quincy Mundt, the university librarian, said he is "thrilled" about the gift. "Dr. Minion has some newspapers that aren't available anywhere else that I know of. His collection is one of the best. We are looking into plans to remodel one floor of the library to house the collection. We would like to make the newspapers available to the public for viewing as well as to researchers." Minion's donation includes more than 7,000 books and 10,301 newspapers. Mundt said the collection is worth at least $133,000.

TRAFFIC LIGHTS

A violent rainstorm passed over the city early this morning. It didn't last long, only a few minutes. But lightning struck one of the power company's substations and knocked out the traffic lights on one of the city's busy streets, McTerril Boulevard. Traffic was backed up for several blocks during rush hour, and several accidents were reported. At least three of them were caused by the lights being out, according to the police chief. Your reporter on the scene says traffic delays of up to forty-five minutes were reported in some areas. "The wet streets from the rainstorm didn't help us any," the police chief said. The power was restored by 8:30.

HISTORY OF THE COUNTY

The county historical society has been working on a comprehensive history of the county for several years. This morning, Lila Bancroft, president of the society, announced that the project has been completed and that a history of the county will be published some time early next year. She said many of the members of the society contributed to the work, but the main author was John Widner, a retired history professor at the university and a native of the county. The book will cover county history from the earliest settlers in the 1700s to the present day. "It's going to be a beautiful book—very well written and with lots of illustrations," according to Bancroft. The prepublication price will be $17.50; after publication, the price will be $25. It will be available in all the local bookstores.

7.8 Writing a Newscast

Construct a two-minute newscast using the following information.

CANINE PACEMAKER

Last week, Marie Bruton's dog was sick. This week it's better. In fact, it's up and running around—"chasing the cat," she says. This is because the dog has had a pacemaker inserted to keep its heart going. Dr. Charles Eulau, a local vet, did the surgery, and he says it's the first time anything like this has been done in this area. Mrs. Bruton: "Wrangler had been pretty listless. Then last week he just collapsed. I didn't know he had a heart problem until I took him to the vet. Now he's doing fine. I think he knows that something has happened to him—that he's been given a new lease on life." Eulau says he used an old pacemaker provided to him by the local hospital. It cost about $100, and he charged $50 for the operation. Mrs. Bruton is a legal secretary for a local law firm.

SENTENCING

A local man has been on trial for several months, accused of poisoning some Halloween candy. His name is Sam Gather. Two days ago, a jury convicted him after a week-long trial. His attorney argued that he was insane, but the jury did not accept that defense. Less than an hour ago, Judge Harvey Eagle sentenced him to five years in prison. This was the maximum sentence the judge could give him, since he wasn't trying to kill the children, just make them sick. At least ten children got sick from eating the candy given to them by Gather. He had put some cleaning fluid onto some hard candy, which he then gave to the kids.

BEERLESS ST. PATRICK'S DAY

M.A.D.D. stands for "Mothers Against Drunk Driving." This organization is working to get drunken drivers off the road and to strengthen laws against them. It also helps victims and families of victims of drunken-driving accidents. Denise Clearly, president of the local chapter, has announced a "beerless St. Patrick's Day party." The party will be on March 17 at Palisades Park. It will feature a cookout and entertainment by a local bluegrass group, Ham 'n' Eggs. It will start at 5 P.M., and according to Clearly, "Everybody is invited. We want to show people that they can have fun without having to drink." She said that information about M.A.D.D. will be available at the party, and interested people may join. The dues are ten dollars a year.

STABBING DEATHS

Frederic Church, a local contractor, and his wife, Sarah, were found in their $300,000 home Sunday, beaten and stabbed to death. Their home is on Lake Smith. Police say they think the couple surprised a burglar because some jewelry and other valuable items were stolen. This morning the police announced that they had arrested and charged a 15-year-old boy with the crimes. They said he is a local youth, but his name is being withheld at this time. His name should be available from the district attorney's office later in the day. The police said he was seen by neighbors leaving the house on Sunday, and they said footprints in the mud outside the house matched a shoe belonging to the boy.

DEPOSITORS

Two months ago, the Trust National Bank was declared bankrupt by the U.S. government. The bank was a state bank and not federally insured, so a lot of people lost their money. A number of people had their life savings invested in the bank, and they have been wondering about it ever since. Today the state claims board, which handles these kinds of things, announced that the state would provide about $60 million to pay back the investors. This amount of money would mean that investors would get about forty cents back for every dollar they had in the bank. The money would be paid out over a period of three years. The state legislature must still approve the plan.

RESIGNATION

The state treasurer is a man named Manness Manford. He has been state treasurer for twenty years, which means that he has been elected to the post four straight times. Today, at the state Capitol, Mr. Manford announced that he is leaving office at the end of this month. He had just been reelected to the position last November. He is leaving to become president of Fidelity National Bank in the capital city. Mr. Manford is from your town, and a lot of people there know him. He is credited with revising the accounting procedures for the state, making it easier for the state legislature to predict the amounts of funding that will be available for the upcoming fiscal years. There have been rumors that he has been ill and not able to do his job. The governor made the following statement: "We believe that Manness Manford has served the state well. He has approached his job with imagination and foresight, and he has made the job of everyone in state government easier. He's my good friend, and I hate to have the state lose his services, but I can understand his desire to go into private business. We all wish him well."

7.9 More Broadcast Writing

Rewrite into radio and television style these stories from print reports. Make a special effort to boil them down into capsule form. Watch for errors in style.

HURRICANE

MIAMI, Fla.—Hurricane Nancy lurched toward the United States today after a brief pause last night during which she whipped up 160-mile-an-hour winds and developed into the most intense storm since 1935.

As the huge storm swung into motion, hurricane watchers warned people in the target area of the possibility of monster tides being pushed ahead of Nancy.

Officials at the National Hurricane Center here said the storm was about 325 miles south of Pensacola, headed for the Florida Panhandle at a speed of 12 mph. At that speed, she would strike the mainland tonight.

She was expected to hit the Panhandle with wind speeds of up to 156 mph.

Residents and travelers were told to move from low and exposed places, which the up to 15-foot tides could cut off from escape routes.

"Nancy is now very similar to the 1935 storm," said Dr. Robert H. Simpson, head of the National Hurricane Center. "She has a very large fury concentrated in an exceedingly small area."

TSUNAMI WARNING STATIONS

WASHINGTON, D.C.—One hundred seismographic stations placed around Africa and Asia could provide the kind of early warning system for earthquakes and ensuing tsunamis that could save thousands of lives. This view was expressed by Harlan Reece at a conference of the National Academy of Sciences meeting in the nation's capital this week.

Earth waves generated by quakes or large explosions provide science with a tool for studying the planet's structure from crust to core. Such waves are recorded by seismographs, Dr. Reece said. Dr. Reece said a network of 100 special seismograph stations could be established around the Indian Ocean for less than $50 million and "operated at an annual cost of several million dollars." Such a system would detect earthquakes and possible tsunamis that might result from them and give nations in the area more time to warn people along their coastlines. Their scientific value alone, he said, would justify the cost.

Dr. Reece pointed to the need for these stations by bringing up the vast tsunami that swept across the Indian Ocean on Dec. 26, 2004 and killed more than 150,000 people. "We could have saved many lives if such a system had been in place," he said.

COLLISION PREVENTION

SACRAMENTO—A device that has the capability of preventing in-flight airplane collisions through use of infrared rays has been described to a radio engineers conference here. The gadget, designed and developed by the Aerojet-General Corp. of Sacramento, uses invisible heat rays received from the oncoming aircraft to trigger an alarm.

Robert G. Richards, operations analyst for Aerojet's Avionics Division, told the Seventh Regional Conference and Trade Show of the Institute of Radio Engineers yesterday that the invisible heat rays are sent out by all engines, motors, electrical apparatus, or anything having a source of heat as part of its makeup.

It took about fourteen years of research to develop the device, which, Richards explained, would have provided a warning in the case of a recent collision of two planes over the Grand Canyon more than three minutes before the collision.

7.10 Interviewing for Broadcast

HIGHWAY DEATHS

The state Department of Transportation today said that the total number of traffic deaths on the state's highways was 120. This is the lowest total in ten years. Your station sends you to do an interview with the State Transportation Commissioner Dick Blocker about why this occurred.

Having the lowest highway death total in ten years is quite an accomplishment.
That's right, it is. I think the people of the state are to be commended for it. I think we must be doing something right.

What do you think we are doing right?
Several things. For one thing, I think people are just being more careful, observing the speed limit, having their cars checked, watching out for hazardous conditions—things like that.

The fifty-five-mile-an-hour speed limit—do you think that's had an effect?
Well, the fifty-five-mile-an-hour speed limit has been in place for more than thirty years, so last year's low figure wouldn't necessarily be due to that. You know, it's interesting about the fifty-five limit. It was originally established to conserve fuel, but its real effect has been to save lives. It's not that everyone is observing the fifty-five limit per se. But I think the fifty-five limit has made people drive more slowly than they would otherwise. So now, instead of the average speed being seventy-five, it might only be sixty-five—and that's an improvement.

Do you know of any specific reason that the death total should have been so low last year?
We're looking into that. One reason has to be the good weather we had generally last year. Hazardous weather conditions create a lot of accidents, and we didn't have much of that last year. Another reason has to be the tough new car safety inspection law the governor proposed and the legislature passed three years ago. I think that's gotten a lot of cars off the road that might have caused accidents.

Is drinking and driving a problem in the state?
Yes, definitely. Eighty out of the 120 people who were killed in automobile accidents in the state last year were killed in accidents where alcohol was involved. Alcohol is still the major safety problem in this state.

What's being done about that?
As you probably know, the governor has sponsored legislation to increase the penalties for those convicted of drunk driving. We were joined in this by M.A.D.D., Mothers Against Drunk Driving. We have also sponsored legislation that would raise the legal drinking age from nineteen to twenty-one. Unfortunately, neither measure was passed by the legislature this session, but we'll be trying against next session.

7.11 Interviewing for Broadcast

HALL OF FAME

A local resident, George M. "Bucky" Barnett, has just been elected to Baseball's Hall of Fame. Barnett spent most of his career as a shortstop for the St. Louis Cardinals, from 1953 to 1968. He also played with the Boston Red Sox before he retired in 1969. He then spent twenty years as a coach and minor-league manager and has been living in your city since leaving baseball. Barnett was best known as a fielder. Grantland Rice, the famed sportswriter, once described Barnett as "personified lightning" on the field. In fact, he had the highest fielding percentage of any shortstop, .993 (fielding percentage is the number of chances handled without making an error). He had a lifetime batting average of .310. Your station sends you to interview him.

How did you get interested in baseball?
When I was growing up, you didn't get interested in baseball. Baseball was just there—kind of like milk. I don't guess it ever occurred to most of us not to be interested in baseball.

What's different about kids growing up today? Why aren't they as interested in baseball as your generation seems to have been?
There are a lot of distractions, I think. When I was growing up, baseball was about all you had, and you simply tried to survive the winter waiting for spring training to begin. Now kids have basketball and football and television to look at if they want to.

I take it you don't think much of football?
I don't have anything against football. It's just that I love baseball so much. Nothing comes as close to being a perfect game as baseball. A good baseball game has lots of little dramas going on the field at the same time, and it takes a keen, intelligent eye to see just a few of them. I'm sorry that many kids today seem to have adopted another sport. I think they're settling for second best.

What was the greatest thrill of your baseball career?
I think it was when the Cardinals won the World Series from the Boston Red Sox in 1967. The Red Sox had a great team with Carl Yastremski as their leading hitter. I don't think anything in my playing career gave me so much joy as beating the Red Sox that year.

People have said that you were the greatest fielding shortstop in the history of baseball.
That's flattering, but I'm not sure it's true. The game has produced several great men at short. It's funny because I always thought fielding was the easiest part of the game. It was just a matter of staying alert, knowing the hitters, and moving with the pitch. Usually, I just wound up where the ball was. Hitting was always the hardest part of the game for me—something I really had to work at. I think I was lucky to have such a high hitting percentage.

chapter eight

Writing
Advertising
Copy

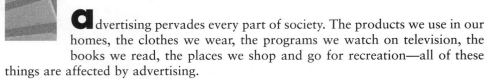

advertising pervades every part of society. The products we use in our homes, the clothes we wear, the programs we watch on television, the books we read, the places we shop and go for recreation—all of these things are affected by advertising.

Advertising is one of the country's major industries. One estimate put the money spent on advertising in 2003 at $163 billion in the United States alone. General Motors, the nation's largest advertiser in 2003, spent $3.7 billion in 2003, while Time Warner, the second largest advertiser, spent $2.9 billion. Major companies routinely spend thousands of dollars on the production of advertisements, and the costs of buying time in the mass media can be astronomical. For example, in late 2000, Toyota launched a $20 million ad campaign to persuade young people to buy its entry-level economy car, the Echo.

Charges for network television advertising time can also boggle the mind. In 1983, thirty seconds of air time during the broadcast of the Super Bowl cost $330,000. For the 1993 Super Bowl, those charges had risen to nearly $900,000. One of the most watched programs in television history, the final episode of "M*A*S*H" in February 1983, cost advertisers about $450,000 for thirty seconds of air time.

Those costs pale in the light of more recent costs. During the 2000 season, thirty seconds on NBC's top-rated "ER" series cost $620,000, and thirty seconds on "Friends" cost $540,000. An average thirty-second prime-time television announcement costs more than $200,000 to produce. The cost of thirty seconds of advertising on the Super Bowl broadcast in 2004 soared past $2 million. The final episode of "Friends" in 2004 also cost advertisers about $2 million for thirty seconds.

People who spend that much money obviously expect a return, and they often get it. Most companies recognize the need to advertise and the benefits of doing so, and they are willing to pay a price for it. Because advertising is so costly, however, there is little room for error or waste. This chapter discusses the writing of advertising copy, but the writing of the ad is only a part of the marketing strategy of a company. Writers of advertising copy must have more on their minds than how the ad will look and what the ad will say.

A LOVE–HATE RELATIONSHIP

Americans have a love–hate relationship with advertising. Many people claim that they never pay attention to advertising. They say that they leave the room when a commercial comes on television and they never read the ads in newspapers or magazines. They never click on banner ads on websites. Many will tell you that they never make consumer decisions on the basis of ads—as if admitting to doing so would mean that something was wrong with them.

More sophisticated critics of advertisements put ads down as insulting and degrading. They criticize ads for creating desires and needs that are wasteful and unhealthy. Advertisers, they believe, use false, misleading, or deceptive measures to foist products on an unsuspecting public. Advertisers, critics say, pollute the public's mind and its environment with their messages.

Despite these criticisms, advertising is one of the vital links in the modern economic chain. It is a major way of getting information to a consumer—information that a consumer often wants and needs. For example, a billboard near an interstate highway telling the location of a gas station may be an eyesore to some, but to the driver who is low on gas, it provides a vital piece of information.

Those who say that they never pay attention to advertising are not being honest. To live in today's society means receiving the messages of advertisers. There are few places people can go where advertising will not reach them. Even "noncommercial" public broadcasting stations air advertisements in the form of credits to those who contribute to the station's programming and promotional spots for upcoming shows. One estimate has the individual consumer confronted with 1,600 advertising messages every day.

Not only do people pay attention to advertising messages, but they often act according to those messages. Advertising works. Check around any room in your house, and you will find plenty of items that were purchased, in part at least, because of the advertising you or someone else has encountered.

THE FIELD OF ADVERTISING

The person who wants to enter the field of advertising has chosen an exciting and challenging profession. Advertising copywriters must be willing to work long and difficult hours researching their products and audiences and straining their creative forces to be successful. Like other writers for the mass media, they must understand the language and be willing caretakers of it. They must be willing to use their creativity in ways that others are willing to pay for and support. The rewards to the few who are able to do well in this profession are great.

Two concepts should form the base of a student's thinking about writing advertising copy. Advertising copy is a different form of writing from the ones that we have studied in other parts of this book. Its purpose is to persuade and motivate. The basic precepts of good writing—accuracy, clarity, efficiency, and precision—remain in force in writing advertising copy as they do in all other forms of writing.

Advertising is based on the assumption that words have the power to produce a change—a change in thinking, attitudes, beliefs, and, ultimately, behavior. Advertising that does not accomplish this change or aid in accomplishing it is worthless. Copywriters must select the words and ideas that will help to produce this change.

The process of writing advertising copy is in many ways the same as the process of writing news. The copywriter must process information and put it into an acceptable form for its medium. Like the newswriter, the advertising copywriter must conduct research before the writing begins. He or she must decide what is important enough to use and what should be left out. The copywriter must choose the words and the structure for the copy that will best fit the product, media, and purpose for the advertising. The copywriter, like the newswriter, is subject to many editors—not the least of whom is the client who is paying for the advertising and whose ideas about advertising copy may differ radically from those of the copywriter.

But what about the creative process? Doesn't advertising copy require more creativity on the part of the writer than newswriting? In some respects, it does. Ad copywriters have a greater variety of forms for their work than do newswriters, and they have more tools with which to work.

Those who are entering the field of advertising make a serious mistake, however, if they believe that because advertising requires creativity, they have complete license to write what they want when they want. A prime example of what many would consider a lack of creativity is found in the advertising for many Procter & Gamble products—household items such as Tide detergent and Crest toothpaste. Advertisements for these products rarely win awards given to the more "creative" or attention-getting ads for the competition. Yet many of these products, backed by a large advertising budget, take a lion's share of their market, and Procter & Gamble remains one of the biggest spenders in the advertising industry. The evidence at the

Figure 8.1   Samuel Johnson on advertising (1759)

The trade of advertising is now so near perfection that it is not easy to propose any improvement. But as every art ought to be exercised in due subordination to the public good, I cannot but propose it as a moral question to these masters of the public ear, whether they do not sometimes play too wantonly with our passions.

cash register is that the ads for these products work, despite their lack of creativity. That is the kind of evidence a client wants.

On the other hand, highly innovative approaches for ads are often effective, especially when products have established and well-rooted competition and when the purpose of the ad is to gain the consumer's attention. Possibly the leading proponent of the off-the-wall approach is Joe Sedelmaier of Sedelmaier Productions in Chicago. In 1984, Sedelmaier created an ad for Wendy's fast-food chain that had an elderly lady in front of a fast-food counter (at the competition's restaurant, not Wendy's) shouting, "Where's the beef?!" That cry was taken up by Democratic presidential candidate Walter Mondale that year and became part of the national lexicon. More important for Wendy's and Sedelmaier, revenues for the fast-food chain jumped 31 percent, net income went up 24 percent, and average sales per restaurant rose 13 percent from the previous year. Much of the credit for these increases was given to Sedelmaier's offbeat approach, one that he has repeated for clients such as Federal Express and General Motors Acceptance Corp.

Sedelmaier demanded total creative control as a condition for taking on a client. His agency was one of the few that can do that. Most clients, whether they are spending a large or small amount of money on the advertising, want a say in the final production of the ad. A copywriter must take copy through a variety of approval stages, a process that demands a great deal of research and discipline. The creative process is a part of the process of producing copy, but it is only a part—and sometimes only a small part—of it.

BEGINNING THE PROCESS: NEEDS AND APPEALS

The process of writing advertising copy begins with a recognition that all humans have certain needs and desires. Effective advertising appeals to these needs and desires in a way that will make people act positively toward a product or an idea. We live in a consumer-oriented society in which the list of needs and desires is a fairly long one. The first step in producing advertising copy is to examine some of the needs and desires of humans in a very general way.

Food and Drink

The need for food and drink is among the most basic and universal needs that we have. We must have food and water daily to sustain ourselves. Beyond that, we want food and drink that are nourishing and palatable.

Shelter, Security, and Comfort

Next to food and drink, one of our most basic needs is for shelter. We need a way of protecting ourselves from the elements.

Following closely on the need for shelter is the need for security—the need to feel that we are protected from various dangers. Rational people understand that they cannot insulate themselves from every danger, but they can take some steps to ensure that they are not victims of certain calamities.

Once shelter and security are established, people want to feel comfortable. Physically, they want to be without pain, they want to be warm when it is cold and cool when it is hot. They want to live, work, and play in a comfortable and pleasing environment.

Sex, Intimacy, and Social Contact

Most people need to have contact with other people. That contact can take various forms in various stages of our lives. Our social relationships are important to us, no matter what form they take. They can be based on sexual intimacy, friendship, or casual contact. Whatever they are, we remain social beings, and lack of such contact can have physical as well as emotional consequences.

Independence, Privacy, Self-Fulfillment, and Power

While we need social contact, we also have a countervailing need for independence and privacy. We need privacy even from those to whom we feel the closest. We have the urge to "get away from it all," and occasionally we do that, even if that means that we simply draw inward rather than removing ourselves physically.

Related to this need is the need for independence. Although we are social beings, we are also individuals, and we need to feel that we can develop our own personalities. This need for individual development continues through adulthood and governs many of our actions. We are all different from one another, and we need to confirm that to ourselves.

Independence is part of a greater need for self-fulfillment, much of which is often met by occupation. We need to be engaged in constructive activity that will give us satisfaction and confirm our worth as individuals. For many, the highest fulfillment of this need lies in the work we choose as adults.

At its best, the need for power means that we are able to make our own decisions and in some way control our own environments. Some child psychologists argue that this need is one of the most important that children have. At a very early age, children need to be able to make choices—even very small ones—so that they can develop their individuality. Adults also need to feel that they are in control of their lives and their surroundings. This need, of course, can develop into a need to control the lives of others. Many of us have this tendency to some degree, and our places in society may dictate that we exercise this power. Parents, particularly, feel the need to control the environment and actions of their children.

Stimulation

The need to be stimulated—to find life interesting—is one of the most important needs that we have. Despite the habits and routines that people have established for themselves, they need to feel that life holds a variety of experiences. They read books, watch television, go to parties, shop, and engage in many other activities in part to

Figure 8.2   Needs and Appeals

This advertisement is fairly simple and straightforward. To what audience is the ad directed? What are the needs and appeals involved? In making this message as simple as possible, what does the advertisement omit?

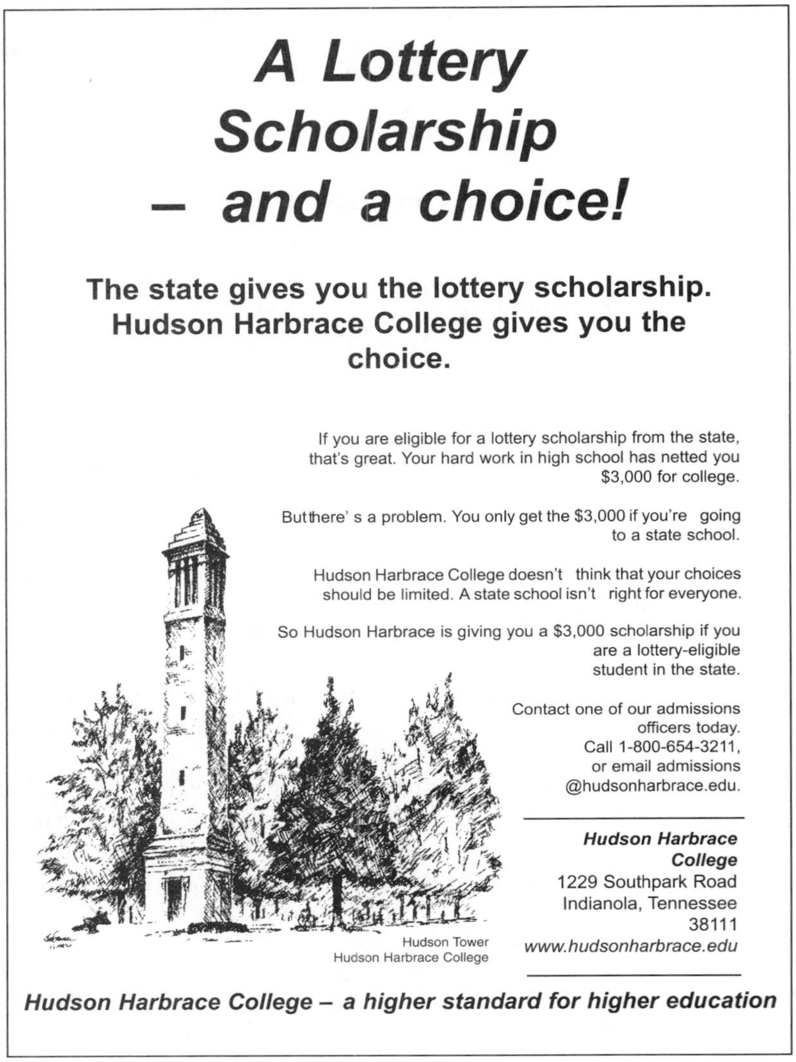

A Lottery Scholarship – and a choice!

The state gives you the lottery scholarship. Hudson Harbrace College gives you the choice.

If you are eligible for a lottery scholarship from the state, that's great. Your hard work in high school has netted you $3,000 for college.

But there's a problem. You only get the $3,000 if you're going to a state school.

Hudson Harbrace College doesn't think that your choices should be limited. A state school isn't right for everyone.

So Hudson Harbrace is giving you a $3,000 scholarship if you are a lottery-eligible student in the state.

Contact one of our admissions officers today. Call 1-800-654-3211, or email admissions @hudsonharbrace.edu.

Hudson Tower
Hudson Harbrace College

Hudson Harbrace College
1229 Southpark Road
Indianola, Tennessee
38111
www.hudsonharbrace.edu

Hudson Harbrace College – a higher standard for higher education

entertain themselves. Occasionally, they need to be excited, to have the feeling that something is going to offer them special enjoyment or a unique feeling.

Acquisition

The number and variety of goods and services that are available to people in modern Western industrial societies would boggle the minds of people in other cultures and from other centuries. The availability of those goods and services has stimulated within many people a need to acquire things. Part of our development as individuals is the acquisition of goods that go beyond basic needs of food, clothing, and shelter.

On occasion, the need overcomes common sense and the bounds of rationality. For instance, news reports coming from the Philippines in 1985 said that Imelda Marcos, wife of the deposed dictator of that country, had had a closet full of shoes—more than 3,000 pairs. Her shoe collection became one of the standing jokes of the year, and she has become a symbol of a consumer whose consumption was beyond conspicuous. What possible use, many wondered, could she have had for so many shoes?

Yet there is some of Imelda Marcos in many of us. Many people acquire things for the sake of acquiring them, not because these items are useful or because we need them for basic purposes. Children "collect" things like dolls, baseball cards, and rocks, and that collecting syndrome carries over into adulthood.

The foregoing list contains just a few of the needs that we all have. There are many others. The consideration of needs is one of the most important parts of the process of developing effective advertising copy. To understand that people need, or feel that they need, certain things is vital to formulating the appeals that advertising can use.

Appeals are the words, phrases, and ideas that advertising copywriters use to tap into the needs of the audience. It is in formulating these appeals that copywriters must choose their language carefully. They must understand that certain words, even those that may have similar meanings, can evoke strikingly different images. The copywriter must have a highly developed ear for the language coupled with an understanding of the needs of the audience (see Figure 2.3).

Just what needs are most salient to an audience? The next section discusses how marketers find this out.

 THE AUDIENCE

Most manufacturers and advertisers want to sell as many units of their product as possible. They recognize, however, that most products are not universal; that is, not everyone will want what they sell. In addition, distributing a product to a massive audience can be costly. Consequently, it is not efficient to try to sell most products to everyone. Marketing a product or service begins with deciding what part of the population is most likely to buy it.

In considering the audience for a product, advertisers need to think about two groups. One is the people who are already using the product. They cannot be taken for granted. Many advertisements are directed at reinforcing the behavior of people who have already bought a product. (For instance, readers of car advertisements in magazines are often those who have already bought the car; they are simply trying to reinforce their belief that they made the correct decision. Many car buyers, once they have made a purchase, will stay with that brand through several more purchases.) Advertisers need to have some idea of how strong a user's loyalty is to a product.

The second group is people who do not use the product but are likely to. These potential users provide the greatest opportunity for product sales to grow. Finding out who they are and what kind of advertising message is most likely to motivate them is the job of market research, and the answers have a direct effect on the advertising copywriter.

How does an advertiser get this information? Researchers can employ a variety of methods for this purpose. They may include personal interview surveys, telephone surveys, mail surveys, focus group interviews, consumer product testing, intercept interviewing (the kind of interviewing that is conducted by people in shopping malls), and many other methods. The data produced by this research are vital to the advertising copywriter.

The major concepts that the beginning advertising copywriter must understand are demographics and psychographics. Demographics is a way of dividing the population into groups on the basis of some obvious characteristics. People who share many of the same demographic characteristics are likely to share many consumer behaviors. In the 1980s, the term *yuppie* was coined to describe an important segment of the population. A yuppie is a young, upwardly mobile professional. In the 1990s, there was Generation X, members of which were thought to share certain attitudes and behavior. After that came Generation Y. In politics, we have had "angry white males" and "soccer moms." All of these categories have particular demographic characteristics, and they provide researchers with a way of looking at different segments of the population.

Psychographics is the concept of putting people into groups based on less obvious characteristics. Psychographics is based on the emotional responses that different types of people have to products or to appeals made through advertising and marketing. Psychographics is a much less well-defined concept than demographics, and sometimes the two concepts are not clearly distinguishable. The following discussion emphasizes demographics but also includes some psychographic variables and ideas.

There are many demographic categories. The following section discusses some of the most basic demographic and psychographic characteristics.

Age

How old people are is one of the most common determinants of how likely they are to use many products and services. Our needs and desires change as we get older, and often they change in the same way for the majority of people. Most children want toys, but as they get older, the desire for toys decreases and the desire for other products increases. The changes that accompany age are not only physical, but also psychological and emotional.

Gender

Boys and girls are different; men and women are different. These differences are of primary importance to the advertiser. These groups have different needs and desires, owing not only to different physical characteristics, but also to differing roles they are likely to play in society. For instance, within a household, a man is more likely to earn more money, but a woman is more likely to make most of the household buying decisions.

Income

How much money people have to spend is important in determining how likely they are to buy a product. Some products and services are marketed to people who do not have as much income as others, and the appeal that advertisers use is often based on price. This kind of appeal is likely to motivate potential customers. On the other hand, many producers want to direct their advertising toward an "upscale" audience—those who have high incomes or whose incomes are likely to increase.

Education

Education is an important demographic variable for two reasons. One is based on the assumption that education changes people; it changes their attitudes and values. For instance, the more education people have, the more likely they are to place a high value on getting an education. The second is that education is often related to the demographic characteristic of income. The more education a person has, the more likely that person is to have a higher income.

Marital Status

If a person is married, that means he or she most likely lives in a household of two or more people. That inevitably leads to different consumer behavior than if that person were single. Knowing whether or not a person is married is important for the advertiser because of the different appeals that may be used to sell a product.

There are many other demographic characteristics that advertisers may need to consider in finding the consumers for their products. For instance, race, home ownership, number of adults and children in a household, occupation, place of residence, and type of housing are just a few of the many variables that researchers can examine.

As a step in developing an advertisement, an advertiser might want to draw a demographic profile of those who use the product already or those who are potential users. For instance, a manufacturer might find that those who have used the product are women between the ages of eighteen and thirty, single, with at least a high school education. Chances are that not all consumers who fit this profile are buying the product, so advertising directed at this group might not only persuade others to buy it, but also reinforce those who already do. On the other hand, an advertiser may decide that the product could be marketed to older women as well as to those who are already likely to buy it. In that case, the advertiser might use a different appeal—one that would work both for women thirty-one to forty years old and for younger women.

In addition to these demographic factors, advertisers must take into account psychographic variables. Market researchers want to know what people believe is important and valuable. If people use a product, market researchers want to know how they feel about that product and whether they are likely to use it again.

As you can tell, making decisions on the basis of just this small amount of information is not a simple task. An advertiser may take a variety of routes in marketing a product. Good research is essential to making the correct decisions about marketing and advertising. But the audience is only one factor to be considered in trying to sell a product; of equal importance is the product itself.

THE PRODUCT

Knowledge of the product—particularly from the standpoint of developing advertising for it—is not as simple as it might first seem. A *product* is anything the advertising is designed to promote. It could be an item (such as a vacuum cleaner), a business (such as an auto body repair shop), or an idea (such as quitting smoking). The advertising copywriter must ask, "What is it about this product that I am trying to sell that might appeal to the user?" The answer may come from a close examination of the product, and it may be surprising.

What the Product Does

First, the copywriter should know what the product does. A vacuum cleaner may clean a floor, but how it cleans the floor may be important to the advertising of the product. Does it introduce some new cleaning method, something that no other vacuum cleaner on the market does? A line of sofas may come in fifteen different patterns; it may also be comfortable to sit on. Which one does the copywriter emphasize? A copywriter may find that there are a number of facts about any product that can be advertised, and someone—the copywriter, the advertiser, or a combination of them—will have to decide which of those facts are most relevant to the advertising situation.

Physical Characteristics of the Product

The physical characteristics of the product also provide the copywriter with some useful considerations in developing the advertising. Sometimes a product will be designed to do a job more efficiently than competing products. Sometimes it will be designed to do a particular part of a job. Small, hand-held vacuum cleaners are still vacuum cleaners, but they are not meant to vacuum an entire house or even an entire room. They are for small jobs that need to be done quickly. The physical characteristics of the product help to promote the feeling that the product can do these simple jobs.

Sometimes the physical characteristics of a product can have little to do with how the product works, but they can still be useful in helping to sell the product. When the Macintosh computer was introduced by the Apple Computer Company in 1984 (with an engrossing surreal commercial that was aired only once, during the Super Bowl broadcast that year), one of the characteristics that helped to set the Macintosh apart from other computers was its unique small, boxlike design. That design helped to establish the Macintosh as "the computer for the rest of us," as its advertising slogan said. One of the legendary campaigns in the history of advertising, the 1960s promotion of the Volkswagen Beetle, used the car's unique shape to distinguish it from other cars. Some of the ads even poked some good-natured fun at the car to establish this difference in the minds of the consumers.

History of the Product

The history and reputation of a product are characteristics that also need consideration in formulating advertising. A product may have a long history, and that may be something that a copywriter will want to emphasize. Many businesses use the phrase "Established in — (year)" to let people know that the business has been around for a long time and therefore can be considered reliable and stable. If a product has existed for only a short time but has gained a good reputation, the advertisement may reflect that reputation.

Sometimes an advertising campaign will be designed to overcome a product's history or reputation. It could be that the product has not worked particularly well and a manufacturer has taken steps to correct that. Or it may be that the manufacturer wants to sell the product to a different audience. One classic case of this redefinition of a product was done by Miller Brewing Company. For many years, its main product had been known as the "Champagne of Bottled Beers." The slogan had little appeal for the Sunday afternoon, football-watching crowd, who were mostly men. When Miller began making a low-calorie beer, Miller Lite, the company sponsored a series of commercials that had ex-athletes arguing as to whether the product "tastes great" or was "less filling." The commercials were good entertainment in themselves, but they also established Miller Light as a beer that could be enjoyed while watching a football game.

Another classic advertising campaign that reestablished a product was the one the Chicago-based advertising agency Leo Burnett developed for Marlboro cigarettes. Marlboro had been a red-filtered cigarette when filtered cigarettes were thought to be products for women. Marlboro also had the slogan "mild as the month of May." Burnett developed a series of ads that put the cigarette in the hands of men and put those men outdoors. Eventually, the Marlboro Man, a rugged outdoorsman (usually a cowboy with a horse), became a staple of the advertising industry. The campaign was so successful that the Marlboro Man is still with us today, fifty years after he was created.

Who Makes the Product

The manufacturer of a product is another characteristic about a product that an advertising copywriter may want to give attention to. Many products are indistinguishable from their competition, but if the manufacturer is well known and has a reputation for reliability and stability, that can help to set the product apart. International Business Machines (IBM) has a reputation for servicing its products, and that has established for IBM a broader reputation for reliability. IBM often uses this reputation in advertising its individual products. More recently, IBM advertising has tried to build on this reputation by emphasizing its ability to find innovative solutions to computing problems.

Many advertising and marketing campaigns emphasize the brand name of a product. This emphasis occurs for a number of reasons. Consumers often exercise what is called *brand loyalty*. Having made a decision to buy a product at some point, many people are reluctant to change. A brand may also be positively associated with other products that carry the name. The Nabisco brand, for example, appears on a number of crackers and cookies because of the strong brand identification that name has. Such identification makes a product, especially a new one, easier to sell.

One of the most important product characteristics is price. People want to know how much something costs. They also want to believe that they are getting the best product for the money they spend. Sometimes, price is the most notable factor about a product, and it will be the characteristic the copywriter will want to feature.

Another factor copywriters will want to consider is the competition that a product has. Much of what we have already said has made reference to a product's competition and the means by which advertising can distinguish it from others like it. Rarely is a product the only one of its kind. It may have some distinguishing characteristics, but there are usually other items that will accomplish the same task. One of the copywriter's main jobs is to set a product apart from its competition. An important concept in advertising and marketing is *positioning*. Manufacturers of a product that has a lot of competition try to "position" the product in the minds of the consumer. Most people buy toothpaste; advertisers try to get consumers to think about a certain toothpaste if they want it to perform a particular task. For instance, if you want to prevent cavities, you should buy Toothpaste A; if you want to whiten your teeth, you should buy Toothpaste B; and if you want to have fresh breath, you should buy Toothpaste C. Advertising will help to place each of these brands into the position to solve these problems.

The list of product characteristics just discussed is only an indication of the many variables that may be considered in developing advertising for a product. The key here is that the copywriter should know as much about the product as possible so that the best characteristics may be selected for the advertising.

In advertising terms, this process is called finding the *unique selling proposition* (USP). A product's USP will give potential consumers their first clue as to why they should want to buy that product. Once a USP has been identified, the selling process has begun.

Finally, advertisers must recognize the social aspects of their advertising; that is, how do their products and advertising fit into society, and are the advertising approaches they use appropriate? For example, many women feel that much of the advertising for and about them is degrading. One watchdog group, Women Against Pornography, annually gives awards to advertisers who use nonsexist approaches in their advertising; at the same time, the group criticizes advertisers who, according to the group, degrade women. In 1983, the group criticized the Hanes company for the way it implied in its hosiery ads that men preferred women with "shapely, sexy, silky legs."

More recently, the British auto maker Austin Rover received many complaints about an ad that focused on the walnut interior of one of its cars and quoted an old English saying, "A woman, a dog, a walnut tree, the more you beat them, the better they'll be." The makers of Opium and Obsession perfumes have also been criticized by those who believe that the names of these products and their advertising glamorize degrading conditions within society.

The Center for Science in the Public Interest has criticized the alcoholic beverage industry for ads that it said were aimed at starting young people to drink and at inducing alcoholics to return to the bottle. Ethnic minorities are often sensitive to the way in which they are portrayed, and advertisers are wise to be aware of their concerns.

This is not to say that advertising should always avoid controversy and that advertisers should construct ads that are so bland that absolutely no one could be offended. Controversy might well be an advisable marketing strategy, as when Burger King directly criticized McDonald's in one of its advertising campaigns. The point here is that advertisers should never be surprised at the effects of their ads. They should know what society, or groups in society, expect of them, and they should have thought through their advertising campaigns well enough that the ads produce the intended results.

THE ADVERTISING SITUATION

The marketing environment is an important consideration in the development of an ad. This environment is created by the audience and product—factors that have already been discussed—but also by the more immediate situation surrounding the advertisement. We are at the point at which the copywriter is beginning to make decisions that will determine the content of the ad.

First, ad writers must know and be able to state the *key fact* about an advertising situation. This key fact sets the stage for the thinking about an ad, and writers who do not have a key fact clearly in mind will be confused and prone to wander in several directions. The key fact may involve the market share: A new product may have entered the market two years ago and now accounts for more than 50 percent of the sales in the market. The key fact may involve the audience: Few people know about the product. The key fact could involve the product itself: Some improvements have been made in the product. Discovering this key fact is sometimes difficult and time consuming. It often takes extensive research and discussion with the manufacturers. But being able to write down the key fact of the situation orders the thinking of the advertiser and helps to produce more effective ads.

Distilling the key fact of the advertising situation leads directly to the next step in the process of ad development: stating *the problem* that the ad should solve. The problem statement should be a specific one and should evolve from the key fact. For example, the key fact may be: A product's percentage of the market is down. The problem then would be: The product's share of the market needs to be raised. Problems may also involve the product itself: The product has a bad reputation, or the product costs more than its competitor's products.

If the key fact and the problem of the advertising situation are clear in an advertising copywriter's mind, the third step in the process should follow: the *objective* of the advertisement. The objective needs to be stated clearly and precisely. Just what is the advertisement supposed to do? The following are some statements of advertising objectives:

- The ad should make people aware of the product.
- The ad should change people's attitudes toward the product.
- The ad should tell consumers of the product's improvements.
- The ad should encourage people to shift from buying another product to buying this product.

Once an advertiser has thought through to this point—and assuming that the proper amount of research has been done—the next step is to develop a copy platform.

COPY PLATFORMS

A copy platform is a way of getting the ideas and information of an advertising situation down on paper and of organizing those ideas in such a way that effective advertising copy can be produced from them. A copy platform is not an ad itself, but it will contain many of the ideas that will later appear in the ad, and it will provide valuable information for the ad copywriter. Figure 8.3 shows one version of a copy platform, but it is not the only type of copy platform. Copy platforms vary according to the advertising agency and the advertiser, but most contain the same basic information.

The copy platform is where many of the factors in developing an ad begin to come together. The copywriter must finally commit to paper what he or she has learned about a product and about an audience and must develop ideas from the information that is there. The example of the copy platform in this chapter shows some of the elements that make up the platform. Note that the advertising problem is the first piece of information that is called for in the copy platform. Stating this problem simply and directly sets the stage for many of the other ideas that will appear on the copy platform. A problem may be encountering a number of different advertising situations, but generally the copywriter will zero in on just one—the one that the advertiser considers the most important. The product characteristics are those that might be helpful in formulating the ad. This list cannot be all-inclusive; the copywriter will have to limit the list to those items that relate directly to the advertising problem and items that might otherwise make the product distinctive and beneficial to the consumer.

The advertising objective is then drawn directly from the advertising problem. The objective should be a way of solving the problem.

The target market is the audience to whom the advertising will be directed. A description of this audience should be stated as simply and specifically as possible.

Figure 8.3   Copy Platform

A copy platform is a way of gathering information about a product and matching it with the advertising situation. Not all of the product characteristics need to relate to the advertising problem, but in listing them together, some creative theme might suggest itself. The platform here lists a number of characteristics that could be emphasized in an advertising campaign depending on the advertising problem that needed to be solved.

Ad subject: The Reps Fitness Club

Ad problem: Many people say they want to join a fitness club but can't fit it into their schedules.

Product characteristics:

- Clean, modern facilities
- Plenty of facilities: stationary bikes, swimming pool, all types of fitness equipment, saunas and steam baths
- Open 24 hours
- Supervised nursery available for children under six years old; available from 7 A.M. to 7 P.M.
- Certified coaches and trainers available for single advisory sessions or regularly scheduled workout sessions
- Special equipment available for people with back problems
- Joint memberships: join with a friend and second membership is half priced; basic membership is $30 a month or $250 a year

Advertising objective: Let the target market know that this fitness club has many options for fitting into a busy schedule.

Target market: Women, ages 25–40, particularly those with young children

Competition: Most other fitness clubs and centers in the area began catering to men; while some have tried to shift their focus to women, they seem to have targeted single women rather than women with children.

Statement of benefit or appeal:

- Free child care available 12 hours a day
- Train alone or with a professional

Creative theme:

- Fitness that fits your schedule

Supportive selling points:

- Always open, always available
- Clean facility, friendly atmosphere

Knowing exactly who the audience is will help the copywriter come up with the next, and most important, part of the copy platform: the statement of benefit and appeal.

Advertising should tell its audience the benefit of a product, the answer to the question "What's in it for me?" The advertising should state, implicitly or explicitly, why the product or service is good for the consumer, why the consumer should buy it, or what the consumer can expect from it. This statement of benefit and appeal is the most persuasive part of an advertisement, and its importance cannot be overestimated. Here are a few examples:

You'll save money if you buy our product.

You'll be safer if you use our product.

You'll live in more comfort if you have our product.

These benefits relate directly to the discussion of needs and wants at the beginning of this chapter. Such appeals are highly potent ones for advertising, and they have been highly effective in many advertising campaigns.

The creative theme in a copy platform allows the copywriter to use some imagination in formulating the appeals of the advertising. The creative theme might be a slogan, or it might be a description of the way in which the advertising will be presented.

The supportive selling points are a list of product characteristics or factors about the advertising situation that will help to sell a product. They may vary somewhat from the main statement of benefit, but they can be used to reinforce a tendency to use the product.

WRITING THE AD

With the copy platform in place, the copywriter is almost ready to write an ad. Among the decisions that still need to be made are which medium or media the advertisements will appear in, how many ads there will be for a product, when they will be placed, and how large or long the ads will be. All of these are marketing decisions that go beyond the scope of this book. Our focus here is on the writing of the advertisement.

This section looks at some of the common advertising writing practices and guidelines. There are few rules in the writing of an advertisement, and there are no dominant structures for ads, as there are for news stories and for broadcast news. Instead, each ad is a combination of the factors we have already discussed in this chapter plus the limits and opportunities provided by the medium in which the ad is placed.

Still, there are some things that we can say generally about the writing of advertisements. One of the oldest advertising copywriting formulas is A-I-D-A: attention, interest, desire, action. According to this formula, an ad should do four things, in order.

First, it should gain the attention of the viewer or listener. An ad that doesn't do at least that is not going to be able to do anything else.

After getting the consumer's attention, the ad must hold his or her interest. The ad should use words and pictures that will draw the reader or listener into the ideas that the ad is trying to present. An ad may be about an interesting or important subject, but it can be so dull that the consumer is lost before the message gets across.

The ad should create a desire for the product, service, or idea presented in the ad. It is important for the copywriter to choose the appeal, the benefits, and the proper words that will develop this desire.

Finally, the ad should stimulate the consumer to some action. In most cases, what you want the consumer to do is go out and buy the product.

With this formula in mind, we will look at some of the commonly accepted guidelines for writing effective advertisements.

Use Clear, Simple English

This rule reappears throughout this book. It is basic to communication in the mass media. Obscure words and complex sentences will not encourage people to read an advertisement. You cannot impress someone with your wide vocabulary in an advertisement.

Another reason for using simple language, particularly in advertising, is that it is more believable. People will tend to believe advertising messages that are presented to them in language that they normally use or are used to hearing.

Pay Attention to the Verbs

Verbs are the most important part of the language. If your ad has mostly "to be" verb forms (*is, are, was, were,* etc.), the ad will probably sound flat and lifeless. If it contains mostly action verbs, it will be lively and interesting.

Good copywriters use verbs rather than adjectives to describe their product. They associate verbs with how the product looks, what it does, and how it makes the user feel. A list of those verbs helps them to develop good advertising copy.

Another rule about the verbs in advertising copy is to stick with the present tense (whenever appropriate) and the active voice (almost always). The present tense implies immediacy and puts the reader into an advertisement quickly. The active voice allows the writer to make a stronger statement than the passive voice does.

Be as Specific as Possible, but Don't Let Too Many Details Get in the Way of the Advertising Message

An advertisement should be balanced. Facts—specifics—are more likely to sell a product than are general ideas or concepts. Yet too many facts are likely to confuse the reader or listener. Consumers like to have reasons to buy a product, and an ad should give them enough of those reasons that they will be motivated to do so.

Be Precise in the Use of the Language

Here's where intelligence, art, and creativity combine for the copywriter. The copywriter needs to know the language intimately. He or she should be sensitive to the subtle meanings of words—not just their dictionary meanings but the images they provoke.

For example, the words *laugh, giggle,* and *guffaw* have essentially the same meaning, but they evoke different images. Most of us laugh; little boys and girls giggle; old men don't usually giggle but guffaw; and so on. Writers need to understand the subtle differences between words and take unusual care with them. They need to select the words for their copy that evoke exactly the images that they want to convey and that will describe the product in exactly the way they mean for it to be described. You should select the words that relate directly to the benefit you are connecting to the product.

Some advertisements will occasionally use poor grammar. If this is done, it should be a deliberate decision on the part of all who are concerned with producing the ad. Those people should recognize the dangers of doing this—the possibility of degrading the product, distracting attention of the audience away from the product, bringing the advertising copywriter into disrepute, and insulting the audience. Any of those things would be a high price to pay for whatever benefits the use of bad grammar might gain for the product.

Use Personal Pronouns When Appropriate

Let the reader, listener, or viewer of an advertisement know that you are talking directly to him or her. Using personal pronouns, especially *you,* is an effective way to do that, but like any good idea, it can be overdone. Occasionally, you should ask a question (although only occasionally; we'll discuss this more in the next section).

Don't Be Afraid of Contractions

Contractions are a good way of making sure that your tone is informal, and the informal tone is preferable in most advertisements. Like personal pronouns, contractions can be used too much, particularly if they sound forced. A copywriter should develop an ear for the language and recognize when the advertising copy "sounds" right or wrong. If a contraction sounds right, use it.

Inspire Confidence in the Product and the Advertiser

Ads should contain messages that will help people to believe the advertiser and trust a product. Advertising copywriters should not sacrifice long-range trust for a short-term goal. They should, however, tell an audience that the product being advertised is one that will benefit them and will live up to expectations. Not only should the messages in an ad inspire such confidence, but the ad itself should also contribute toward this goal. Ads that are in good taste, use English properly, are not cutesy or smart-alecky, and do not insult the audience are the kinds of ads that build confidence. A manufacturer should be as proud of the ads that it commissions for a product as of the product itself. Advertisement writers should feel that same pride in what they produce.

Give the Audience All the Information It Needs

An ad does not have to tell everything about a product or a manufacturer, but it should not leave any major questions about the product or service unanswered. For example, a power company advertised that energy audits were available to its customers. These audits involved representatives of the power company coming to the home, inspecting it, and recommending actions to increase the efficient use of energy. The service was free. What the ad did not say was how a customer could get this service: Whom should the customer call or write? What was the procedure? The ad left the clear impression that the power company was not very interested in having customers take advantage of this service.

ELEMENTS OF A PRINT AD

Unlike the newspaper reporter, who generally does not have anything to do with the physical appearance of a story in the newspaper, an advertising copywriter must always be aware of the design of an ad. Design is an integral part of the ad-writing process, and it often is a determining factor in what the ad says. In this section, we

Figure 8.4   Copy Sheet for Print Ad

This ad shows how the copy on the copy sheet is translated into a print ad.

Product: The Reps Fitness Club

Medium: Newspaper

Client: The Reps Fitness Club

Writer: Smith

Headline: Fitness—Anytime You Want It

Subhead: 24/7. All you have to do is show up.

Body copy:

You know you need to do it; you just don't have the time. At least, you think you don't.

The Reps Fitness Club thinks you do. And whenever that time comes along, we're ready—open 24 hours a day, 7 days a week. If you have kids to tend to, bring them along. Our supervised and spacious playroom is filled with toys and videos that will occupy the young ones while you do what you need to do:

- Get into shape
- Feel better

Check us out today—all 24 hours of it. Call 276-555-0055 right now.

Subhead or slogan:

Fitness that fits your schedule.

Signature:

The Reps Fitness Center, 1818 Blackoak Drive, 276-955-0055

will discuss the different parts of a print ad, keeping in mind that, depending on the work situation, it may or may not be the copywriter's job to design the ad as well as write the copy.

Illustration

The illustration that an ad uses is often the most important attention-getting item in that ad. It is the part of an ad that is most likely to achieve the attention-getting part of the A-I-D-A formula. While we are not concerned here with the design of the ad or the selection of the illustration, the copywriter will often write the copy on the basis of the kind of illustration that is used. The illustration, the headline, and the body copy—the three most important parts of the ad—must be closely tied to one another. If the relationship between these three elements is not readily apparent, the ad runs the risk of losing the reader who will not want to figure it out.

Headline

After the image, the headline is often the most important part of an ad because it gives the reader the first solid information about the product. The headline will most often achieve the "interest" part of the A-I-D-A formula and will determine whether or not the reader's interest is aroused enough to read the rest of the ad.

The most effective headlines appeal to the self-interest of the reader—the answer to the question "What's in it for me?" The copywriter must decide what appeal is being made and what benefit is being offered.

The headline should consist of just a few carefully chosen words (many ad writers say that the limit is eight words) that will set the tone for the ad and implicitly promise some reward to the reader for reading through the ad. Many advertising copywriters believe that headlines in ads should be treated much like headlines for news stories in newspapers; that is, they should give the reader some information that the reader does not already have. Although this is not the only approach to writing headlines in ads, it is a useful one for many ads.

A headline may deliver a promise about a product. It might challenge an assumption on the reader's part. It might make a claim about a product. It may play on the reputation of the advertiser. It may simply try to provoke a mood for the reader.

Above all, headlines should involve the reader in the ad quickly. They may do this by asking a question ("When will you get an opportunity like this again?"), offering some information ("How to save money"), or making a provocative statement ("Not all men are created equal").

Finally, caution should be exercised in writing headlines. Some headlines are clearly misleading and inappropriate, and an advertiser uses these at his or her peril. Misleading or deceptive headlines can get an advertiser into legal trouble, and inappropriate headlines can destroy the advertiser's credibility with the reader.

Subheads

Subheads allow the copywriter an opportunity to expand on what has been said in the main headline. They also allow the writer to introduce new material that may draw the reader into an ad. Subheads are set in a smaller size of type than the main headline, and they are generally longer. Most often, the thoughts that are presented in a subhead are tied to those that are presented in the main headline. For instance, if the main headline poses a question, the subhead may answer it, as in the following example:

IS NOW THE TIME TO BUY A NEW CAR?
Most experts agree that it is.

Not every advertisement needs a subhead. They are not attention-getting devices; rather, they are informational devices, and they should be used only when necessary and appropriate.

Body Copy

The body copy is the heart of the advertisement. If the illustration and headline get the reader's attention, the body copy is where the reader should be rewarded for taking the time to read the ad. That reward should come in the form of information about the product being advertised and answers to questions that are raised explicitly and implicitly in the headline.

Writing body copy can take a number of approaches. The factual approach is a direct one. Essentially, it says: Here is some information about the product; here is why you should buy it. The narrative approach is a less direct one. It generally tells a story about the product, emphasizing the selling points of the product. The narrative approach is used when the ad needs to hold the attention of the reader. The stories or situations that are used in a narrative approach should be projective. That is, they should be situations that the readers can relate to or imagine themselves in.

The rules for writing body copy are the same as those for writing in any part of the mass media: simplicity, brevity, word precision, and so on. Advertising copywriters take special care with the verbs they use and think of verbs as the chief descriptors of a product.

Avoid mistakes in grammar. Mistakes call attention to the writing and not to the message. Sentence fragments—one or two words or short phrases that do not make complete sentences—can be acceptable, but they must be deliberate, and the writer should exercise complete control of the language.

Avoid exaggeration. Saying that something is the "greatest in the world" or even "the cheapest in town" is not likely to help sell a product. Readers are more likely to want facts and specifics.

The writer should have a simple message in mind, and everything in the body copy should relate to that message.

Tell the reader what you want him or her to do: "Call today," "Go out and buy it," or "Clip this coupon." Whatever the action is, do not assume that the reader will know it without being told.

Above all, the copy should be interesting or even compelling.

Closings

Closings may be thought of as subheads that come after body copy rather than before it. A closing will make a strong point for the reader. Often, it will summarize what the body copy has been implying. Sometimes, it will give a direct command to the reader; at other times, it will only suggest that the reader do something. Like the subhead, a closing may not be necessary for every advertisement.

Mandatories, Including Legals

Mandatories are items that must be included in the advertisement. For instance, an advertiser may want an ad to mention the name of the company president or that a product is manufactured in a certain area. The words "an equal opportunity employer," are a mandatory for the employment ads of many organizations.

Legals are items that are required by law to be in an ad. For instance, all cigarette ads must include the Surgeon General's warning; all automobile ads must include the mileage ratings. The Federal Trade Commission and other federal agencies, such as the Food and Drug Administration, have issued many regulations about the content of advertisements. These regulations often require that certain things be in an advertisement. A professional copywriter must be familiar with these regulations if the ads he or she writes are to remain legal.

Slogans, Logos, and Signatures

These items may be included in an ad, although they are necessary in every advertisement. *Slogans* are short phrases that become identified with products. A slogan should be short, easily understood, and appropriate to the product. Sometimes, whole advertising campaigns are built around slogans, such as Coke's slogan "Coke Is Real." or that of McDonald's, "I'm lovin' it."

A *logo* is a design that represents a company. The Volkswagen logo, for instance, is a "V" sitting in the middle of a "W," all of which is in a circle. Volkswagen has been using this logo for decades. It has become a symbol of the company. Advertisers will want to use well-designed logos in their ads because of the distinctiveness they add to the advertisement. *Signatures* generally refer to the name and address of the company, which are often necessary or useful in an ad.

WRITING ADVERTISING FOR BROADCAST

Much of the advertising that we pay the most attention to comes from the broadcast media: television and radio. Broadcasting has advantages over print in being able to deliver a message with immediacy and impact. It can bring a product to life and show it in action. But broadcast advertising is expensive to produce and air, especially on television. And broadcast advertising gets only one chance at a time with the listener or viewer. If the message is not delivered immediately, the consumer cannot turn back the page and listen to it again.

Figure 8.5   Radio Script Sheet

This thirty-second radio ad limits itself to making a single point and giving the listener some essential information about the product. Note that it ends with a call to action.

Product: The Reps Fitness Club

Client: The Reps Fitness Club

Title: Out of excuses

Writer: Smith

Length: 30 seconds

Source	Audio
Announcer 1	Need to get fit, feel better, lose a few pounds?
	Of course you do. We all do.
	But (affected voice) you don't have the time, right? Wrong!
	(SDX: Workout music, heavy beat)
	The Reps Fitness Club gives you time—24 hours a day, 7 days a week. All the equipment and space you could ever want, plus a nursery for the kids.
	You're not out of time. You're out of excuses.
	Call The Reps Fitness Club today. 276-955-0055.
	Fitness that fits your schedule.

Whereas print ads are space oriented, broadcast ads are time oriented. Broadcast ads should be simple. They should be designed to achieve maximum impact in a short amount of time. In addition, copywriters should write for the ear. The visual and oral messages should complement one another. They should key in on the sounds, words, and pictures that will help sell the product.

The copywriter for broadcast advertising has certain tools available, and it is useful to take a brief look at what they are and how they can be used.

Voices

The most commonly used tool of the broadcast advertiser is the voice. Talking is the most direct and effective form of communication for broadcasting and the easiest to produce. Most of what the advertising copywriter will write for broadcast advertising is a script for what people will say. To write conversational language, however, is neither easy nor simple. It takes practice and much writing and rewriting. The script must be suitable for the voice that is using it as well as the other elements of the ad.

Sound Effects

Like voices, sounds can be a very effective means of communication. Sound effects are often vital to radio ads. Car engines, crowds cheering, birds chirping in the trees, children laughing—all of these sounds can take listeners to the scene of an advertisement. They evoke pictures and images inside the heads of the listeners. They can demonstrate the way a product looks or works.

Music

As with sound effects, music can provide the proper background for a commercial, or it can be the main part of the commercial's message. Selecting the proper music for a commercial's background is an important consideration for the producers of an advertisement. The haunting music of Vangelis (part of which was used in the score for the movie *Chariots of Fire*) was one of the most memorable parts of the famous Ernest and Julio Gallo "Wedding" commercial. The commercial needed only the music, the superb photography, and the tag line, "All the best a wine can be" to get its message across.

In the days when radio was the dominant broadcast medium, the *jingle*—the one- or two-line musical message about a product—was one of the most popular advertising techniques. The jingle is still popular for radio and has also become a staple of the television commercial. In fact, the simple one- or two-line jingle has developed in a number of ways. Some advertisers have produced orchestra-backed songs to promote their products, and Coca-Cola's "I'd Like to Teach the World to Sing" became a popular hit when it was recorded and sold to the public.

Pictures

Pictures are not available for radio, of course, but they constitute one of the major advantages of television. Not only can television show pictures, but a well-produced advertisement can direct the eye to exactly the images that it wants the audience to see.

Pictures bring a commercial to life. They can show real people talking to one another and doing real things. Although most people realize that commercials are most often dramatic presentations (not pictures of real life), commercials still have a believability about them that makes people accept them and consider the messages they have to send.

Visual Effects

Graphics and special effects have always been a part of television and have proven themselves to be a useful tool in the production of television advertising. Today their value has been enhanced because the computer hardware and software to create complex and eye-popping graphics are readily available and easy to use.

Although broadcast commercials can vary widely in approach, there are two basic formats: dramatic formats and announcer formats. Dramatic formats emphasize the action on the screen or within the script. One of the best and oldest ways to make a point is to tell a story. Radio and television commercials are often small dramas packed into just a few seconds. They may also be just a set of scenes and sounds

Figure 8.6   Television Script Sheet

An idea for a television ad may get its first incarnation as a simple television script sheet such as the one shown here. Later it may become a storyboard (see Figure 8.7).

Product: The Reps Fitness Club

Client: The Reps Fitness Club

Title: Maybe I do have the time

Writer: Smith

Length: 30 seconds

Video	Audio
(Two women in a grocery store; small child in one of the shopping carts)	
Woman 1	Rachael, long time no see. Hey, you look great! Been working out?
Woman 2	Sure have.
Woman 1	Really? How do you find the time with all that you do and your kids?
Woman 2	The Reps Fitness Club. Open 24 hours a day, all kinds of equipment—and there's a nursery. Little Sara here loves it.
(VO: Inside of Reps Fitness Club)	
Woman 2	The Reps Fitness Club. Maybe I do have the time.
Announcer	The Reps Fitness Club. Call today, 276-955-0055.

that lead to a point about a product. While they may use announcers, the announcer plays only a partial role in the ad. There are four types of dramatic formats.

Problem Resolution

Presenting a problem and then resolving it is one of the most common ways of selling a product. The outline for a problem-resolution commercial is a simple one. For instance, a person has a headache; he takes a brand of aspirin; he no longer has a headache. The problem-resolution technique is popular with advertisers because it can make a strong point in a short amount of time.

Whatever the problem is, the commercial is structured so that its solution is directly attributed to the product. You can think of the problem-resolution commercial as a before-and-after structure: Before using the product, we had this problem; after using it, we no longer have the problem.

One of the secrets of the problem-resolution commercial's success is the speed with which a problem can be established. A copywriter need waste no time in letting the audience know what the problem is. Usually, that is done with the very first words and pictures. The idea of the problem has to be clear and simple: The people in the commercial are hungry, or they're uncomfortable, or they're looking for something, and so on. The product then comes to their rescue just as quickly. All this is done usually within the space of thirty seconds, sometimes even fifteen seconds.

Slice of Life

Normally, the slice-of-life-commercial shows people doing things in which the advertised product is involved. These may be minidramas with a problem and resolution that have little to do with the product itself, but they show the product in a very good light. Or they may be sketches that revolve around the product. For example, a popular commercial for Coke shows a baseball team on a bus after a game that the team won; the team is hot and thirsty, and the bus stops at a small diner; the team descends on the diner, and everyone who works at the diner must work harder; finally, the team quenches its thirst with Coke, and one of the team members gives his baseball cap to one of the waitresses right before the team leaves.

In a similar type of commercial, a father drives his preteen daughter and her friends to McDonald's, where they may run into some boys they have been discussing. When they get to McDonald's, the father gets out, and his daughter, horrified, says, "You're not going in, are you?" The father waits in the car, realizing that his daughter is growing up. He takes comfort in eating some McDonald's french fries.

Slice-of-life commercials must be entertaining, but more important, they need to identify the product with a situation or feeling that is familiar and comfortable. They try to demonstrate that the product is part of the life that the people on the screen are living, and it should also be part of the viewer's life.

Documentary/Demonstration

These kinds of commercials use fewer dramatic techniques than others. They may simply show how a product works (for example, how a fabric cleaner lifts out the stain from a sweater). They may demonstrate how a product works in comparison to its competition. They put a product in an unusual situation to demonstrate something about the product (such as Timex watch's once famous slogan, "It takes a licking and keeps on ticking," or Master Lock's demonstration of the durability of its lock by firing a rifle bullet into one of them). Occasionally, a commercial will present the way a product is made in order to demonstrate something about the product.

Fantasy

Putting people and products in unreal or abnormal situations is another way of making a point about a product. Fantasy also includes the use of animation, such as that used in commercials for Keebler cookies or Green Giant products, and special camera techniques, such as dancing cats and talking dogs.

Fantasy characters are not always without controversy. During a mid-1980s campaign, Energizer used a fuzzy, pink bunny beating a small drum to say that its batteries lasted longer than those of the competition. One member of the competition, the Eveready Battery Company, took exception to this message and brought out an ad featuring a garish, hot-pink bunny with sunglasses pounding a bass drum. "For years, one of our competitors has been telling you they have the longest-lasting battery. But they haven't invited us to the party," the voiceover announcer says. The Energizer bunny has proved to be remarkably long-lasting as an advertising character. Several years after it originated, its new tactic was to interrupt fake commercials with the tag line "Still going."

Dramatic presentations have either no announcer at all or an announcer who plays only a minor part in the commercial. Announcer formats are those in which the announcer is the main character or one of the main characters in the commercial. There are three types of announcer formats: the spokesperson, the testimonial, and the anonymous announcer.

The Spokesperson

The spokesperson is another popular format for broadcast commercials. Spokespeople may range from celebrities to unknown but real people to actors. They may or may not be experts on the product they are advertising. The Federal Trade Commission has a wide variety of rules governing the use of spokespeople in advertisements. In general, celebrities who endorse products have some responsibility for the claims that are made about the products; people who are identified as "real people" or "typical users" in advertisements must be who the ads say they are; actors may play the part of "real people" or "typical users" as long as they are not identified as such. In other words, if a commercial identifies a speaker as "Joe Smith of Hoboken, New Jersey," that speaker must be Joe Smith of Hoboken, New Jersey.

Famous people (usually actors or sports stars but not always) can become spokespeople and even symbols for the manufacturers that hire them for their products. Basketball star Michael Jordan became so identified with Nike shoes that the company developed a major brand and named it after him. Tiger Woods is another sports figure who stands to make far more from his endorsements than from his sports career. Actor Jessie White was for two decades the Maytag repairman, "the loneliest guy in the world." The advertising industry took special note when Maytag announced in 1989 that Gordon Jump, a star of the "WKRP" comedy series, would replace White in this role. When Jump retired in 2003, actor Hardy Rawls took over the role.

Testimonial

Closely associated with the use of the spokesperson is the testimonial commercial. The testimonial differs from the spokesperson commercial because of the credibility of the person doing the testimonial. In the testimonial, the person in the commercial is saying, in effect, "I have some expertise about this product, and I think it's the best there is." Sports figures are often asked to endorse sporting goods products because it is believed that they have high credibility in this area. In some cases, their endorsements have gone as far as allowing their names to be placed on the product itself, such as with Michael Jordan's line of sports shoes.

Anonymous Announcers

In the anonymous announcer format, the announcer does not appear and is not identified but is only heard. This format is popular with advertisers who want to direct all the attention of the audience to the product itself. The attributes of the product, not the spokesperson, are emphasized.

Sometimes "anonymous" announcers are not so anonymous. A number of people have such distinctive and widely recognizable voices that viewers of a commercial will know who is speaking even when he or she is not identified. For a number of years Cable News Network used the very distinctive voice of James Earl Jones to say simply, "This is CNN." Short as the voiceover was, there was no doubt it was Jones. This technique of having a recognizable voice in a commercial can heighten the interest in a product without distracting from the message of the commercial.

Students should recognize that many commercials do not fall strictly within the categories just outlined. They are often combinations of two or more of the types of commercials. They use techniques from a number of sources to help sell their products. On the other hand, you should remember that the most common characteristic of a television ad is its simplicity of structure. The time constraints of a television commercial demand that you get the message across to the viewer simply and quickly.

One of the most useful tools that writers of television commercials have is the television storyboard. The storyboard allows a writer to begin visualizing the commercial as it is being written. It uses a series of scenes from the commercial along with the words to give the writer an idea of how the commercial will look when it is produced. An example of a television storyboard can be found in Figure 8.7.

Storyboards are useful in other ways. Besides helping the writer to visualize the commercial, a storyboard can give a client an idea of what a commercial will be like before any expensive production work has begun. It can also give the producer and director of the commercial insights into what the writer has in mind for the commercial.

No one has to be a good or clever artist to use a storyboard. The most basic drawings of commercial scenes, even using stick figures if necessary, will be sufficient for transmitting the visual ideas in a commercial.

OTHER MEDIA

Three other types of media should be mentioned briefly as part of our overall discussion of advertising: point-of-purchase advertising, outdoor advertising, and direct mail. These are important forms of advertising, particularly in supporting advertising campaigns that are carried on in other media. Because they involve many decisions beyond those of the copywriter, however, they are discussed only briefly here.

Point-of-purchase advertising refers to the packaging and display of a product. One study by the Point-of-Purchase Advertising Institute indicated that as many as two thirds of buying decisions are made after the customer has entered the store. All other advertising is useless unless a product can be found. That means that it must be well packaged and well displayed. It must stand out from other products—

Figure 8.7   Television Storyboard

Television storyboards, even ones as crude as in this illustration, can give advertisers an idea of how the visuals will work with the sound in a television advertisement.

TELEVISION STORYBOARD

Product:	The Reps Fitness Club
Client:	The Reps Fitness Club
Title:	Maybe I do have time
Writer:	Smith
Length:	30 seconds

Video   **Audio**

Frame time 5 seconds		Rachael, long time no see. Hey, you look great. Been working out?
Frame time 2 seconds		Sure have.
Frame time 5 seconds	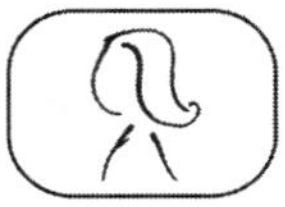	Really? How do you find the time with all that you do and your kids?
Frame time 7 seconds		The Reps Fitness Club. Open 24 hours a day, all kinds of equipment – and there's a nursery. Little Sara here loves it.
Frame time 5 seconds		The Reps Fitness Club. Maybe I do have the time.
Frame time 6 seconds	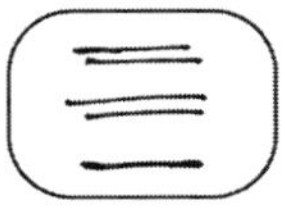	The Reps Fitness Club. Call today, 276-955-0055.
Frame time		

particularly the competition, which is likely to be displayed beside it on the store shelves.

The effectiveness of point-of-purchase can be found in the history of one product: Hershey's candy bars. For decades, Hershey's declined to advertise in any media except its own packaging. Its marketing strategy was known as *mass availability*. That is, the company tried to place its product in as many locations as it could. That strategy worked, and Hershey's candy bars became some of the most popular in their product area. Only in 1970, in the face of increasing competition, did the company start to produce mass media advertising.

Outdoor advertising is a multi-million-dollar business. In 2003, advertisers spent about $5.5 billion on this medium, about $3 billion on billboards alone, according to the Outdoor Advertising Association of America. Because the messages on almost all types of outdoor advertising must be brief, this medium is also used to supplement advertising campaigns in other media. One of the chief assets of outdoor advertising is its repetitive nature. A person may pass a poster or billboard many times, yet the advertiser has made only one advertising purchase.

Finally, *direct mail advertising* offers an advertiser many possibilities and advantages. Direct mail includes a variety of marketing techniques, including sales letters, postcards, pamphlets, brochures, and catalogues. Direct mail allows advertisers to target a very specific audience and to get a message to that audience very quickly. It can carry a great deal of information. One of the problems with direct mail is that it can be very expensive. It can, however, give an advertiser some fairly precise information about how well an advertising campaign has worked.

CONCLUSION

Writing advertising copy calls for a high degree of intelligence, hard work, creativity, and competitiveness on the part of the writer. It is not a job that everyone can do, but it is one that has great rewards for those who are successful.

POINTS FOR CONSIDERATION AND DISCUSSION

1. The text lists some major demographic characteristics that advertisers want to know. Can you think of other demographic variables that would be important to advertisers? What would make these important in selling a product?
2. Think of a member of your family. What needs are most important to that person? What advertising appeals would work best to sell that person a product that would meet those needs?
3. Take an ad from a magazine. To what audience, in terms of demographic variables, is that ad targeted? What appeals does the ad use?
4. The text says that ads should tell people what they should do (e.g., "Go out and buy one today."). Find an ad that does not do this, and then find one that does. Which do you think is more effective?
5. Select an ad that you think is a good one from a magazine. List the verbs that are used in the ad. Does this tell you anything about how the ad was written?
6. What characteristics does advertising copy writing have in common with news writing? How are they different?

FURTHER READING

Applegate, E. (2004). *Strategic Copywriting: How to Create Effective Advertising.* Lanham, MD: Rowman & Littlefield Publishers.

Burton, P. W. (1999). *Advertising Copywriting* (7th ed.). Lincolnwood, IL: NTC Business Books.

Parente, D. E., Barban, A. M., & Vanden Bergh, B. G. (1998). *Advertising Campaign Strategy.* New York: Harcourt Brace College Publishers.

WEBSITES

Advertising Age: **www.adage.com**

Advertising Media Internet Center: **www.amic.com**

American Advertising Federation: **www.aaf.org**

EXERCISES

8.I Print Advertising Critique Sheet

Answer the questions below about a print advertisement.

Name: _____

Advertisement: _____

1. What is the promise of benefit offered by this headline?

2. How does the illustration demonstrate the product? How does this illustration attract attention?

3. What proofs of the promise of benefit in the headline are offered by the body copy?

4. What action does this ad tell readers to take?

8.2 Radio Advertising Critique Sheet

Answer the questions below about a radio advertisement.

Name: _____

Advertisement: _____

1. What sound effects are used to define location?

2. What sound effects are used to define action?

3. Was the announcer overused?

4. Give two examples of how dialogue is used to let the listener know what actions are happening.

5. What is the target market of the ad?

6. What benefits are offered by the ad?

7. Is there a call to action in the ad?

_____

8.3 Television Advertising Critique Sheet

Answer the questions below about a television advertisement.

Name: _____

Advertisement: _____

1. What visual effects are used to define location?

2. What sound effects are used to define action?

3. What type of format is used?

4. Write a brief (three or four sentences at most) synopsis of the ad.

5. What is the target market of the ad?

6. What benefits are offered by the ad?

7. Is there a call to action in the ad?

8.4 Writing Advertising Copy

Write the copy for three print advertisements based on the information below. The body copy in each should be from fifty to seventy-five words long. You may want to use the layout sheet in Appendix D for this assignment.

CAR REPAIR SHOP

Wright's Auto Repair, located at 126 Wesley, is the oldest car repair shop in town. It has operated continuously in the same location since 1923. In fact, that makes it one of the oldest businesses in town.

At least, that's what it wants to be known for. Hank Wright, the current proprietor, has just taken over as manager of Wright's from his dad. It was Hank Wright's grandfather who began the business in 1923.

Hank wants a set of advertisements that emphasize the reliability of the work he does. He wants to appeal particularly to people who have been using other repair shops—especially those who use the shops at dealerships where they bought their cars and have been dissatisfied with them. Hank says that his shop offers not only a guarantee on the work, but also a guarantee on when the work will be finished. If the shop cannot meet that deadline, it will provide a loaner car to the customer if needed. The shop takes care of all types of car work, from maintenance (changing oil and filters) to engine and brake repair. They also have a specialist who is trained in repair of car radios and sound systems.

8.5 Writing Advertising Copy

COLLEGE PROMOTION

Pick a slogan or theme for an image advertising campaign for your college or university (example: "It's a great place to learn") and write 200 words of copy for three ads centered on that theme. You will also need to write a four- to ten-word headline for each of the ads.

Do a rough drawing of one of the main buildings on your campus, or use the image in Figure 8.2.

8.6 Developing an Advertising Strategy

Use the information below to develop a series of print and/or broadcast advertisements for the following product. Follow your instructor's directions in completing this assignment.

CREATIVE WORK PLAN

Cowabunga Cream Bars

Key fact: Cowabunga Cream Bars are made with all-natural ingredients and packaged using 100% recyclable materials.

Advertising problem: Many people feel that pure ice cream is not healthy and are switching to yogurts and low calorie products instead.

CREATIVE STRATEGY

Principal competition: Cowabunga Cream Bars are new to the market but will be priced and marketed similarly with Häagen-Dazs products. Häagen-Dazs is the current leading brand among gourmet ice creams.

Customer profile: Men and women age 28–35, with total household income of $50,000 or more. Usually with families.

Customer Benefit: Cowabunga Cream Bars come in seven flavors and are easy to eat, with no messy scooping involved—plus, their packaging is environmentally safe.

Reason why: The makers of Cowabunga Cream Bars care about the environment as well as making the best-tasting ice cream available.

Tone and manner: Advertising messages should be lively and upbeat with humor involved.

Mandatories: Do not mention competitor by name. Do not attack competitor's product. All advertising should use the tag line: "Mooove closer to udder perfection."

Cowabunga Cream Bars come in the following flavors: chocolate, vanilla, banana, coconut, strawberry, boysenberry, and peach.

8.7 Developing a Product Marketing Scheme

Develop a series of print and/or broadcast advertisements based on the information below. Follow your instructor's directions in completing this assignment.

- Sponsor: Kraft Foods
- Product: SodaBurst

THE PRODUCT

SodaBurst is an instant ice cream soda consisting of a single unit made of ice cream, syrup, and frozen carbonated water fused together and packaged in a "miniature" cylindrical ice cream container of aluminum foil. The ice cream soda is prepared by slipping the single unit (ice cream, syrup, and frozen carbonated water) from its cylindrical container into a large glass and adding tap water. On contact with the tap water, the frozen carbonated water is released and mixes with the syrup. After one minute of stirring, the soda is ready to serve.

At this time, the product is available in two flavors: chocolate (vanilla ice cream with chocolate syrup) and strawberry (vanilla ice cream with strawberry syrup). The product will be sold from ice cream cabinets in retail outlets and must be kept in the freezer section of the home refrigerator until ready for use. SodaBurst will be sold in a four-soda-size carton at a suggested retail price of $2.00. (A package design firm is now completing work on the carton.)

MARKETING RESEARCH

Research conducted in the course of SodaBurst's early product testing indicated that about 70 percent of adults and 80 percent of teens and children drink sodas. Research also revealed that on a year-round basis, housewives reported their own consumption of ice cream sodas at two per month, other family adults at two per month, children age 5–11 at three per month, and teens age 12–17 at four per month. No research indicated that a specific sociogeographic area purchased more than any other.

Early exploratory research indicated that housewives did not see the product as a substitute for fountain ice cream sodas, particularly for themselves, because it could not furnish the highly valued "going-out" experience associated with consuming fountain sodas. Rather, they saw the product as a family snack, competing with the whole spectrum of at-home snacks, from traditional snack foods such as peanuts or corn chips to newly introduced, nontraditional snack foods such as beef jerky. (SodaBurst would be entering a very large and highly competitive category.)

In response to questions about what specific things they liked about SodaBurst, housewives, after the home-use test, cited four major areas: flavor/taste, convenience, ease of preparation, and packaging/storage. Exploratory research had also revealed that ice cream sodas, in contrast to many other snack foods, are regarded as wholesome and that SodaBurst was seen by the majority of respondents as "wholesome" and/or "nutritious."

TEST MARKETING PLANS

Because it appears that all family members would be prospects, it has been decided that spending levels will be substantial (at least on a $5 million national level) and varied media will be employed in a mix emphasizing television.

The creative message must be distinctive to break through the saturation of the snack product market. After extensive discussions, the following message strategy statement was agreed upon between client and agency:

- Advertising copy will be directed to an all-family audience, with particular emphasis on housewives in homes with children aged 5–17.
- Copy will be designed to appeal to consumers in all geographic areas and among all socioeconomic groups.
- The principal objective of the advertising will be to announce that all the familiar taste enjoyment of an ice cream soda is now quickly and conveniently available at home with SodaBurst.
- A secondary objective will be to convince housewives of the product's quality/wholesomeness that makes it suitable for all-family consumption.
- The copy will dramatize the interest and excitement that are inherent in the totally new product concept represented by SodaBurst.

8.8 Developing Print Advertisements

Design a series of four ads to run in the local newspaper in four succeeding weeks. Each ad should carry the same slogan but have a different headline and body copy. Each block of body copy should be about fifty words long. You may want to keep the same design and illustration for the ads, or you can change things around. You may use the layout sheet in Appendix D for this assignment.

LOCAL FLOWER SHOP

Pearsall Florist Shop, the manager says, "wants to put a flower in every business in town at least once a week." She wants to promote the idea that fresh flowers enliven a business and make both customers and employees feel better about that business. The advertising will be pitched to downtown area businesses where the flower shop is located. (It's at 222 Main Street, and the telephone number is 643-ROSE.) For businesses that order one bouquet of flowers each week for a month, there will be a 20 percent discount. Because the shop is located in the downtown area, it can offer quick delivery to businesses in the area. In fact, it guarantees delivery within two hours of getting a telephone order. The manager says that the florists at the shop are experts in designing specialty bouquets for special occasions or locations and that they can design something that is appropriate for any business.

8.9 Writing Advertising Copy

Write four print advertisements for the product below. The advertisements should include a headline, subhead, and seventy-five words of copy.

WEDDING DRESSES

A local wedding shop wants to run a series of ads in April and May with the idea that it has "the best prices in town" on wedding dresses and accessories. Wedding dress prices begin at $250, and bridesmaids' dresses begin at $150. The shop has lots of sizes and colors, and it also carries many accessories for weddings, such as veils and ring pillows. The store, the Bride's Boutique, is going to remain open extra hours during these two months for its sale. It will be open until 9 every night and from 1–5 P.M. on Sundays. One of the owners says she especially wants the ads to mention that brides who have looked everywhere else in town and haven't found what they wanted should come to the Bride's Boutique. They'll probably find something they like.

8.10 Preparing Print Advertisements

Prepare a series of print advertisements for the product below. Follow the directions given by your instructor.

- Sponsor: Marriot Foods
- Product: The Cardinal Club

THE PRODUCT

The Cardinal Club, located on the first floor of the College Center, is a fast-service food cafe. Customers can eat in the dining area or take the food with them.

The cafe is open from 11:30 A.M. to 1 A.M. Monday through Thursday with weekend service: Friday, 11:30 A.M. to 2 A.M.; Saturday, noon to 2 A.M., and Sunday, noon to 1 A.M.

Lunches available: Fast foods from the grill. Deep-fried specialties: mozzarella sticks, mushrooms, and onion rings in addition to french fries. Soup changes daily.

Sandwiches: Turkey croissants; ham salad, tuna salad, or egg salad croissants.

Garden salads and cottage cheese.

Drinks: Coca-Cola products, coffee, tea, milk, fruit juices.

Specials: Wild Pizza. Hand-made crust and sauce. Fresh grilled sausage and meats. Phone number for delivery from 6 P.M. to 1 A.M. daily: 1588.

Dole Whip. A frozen fruit drink. Available in a variety of flavors.

The staff, made up of students from the college, are well known and liked on campus. This personal touch makes it a fun place to meet where students can find the types of foods that they desire.

Entertainment features of the Cardinal Club include a big-screen TV, pool tables, and video games.

MARKETING RESEARCH

Research conducted indicated that about 80 percent of students (but fewer than 40 percent of faculty and staff) have eaten at the Cardinal Club. Research also revealed that on a year-round basis, students tend to use the Cardinal Club more in the wintertime than in the fall and spring. Students were likely to use the Club if they did not have a class near lunchtime. No research indicated that students from a specific dormitory purchased more than any other.

Early exploratory research indicated that students see the Cardinal Club as a substitute for the dining hall, particularly for themselves, because it could furnish the highly valued "going-out" experience associated with restaurants.

In response to questions about what specific things they liked about the Cardinal Club, students cited four major areas: flavor/taste, convenience, to meet with friends, and pizza.

The creative message must be distinctive to break through the saturation of the food-vending market. After extensive discussions, the following message strategy statement was agreed upon between client and agency: Advertising copy will be directed to students and faculty with emphasis on student use.

Copy will be designed to appeal to on-campus consumers who want a place to socialize.

The principal objective of the advertising will be to announce that nutritional foods are available fast. A secondary objective will be to convince students that the product provides advantages that are primarily associated with ambiance.

The copy will dramatize interest and excitement.

8.11 Writing Radio Advertising Copy

Write a series of radio advertisements for the product below. Follow your instructor's directions in completing this assignment.

CLASSICAL RECORD SALE

A local shop, Sound Advice, normally advertises and sells a lot of rock and country recordings. The owner wants to expand his business by offering "the best collection of classical records in the area." He wants you to write some ads promoting this part of his business. But you must be careful, he says, because he doesn't want to drive away his current customers. He is starting the new part of his business by offering all his single classical records and tapes for $4.99 for this weekend only. Come up with a slogan that the owner can use for this expansion in his business and write the ads, which will run in the local paper on Thursday, Friday, and Saturday. The owner says that he has a full line of classical music, from Bach to Stravinsky.

8.12 Preparing Advertising Copy

Write three print advertisements using the same theme or slogan. The ads should be at least seventy-five words each. Write three 15-second broadcast advertisements that refer to the print ads in the local newspaper.

DAYCARE CENTER

Daycare is one of the fastest-growing parts of the service sector. As more and more women work outside the home, the demand for quality, affordable daycare has skyrocketed.

The Sunshine Daycare Center is open from 6:30 A.M. to 6:30 P.M. It is located at 1212 Wiltshire Blvd., one of the city's major thoroughfares, so it is convenient for many people, especially to those who work downtown. The center takes children up through kindergarten ages and has a fully accredited kindergarten class.

The center knows that one of the major concerns that parents have about their child's daycare is to make sure that the child is properly cared for and that the child gets a lot of individual attention. Responding to this concern, the center makes sure that there is at least one adult for every ten children at all times in the center. Most of these adults have some academic or professional training. The center has an open, bright environment inside, with a large, well-equipped playground in the back.

Current advertising should be pitched toward people who work downtown and who are concerned about the quality of care that their children receive during the day. These people are not as concerned about price (the Sunshine Daycare Center is one of the most expensive in town) as about convenience and quality.

8.13 Writing Advertising Copy

Write five advertisements for this product that will run in successive issues of *Vogue*. Each ad should have a headline and about fifty words of copy. The ads will have a common illustration: a gorgeous woman, dressed in a leopard-skin dress and accompanied by a leopard.

PERFUME

The Soft Lights Perfume Company has been marketing Wild Abandon perfume for a number of years, and it has recently found that its share of the perfume market has been decreasing. Essentially, the company wants to advertise a "new and improved" Wild Abandon perfume, but company officials are uncertain exactly how to do this. They tell you that this new perfume, which they want to market under the same name, has a slightly stronger scent and that it comes in a variety of colors, including purple, crimson, and gold. (It used to be clear.) In a radical move, the company has decided to increase the price of the perfume by 50 percent, so that now it costs sixty-five dollars for a half ounce.

8.14 Developing an Advertising Strategy

Write a slogan for Smart Tops hats that can be used in all the company's advertising. Write two print ads, each with a headline and at least fifty words of copy. Be sure to use the slogan you have written. Write a thirty-second radio spot or a thirty-second TV storyboard, also using the slogan you have written.

SMART TOPS, INC.

Most men don't wear hats. That's what the research shows. Smart Tops, Inc., is going to try to change that. Smart Tops is a small firm but is owned by the clothes conglomerate Giant Size, a respected name in clothes. Giant Size isn't a charity, however, and Smart Tops has been losing money for years. The managers of Smart Tops fear that Giant Size will close the company down unless they can show a profit in the next two years. They have decided to embark on a major advertising campaign and have come to your agency for help.

The research that your agency has done into why men do not wear hats has come up with two major reasons: Men don't wear hats because they don't consider them necessary, and they don't wear hats because they think hats are for "older" men. Smart Tops wants to market its hats to younger men, those in the 25–40 range. The managers aren't sure which would be the most effective advertising campaign. Should they take on the "old" characteristic directly and try to convince men that wearing a hat is a "young" thing to do? Or should they try to counter the negative characteristic that hats are unnecessary with some convincing arguments that hats really are necessary?

Your agency wants you to pick one of these advertising strategies and design some advertising for Smart Tops. The following is some information that the agency research office has provided you which may eventually go into a copy platform.

Competition: Smart Tops now has about a 7 percent share of the market, down from 10 percent two years ago. Almost every other manufacturer of men's hats has seen a drop in sales during the past two years also, so there is no evidence that hat wearers have anything against Smart Tops. The biggest advertiser in the market is Smith, Inc., which manufactures a line of hats known as Good As Gold. These are some of the most expensive and well-made hats on the market. Other hat manufacturers do relatively little advertising.

Supportive selling points: Smart Tops says that its hats are as well made as the Good As Golds, but Smart Tops hats sell for an average of 25 percent less. The hats range in price from $15 to $50. All the hats contain at least 50 percent natural fibers, especially cotton and wool. They are extremely well crafted and are backed by years of tradition and experience. Smart Tops has been making hats since the 1880s. The hats are guaranteed against any defect in workmanship and against any damage for a year. If a customer is dissatisfied with anything about a Smart Tops hat, all he has to do is send the hat to the company office, and he will receive a full refund. Smart Tops can also be counted on to provide the latest in new styling in men's hats, as well as a wide variety of traditional styles.

Audience: The marketing research has turned up the fact that women make about 40 percent of all hat purchases for men.

8.15 Solving Advertising Problems

Read through the following information and identify some of the possible advertising problems. Follow your instructor's directions on handling this advertising situation.

HERSHAL'S DEPARTMENT STORE

Hershal's Department Store is one of the largest department stores in town. It is located in the same shopping mall as a Sears and a J.C. Penney store, but Hershal's has a larger variety of clothes than either of these two chain stores. The store's line of women's clothes is especially large, and the store has a reputation for having the most up-to-date styles of women's clothing. It is locally owned and has been in operation for more than fifty years. The president of the board is John Hershal, Jr., the son of the founder. The store's general manager is John Hershal III, the president's son. Hershal's is considered to be the major store in the mall where it is located.

Hershal's recently conducted a marketing survey, as it has for several years, but this survey turned up some surprising results. The survey found that there is a reservoir of goodwill about the store, something that Hershal's has cultivated for many years. For instance, people in the survey said that they liked Hershal's refund policy, which has always been a very liberal one. However, the survey found that people did not like a number of things about Hershal's: The store hours were not long enough (Hershal's closes at 8 P.M., while the other stores in the mall stay open until 9 P.M.); it takes too long to check out; many of the departments don't have enough people to wait on the customers adequately; there is some feeling that Hershal's has raised prices more than other stores have; and many younger women try smaller shops, especially those close to the local college campus, before shopping at Hershal's.

In light of these findings, Hershal's has done several things: Store hours will be extended to 9 P.M. beginning next month; new salespeople will be added to departments that have been understaffed; and the store, which conducts three major sales each year, will conduct five during the coming year.

Hershal's also wants to increase its advertising and has come to your agency for help.

Writing for Public Relations

In today's business and social environment, an organization—no matter what its function or purpose—must pay attention to its communication at every level. Public relations (PR) is a management function that helps organizations to communicate and that involves communicating with targeted publics. Public relations practitioners are communication specialists, hired by organizations to perform and advise on a variety of communication tasks.

Only a few years ago, many organizations, particularly private businesses, saw no need to have such specialists. The organizations sold their products or performed their services for a specialized public and were content to believe that they were doing all the communicating that they needed to do.

One example is a large corporation that specializes in operating sites around the country that handle toxic chemical waste material for other industries. The company performed this necessary but unpleasant task and did so within the legal regulations that governed such operations. The company managers felt that the company had little need to communicate with the public. After all, it was not trying to sell a service to the general public. It dealt exclusively with other industries. In the last few decades, however, with more public attention focused on the environment—and on dangerous toxic waste sites—the company found that it could no longer afford to take such a cavalier attitude toward its communication needs. As the issue of hazardous waste disposal has become not only an industrial one but also a political one, this company and many others like it have found themselves in the communication business.

Situations like the one described above have occurred for many organizations. Corporate chiefs are discovering that they need professional communicators as well as budget managers, salespeople, scientists, engineers, and secretaries. The field of public relations has expanded a great deal in the last few years, and more and more students are finding excellent employment opportunities in this field. In fact, the public relations major has become a highly popular field of study in mass communication.

Traditionally, the career path into public relations has been through journalism programs and working in the mass media. People who had either or both of these credentials were thought to make good public relations practitioners. Although this is still the case, many colleges and universities have instituted public relations majors. These programs teach many of the specifics of working in the field of public relations. More and more students are obtaining internships in public relations agencies and PR departments within companies and organizations.

Despite these burgeoning opportunities, public relations remains a very competitive field. The person who would enter this line of work must be intelligent, disciplined, and willing to work difficult and long hours. Public relations jobs carry with them a great deal of responsibility, and the people who accept them must be willing to live up to that responsibility. Many public relations practitioners work for nonprofit or governmental organizations. Others are employed by public relations agencies or in corporations that have public relations offices. Regardless of the field, practitioners find that the most important skill they need—the one they use every day—is the ability to write. That is what this chapter focuses on.

THE WORK OF THE PR PRACTITIONER

People who work in public relations jobs do a great many things. In fact, that is one of the attractions of a career in PR. The variety of activities that a practitioner can engage in is enormous. On the other hand, that variety requires that practitioners be skilled in many areas and that they be able to deal with many differing and sometimes conflicting assignments. They should also be comfortable with many different people.

Following are some of the tasks of a public relations practitioner.

Handle Communication with the External Publics of an Organization

The term *publics* is at the heart of public relations. External publics are those groups outside of the organization with which an organization wants to communicate. They may include the public at large, buyers of a product, users of a service offered by the organization, potential contributors to the organization, members of the news media on whom the organization depends to distribute its information, or any number of other groups. A public relations practitioner must assist not only in getting information out but also in making sure that the information is properly interpreted. Some of the means by which information from an organization is distributed are news releases, letters, brochures, and quarterly and annual reports.

Counsel Management and Other Organization Employees on How Best to Deal with Important Publics

PR practitioners are called on to help an organization tell its story to a targeted public. The organization, of course, should be doing the right thing—that is, performing for the benefit of its public. The PR professional, then, must help the organization to get its message out. PR counselors often serve as the conscience of an organization when it makes mistakes or when management is considering what actions to take. Ethical PR professionals are there to remind management personnel of the long-term benefits to the organization of telling the truth; they should never condone deliberately misleading the public.

Handle Communication with the Internal Publics of an Organization

Just as there are groups outside the organization that need to be reached, there are also groups within the organization that must receive information. These are the internal publics. They can include employees, independent contractors, stockholders, members, and the families of any of these groups. In companies that have a larger number of employees, this communication function is often critical to the organization. Keeping employees properly informed is often vital to the company's health. Associations—those that have memberships who are not part of the day-to-day operation of the organization—also depend on good communication with their members to keep their organizations healthy. Communication with these internal publics can take the form of newsletters, company magazines, letters, notices, memoranda, and periodic reports.

Work with the News Media to Get Information about the Organization

In most organizations, one of the chief responsibilities is that of media liaison. The PR professional is called on to help find out information about the organization that would be useful to the news reporter in putting together a story. This kind of information goes beyond that produced in a press release. The PR practitioner must find the person within the organization who has the information the reporter wants and must often make arrangements for those people to meet. The other side of this responsibility for the PR practitioner is that of advising the organization's officials on media relations. When and how to release information is often the responsibility of PR practitioners. They may also have to give advice on speeches, press conferences, and interviews that the organization's officials may give. In short, any time the news media deal with an organization, a PR person will be involved.

Help to Produce Public Functions and Events

Public relations practitioners are often involved in the organization's public activities. For example, a company may announce an advertising campaign; officials of a local charity may hold a news conference to kick off its annual fund drive; a local business may make a donation to a school with a ceremony marking that donation; or a university may break ground for a new building. Any number of events may occur, and PR practitioners are usually a part of the planning. They are most likely the ones who ensure that the public is properly informed about such events. Almost all organizations have the need to sponsor public events at some point, and the public relations practitioner will have a major responsibility for their success.

These are some of the day-to-day activities in which PR practitioners might be involved. On a more general level, they contribute to their organizations by helping formulate a continuing, long-range public relations plan. That plan may have many parts and may certainly be revised as new needs arise and old needs subside. At this level, most experts agree that public relations consists of four parts.

Research

Public relations activities and plans begin with research, whether formal or informal. PR practitioners must find out everything possible about their client, the problems or opportunities being faced, and the publics that need to be addressed. These factors in the PR situation are complex and often defy simple answers or solutions. A public relations person will need to have these answers if a plan is to be properly executed.

The process of research may involve talking with people in the organization in order to write a news release. It could mean poring over financial and technical papers and holding long discussions with many of the organization's top officials in order to put together an annual report. It could involve examining how similar organizations have dealt with similar challenges. It could also involve holding focus groups with members of targeted publics. Or it could mean conducting formal surveys or experiments.

Planning

An organization should develop a plan for how it intends to deal with its publics. Some means of communication are not appropriate for certain publics, while others are. A well-conceived plan will allow the organization's officials to figure out what publics they need to communicate with and how that communication should take place. An integral part of planning is setting measurable impact and output objectives for the various communications with the organization's publics.

For example, an impact objective might be "to persuade 10,000 employees to sign up for the optional retirement program by December 31." An output objective might be "to host an information fair for employees on May 1 to inform them about the optional retirement program." Once measurable objectives are set, the PR practitioner develops strategies for achieving those objectives.

Communication

This is the part of the process that we are concerned with most in this book. Putting information into the proper form—and often doing it very quickly—is one of the most important jobs that the PR person can perform. A PR practitioner's ability to do this, more than anything else, will determine that person's worth to the organization.

Evaluation

The evaluation phase of the practitioner's work is when he or she asks, "Did our plan work? Did we get the right information out to the right publics? Did our efforts have the effect we wanted? Did we accomplish our objectives?" Plans need evaluation to determine whether they are working, and it is often up to the public relations person to evaluate the plan.

If an organization's objective is to gain new members, evaluation is fairly easy. Looking at the number of new members who joined while the plan was being executed is a straightforward means of evaluating the plan. Sometimes, however, objectives are much more complex, and evaluation is more subjective.

CHARACTERISTICS OF THE PR PRACTITIONER

Whether you work for a major public relations firm, a particular company, a government agency, a hospital, a university, or another institution, chances are quite good that you will have to write a lot and in a variety of formats. Public relations departments produce brochures, press releases, letters, speeches, scripts, public service announcements for television and radio, posters, reports, books, formal documents, magazines, newsletters, newspapers, and websites on a wide variety of topics. While photographers, artists, designers, production managers, and editors may also be required in producing such items, each project requires a writer. Even a flier announcing a company picnic has to be written by someone.

Gathering information and structuring it for specific formats is the basic process for all writing. The best people in the public relations profession can take a scribbled set of ideas and produce a fifteen-minute speech for a vice president to give at a company dinner in much the same way that a good reporter takes a tip from the telephone and eventually produces a polished story. The differences between public relations writing and news writing are primarily differences created by the intent inherent in public relations writing. A public relations writer must bear in mind a complex set of purposes and interests while producing any piece of copy for any particular publication.

If you wish to write in a public relations environment, you should be prepared to work very hard on assignments directed at targeted publics. It is not unusual for a piece of writing to be scrutinized by several "editors" (that is to say, your bosses), who will criticize and often change your work. Unlike the journalist, who does not have to show a story to his or her sources before it is published, a PR specialist has to make sure that anyone who is quoted speaks clearly and accurately. A PR writer should correct grammatical or factual errors in someone's quotation and then should show these corrections to the source or someone else who has the authority to approve the story.

Public relations writing is usually done for an explicit purpose, and the expenditures that are involved in producing any item must be justified by the degree to which the writing fulfills that purpose. For example, if you are asked to write an article for a company publication outlining a new policy about how raises are awarded, you will be expected not only to write a factually correct story but also to express the attitudes and intentions of management in a manner acceptable to employees.

This idea of intent in public relations writing puts an extra burden on the writer. All of the rules of good grammar, spelling, usage, style, and structure apply to public relations writing. The requirements of brevity and clarity that help to make for crisp news stories also hold for writing brochures. Above and beyond these considerations, public relations writers must constantly bear in mind the interests of the institutions for which they write and the purposes of their writing.

Public relations writers are not merely propagandists for the people who pay them. Rather, the good public relations writer is a professional, able to write honestly and clearly about complex and varied issues in a manner that is acceptable to people who may know little or nothing about writing but who know a great deal about what they want to see in print.

Public relations writers have a dual role, however. Their responsibilities extend not only upward to their employers but also outward to those who will read what they write. In a sense, public relations writers act as translators. They must completely understand the company or institution they write about. If it is a company that makes computer parts, they must know a great deal about computers. If it is a hospital, they must have a working knowledge of medical terms and procedures. Yet they must write about these things in ways their readers can understand. Their role becomes much like that of newspaper reporters covering particular beats they know intimately.

This intimate knowledge of the institution that a writer covers engenders a particular problem with the use of language. Public relations writers should take care not to become so immersed in their topics that they take on the company's jargon to an inordinate degree. Readers of newspapers that use press releases from a hospital may not know what a "cardiovascular microsurgery specialist" really does unless the writer explains cardiovascular microsurgery in simple terms. The same is true for any highly specialized topic. Central to this concept is the idea of audience. As a public relations writer, you will write for a variety of people—company employees, shareholders, customers, the media, management, government officials—and the use of language will change depending on who the audience is. A piece that is intended for the board of trustees of a university may differ substantially in tone and content from something that is intended for release to state newspapers, even if the topic (the hiring of a new dean, for example) is the same.

A public relations writer must be something of a verbal acrobat, leaping from form to form. One person may be required to write speeches, letters, brochures, news releases, promotional copy, and formal reports—all on the same topic and all in the same week. This is particularly true of small firms or departments. Doing this kind of work requires an absolute command of the basic tools of writing, good reporting abilities, and a mental flexibility that allows the writer to think about the same or related topics in a multitude of ways.

A final point should be made about PR writing. Essential to all writing for public relations is understanding the purpose of the communication and knowing who the public is for the communication. In other words, a writer needs to know why he or she is writing and what the public is likely to do with that information. That knowledge comes not only from the research the writer does on what he or she is writing but also from the sensitivity and respect the writer has for the public.

The ability to write—and to use language effectively—is at the heart of almost all public relations activities, but it is not the only skill the successful public relations person needs. That person must also have the ability to deal effectively with many people in various situations. He or she must know how to use tact or persuasion in obtaining information from others within and outside the organization. The PR professional must be able to satisfy the various publics with whom the organization communicates. The professional must also be persuasive with the leaders of an organization in advising them on their public relations efforts. The PR practitioner is often one of the most visible people within the organization and must keep the purposes and goals of the organization in mind during all of his or her contacts.

The successful PR practitioner must have the ability to organize effectively and work efficiently. That means meeting deadlines that are imposed quickly and sometimes arbitrarily. That person must be a quick study—one who can quickly grasp an idea or situation and give it form and substance. And that person must be able to make sound judgments about the effectiveness of public relations efforts.

The PR professional should combine a belief in the goals of an organization with a high standard of personal ethics and integrity. In the tenth century, so the story goes, Eric the Red sailed west from his native Iceland and discovered a large, desolate land. He wanted to colonize it, but the land was so forbidding that he thought that even the hardy Icelanders would be reluctant to do so. To make the land more appealing, he named it Greenland. With this name, Eric the Red was able to persuade a number of people to follow him to a place that is covered mostly with snow and ice. Eric the Red, many have said, was one of the world's first publicists.

Public relations has had a widespread reputation of being practiced by "flacks." These are people who stretch or ignore the truth to gain something for their organization. They spout the "company line," knowing but not caring that it is self-serving and inaccurate. They seek only publicity, even if it is bad publicity. Such people, unfortunately, make it into almost every profession, and the public relations field has certainly not been immune to them.

Yet most PR practitioners consider themselves professionals with high standards of ethics and a deep regard for accuracy. They seek to serve not only the good of their organization but also the public good. The people who believe in what their organization is doing and make genuine efforts to provide accurate and useful information to the organization's publics make the best PR professionals.

WRITING NEWS RELEASES

One of the most common forms of public relations writing is the news release (see Figure 9.1). The news release is information, usually written in the form of a news story that an organization wishes to make public through the news media. A news release, like a news story, should follow a consistent style; it should be written as concisely and precisely as possible; it should answer all of the pertinent questions about the story; and it should emphasize what an editor will think is the most important part of a story. In short, a good news release differs very little from a good news story.

The last point about news releases—that they should emphasize what an editor will think is the most important part of a story—is one that sometimes gives public relations writers some problems. PR professionals must know and be able to apply the news values discussed in Chapter 4. This can be challenging, especially when their bosses do not understand news values and expect PR professionals to spout the company line rather than offering what editors might want.

Editors discard most of the news releases they receive. Fewer than 10 percent of all news releases are published, although many editors and television news producers use the information in a news release as the source for their own stories. This third-party endorsement (having someone else tell your story) can sometimes be a more effective way of getting your message to your publics, although you give up control over the content.

Figure 9.1   News Releases

Good news releases generally follow the rules of writing a good inverted pyramid news story. This news release emphasizes what is important to the readers, not necessarily what is important to the company. Note also that AP style rules are observed.

News from

AS

American South

```
For more information contact
James E. Smith
American South Corporation
(555) 556-5555
jesmith@ameri-south.com

For release after 10 a.m.
Friday, Oct. 13

NEW PLAN TO OPEN IN MIDVILLE NEXT YEAR

     A new plant employing up to 200 people and manufacturing wiring
products will open in Midville in January, the American South Corporation
announced today.
     John Jones, president of American South, said the plant would make
copper wiring products for distribution around the world. The plant will
be located in the Frank O. Story Memorial Industrial Park on Old Niles
Ferry Road.
     The plant will employ about 75 people initially, but as its capaci-
ty grows, it will give work to about 200 people, Jones said.
     The copper wire plant will be part of the industrial parts divi-
sions of the company. Construction on the plant will begin immediately.
The major contractor for the construction of the plant is Midville
Construction Company.
     "We plan to hire many people from the Midville area to work in
this plant, but a number of them will have to be trained in the process
we use," Jones said.
     "We will be taking on workers and giving those people training as
soon as possible."
     American South has plants in more than 30 states and manufactures a
variety of materials used in heavy industrial plants around the world.
The company employs more than 15,000 people and is headquartered in
Atlanta.
     "We looked at a number of sites but chose Midville for a number of
reasons," Jones said. "Among them were its closeness to a major rail sys-
tem and the overall quality of life there.
     More information about the company and the plant in Midville is
available on the company s Web site at www.ameri-south.com.

                              -- 30 --
```

One reason that editors do not think much of news releases, according to some researchers, is that news releases are poorly written, are not localized for the editor's audience, or simply are not newsworthy. Another reason is that editors have a prejudice against running news releases. They see news releases as propaganda or promotion—or even free advertising.

A writer can overcome these problems by writing a news release in a form that is as close to the news story form as possible. Editors are much more likely to use news releases that have the most important information in a simply written lead paragraph and that follow a consistent style than those releases that do not.

Many corporate managers do not understand news values, and they often want a nonnewsworthy item emphasized in a release. For instance, a manager may want to announce a new plant opening in the following way:

> John Jones, president of the American South Corporation, announced today that American South Corporation will open a new copper-wire manufacturing plant in Midville next year.
>
> Mr. Jones said the plant will employ about 75 people initially and about 250 when it is fully operational.

The public relations writer will have to convince the manager that this style will not help the news release get used. A better way of writing this release would be the following:

> A copper-wire manufacturing plant, which will employ about 250 when it is fully operational, will open in Midville next year, according to officials of the American South Corp.
>
> The opening was announced by John Jones, president of the corporation.

Although the content of a good news release is the same as that of a good news story, the form differs slightly. Generally, a news release should contain three things at the top of the first page. One is a headline or slug line telling what the story is about. The styles used by various public relations departments are different, and the writer must learn what style his or her department uses. In the example above, a headline might look like this:

NEW PLANT TO OPEN
IN MIDVILLE NEXT YEAR

A second item that should be at the top of a news release is the name and contact information of a person in the organization who can be reached for more information. Again, the format will differ according to various public relations departments, but this information should always be there. Editors who are interested in using a story may want to know more about it. They are more likely to pursue a story if a name and contact information are easily available to them. The form this information takes could be as simple as the following:

For more information contact
James E. Smith
American South Corporation
555-1616, jsmith@ascorp.com

A third piece of information that should be at the top of a news release is a release time. This tells the editor when the information may be used. Often, the information may be used as soon as the editor gets it; in this situation the words "FOR IMMEDIATE RELEASE" should be used. Sometimes, however, editors may be sent releases before they should be used. In our example, let's say that the American South Corporation is planning to announce the new plant at a ceremony in the mayor's office at 10 A.M. Friday. The PR practitioner, sensitive to the news media's deadlines, might send out a news release about the announcement so that the reporters can start preparing their stories but *embargo* (or forbid the information from being released) the story until after the ceremony takes place. An embargo may look like this:

For release after 10 A.M.
Friday, October 13

Editors generally abide by embargo times, not releasing information before they should. There is nothing an organization can do, however, if an editor chooses to run information before an embargo. Consequently, public relations practitioners should be careful in releasing information with an embargo and should do so only to those editors who can be trusted.

News releases generally are written in an inverted pyramid form. The most important information is presented first, and the information comes in descending order of importance. For the writer of the news release, this means that the background information that often must be included about the organization should come at the end of the story rather than toward the beginning.

The writer of a news release, like the writer of a news story, should keep in mind the commonly accepted news values that contribute to defining news when writing the release. The writer should ask, "Is the story timely? What impact will it have? Is there conflict in this story? Are prominent people involved in the story? Is there something bizarre or unusual about this story?" Reviewing the news values of a news release will help the writer to produce a release that is more likely to be used.

The most important part of a news story—and also of a news release—is the lead paragraph. Remember, the first reader of a news release is likely to be a busy editor who must decide whether or not to use it in his or her publication. You should let that editor know quickly what your story is about. Just as a news writer needs to "sell" a story with a lead that is interesting or informative (or even both), the writer of a news release needs to sell an editor on the story in the same way. If the editor thinks the news release is interesting or important, he or she is more likely to use the information.

Another point about news releases should be made here. A news release might have only one reader: the editor or reporter to whom it is sent. Yet if that person uses the information it contains in a story or uses it as the basis for getting more information, the release has been a success. In most cases, particularly in larger cities, newspapers and trade publications rarely run press releases, so the writer of a news release rarely expects to see his or her own words in print. The purpose of a news release is to get information to the people who work in the mass media. If the information in a news release results in the information being used by the media, the news release has done its job.

The rules about sentence and paragraph structure apply to news releases just as they do to news stories. Sentences should be short, and the paragraphs should be reasonably brief. Editors, like newspaper readers, do not want to get involved with long paragraphs.

A news release writer has to pay particular attention to jargon and wordiness that might creep into a news release. Every organization or association develops its own language—abbreviations and acronyms that speed up communication among those with a knowledge or interest in the field. PR practitioners must know this language in order to communicate within the organization, but they should be careful to use only language that is widely familiar in their news stories.

Wordiness is another danger to the well-written news release. Wordiness is particularly a problem if a news release must be approved by those who are not professional writers. People who do not understand how to use language often believe that the more words you can use, not the fewer words, the more you will impress the reader and the more likely you are to get your point across. Professional writers know that just the opposite is the case. A news release should use only the number of words it takes to create your message. Anything more is wasted.

News release writers should pay particular attention to proper identification of all the people who are mentioned in a release. A news release is an official document coming from the organization. Journalists count on a news release to be correct when it mentions information about the organization. Journalists may also want to directly contact the people who are mentioned in the news release. They assume that those who are mentioned in a news release are correctly identified and that their names are spelled correctly. A PR practitioner who fails in either of these tasks can cause much embarrassment for everyone involved.

Another form of the news release with which PR practitioners must deal is the *video news release* (VNR). The VNR can range from a short news story produced by the organization on videotape and distributed locally to longer feature items (or even half-hour shows) that large companies distribute nationally. VNRs for news items are written in much the same way that broadcast scripts for news stories are written. They are "reported" by someone within the organization or someone hired by the organization, put on videotape, CD or DVD, and distributed to TV news departments in the area. Larger companies produce longer, more expensive VNRs that are likely to emphasize the generic products they sell rather than the brand names. For instance, a soup manufacturer may produce a VNR about the nutritional value of soup, or a brokerage firm might produce one about the advantages of buying stock.

Sometimes a company will create a VNR during a crisis to get the company's side of the story to the public. When syringes started appearing in cans of Diet Pepsi, PepsiCo released three VNRs that received much national exposure. One contained footage of a Pepsi production line, to prove that it would be impossible to insert anything into the fast-moving cans. There was also footage from a convenience store surveillance camera showing a woman inserting a syringe into a Diet Pepsi can.

From the PR practitioner's point of view, the two major problems with producing VNRs are the expense and the uncertainty about their use. VNRs can take a lot of time and money to produce. The people and equipment that are involved in producing a high-quality VNR can cost thousands of dollars. The costs may not seem out of line for a company with many assets, but for smaller organizations, spending several thousand dollars—or even several hundred—on a single item such as a VNR is not worth it. The second problem is getting VNRs used by television stations. Many stations are unwilling to use material that is not produced by their own news departments because the quality may not be high enough or because they view VNRs as advertisements. Even when stations are willing to use this material, they may not have the air time to do so.

VNRs may be produced for internal as well as external publics. Larger organizations find VNRs using a news format excellent tools for explaining new policies or for persuading employees to think or act in ways that would benefit the company. Even if a video of this type is contracted to an independent production agency, companies often consider the large amount of money they spend worth the cost because it bypasses one of the major problems with the use of VNRs: the control of their use.

Despite these problems, VNRs remain a valid tool for information distribution by an organization. With improvements in video technology, the costs of producing and distributing a VNR are coming down, and more and more companies are finding video a useful means of providing information to their publics.

LETTERS

Despite increased use of the telephone and advances in other forms of communication, such as e-mail, letters are still one of the most important and effective means of communicating in the business world today (see Figure 9.2). In fact, they increased in importance with the installation and use of fax machines. The well-written letter is impressive and appreciated by the receiver. The poorly written letter can establish negative feelings on the part of the receiver that are extremely difficult to overcome. PR practitioners are often called on to write letters for their organizations. These letters may serve a variety of purposes, such as selling a product or idea, explaining company policy, answering complaints, and raising funds. Each of these letters must be carefully crafted to accomplish its purpose.

Letters are a good way to direct a message straight to the people you want to receive that message. Most people read their mail; at least, they begin to read their mail. If a letter does not quickly give its information and make its point, it is likely to irritate or lose its reader—or both. Letters are expensive for organizations to produce and send. They take time and care to write. Like all other communication, they must accomplish their mission for the organization.

Just as in any other kind of writing, letter writing requires a precise and concise use of the language. Letters require that writers come directly to the point and not waste the time of the receiver. Even if a letter is obviously written for a large number of people, the reader should get the feeling that the letter was written to and for him or her.

One technical requirement is that letters should never contain any spelling, grammar, or punctuation errors. They should also never show any editing.

The first rule of letter writing is to understand the purpose of the letter. The letter writer should ask, "Why am I writing this letter?" and, if necessary, should make a list of reasons. There may be a number of reasons for a letter to be written, but there should be one overriding purpose. If that purpose is not evident from the list the writer makes, then he or she should give more thought to the letter itself.

Following closely on the purpose for writing the letter is the action that is expected of the recipient. Again, the letter writer should ask a question: "What do I want the reader to do after reading the letter?" Sometimes the answer is a simple one and comes directly from the purpose of the letter. At other times, the intended action of the reader may not be apparent. Again, the writer should have this action clearly in mind before starting to write the letter. In any case, the action of the reader should be as specific as possible.

The table in Figure 9.3 shows some examples of purposes and intended actions for a letter.

Once the purpose of the letter and the intended action on the part of the reader have been established, the writing can begin. One of the first and most important considerations a writer should give to a letter is its tone. The proper tone is essential to the effectiveness of a letter. In most cases of business correspondence, a letter must be both personal and professional; it must show the right mix of these qualities. A letter that is too personal—especially if the writer and recipient are not personal friends—may offend the recipient as an invasion of privacy. A letter that is too formal may make the recipient feel that he or she is not very important to the writer.

Following are some guidelines that will help writers to avoid being too personal in a business letter.

Don't Be Obsequious

The dictionary defines *obsequious* as "exhibiting a servile attentiveness or compliance." In letter writing, avoiding being obsequious means not thanking someone too

Figure 9.2   Parts of a Letter

Letter writing is an important part of the duties of many PR professionals. This illustration shows the different parts of a business letter. Read the letter itself, and take note of the straightforward, businesslike language that is used. Every sentence in the letter contains some information or asks for action from the reader.

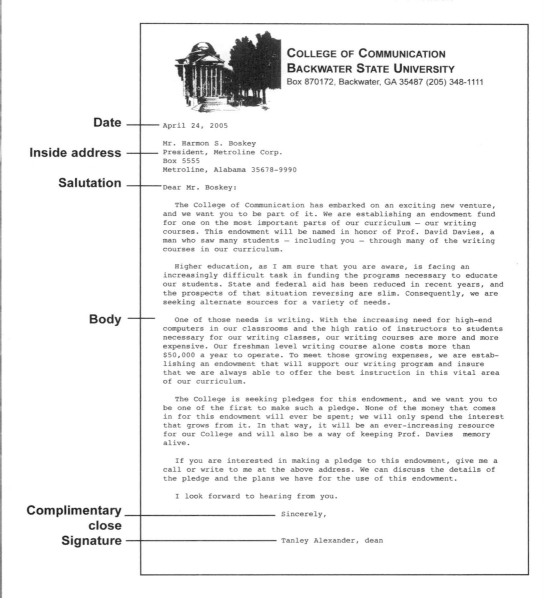

COLLEGE OF COMMUNICATION
BACKWATER STATE UNIVERSITY
Box 870172, Backwater, GA 35487 (205) 348-1111

Date — April 24, 2005

Inside address —
Mr. Harmon S. Boskey
President, Metroline Corp.
Box 5555
Metroline, Alabama 35678-9990

Salutation — Dear Mr. Boskey:

The College of Communication has embarked on an exciting new venture, and we want you to be part of it. We are establishing an endowment fund for one on the most important parts of our curriculum — our writing courses. This endowment will be named in honor of Prof. David Davies, a man who saw many students — including you — through many of the writing courses in our curriculum.

Higher education, as I am sure that you are aware, is facing an increasingly difficult task in funding the programs necessary to educate our students. State and federal aid has been reduced in recent years, and the prospects of that situation reversing are slim. Consequently, we are seeking alternate sources for a variety of needs.

Body —
One of those needs is writing. With the increasing need for high-end computers in our classrooms and the high ratio of instructors to students necessary for our writing classes, our writing courses are more and more expensive. Our freshman level writing course alone costs more than $50,000 a year to operate. To meet those growing expenses, we are establishing an endowment that will support our writing program and insure that we are always able to offer the best instruction in this vital area of our curriculum.

The College is seeking pledges for this endowment, and we want you to be one of the first to make such a pledge. None of the money that comes in for this endowment will ever be spent; we will only spend the interest that grows from it. In that way, it will be an ever-increasing resource for our College and will also be a way of keeping Prof. Davies memory alive.

If you are interested in making a pledge to this endowment, give me a call or write to me at the above address. We can discuss the details of the pledge and the plans we have for the use of this endowment.

I look forward to hearing from you.

Complimentary close — Sincerely,

Signature — Tanley Alexander, dean

much (twice is the maximum for a letter, once is better); not continually apologizing; not saying *please* more than once in a letter; not using or repeating phrases such as *I hope you'll understand*. All of these things can irritate the reader; most people want to be spoken to, or written to, in a straightforward manner.

Figure 9.3   Purposes and Intended Actions

This table shows the variety of purposes and intended actions that letters might have. Letter writers should have a good sense of both of these concepts.

PURPOSES The purpose of the letter is:		INTENDED ACTIONS The intended action on the part of the reader is:
To answer a complaint from a customer	→	To understand why the situation occurred
To explain a policy to a member of the organization	→	To know what the policy is
To announce a new procedure for applying for promotion	→	To follow the new procedure when applying for promotion
To persuade someone to subscribe to our magazine	→	To fill out the subscription card
To ask someone to join our organization	→	To fill out the membership card
To get someone to pay a bill	→	To send the payment
To tell someone that he or she did not get a job	→	To know that he or she didn't get the job but to feel that he or she received fair treatment

Don't Be Overly Complimentary

Compliments are good interpersonal actions and should be offered when they are appropriate, but sometimes compliments can sound insincere and gratuitous. In a letter telling a job applicant that he or she didn't get the job, the following might be appropriate:

> The experience listed on your resume shows that you are very well qualified for a number of positions.

But going too far beyond that, particularly if some of the complimentary statements are questionable, gives the impression that the writer is insincere or doubtful about not hiring the recipient.

Generally, Don't Try to Be Funny

Humor is not expected in business correspondence and is likely to get in the way of your purpose for writing the letter. In addition, few people can write humor well enough to be understood, so the best rule is: Don't try.

Avoid Referring to the Personal Characteristics, Habits, or Feelings of the Reader

If you are dealing with someone on a professional basis, you probably do not know much about their personal habits or feelings. Even if you think you do, you shouldn't make too many assumptions about them. In a letter telling a person that he or she did not get a job, suppose the writer had said:

> I know this news will disappoint you.

It is possible that the recipient would actually be glad not to have gotten the job offer. The recipient may have gotten a better offer from another company. In that case, the writer would look pretty silly.

To avoid sounding too formal in your letters, here are some things you should consider.

Use Personal Pronouns

Used appropriately—that is, not too often—personal pronouns can humanize a letter without letting it become too personal. A reader wants to be recognized as a human being with attitudes and feelings. The use of personal pronouns, especially *you* to address the reader, is a good device for business correspondence.

Avoid Impersonal Constructions

Impersonal constructions are those such as "It is" and "There is." These constructions also include those that place the blame on "it," as in "It has been decided." "It" does not decide anything; some person or group does. Writers use these constructions in the hope that readers will not attribute an action to a particular person (especially themselves). Readers are usually sharper than that, however, and can see right through this ploy.

Avoid the Passive Voice

In business letters, as in all other forms of writing, the passive voice deadens writing. It robs any piece of writing of its vitality. Active verbs make a letter much more likely to be read and understood.

Avoid Using Technical Language That May Mean Nothing to the Reader

A person who has a complaint will not be pacified by a letter that he or she does not understand. In fact, it is likely to confirm the feeling that the complaint is valid. Such a letter is also likely to offend the reader by its condescending tone.

Be careful about referring to policies, rules, and regulations. If a policy or rule is the reason that something occurred and that needs to be explained in the letter, the policy or rule should be stated in the simplest terms possible. In many large, bureaucratic organizations, such rules are written in an obscure form of bureaucratese. The writer needs to translate this for the reader into the plainest terms possible. In most cases, the writer should not make technical references, such as "Regulation 33.b states," unless that is something the reader will readily understand.

Avoid Wordiness

Lots of words, long sentences, and long paragraphs will obscure the message of the letter. They may sound impressive to the person who writes them, but they will not impress the reader. One of the best ways to strike that mix of the formal and personal necessary to a good letter is to write in simple, down-to-earth language.

Sending letters across the Internet or through some other wired or cable communication system is a growing part of business and personal communication. E-mail is a form of communication that professional communicators need to master along with all the others they use.

In general, e-mail messages are shorter and more succinct than "snail mail" letters. E-mail systems are equipped with a function for attaching documents to the e-mail communication so that the main message can remain short and to the point.

One of the factors that contributes to this succinctness is that many e-mail messages are sent as direct replies to a previous e-mail message. The original message can be carried along with the reply. Consequently, there is no need to repeat information that may have been in the original e-mail. In this way, e-mail sometimes resembles ordinary conversation more than letter writing.

E-mail messages are often less formal than those of ordinary letters. One reason for this is that people who use e-mail assume that they have at least one experience in common with their fellow correspondents: Both sender and receiver use the computer. This common experience puts them on a more intimate or friendly basis with their fellow e-mailers. The fact that e-mail messages can be sent and received very quickly—in many cases, almost instantly—also contributes to the lessened formality.

One consideration of e-mail that the writer must keep in mind is that a message that is meant for only one person can quickly be forwarded to many other people. Nothing prevents a recipient of an e-mail from doing this. Consequently, a writer of an e-mail should be careful about what is said and how it is said.

Despite greater directness and less formality, the rules of good writing apply to e-mail messages just as they do any other writing. The writer of an e-mail message must be clear and precise in the use of the language. The words must convey the information and meaning that the writer intends and the receiver will understand. Good e-mail messages are just as important to an organization's and an individual's image and goals as good letter writing is.

COMPANY PUBLICATIONS

News releases and letters are very important and common forms of public relations writing, but they are by no means the only ones. Organizational publications abound, and the public relations people in an organization are usually responsible for them.

In dealing with these publications, the public relations practitioners may be responsible for more than writing. They should know about editing, typography, design, layout, photo selection and cropping, and other parts of the publication process. Those topics are not covered specifically by this book. Rather, the focus here is on the basic writing skills that are a part of any of these jobs.

Three major kinds of publications that organizations produce are newsletters, pamphlets and brochures, and company reports.

Newsletters

Newsletter is a basic term for a wide variety of publications a company may produce. Working on a newsletter is a common task of a beginning PR practitioner. The newsletter may range from a single photocopied sheet to a slick, full-color magazine to an interactive website. The form that a newsletter takes will depend on the company, the amount of money that is spent on the newsletter, and, most important, the public.

Newsletters are directed at a particular public, and a writer for a newsletter must keep this in mind to be successful. Most company newsletters are internal; that is, they are targeted to publics within the company. One of the most popular types of newsletters is the employee newsletter. This one gives employees information about the company and focuses on the employees' interests and concerns. Newsletters may be specialized to the point of aiming at a certain set of employees within a company.

The style of writing that a newsletter uses will depend on the purpose and the targeted public. Many newsletters are purely informational. They try to get as many facts as possible to the targeted public as quickly as possible. Other newsletters are for information and entertainment. Either way, the writing in a newsletter must be concise and precise. No newsletter should waste the reader's time. Few companies will require that their employees read a newsletter. Rather, employees are encouraged to do so, and one of the means of encouragement is an efficient writing style.

Many newsletters are produced in-house; that is, they are designed and even printed by facilities within the organization. Consequently, the PR practitioner must have a basic understanding of design and must have the skills to produce a newsletter from writing to printing and distribution.

Another new format is the e-mail newsletter (discussed more fully in Chapter 6). The most common form that an e-mail newsletter takes is to have headlines and summaries of articles with links to an organization's website. These newsletters allow readers to respond quickly to inquiries and opportunities that the company might offer.

Newsletters are most effective when they are consistent in their writing, design, and publication schedule. Those who read newsletters should know what to expect in them and when to expect it. The PR practitioner who publishes a newsletter must understand the value of this consistency to the effectiveness of the newsletter.

Pamphlets and Brochures

Unlike newsletters, pamphlets and brochures are usually directed at external publics—people outside an organization. They are not published periodically, as a newsletter is. Rather, they are published once and for a specific purpose. These kinds of publications are important because they are often the first and sometimes the only contact a person has with an organization. These publications must catch the eye of a potential reader and then deliver content that is substantial and well written. Like an advertisement, the pamphlet or brochure, through its appearance, will promise something; that promise should be fulfilled by the content.

There are two kinds of pamphlets and brochures: informational and persuasive. The informational brochure tells about an organization or procedure. The writing in this kind of brochure must be down-to-earth, practical, and efficient. A brochure on how to hang wallpaper, for instance, should take the reader through a step-by-step process, giving the reader enough information to do the job but not wasting the reader's time. The persuasive brochure is one that tries to make a point, to sell an idea, or to persuade readers to adopt a certain point of view. Many examples of this kind of brochure exist. An American Cancer Society brochure on the dangers of smoking is one. Others include a local chamber of commerce brochure on why businesses should locate in that area and a professional association brochure on why people should join the organization. The writing style may vary in this kind of brochure, but one thing the writer should remember is that opinions should be based

Sidebar 9.1
Reader-Based Writing

Public relations practitioners too often begin their writing with what has been called *writer-based prose*. That is, the writing is composed from the writer's point of view rather than the reader's point of view. For instance, the writer of a brochure might begin with the following:

> The University of Knowledge was founded in 1992 by a group of Midwesterners who were unhappy with the educational opportunities available to their children. UK has 400 faculty and 5,000 students.

This passage is writer-based in that it focuses on information the writer (or his or her employer) thinks is important. Historical or background information is often in the forefront of writer-based prose. *Reader-based prose* focuses on the reasons why someone might need something. The beginning of a reader-based recruitment brochure might read like this:

> Are you looking for an enriching college experience where you can combine class-room learning with real-life applications? If so, the University of Knowledge is the place for you.

Writers who work for organizations sometimes unconsciously write to satisfy those within the organization rather than those to whom the writing is directed. Reader-based prose is what is likely to do the organization the most good, and that is what the writer should be aiming for.

LaRae Donnellan, Ph.D., APR, CPRC

Florida A & M University

on information. A writer may express opinions very strongly, but these expressions are not nearly as persuasive as facts. For instance, a writer may say, "You ought to give up smoking because it is bad for your health." It would be more effective to say, "Doctors say that more than half the cases of lung cancer they treat are caused by smoking." The second statement is much stronger because it gives the reader facts, not just opinions.

(For the rest of this section, the term *brochure* will refer to both pamphlets and brochures. A pamphlet is usually smaller than a brochure, has a narrower purpose, and often has a shorter life. Beyond that—for the purposes here, at least—the differences between a pamphlet and brochure are not significant.)

The brochure is a common means of introducing an organization to the public. Its strength is that it can be designed for and delivered directly to an audience of the organization's choosing.

Design is a very important part of a brochure and has a great deal to do with the writing in it. A wide variety of formats and an infinite number of designs can be applied to a brochure. The people who are in charge of the production of the brochure need to decide first on the purpose it is to serve. They should ask, "Why is this brochure necessary? What problem will it solve? To what audience is it directed?"

Following closely on these questions is the message that the brochure is to convey. Is the brochure supposed to describe the organization in general, or does it have a more specific message? Is it to persuade its public to do something, or is it simply to inform? (The thinking that goes into a brochure is much like the thinking that goes into an advertisement. In fact, a brochure can be considered a kind of advertisement for an organization. For a more in-depth review of this process, see Chapter 8.)

Once the purpose and message of a brochure have been decided, the design and writing decisions are made. These decisions may be simultaneous; that is, the writing and design may take place at more or less the same time. A PR practitioner who is proficient in both writing and design will often do this. Or one decision could follow the other. For instance, a designer may come up with a design for a brochure and then give it to a copywriter, or a writer may write the copy first and hand it over to the designer. In any case, the design and writing are closely linked.

Many people make the mistake of thinking that simply presenting information is persuasive. Although information is necessary for a persuasive argument, it usually needs to be crafted in a way that will emphasize its persuasive factors. Sometimes that can be done by the order in which the information is presented. Very often, it is done by the graphic techniques in the brochure. If a PR practitioner is not good with design and layout, he or she needs to find someone who is and work closely with that person.

Annual Reports and Other Types of Reports

Companies that sell stock to the public are required by law to produce an annual report. Many other organizations that do not come under this requirement also produce annual reports. These reports give people inside and outside the company an idea of what the company is all about and how the company is doing financially. Many companies, particularly larger companies, consider the annual report one of the most important forms of communication they have. One legal requirement for annual reports is that they must be truthful. Although a company may put on its best face in an annual report, the information the report contains must be factual.

Annual reports must contain financial information about the organization and some descriptive information about the company's structure and activities for the year. Beyond that, companies have a wide latitude in what they may include in an annual report. Large organizations sometimes put thousands of dollars into the production of an annual report, and they target these reports for specific audiences and purposes, such as attracting investors, holding onto stockholders, and creating a stable image within a field of competition. For nonprofit organizations, the purpose of an annual report might be to attract members, increase visibility in the community, and report on otherwise hidden activities.

The writer of an annual report—usually someone in the company's public relations department—is often required to translate a lot of complicated financial data and industry jargon into a simple, clear account of the company's activities and position. The writer must use understandable English and write for an audience that does not know the ins and outs of the company.

Other kinds of reports that a company may publish are quarterly or semiannual reports or reports about an organization's activities that are directed to a special audience. Nonprofit organizations may compile these kinds of reports when they embark on fund-raising campaigns. Writing these kinds of reports takes a lot of intelligence and skill in using the language.

Websites

Other types of publication activities that may be the responsibility of the public relations department are the development, design, and maintenance of the organization's website on the Internet. Access to the Internet has grown phenomenally, and most organizations understand that they must have a presence on the World Wide Web. A "www" site is an integral part of an organization's public posture.

The people who are in charge of developing the website must have the practical knowledge of how to hook up to the Web. Usually, this is done through a local or national Internet access provider. The company that provides access to the Web will also offer technical assistance about how to establish an Internet site. If the organization decides to maintain its own site (rather than subcontracting it to another company), someone within the organization will need to learn how to write the Hypertext Mark-up Language (HTML) code that is used to format websites. The technical aspects of creating and putting up a website are not difficult to execute.

The harder job is to understand the purpose of the website for the organization and to design the site according to that purpose. A website may exist simply to inform Internet surfers about the organization. It may be intended to sell a product. An organization may want the people who visit the site to interact with it. Websites may serve these and many other purposes. Understanding the purpose of the website is the first step because—just as with the brochure—a website may be a person's first contact with the organization. That first contact is always important.

ORAL PRESENTATIONS

Speeches, statements, and other oral presentations are among the most common forms of public relations writing. The major difference between this kind of writing and the writing that we discussed previously is that, writing for broadcasts, oral presentations are written for the ear, not the eye. They are written to be spoken, not read silently. Consequently, many of the principles of broadcast writing apply to this kind of writing.

Oral presentations should be written in simple, clear, concise language. Sentences should be short. Modifiers and modifying phrases should be kept to a minimum. The content of the speech should be simple; the points that are made should be easy to follow.

In writing any oral presentation, the PR practitioner must take three major factors into consideration: the targeted audience, the speaker, and the subject of the presentation.

The writer should know, as precisely as possible, who will be listening to the speech. For instance, a company president may be asked to speak at a high school graduation. The writer should understand that although the speech may be directed to the graduates, their parents and other relatives are likely to be present. This can make a difference in how the speech is structured. The writer will also need to have some idea of what the listeners are expecting to hear and how important it is to meet those expectations. For instance, if the local college football coach is asked to make a speech before the Lion's Club in early August, the listeners will expect him to comment on the upcoming football season. They are likely to be disappointed if most of his speech is devoted to the previous season.

The speaker is an important part of how writers approach a speech. The speaker's personality will have much to do with the content of the speech. For instance, the writer may need to know if the speaker is comfortable telling funny stories or if the speaker likes to quote certain people. The speaker may have some ideas he or she wishes to use in the speech, or the speaker may even want to write a draft of the speech for the writer to polish.

The subject of the oral presentation, of course, is an all-important factor for the writer. The subject is usually connected with the position of the speaker. For instance, a speech by a U.S. senator will usually have something to do with politics or legislation. But this is not always the case. In a high school graduation speech, a company president is not expected to talk much (if at all) about his or her company. Too many comments about the organization might be inappropriate in this setting. In other cases, however, the audience will expect to hear about the organization that the speaker represents.

Three of the most common types of oral presentations that PR practitioners are asked to write are slide presentations, statements, and speeches.

Slide Presentations

This is a popular method of presentation with many organizations. Slide shows can be used easily with small groups. They are especially helpful in sales presentations. Slides should serve as an outline for the speaker and can help to focus the attention of the audience on the points that the speaker wants to make.

Software programs that help to produce slide shows have become increasingly sophisticated and easy to use. Microsoft's PowerPoint and other programs place a variety of visual tools at the fingertips of a presenter, and a PR practitioner needs some advanced knowledge of how these programs work and what they do.

The writer of a script for a slide presentation needs to understand the relationship between the script—that is, what the presenter will say—and the slides themselves. The slides should be used to outline what the speaker is saying, with the main information coming from the speaker. The slides themselves should be simple and uncluttered and should have a consistent format. The script contains the major part of the information in the presentation.

Another concept that the writer of a slide script needs to understand is that of pacing. Pacing simply means how fast the slides appear to the audience. Some presentations need to be fast-paced; that is, the slides are shown rapidly throughout the presentation, possibly as many as ten per minute. A fast-paced script means that the slides contain no detailed information that the audience must absorb. If the slides do contain such information—such as graphs that indicate something about an organization's progress—the presentation should move at a slower pace. Some presentations call for slides to be shown at a rate of only one or two per minute. A good guideline is to have no more than six brief, bulleted lines on each slide.

Statements

A statement is a short oral presentation; its length depends on the forum in which it is presented. A statement that precedes a question-and-answer session at a press conference should be relatively short—one to two pages at most. A statement that is read to a legislative committee might be longer, depending on the subject and the time allotted to the speaker. A statement has few of the formalities of a full-blown speech. It is an attempt to summarize facts and make points as efficiently as possible. It often sets the stage for what is to come later, particularly if it precedes a news conference. A statement should be cleanly and efficiently written. It should present its facts and make its points and then stop.

Speeches

Speeches come in a wide variety of forms. They may be informative, persuasive, entertaining, or a combination of all three. They may last only a few minutes or all day (although modern Western audiences are likely to think a speech is too long if

Figure 9.4

Speeches

Most of the speeches with which we come into contact come from the political arena. The speech is still one of the major forms of communication of politicians, and that is most evident during an election campaign. Speeches are important in many other areas of business, too.

Sources: www.WhiteHouse.gov; www.JohnKerry.com.

it exceeds thirty minutes). Many of our most memorable sayings were delivered in speeches. For instance:

> And so, my fellow Americans, ask not what your country can do for you; ask what you can do for your country. (John F. Kennedy, inaugural address, 1961)

> The only thing we have to fear is fear itself. (Franklin D. Roosevelt, inaugural address, 1933)

> I never met a man I didn't like. (Will Rogers, speech in Boston, 1930)

> Four score and seven years ago our fathers brought forth, upon this continent, a new nation, conceived in Liberty, and dedicated to the proposition that all men are created equal. (Abraham Lincoln, Gettysburg Address, 1863)

> I have a dream. (The Reverend Martin Luther King, Jr., speech given at a civil rights march in Washington, D.C., 1963)

Writing a speech is not an easy task, but it is a common one for many PR practitioners. Writers may begin their work by thinking of a speech as consisting of three parts: an opening, a middle, and an ending.

The opening should do a number of things. It should allow the speaker to introduce himself or herself to the audience with some sort of personal reference. In most cases, an audience will already know something about a speaker; the speaker may have been formally introduced by someone else. The opening allows the speaker to establish a relationship with the audience.

Many speakers also use the opening to warm up the audience with a humorous story. Such a device works best when the point of the story can be directly related to the points that the speaker is trying to make in the speech. A funny story for its own sake may help the speaker to get going, but it is not as effective as one that is part of the speaker's message.

Most important, the opening of a speech should establish the speaker's subject and should give the audience clues to the direction in which the speaker is headed. An audience should detect in a speech a logical progression of thought, and that progression should be evident from the very beginning of the speech.

The middle of the speech should take whatever points are made—or alluded to in the opening—and expand on them. A speaker may use a variety of techniques to do this. One of the most effective is telling a story. People of all ages like to hear stories; they enjoy following narratives. The stories, of course, should support the points that the speaker is trying to make in the speech, and they should do so in a fairly obvious way. A speaker who tells a story and then tries to explain what that has to do with the points in a speech has failed in using this device.

Another useful technique for a speech writer is the striking quotation. A speaker who can use quotations from other sources can add interest, strength, and credibility to his or her own remarks. Consider these remarks from a Vietnam combat veteran who was asked to speak to a local civic club about his war experiences:

> Occasionally, I am asked to describe what it was like to be in Vietnam. From the perspective of those who lived in America during that time, Vietnam was somehow a different kind of war. It has often been pointed out that it was the first war we saw on television. To the combat soldier, however, that made little difference. We knew that all wars are essentially the same. William Tecumseh Sherman, speaking more than a hundred years ago, summed up our feelings about war when he said, "I am tired and sick of war. Its glory is all moonshine. It is only those who neither

fired a shot nor heard the shrieks and groans of the wounded who cry aloud for blood, more vengeance, more desolation. War is hell."

Adapting an ancient quote to a modern purpose is another useful way to add interest to speeches. A person speaking on the environment used a biblical quote in this way:

The Book of Ecclesiastes says there is "a time to cast away stones, and a time to gather stones together." Generations before us in this century have been casting away the stones of our environmental systems. I firmly believe that it is the charge of our generation to gather those stones together. Now is the time.

Making a striking statement is another technique that speakers can use to make a point and gain the attention of their audience. Sometimes that statement can come in the form of challenging conventional wisdom, as in the following:

Most people believe that the Golden Rule—"Do unto others as you would have them do unto you"—is the simplest and best formula for good human relations. I'm here to tell you that it isn't. In fact, that formula, despite the best intentions of some people, is a disaster.

Sometimes an obscure but striking fact can gain the attention of the audience in the same way. The following is from a speech about how people can rebound from failures early in life and go on to success later:

Back in 1919, the New York Yankees were looking for an outfielder who was also a good hitter. They thought they had a promising young man, but he managed only two hits in twenty-two at bats. The Yankees then went out and purchased Babe Ruth from the Boston Red Sox. Everybody knows what Babe Ruth accomplished, of course. But what about that young man who only got the two hits? Whatever happened to him? He decided that baseball wasn't his game after all, so he gave football a try. That game was obviously better suited to his abilities, and he became a star. In fact, many consider him to be the father of professional football. His name was George Halas, the long-time owner of the Chicago Bears.

These are just a few of the techniques that a writer can use to expand the body of a speech. Whatever techniques are used, the speech should follow a logical line—one that the audience can follow, too. If the speech goes off on tangents and never returns, the points will be lost and the audience will be dissatisfied.

The closing of a speech can be used to make the final, major point of the speech, or it can offer the audience a summary of what the speaker has already said. The same rhetorical devices that you can use in any other parts of the speech—telling stories, using quotes, making striking statements—can be used to close a speech. Speech writers should remember, however, that a good speech does not need a dramatic flourish at the end. It can simply end with a story that summarizes the subject of the speech, a listing of the points already made by the speaker, or a conclusion that can be logically drawn from what the speaker has said.

CONCLUSION

Public relations work is mostly writing. Employers will look for people who can write to fill their public relations jobs. Public relations writing requires a versatility on the part of the writer that is demanded in few other jobs. While it is exciting and rewarding, the field of public relations is one that demands intelligence, skill, and hard work.

POINTS FOR CONSIDERATION AND DISCUSSION

1. At the beginning of this chapter, the author describes the field of public relations and some of the things that public relations practitioners do. From this description and what you know about the field, what is the most attractive thing about public relations work to you? What is the part of the work that you would like the least?

2. Many people who work in journalism and elsewhere have a very negative opinion of the field of public relations. Why do you think they have such an opinion?

3. A public relations practitioner has to have a wide range of knowledge and understanding to do his or her job well. What other courses in the curriculum of your college or university would you think a person should take if he or she is interested in becoming a public relations practitioner?

4. What are the advantages and disadvantages of writing a letter as opposed to making a telephone call when you want to make personal contact with someone?

5. The author says that the design and the content of a brochure or pamphlet are closely related. Try to find some examples of brochures or pamphlets and see whether you think the people who put these together did a good job of relating the design and content.

6. The author lists several techniques for writing speeches, such as adapting ancient quotes and telling personal anecdotes. Can you think of others?

FURTHER READING

Cutlip, S., Center, A. H., & Broom, G. (2000). *Effective Public Relations* (8th ed.). Upper Saddle River, NJ: Prentice Hall.

Foster, J. L. (2001). *Effective Writing Skills for Public Relations*. London: Krogan Page Ltd.

Wilcox, D. L. (2004). *Public Relations Writing and Media Techniques*. Boston: Allyn and Bacon.

WEBSITE

Public Relations Society of America: **www.prsa.org**

EXERCISES

9.1 News Releases

Write news releases based on the following information. Follow the directions given to you by your instructor.

YMCA

You work for the YMCA in your city, and as part of your job, you have to write news releases about the organization's many recreational and educational programs. One such program is an ongoing series of swimming lessons for children, young people, and adults. You have to write a release including the following information about the fall series:

Children's classes begin August 25 and are held on Mondays, Wednesdays, and Fridays. One class is held for each of five different age groups: tiny tots (ages one to three), kindergarten (ages four to six), elementary (ages six to nine), youth (ages ten to thirteen), and teens (ages fourteen to seventeen). All of these classes meet twice each week until November 30 on the following schedule:

Tiny tots meet on Mondays and Wednesdays from 1 P.M. until 2 P.M.

The kindergarten class meets on Mondays and Wednesdays from 2 P.M. until 3 P.M.

Elementary students meet from 3:30 P.M. until 4:30 P.M. on Mondays and Wednesdays.

The youth class runs from 4:30 P.M. until 5:30 P.M. on Mondays and Fridays.

The teen class meets from 5:30 P.M. until 6:30 P.M. on Mondays and Wednesdays.

Two classes are held for adults (ages eighteen and older). One meets on Monday and Tuesday nights from 7 P.M. until 8 P.M. The other meets on Saturday from 1 P.M. until 3 P.M.

Registration will be held at the YMCA office from August 15 until August 22. Classes are limited to fifteen students each, and the registration cost is twenty dollars per child or twenty-five dollars per adult for YMCA members, thirty dollars per child or thirty-five dollars per adult for nonmembers.

Information: Mrs. Bertha Bucher, 774-4567.

Registration: See Mr. Bob Driver at the YMCA office.

No cash refunds for registration fees will be given. Those who register for classes but find it necessary to cancel should be sure to notify Mrs. Bucher immediately so that a credit memo can be issued for the amount of the registration fee. This memo can be applied to registration for other YMCA classes at some future date.

DEPARTMENT HEAD LEAVES

You are the public relations director for a local private hospital, Mountain East Medical Center (MEMC). During the past few months, there has been considerable friction between the hospital's board of directors and the head of the purchasing department, Bob Wilkinson. Wilkinson's tight-fisted purchasing practices have been criticized by some of the medical staff in spite of the fact that the board of directors had ordered him to cut costs by 15 percent.

Write a press release using whatever of the following information you feel is important.

Wilkinson's resignation is effective immediately. He will be replaced by the assistant head of the department, Johnny Toler, who has been with the hospital for thirteen years.

Wilkinson was a 1972 graduate of the state university's school of hospital administration. He came to Mountain East Medical Center in 1975 after working for a small rural community hospital as purchasing chief. He will take a job as a purchasing agent with City Memorial Hospital.

Toler's background is in pharmacy. He began as an assistant druggist in the hospital pharmacy thirteen years ago and was moved to the purchasing department in 1978 as an assistant after the hospital pharmacy closed. Toler's wife, Carolyn, is head of the gynecology department at MEMC. They have two children.

Hospital administrator Harry Illscott had this comment: "Bob's abilities will be greatly missed at this hospital, but I know that Johnny Toler is a person we can all depend on to do whatever is necessary to keep his department going. I have great faith in him and in this hospital."

Toler gave the following statement: "This hospital means a great deal to me and my family, and I will give my best efforts to making our purchasing department the best. I learned from a fine man—Bob Wilkinson—and I hope I can continue to build on the foundation he established."

HONORARY DEGREES

Each year, your university awards honorary degrees to people who have made outstanding contributions to the state or to society in some way. This year two honorary degrees will be awarded at the commencement exercises, which will be held at 11 A.M. on May 14 in Memorial Coliseum.

You work part-time at the university's public relations department, and your boss has asked you to write a press release announcing that the following people will be receiving honorary doctorates at the Saturday morning ceremony:

George T. Hale, age sixty-three, a 1965 graduate of the university who established the state's first educational television cooperative back in the late 1960s, will be cited for his "ability to envision the future and make it a reality for the state's telecommunications industry." When he retired from the presidency of Hale Communication, Inc., last year, the company had more than 40 percent of the cable market. Hale, a multimillionaire, has donated thousands of dollars to the development of educational television at both major universities in the state. In addition, he built a camp for physically handicapped adults on his mountain estate and sends more than 300 individuals there each spring and summer for an extensive recreation training program. Hale lives in Birmingham with his wife of thirty years, Elizabeth. They are the adoptive parents of two Korean children: Lee, twenty-one, and Ben, eighteen.

Rachel Cabanis, age forty-four, an Alabama native and 1982 graduate of Goucher College, completed law school at Harvard after a twenty-year career as a legal secretary with her husband's law firm in Montgomery. Her famous book about her decision to go to law school and her experiences there, *Breaking Through,* has been lauded as "the greatest statement of one woman's choices written in this decade." It won her a Pulitzer Prize (and at least a year's worth of speaking engagements). Mrs. Cabanis, now separated from her husband, Roy Cabanis, will return to Montgomery as a full partner in another law firm. She is being honored by the university for her "honesty and integrity in making difficult choices in a complex world and succeeding despite numerous obstacles."

NEW PLANT

You work for the Holesome Donut Company of Wilmington, Delaware. Your company wants to open as many plants as possible in the Sunbelt, and company officials have decided to establish a new doughnut factory in Repton, Alabama.

Write a press release announcing plans for the complex. Include as much of the following as you believe is significant.

Repton city officials had been bargaining for the new plant for two years. At least twelve small towns in Tennessee, Georgia, and Mississippi also wanted to be the site of the new plant. Repton was chosen because of its desirable location, the low interest rates local banks offered for development, and the willingness of city officials to help build roads and sidewalks, waste disposal facilities, and recreation areas near the plant.

Repton currently has a 14 percent unemployment rate, slightly below the state average. However, its main industry, a shoe factory, is reducing its payroll by half at the beginning of next year.

Construction on the $3 million doughnut factory is slated to begin on March 31. A tentative completion date of November 15 is set, and the factory should be in full operation by the beginning of next year.

The plant will provide 700 jobs for local people, and more than 100 families are expected to be brought in to work for the company.

The plant will make and package doughnuts for shipping to all parts of Alabama.

Company president Lonny Joe Underwood, an Alabama native who once owned a grocery store in Repton, made the following comment: "We believe that the future of America, like its past, lies in small towns like this. We want to be an integral part of this community and make it just as prosperous as it should be."

TUITION DECREASE

You are working in the public relations department of your university. The board of trustees is about to meet to consider tuition costs for next year. One of the proposals before the board is that tuition be lowered by 10 percent for all students: in-state, out-of-state, graduate students, and undergraduates. The president of the university has already polled most of the board on this issue and has general agreement from the board on this action. Your first assignment is to prepare a news release on this action with an embargo time of 11:45 A.M. Friday, which is when the board meeting will be finished.

You can use the following information to prepare your news release:

The president's statement: "I am extremely pleased that the board has seen fit to follow our recommendations on lowering tuition costs. During the past several years, we have had to raise tuition a number of times for all of our students. Out-of-state students have been particularly hard hit. For some time, we have been afraid that we have been pricing ourselves out of the market, even with in-state students. With more and more people attending junior colleges and other universities in the state, we have recognized that those who want to come to this university must have some relief.

"Unfortunately, of course, the board's actions will have some negative effects on some parts of the university. Cutting tuition means a reduction in our income, and that reduction will have to be made up in other areas. No faculty or staff member will lose his or her job because of these cuts, but we will not be able to offer as many of the programs as we have in the past. The faculty and staff members whose programs will be eliminated will be absorbed into other areas of the university. I am very pleased about that. The students attending these programs, of course, must find alternatives."

The programs to be cut are Women's Studies, Ornithology Department, Arts and Sciences Honors Program, Women's Golf Team, Men's Golf Team, Human Resources Management Institute, University Hosts and Hostesses Program, and the Department of Eastern Languages; the Geology Department will be merged with the Geography Department.

Tuition costs during the last five years (tuition per semester):

Undergrad (in-state)	$500	$550	$650	$800	$1050
Undergrad (out-of-state)	$800	$800	$100	$1200	$1400
Graduates (in-state)	$600	$650	$750	$900	$1200
Graduates (out-of-state)	$850	$1000	$1100	$1200	$1700

Each of the final figures in the table above will be reduced 10 percent for the next term.

Overall enrollment increased at the university in the last five years from 14,500 students five years ago to 16,275 this year; however, last year the total enrollment was 16,700. Applications for next semester are down, and if they continue at the current rate, a 10 percent drop in enrollment from this year's figure is anticipated.

After the news release, you are to prepare two advertisements to run in the state's major newspapers telling about the new tuition rates at the university.

PRESS ASSOCIATION

You are the public relations officer for your state's press association. This association counts as its members all of the state's daily and weekly newspapers, and it performs a number of services, such as a statewide advertising bureau (if an advertiser wants to advertise in all of the state's newspapers, he or she can come to the press association and place the ad rather than going to the individual newspapers), information about the state's newspapers, a professional training program with a local university for people who work with the state's newspapers, and a lobbying service in the state legislature on bills that affect the press.

Recently, the press association's board of directors decided that your office should do some special promotion for National Newspaper Week. Also, the press association has recently hired some university professors to conduct a survey about newspaper leadership in your state. That survey has been completed, and the board has decided to release the results and have them serve as the basis for this promotion.

Consequently, the press association has called a press conference for next Monday, the first day of National Newspaper Week. The press conference is scheduled for 10 A.M. The executive director of the press association, Ken Billiard, and this year's president of the press association, Slade Luketon, editor of the Rogersville *Register*, will be there to announce the results of the survey and to talk about newspapers.

Here are some facts about the survey: The survey was conducted during a two-week period in the fall by a polling organization at the state university. The number of people surveyed was 500, randomly selected from all across the state. The margin of error for the results is plus or minus 4 percent. The survey showed the following things: Newspaper readers are a "quality audience" (they tend to be married, be more highly educated than the average person, have more annual income, own their own home, and vote regularly); newspaper readership is positively linked with income (only 43 percent of those with incomes of less than $30,000 read a newspaper regularly while 96 percent of those with incomes of more than $30,000 read a newspaper regularly); and 80 percent of everyone in the state reads a newspaper regularly; on the average, two newspapers are read in each home; more than half the people in the state read a newspaper every day; newspapers were named by 70 percent of the people as the most "thorough" medium (that is, giving the most complete reports), by 65 percent as the "most trustworthy" medium (as opposed to television, 25 percent, and radio, 10 percent); and about 85 percent of the people in the survey said that they regularly made decisions on the basis of newspaper advertising.

Luketon's statement, to be released at the time of the press conference, is as follows: "The results of this survey show that newspapers are a trusted and useful medium. We believe that a newspaper is the best buy that an advertiser or a consumer can make in today's market. Newspapers have been hiding their lights under a bushel for a long time. We haven't bothered to tell people how good we are and what we can do for them. We hope that our attention to National Newspaper Week will help us tell this story."

Billiard's statement: "These results clearly show that newspapers are here to stay. While a few have gone out of business elsewhere, the newspapers in this state have a strong following among many people. Those newspapers plan to continue to provide the excellent service to advertisers and readers that we have provided in the past."

You are to prepare a 250-word press release incorporating these statements and summarizing the results of the survey. The press release will be handed out to other media in the state.

You are also assigned to prepare two advertisements based on the survey results. At least one should be for print and will run in the state's newspapers. The other may be for print, radio, or television.

9.2 Speeches and Statements

The following situations require that you draft speeches or statements. Follow the instructions below or those given to you by your instructor.

COMMENCEMENT SPEECH

You are working in the public relations department of a local company that manufactures computers, computer parts, and computer-related equipment. The president of your company has been asked to be the commencement speaker for this year's high school graduation ceremony. The president asks you to draft a speech for him that should be about five to ten minutes long. He tells you that he wants to bring a hopeful message—one that says that despite a period of locally high unemployment, the future looks bright for today's high school graduates.

KIWANIS SPEECH

Look at the press release on page 278. The president of American Southern has been invited to make a short speech to the Midville Kiwanis Club after this announcement has been made. He wants to tell them a little more about why his company chose Midville for the location of the plant. Here are some of the reasons:

- The educational system: Midville has one of the best in the state; a high percentage of students graduate from high school and go on to college (85 percent and 62 percent, respectively; the company feels that this is the kind of community that it can ask its managers and their families to live in.)

- The waterways: The manufacturing process that will be used in the new plant will require abundant sources of water; it will also require rivers that can be navigated to major shipping areas; the Blount River in Midville is such a river.

- A generally favorable business climate: The state has some of the lowest business taxes in the region, and that is what prompted American Southern to look at the state for a location here in the first place.

You may also use information found in the press release.

The Kiwanis Club is a service organization. The members get involved in a lot of community projects. They will want to know about American Southern's planned involvement in the community. The president wants to tell them that community involvement is important to the company; the company often contributes money and people to causes such as the United Way and generally sponsors YMCA soccer, basketball, and baseball teams in the youth leagues. He wants to tell the Kiwanis Club that once American Southern is located in Midville, it will look at what the needs of the community are and try to help out.

The speech should be 750 to 1,000 words long.

COLLEGE DAY

The Chamber of Commerce in your hometown is sponsoring "College Day," and the president has asked you to come back and tell them about your experiences in college. You'll be one of three people who have been asked to speak at the meeting that day on this subject. The president tells you that he wants you to talk purely from your own experiences. Try to give the listeners a sense of what it was like to go to the college you attend; how you felt about going to your first class; when and how you made friends; how much money it costs; what some of the things are that they could tell their high-school-age children about college.

The speech should be 500–750 words long.

9.3 Letters

Write letters based on the following information. Follow the directions given by your instructor.

LETTER OF APOLOGY

Just after Christmas, a large department store receives a letter from a woman complaining about the rudeness of the salespeople in the women's sportswear department. The woman is not specific about her complaints but says that she was in the store twice before Christmas and was ignored completely once and spoken to rudely by a young sales clerk the other time. The department head, on seeing the letter, says that Christmas was a very busy season, the store always seemed to be crowded, and the department had to hire some temporary and untrained people to work during that time. She says she doubts that the woman would feel slighted by the regular employees. Draft a letter of at least 150 words for the store manager's signature responding to the woman's complaint.

EMPLOYEE DINNER

You are working in the public relations department of the home office of an insurance company. The company is planning an employee appreciation dinner for home office employees. This is the fifth year the company has had such a dinner. One of the employees will be named Outstanding Home Office Employee for the year. Another will receive the Community Service Award, which is given to the home office employee who has contributed the most to the community. A string quartet from the local university will provide the entertainment for the dinner, and Paul Harvey, the radio commentator and newspaper columnist, will give a speech. You should draft a letter to all the employees to encourage them to attend. The dinner will begin at 6:00 P.M. at the Hilton Hotel on April 5. There is no charge for the dinner, but employees who plan to attend should inform their supervisors by April 1.

FUND-RAISING LETTER: CONSOLIDATED GIVING FUND DRIVE

The president of your university wants to send out a letter to all employees encouraging them to support the annual community Consolidated Giving fund drive. As a member of the PR department, you have been assigned to draft the letter. The letter should make the following points (but not necessarily in this order):

- Contributing to the Consolidated Giving fund is easy and convenient; employees can sign up for a monthly payroll deduction; the card to do this with will accompany the letter.

- The university has always been a major contributor to the community's Consolidated Giving fund; last year, more than $200,000 was raised from university employees alone; this year's goal is $250,000.

- Consolidated Giving supports more than fifty community projects; more than 95 percent of the contributions will stay within the community.

- Each department within the university has been given a goal; it is important for every individual employee to respond.

The letter should be between 150 and 200 words.

FUND-RAISING LETTER: PUBLIC RADIO

The manager of the local public radio station (for which you are a volunteer) has asked you to draft a letter announcing an on-air fund-raising campaign for the station. The campaign is to begin in two weeks and will run for five days. The goal is to raise $50,000 from the listeners. The letter that you are drafting will go to people who contributed last year. These people already have supported public radio, and they know the kind of programming that public radio has: the news shows "Morning Edition" and "All Things Considered" from National Public Radio; the classical music during the weekdays and the jazz and bluegrass on the weekends; the special broadcasts of musical events in the community.

This year's fund-raising campaign is particularly important, and it is important that the station get off to a good start with early contributions from previous supporters. It is important for the following reasons:

- The station needs a new emergency generator; bad weather had knocked the station off the air a number of times.

- The station needs to purchase a new compact disk player to replace one that is malfunctioning.

- The cost of many of the programs that the station has to buy has gone up during the past year—some by as much as 25 to 30 percent; some of these programs may have to be dropped if the station doesn't get more money.

The letter should be between 150 and 200 words.

9.4 Pamphlets and Brochures

SWIMMING

You have been asked to design a pamphlet that the local YMCA wants to publish and distribute about the benefits of a regular swimming program. The purpose of the pamphlet is to get people to join the Y and begin swimming or doing some form of exercise. The pamphlet will be distributed to local businesses, especially those close to the Y.

The pool at the YMCA is open during the following hours: 7–9 A.M., 11 A.M.–1:30 P.M., and 4:30–7:30 P.M. on Mondays through Fridays; 3–6 P.M. on Saturdays. People who want to join the Y should come by or call, 876-0987. A year's membership costs thirty-five dollars.

Here are some of the benefits of swimming:

- It's aerobic exercise, meaning that it conditions the heart and lungs; this exercise can help to prevent heart disease, the nation's number-one killer.

- It can help control body weight.

- It can help to build up stamina in a person.

- It can relieve tension; many doctors believe that exercise is a good antidote for depression and other emotional stress.

- Swimming is a particularly good exercise because it is not hard on the joints; this is important especially for elderly people, who are more likely to suffer from arthritis; swimming often offers a lot of relief for arthritis.

- Swimming exercises almost all the major muscles of the body.

- Regular exercise is good for the self-image; you just feel better about yourself.

YMCA officials also caution that people may need to consult their doctors or physicians before beginning an exercise program.

You need to write about 300 words of copy for this brochure.

TRAVEL BROCHURE

The Chamber of Commerce for the county next to the one you live in wants your public relations agency to design and write a short travel pamphlet about the sights in the county. This pamphlet will be distributed by the state Department of Tourism and will be found in hotels, travel bureaus and agencies, and interstate rest stops.

Write about 300 words that would persuade a traveler to visit that county. You may also want to suggest a general design for the pamphlet. Here are some facts that you can use:

Probably the major scenic attraction of the county is the four covered bridges; all have been well preserved and date back to the 1800s. They are (1) the Morton Mill Bridge, the highest covered bridge above water (about seventy-five feet), located five miles east of Smithville on Highway 6; it's 220 feet long; built in 1877 and restored in 1976; located next to the bridge was Morton Mill, where farmers brought their corn and wheat to be ground from about the time the bridge was built until the 1930s; (2) the Ensley Bridge, the oldest one in the county, built in 1821; legend has it that there was a skirmish between companies of Confederate and Union soldiers during the Civil War; several soldiers were killed, and locals say you can hear the ghosts rustling through the grass and trees at dusk; it's located on Highway 42 west of Springtown; (3) the Swann Bridge, built in 1921, the newest of the four bridges; it is on the Old Barterville Highway, just south of Masontown; there was also a mill located next to it, and part of that mill building has been restored and is open to tourists; (4) the Nactor Bridge, built in 1900 and found in the western part of the county on Highway 69 west of Smithville; the reason it was built is unclear, although some say that a mill was located next to it for a while; if that's the case, it wasn't there very long because there are no records of it. Just why covered bridges were built is not exactly clear, although the ones that were located next to mills were probably built so that farmers would have some protection from the weather while waiting to get their wheat and corn ground. Since this is a small and still mostly rural county, the covered bridges are a big part of the heritage of the people.

The county offers some other attractions. It has several lakes and recreation areas, plus Rickwill Caverns, a 280-acre state park that is open all year. The park features a restaurant that is actually located inside the cavern; you can also explore the caverns for a small admission fee.

Finally, every October, there is the Old Times Festival, a week-long fair that features everything from a tennis tournament to a quilt show; special tours of the covered bridges are conducted then.

9.5 Writing for the Web

ORGANIZING A WEBSITE

Pick an organization that you are familiar with. It could be a church, a fraternity, a sorority, your academic department, a high school, a civic or service organization, a club—or even your family. You assignment is to develop a website for that organization.

First, ask yourself these questions: What would I want a person surfing the Internet to know about this organization? How would I want that person to feel about the organization once he or she saw the website? What would I want that person to know about the organization?

Second, reread pages 289 to 290 of this book. Many websites are organized in a treelike structure. That is, there are a few major organizational units, and those units are broken down into smaller and smaller blocks.

As you are considering the organization and text content of the website, you must also consider what pictures and graphics that you want to use. Does the organization have a logo or symbol of some type? Are there pictures of people that are relevant?

What text materials already exist that should be included on your website? An organization might already have a constitution, set of rules, or code of ethics that you should include. If so, you won't necessarily have to retype this material (particularly if it already exists as electronic files), but you will have to write a short introduction for it.

One organizational scheme that applies to many organizations is the following: structure, people, activities, calendar. That, however, is just one approach. Every organization is different, and each needs to be organized differently.

As a way of preparing for this assignment, you should examine closely several websites that are of interest to you or that have been set up for organizations similar to yours.

Here is what you should have to complete your assignment:

1. A statement of what you want to accomplish with the website—what you want surfers to know about your organization
2. A structure or outline to show how the website will be organized
3. Introductions for all of the first-level and some of the second-level parts of the website
4. A list of graphics and pictures that could be used for the website
5. An explanation of some of the links that web surfers could use in getting to different parts of the material that you are showing on the website

The Writer and the Law

By Matthew Bunker
University of Alabama

for better or worse, law is an important part of mass communication. The law is not always a threat to writers, of course. It can even be a positive force. For example, the law can help writers by enabling them to protect their work against theft by obtaining a copyright. On the other side of the coin, the law places limitations on what writers may say by allowing civil lawsuits against writers for defamation and invasion of privacy. The federal government also limits writers' freedoms when it regulates such activities as broadcasting and false advertising.

This chapter is a brief sketch of some legal areas that may affect mass media writers. It is, of necessity, somewhat simplified. Legal matters are rarely black and white; in fact, legal doctrine is often enormously complex. Moreover, law is not static; it is always changing and evolving, both "on the books" and through the interpretations of courts. For these reasons, writers who run up against possible legal difficulties should consult with editors, producers, and other supervisors who can determine whether it is time to call the lawyers.

THE FIRST AMENDMENT

Writers in the United States have a great deal of freedom in their work; much of this freedom derives from the First Amendment to the U.S. Constitution. The First Amendment, which was ratified in 1791, provides significant protection for spoken and written communication. Although the First Amendment also protects other rights, such as religious liberties, this chapter will focus on the free speech aspects of the amendment.

The relevant portion of the First Amendment states as follows: "Congress shall make no law . . . abridging the freedom of speech, or of the press. . . ." This broad, general language leaves much to the imagination. What exactly is "the freedom of speech"? What sort of law or regulation would constitute "abridging" that freedom? Perhaps not surprisingly, these issues are still being argued about in the courts as our understanding of free speech evolves. Some would argue that the malleability of the First Amendment—the ability of the free speech principle to adapt to changed circumstances—is one of its greatest strengths. Others suggest that when the outlines of constitutional rights are uncertain, government may subvert basic liberties.

One point that is worth noting immediately is that the First Amendment states that "Congress" cannot abridge free speech. At a first reading, that might suggest that only the federal government is limited by the First Amendment, because "Congress" is the federal legislature. That is not the case, however. The U.S. Supreme Court has ruled that the First Amendment applies to all governmental authorities in the United States, including federal, state, and local authorities. Thus, the First Amendment applies not only to Congress, but also to state legislatures, local city councils, and even state-funded institutions such as public universities. None of these institutions can trample on the right of free speech.

The First Amendment protects speech about politics, religion, and culture most strongly. Government can rarely stop such speech ahead of time, a practice called *prior restraint,* or punish its dissemination after the fact. Fully protected speech, such as political, religious, and cultural speech, can be restrained or punished by government only in dire circumstances. Other forms of speech, such as advertising and indecent speech, receive less protection, although there are still many circumstances in which such speech is protected by the First Amendment. Finally, certain types of speech, such as obscenity and criminal threats, are completely unprotected by the First Amendment. This means that government can regulate such "low value" speech as much as it likes.

Figure 10.1 James Madison on freedom of the press

Congress shall make no law respecting an establishment of religion, or prohibiting the free exercise thereof; or abridging freedom of speech, or of the press; or the right of the people to peaceably assemble, and to petition the Government for a redress of grievances. (First Amendment to the U.S. Constitution)

Whatever facilitates a general intercourse of sentiments, as good roads, domestic commerce, a free press, and particularly a circulation of newspapers through the entire body of the people . . . is favorable to liberty. (National Gazette, 1791)

It is to the press mankind are indebted for having dispelled the clouds which long encompassed religion, for disclosing her genuine lustre, and disseminating her salutary doctrines. (Speech in the Virginia Assembly, 1799)

Although the basics of free speech protection seem reasonably clear, in recent years writers and media organizations have faced novel legal assaults that have left their rights in question. A number of individuals and companies, unable to attack the media directly because of First Amendment rights, have launched peripheral or "end run" legal attacks that try to evade free speech protections. For example, companies that are unhappy with media coverage have sued the media not on the basis of the information presented, but on the basis of how that information was gathered.

In a famous case, the Food Lion supermarket chain sued ABC for an undercover news story that purported to show questionable food handling by Food Lion employees. Food Lion chose not to sue for defamation—that is, to challenge the truth of the story—but instead brought claims for fraud and trespass based on the methods ABC used to get its hidden cameras into Food Lion stores. For instance, ABC producers used false resumés to gain employment in the stores. In another widely reported case, CBS made a controversial decision not to air a story that was critical of the tobacco industry because of possible legal action. Once again, the potential legal claim was based not on the truth or falsity of the story but how the information was acquired. In this case, tobacco company lawyers could have sued, claiming that CBS had acted improperly by persuading a former tobacco company employee to break his confidentiality agreement with his former employer and talk to CBS about the company. In other cases, companies have brought trademark suits against media organizations that used company symbols to parody a company's actions or provide social commentary.

The central theme of these cases is that companies that feel mistreated by the media are finding ingenious ways to punish or deter the press, using legal actions that do not bring free speech protections into play. It is a disturbing trend to many who value free speech and a free press.

DEFAMATION

Defamation is the legal term for harming someone's reputation. It is a great concern for those who work in media industries, because defaming someone can result in large damage awards against media companies, as well as the possibility of lost employment for the writers and editors who are involved. U.S. defamation law, which has evolved from English law, regards a person's reputation as a piece of his or her property, just like a house or car that person might own. If you harm an individual's reputation by stating something false about him or her, you may be required to pay that person damages, in the same way that you would have to pay to repair the person's car if you dented the fender. It is important to note that reputation refers to how others see us, not how we feel about ourselves. However, our reputations die with us. One cannot defame the dead.

Defamation consists of *libel*, which is written defamation, and *slander*, which is spoken defamation. Libel is the more serious of the two, because more people may come across a written statement over a longer period of time, causing greater harm to reputation. Many state laws treat defamation on radio or television as libel, even though it is not written. The remainder of this chapter will address only libel, rather than slander, since libel is the chief concern of writers.

Libel in the United States is generally not treated as a crime. It is, instead, often the subject of a civil suit, which is a lawsuit brought by one private person or corporation against another. Civil suits seek monetary damages rather than determinations of guilt or prison sentences. In a civil suit, the plaintiff is the person bringing the suit, while the defendant is the person being sued. Anyone can be sued for libel, but media companies are frequent libel defendants.

Figure 10.2   Libelous Words

Libel actions usually develop out of lack of thought or temporary mental lapses on the part of the communicator. No list of problem words and phrases is ever quite complete, but this is a beginning. Use these words and phrases with caution.

adulterer	incompetent
AIDS victim	infidelity
alcoholic	influence peddler
ambulance chaser	informer
atheist	insane
attempted suicide	intemperate
bad morals	intimate
bankrupt	Jekyll-Hyde personality
bigamist	junkie
blackmail	kept woman
bordello	Ku Klux Klan
briber	lascivious
brothel	lewd
cheat	liar
collusion	mental disease
communist	mental incompetent
con man	molester
convict	moral degenerate
corrupt	murderer
coward	nazi
death-merchant	paramour
divorced (when not)	paranoid
drug addict or druggie	peeping Tom
drunk	perjurer
embezzler	pervert
ex-convict	pimp
fascist	plagiarist
fink	pockets public funds
fixed game	price cutter
fool	profiteer
fornicator	prostitute
fraud	rapist
gambling house	recidivist
gangster	rogue
gay	sadist
grafter	scam-artist
herpes	scandal monger
hit-man	scoundrel
homosexual	seducer
hypocrite	short in accounts
illegitimate	shyster
illicit relations	skunk
incest	sneak

(continued)

Figure 10.2   Continued

stuffed ballot boxes   unsound mind
underworld connections   vice den
unethical   villain
unmarried mother   viper
unprofessional

THE PLAINTIFF'S CASE

To succeed in a libel suit, a plaintiff must prove five points, or elements. These five elements are as follows.

Publication

The plaintiff must prove that the libelous statement was published. This can be shown, for example, by proving that a libelous statement appeared in a newspaper, on a television news broadcast, in an advertisement, or as part of a public relations press release. Publication of libel can also occur when a statement is transmitted not to the general public but to a small audience, such as the recipient of a letter.

Identification

The plaintiff in a libel suit must prove that he or she has been identified. This is relatively simple if the story contains the plaintiff's name, but there are many other ways to identify someone. For example, a photograph that is accidentally juxtaposed with a libelous story can create problems. Likewise, a detailed description of a person (age, lifestyle, occupation, and the like) can tip others off to the person's identity even if the individual's name is not mentioned in the story. Finally, writers may accidentally identify someone in a libelous story by getting a name wrong or by failing to separate the person they intend to identify from others with the same name. Remember, there are many people named Joseph Smith who are not criminals, even if one Joe Smith happens to run afoul of the law. For this reason, it is often wise to include identifying information to narrow the range of possible misidentification; middle initial, age, address, and other specifics are helpful.

Keep in mind that one can libel a corporation, which has its own legal identity and reputation. It is also possible to libel individuals by writing defamatory statements about groups, although the courts have held that the group must be rather small for the individual members to bring suit successfully. For example, individual members of a five-member city commission could be libeled by a story stating that most of the commissioners took bribes, even if no names were mentioned. When groups get very large, the danger of a libel suit diminishes. For example, the statement that "all lawyers are corrupt" is about such a large group that no individual attorney could succeed in a libel suit based on the statement.

Defamation

This element means that the plaintiff must prove that the story has harmed his or her reputation. It could be that the story has made others hate the plaintiff or perhaps simply shun him or her. Classic danger areas include false statements about (1) political beliefs (calling someone a nazi is not recommended); (2) illnesses, particularly mental illnesses or other diseases that might lead people to avoid the plaintiff; (3) business practices or professional competence (damage awards can be particularly large when a story affects an individual's livelihood); and (4) criminal activity. Moreover, the use of the word *allegedly* will not shield a writer from liability. *Allegedly* simply implies that someone other than the writer is making the claim. It has no legal effect because someone who repeats a libelous statement is just as responsible for damages as is the person who originated the statement.

Fault

The plaintiff must show that the writer was at fault in some way. The strength of this showing varies depending on the identity of the plaintiff, as we will see in the next section. Ordinary libel plaintiffs must prove that the writer was *negligent,* or careless. A simple typographical error might warrant a finding of negligence. Plaintiffs who hold public offices or are public figures have a more stringent burden of proof, called *actual malice.* Actual malice, as will be discussed more fully later, means roughly that the writer was aware that a statement was false and published it anyway.

Damages

The plaintiff must prove that he or she was harmed in some way. Damages can be shown, for example, by a professional person whose revenues decreased after a libelous story appeared. Plaintiffs can also prove damages by demonstrating that their standing in the community was diminished by a libelous statement, even though it may be hard to place a precise dollar figure on the loss. Courts and juries can also award *punitive damages* to punish the defendant if the libel was particularly egregious.

AFFIRMATIVE DEFENSES

To defend against a libel suit, the defendant can try to prove that some element of the plaintiff's case is lacking. For example, the defendant might try to show that the plaintiff was not identified in the news story in question or that no damages had accrued because of the story. In addition, libel defendants have a number of affirmative defenses that they can assert. Affirmative defenses include the following.

Truth

Truth can be an excellent defense against a libel claim, although procedurally, defendants are not always required to prove truth. If a defendant can establish that a story was true, the defendant will almost certainly win the case. Libel, by definition, is a false statement about someone. It is worth keeping in mind, however, that truth is often a slippery subject. Even though a writer may be convinced that a story is true, judges and juries often will not be persuaded simply by a sincere statement from the witness stand. Ideally, the writer should have documents, credible eyewitnesses, or other concrete evidence that establishes the truth of claims made in a story.

Qualified Privilege

Writers are generally entitled to quote from government officials who are acting in an official capacity, even if those officials make libelous statements. Thus, for example, a writer has a qualified privilege to quote from a police report stating that Joe Smith has been arrested for armed robbery, even if Smith is later cleared of the charge. Similarly, statements made by judges during a trial or by legislators while debating a bill on the floor of the legislature are privileged. Writers who assert a qualified privilege must be able to show that their reports were fair and accurate. Also, informal statements made by officials are not always protected.

Statute of Limitations

Libel plaintiffs must bring suit within a specified period of time, often one or two years, depending on the state. If the plaintiff files suit after this time, the limitations period has run out, and the suit is dismissed.

Constitutional Privilege

As was discussed briefly earlier, when public officials and public figures bring libel suits, their burden of proof is higher than when ordinary citizens sue for libel. In a series of cases, beginning with the landmark 1964 case of *New York Times Co. v. Sullivan,* the U.S. Supreme Court has ruled that public officials and public figures must prove actual malice to win libel damages. By using the term *actual malice,* the Court intends a special meaning that is not related to ill will or hatred. Instead, "actual malice" means that when the writer published the libelous statement, the

Figure 10.3

Chief Justice William Rehnquist on criticism of public figures

The sort of robust political debate encouraged by the First Amendment is bound to produce speech that is critical of those who hold public office or . . . public figures. Such criticism, inevitably, will not always be reasoned or moderate; public figures as well as public officials will be subject to vehement, caustic, and sometimes unpleasantly sharp attacks. (*Hustler Magazine* v. *Falwell,* 1988)

writer either (1) knew that the statement was false or (2) had reckless disregard for the truth or falsity of the statement. As you might imagine, imposing an "actual malice" burden of proof on the plaintiff in a libel suit makes it very difficult to win the case. A public official or public figure plaintiff must show, in essence, that the writer knew that the libelous statement was false and chose to publish it anyway—it was a deliberate lie—or, if the writer was not sure the statement was false, at least had serious doubts about it. Very few reputable news organizations operate this way, and very few plaintiffs have won libel suits when faced with having to prove actual malice on the part of the defendant.

Given this extraordinarily difficult burden of proof, it is not surprising that plaintiffs fight hard not be classified as public officials or public figures. Defendants fight equally hard to have the court declare that the plaintiff does fit into one of those categories. Often, the determination of whether the plaintiff is or is not a public official or public figure is the key to the lawsuit.

What criteria do courts use to decide whether plaintiffs are public officials or public figures and thus subject to the actual malice burden? *Public officials* are generally people who either hold an elected office or hold a nonelective public office that gives them significant power of some sort. A good example of this second type of public official would be a public school principal. *Public figures* are famous people who have become household names (Michael Jordan is a good example). A second type of public figure is a person who, although not famous, nonetheless has thrust himself or herself into the public eye to affect some public controversy. A good example of this second type of public figure would be an activist who made speeches, led protests, and otherwise went before the public to influence public sentiment about a cause such as abortion, the environment, affirmative action, assisted suicide, or some other public controversy. The filmmaker Michael Moore probably falls into this category. Because such a person has invited public comment and criticism, he or she would be treated as a public figure in a libel suit.

To summarize, if a plaintiff is labeled a public official or public figure, the Supreme Court has said that he or she must prove actual malice to win a libel suit. In practice, this means that journalists have wider latitude to write critically about people who have achieved fame and power than about the average citizen. Such latitude clearly should not encourage irresponsible or sloppy writing or reporting, but it does provide some degree of legal protection to writers, particularly when they are criticizing government officials.

There are other affirmative defenses available to libel defendants, but those discussed above should give you some idea of how libel defenses work. The best way to avoid libel is not to rely on defenses, however. Instead, writers should strive for accuracy and fairness so that the possibility of a libel suit is diminished. Writers should also consult with a lawyer when it appears that a story has significant legal risks.

PRIVACY

In addition to libel, writers can be sued when their stories invade someone's privacy. Privacy is defined in many different ways, but most states recognize four different ways in which the media can invade privacy. These four methods of privacy invasion are called *torts* of privacy, which simply means that such conduct may result in a civil action. The four torts of privacy are as follows.

Publication of Private Facts

Writers may commit this tort when they publish some intensely personal fact or facts about an individual. Note that, unlike libel, publication of private facts consists of true information that nonetheless may result in damages against the writer. The legal harm in private facts cases is not to the reputation of the plaintiff but instead results from shame or humiliation. The kinds of cases that have led to claims of publication of private facts have included stories about rape, sexual orientation, illnesses, and other topics that most people would prefer to keep private. Writers would do well to pause when they consider writing about this kind of information, even if they know that the information is accurate.

Fortunately for the media, the majority of publication of private facts suits fails. This is because courts generally protect defendants who publish personal information, as long as it is "newsworthy." Because many courts regard almost anything in which the public is interested as newsworthy, plaintiffs who bring publication of private facts suits generally lose. Nonetheless, writers should be careful when venturing into very personal aspects of others' lives. Not only is legal liability still possible, but journalistic ethics often counsel against such revelations. For example, almost no reputable news media publish the names of rape victims, even though the Supreme Court has held that the First Amendment protects such publication.

Intrusion into Seclusion

This privacy tort is committed when a writer trespasses into someone's "personal space," whether physically or using technology. For example, using a telephoto lens to take pictures of an individual in his or her bedroom would be intrusion. Similarly, sneaking into someone's office file drawer to gather information would be legally risky. The crucial issue, courts have said, is whether the plaintiff has a "reasonable expectation" of privacy. That means, for example, that photographing someone in a public place would generally not be intrusion, because when people are in public, they know that others can see them and that it is possible they may be photographed.

Intrusion is different from other torts that we have examined so far in that it does not depend on publication of the information. If a television news crew gathers information by barging into someone's home, intrusion has taken place whether or not the footage is ever televised.

False Light

False light is a privacy tort that looks very much like libel, although there are also some important differences. A writer commits false light by presenting someone as being something he or she is not—that is, portraying someone in a "false light." In a famous case that went before the U.S. Supreme Court, a reporter presented a woman in a false light by writing a story that portrayed her as "stoic" after the death of her husband. In fact, the woman was not stoic. Even worse, the reporter had never interviewed the woman but had simply fabricated the interview after he went to speak with her and found that she was not home.

Notice that in this example, the reporter probably did not commit libel. There is nothing defamatory about being considered stoic after a personal loss. The story would not diminish the woman's reputation. Some people might even applaud her reported strength in the face of tragedy. Nonetheless, because the presentation is inaccurate and would be offensive to its subject, it constitutes false light. Although false light is conceptually distinct from libel, some states have refused to recognize false light as an independent tort. Even where it is recognized, it is often appended as a secondary claim to a plaintiff's libel suit. In any event, it is one more reason for writers to concentrate on accuracy and avoid statements or presentations that would tend to present someone in a false manner.

Appropriation

Appropriation is a tort that arises most frequently in the context of advertising and public relations. This tort is sometimes referred to as an individual's right of publicity. It is defined as the unauthorized use of a person's name, likeness, or other integral part of the individual's persona for commercial purposes. For example, one could not use movie star Brad Pitt's face or name in an advertisement for a product without his consent (and that would almost certainly be accompanied by a hefty endorsement fee, if he consented at all). Generally, the harm from appropriation is not so much a loss of privacy, but the loss of income celebrities suffer when an advertiser uses their persona in a campaign without their consent. It is not appropriation to use someone's name or likeness for legitimate news purposes. Thus, for example, Brad Pitt could not succeed in an appropriation suit against a newspaper or a television station that used his image in an entertainment report.

Sometimes the line is not completely clear between "commercial" uses of someone's name or likeness and other uses. In a lawsuit that involved golf sensation Tiger Woods, Woods' company filed an appropriation suit against a company that marketed an art print called "The Masters of Augusta." The print, created after Woods won golf's Masters Tournament in 1997, featured Woods' image. An Ohio federal court ruled against Woods' appropriation claim, holding that the print was not primarily commercial in nature and was an artistic creation protected by the First Amendment.

Aside from a celebrity's name or picture, appropriation can occur with other attributes associated with him or her. For example, singer Bette Midler won a famous case in which a song in an automobile commercial was sung by a "sound-alike" singer who was able to mimic Midler's vocal style. Although neither Midler's name nor her likeness appeared anywhere in the commercial, her distinctive singing voice was also a legally protected part of her persona that could not be taken without her consent. Thus, any time writers seek to associate an individual's persona with a product for commercial purposes, they should be certain that they have the individual's permission.

COPYRIGHT AND TRADEMARK

Copyright law in the United States originated as a way to protect those who produce creative works by giving them the right to a kind of commercial monopoly on their works. If creators are rewarded, the theory goes, they will work hard and create great artistic works, thus benefiting everyone. In essence, copyright law acts as an incentive for creators. Copyright protection extends not only to writers, but also to composers, graphic artists, sculptors, and many other people who create original works. Copyright law is but one part of a larger area of law called *intellectual property* law, which also encompasses trademarks and patents. It is important for writers to have some basic knowledge of copyright law, not only to protect their own works, but also to make certain that they are using others' works appropriately.

To copyright a work, the law says that the work must be "fixed in a tangible medium." This means that it must exist in some relatively permanent form. It could be a written work stored on paper or on a computer disk, a song recorded on audiotape, a painting on canvas, a motion picture on film, or a variety of other forms of expression.

An important result of the "fixed in a tangible medium" requirement is that ideas or events cannot be copyrighted. Thus, if a writer has a general idea for an advertising layout, the general idea cannot be copyrighted. Rather, only its particular expression in an individual ad could receive a copyright. The same goes for general ideas in fiction. A screenwriter could not copyright the general formula "boy meets girl, boy loses girl, boy loses dog, girl finds dog, boy finds girl." However, the screenwriter could protect his or her particular expression of that idea in a romantic comedy movie script. Moreover, events cannot be copyrighted. Anyone can write an account of the tragic explosion of the space shuttle *Columbia,* for example. What can be copyrighted is an individual writer's particular expression of that event—the way in which that writer tells the story, not the story itself.

Merely fixing words in a tangible medium does not guarantee that the result is copyrightable. Courts have held that for a work to be copyrightable, it must have some minimal degree of creativity. For example, the U.S. Supreme Court held that telephone company white pages, which simply list customers' names alphabetically, were not sufficiently creative to warrant copyright protection. There was no element of creativity in the phone book. Nevertheless, although works must be minimally creative to be copyrighted, there is no requirement that they be good. A poorly written novel is just as entitled to protection as is a masterpiece of fiction.

Copyright protection does not last forever. At some point, works cease to be legally protected and enter the public domain, which means that anyone can use them. For example, filmmakers who have made popular movies based on works by William Shakespeare and Jane Austen are certainly not paying any royalties to the estates of those two literary geniuses. Under current U.S. law, copyright protection remains in effect for the author's life plus 70 years. When a copyright belongs to a corporation rather than to a human being, the term is either 120 years from the date of creation or 95 years from the date of publication, whichever is shorter. The U.S. Supreme Court recently upheld these terms as constitutional, even though the Constitution itself states that copyrights should last only for "limited times."

Corporate copyright ownership brings up an important point for writers: Who owns the copyright when a writer creates a work as an employee? The general answer is that the employer owns the work. Thus, for example, when a journalist writes a news story while in the employ of a newspaper, the newspaper owns the copyright to the resulting story. The same goes for a copywriter who works for an advertising agency. The question of ownership becomes murkier when work is created by a *free-lancer,* who is not a full-time employee but instead works on individual projects, sometimes using the freelancer's own premises and equipment. The law gets complicated here, but the simplest way to avoid problems is to draw up a clear contract ahead of time specifying to whom the resulting copyrighted work will belong. Recently, freelancers have been battling major newspapers in court over the right to take freelance contributions and place them into electronic databases such as LEXIS/NEXIS. The publishers have claimed that the electronic database versions were simply "revisions" of the original publication, and the freelancers have argued that use of their work in a database is a new publication that must be compensated. Again, a clear contractual agreement is the best means of ensuring that writers can maintain control of their works.

The mere fact that a work is copyrighted does not mean that no one other than the copyright owner may use any part of the work. Clearly, wholesale theft of someone else's work would almost certainly result in a finding of copyright infringement by a court. However, the copyright law has created some breathing room for at least some uses by others to which the copyright owner need not consent. This breathing room is the idea of fair use. *Fair use* essentially says that although granting a copyright owner a type of monopoly serves society by encouraging creativity, the monopoly is not absolute. Society also has an interest in the wide dissemination of important works. Recently, copyright infringement cases involving online music services such as Napster, Kazaa, and MP3.com have been testing the scope of fair use protection on the Internet.

How does one know whether the use of someone else's copyrighted material is a fair use? This question is not easily answered, because courts decide the matter on a case-by-case basis. In making fair use decisions, courts use four factors that they weigh to determine whether a use is fair. No single factor dictates the result. The four factors are as follows.

Nature of the Copyrighted Material

Courts look at the length of the original, how much effort went into creating it, and how widely available it is. Less creative works may receive less protection under this factor than those works that exhibit great creativity.

Nature of the Use

Courts look with more favor on a use (borrowing) if it is for educational purposes than if it is solely to make money. For example, it's one thing for a teacher to photocopy a magazine article for classroom use and quite another for the teacher to include that article in a published book of readings to be sold to students. A court might well grant fair use in the former case but almost certainly would not in the latter. Courts also tend to look favorably on "transformative" uses—that is, uses in which the user doesn't simply reproduce the original work verbatim but somehow changes it to produce a new meaning or new message. A good example of a transformative use is a parody of a copyrighted work that uses parts of the original work to comment on or critique the original.

Extent of the Use

Courts look at both the quantity and the quality of the borrowed material. Quantity, of course, is relative to the total length of the work; it's one thing to borrow a single line from a lengthy book and quite another if a line is borrowed from a haiku. Even if the quantity borrowed is relatively small, courts still may find that a use is not "fair" if the borrowed portion is the most valuable part of the work. For example, the "hook line" of a hit song may be a relatively small portion of the entire song, but it is nonetheless the heart of the work.

Commercial Infringement

The final fair use factor looks at the extent to which the borrowing damages the market for the original work. Would the later work somehow serve as a substitute for the original, thus discouraging people from buying the original? If so, courts are less likely to declare the use a fair one.

In contrast to copyright law, trademark law operates to prevent consumer confusion and protect the business relationship between a company and its customers. A good trademark is worth a fortune to the company that owns it. Think what would happen, for example, if all sports manufacturers were free to use the word *Nike* on their athletic gear. Consumers could not be certain they were getting the high-quality products they wanted, and the original trademark owner would lose a great deal of money because of the copycat products. Trademarks can include not only the names of products or services, but also logos, symbols, advertising catchphrases, and other items that denote a product or service.

Because trademarks are so valuable, companies go to great lengths to protect their trademarks. One way in which companies can lose their exclusive right to a trademark is by allowing its use as a generic term. For example, if the Coca-Cola

Company allowed its trademark "Coke" to be used to mean any soft drink (as sometimes happens informally), the company might eventually lose the right to the trademark. The word "Coke" would have *gone generic,* which means that any manufacturer could use it. The same thing would apply if the Xerox Corporation allowed its trademark "Xerox" to be used to refer to any photocopier machine or, perhaps even worse, if the company allowed others to use "Xerox" as a verb to denote the process of photocopying.

All of this means that writers must be careful in their use of trademark names. To maintain their trademarks and prevent generic use, companies often write sharp letters to mass media writers who misuse trademarks. Legal action by the trademark owner is possible. Companies also take out advertisements in media trade magazines, such as *Columbia Journalism Review* and *The Quill,* to alert writers to the proper use of their trademarks.

To use trademarks properly, writers must be certain to use the mark to apply only to a specific product by a specific company, not to a broad class of products. The trademark should generally be used as a proper adjective followed by a generic noun and never as a verb. For example, the word "Rollerblade" is the trademark of Rollerblade, Inc., a company that manufactures the skates. Writers should not refer to in-line skates in general as *rollerblades,* nor should writers use the verb form *rollerblading.* The terms *in-line skates* or *in-line skating* would have to be used. It would be appropriate to write about *Rollerblade skates* only if the writer was referring specifically to that brand.

The International Trademark Association issues a Trademark Checklist that helps writers to avoid such problems. The Trademark Checklist advises writers to use *lip balm* rather than *Chap Stick, drain opener* rather than *Drano, gelatin* rather than *Jell-O,* and *insect trap* rather than *Roach Motel.* All of the capitalized terms are trademarks, as are many other common words that writers may accidentally misuse (see Figure 10.4).

ADVERTISING

Up until fairly recently, advertising was not protected by the First Amendment. The Supreme Court apparently felt that advertising (which the Court calls *commercial speech*) was beneath the notice of the Constitution, which is concerned with weightier issues than ads for products and services. During the last few decades, however, the Supreme Court has gradually created greater protection for advertising. This protection is still not equal to the protection that is granted to political speech, for example, but it is nonetheless significant.

How can one tell whether an individual advertisement is entitled to protection under the First Amendment? First, the Supreme Court requires that the ad be truthful and in no way misleading. If the advertiser promises that its product will do something that it can't do, the ad will not be protected. Second, the advertisement must relate to a legal product or service. For example, an advertisement for illegal drugs would not be protected speech.

If these two conditions are met—the ad is not misleading and concerns a legal activity—the Court requires that the advertisement be subjected to a complicated legal analysis. The gist of this analysis is that the government can regulate an advertisement if it has a very good reason for doing so, such as protecting public health or well-being. If there is no such good reason, the ad is entitled to First Amendment protection and cannot be regulated by the government. Thus, for example, some legal limitations on alcohol advertising aimed at children have been approved because there is a sound reason for doing so. Alcohol use by minors is a serious social prob-

Figure 10.4 Commonly Misused Trademarks

The following are some commonly misused trademarks. These words are the names of products, but writers often use them to refer to the generic product. Each trademark is followed by a term that might be used in its place.

Autoharp: zither
Baggies: plastic bag
Band-Aid: adhesive bandage
Bon Bons: ice cream
Breathalyzer: instrument to measure
   alcoholic content
Brillo: scouring pad
Chap Stick: lip balm
Clorox: bleach
Coke: soft drink
Cool Whip: dessert topping
Dictaphone: recorder
Disposall: food waste disposer
Drano: drain opener
Ektachrome: photographic film
FedEx: overnight delivery service
Fig Newtons: cookies
Frisbee: flying disc
Handi-Wrap: plastic wrap
Hi-Liter: color marker
Hush Puppies: shoes
Jacuzzi: whirlpool bath
Jell-O: gelatin pudding
Kitty Litter: cat box filler
Kleenex: tissues
Kool-Aid: drinks
Krazy Glue: strong adhesive

Levi's: jeans
Lysol: disinfectant
Mace: tear gas
Naugahyde: plastic fabric
Nautilus: weight training equipment
Palm Pilot: personal digital assistant
Pampers: diapers
Ping-Pong: table tennis
Plexiglas: see-through plastic glass
Pyrex: glassware
Reynolds Wrap: aluminum foil
Rollerblade: in-line skates
Sanforized: preshrunk fabrics
Seeing Eye: guide dog
Sterno: cooking fuel
Tabasco: hot pepper sauce
Teflon: nonstick coatings
Vaseline: petroleum jelly
Vise-Grip: clamp
Walkman: portable music player
Windex: glass cleaner
Winnebago: motor home
Wite-Out: correction fluid
X-Acto: knife
Xerox: photocopier
Ziploc: resealable bag
Zippo: cigarette lighter

lem with numerous harmful consequences. On the other hand, a law that limited the distribution of advertising handbills on the street solely because they cause litter probably would not be constitutional. Litter, while unsightly, is not a serious enough problem to justify such a law.

Although First Amendment protection for advertising seems to be expanding, there is still a considerable amount of government regulation. This is particularly true for advertising that may mislead consumers, which is not protected by the First Amendment. The primary federal agency that enforces laws against misleading advertising is the Federal Trade Commission (FTC). Although other agencies at the state and federal level also enforce advertising laws, this section will concentrate on the FTC as perhaps the most important agency in this area.

The FTC is an independent federal agency with five commissioners and a large staff that polices advertisers. Because the FTC cannot look at every advertisement produced in the United States, the agency generally works by responding to complaints about ads.

To determine whether an advertisement is misleading, the FTC examines three criteria. A deceptive ad is one that is (1) likely to mislead (2) a reasonable consumer (3) with a material statement or omission. This definition means, first, that a mere likelihood of deception is all that is required. The FTC need not prove that anyone was actually deceived, only that the ad created that likelihood. Second, the FTC looks at ads that might be deceptive from the vantage point of the reasonable consumer— sort of the average "Joe or Joan Sixpack." How particularly bright or naive consumers would react to the ad is irrelevant. Finally, a material statement or omission is something of consequence—a statement or omission that would actually cause consumers to buy the product on the basis of the misrepresentation.

From the standpoint of those who write advertising copy, all of this means that the writer must be extraordinarily careful to describe products accurately in ad copy. Mere puffery (subjective claims about a product) is generally not regulated by the FTC. So, for example, claiming that a cookie is the "the most fudge-a-licious snack around" or that a sports car is "the ultimate high" would not lead to FTC action. However, inaccurate factual claims about actual performance that can be verified (e.g., "our ice cream is 100 percent fat free") could generate a response from the FTC.

Not only can the FTC act against misleading advertising, but competitors of companies employing misleading advertising can also bring legal actions. Recently, for example, makers of over-the-counter heartburn medications have been battling each other in court over the accuracy of various advertising claims. Competitor lawsuits are one more reason that advertisers must strive for a high degree of accuracy in their ads.

BROADCAST REGULATION

Broadcasting is different from other media. In particular, the government has much wider latitude to regulate broadcasting than most other forms of mass media. Most broadcasting regulation is done by the Federal Communications Commission (FCC), a government agency that also regulates telephone, cable, and other communication technologies.

Broadcasting, which includes both radio and television broadcasting, is unique in that it uses the public airwaves for transmission of its messages. Because broadcasters use this scarce public resource and because broadcasting is easily accessible to children, the U.S. Supreme Court has ruled that the content of broadcast media can be regulated much more intensely than the content of other media, such as newspapers or magazines. To understand what broadcasting is, it is important to understand what it is not. For example, a local television station that uses the airwaves is a broadcaster, whereas a cable service such as HBO, MTV, or ESPN is not. These cable services are delivered to cable companies by satellite and then to subscribers' homes via coaxial cable. Because the cable services do not use the public airwaves, their content is less regulated than is that of the broadcasters.

Writers need to be aware that radio and television broadcasters are limited in their use of "indecent" material, and can be subject to fines or other FCC punishment if indecent matter is broadcast. For example, sexual or excretory expletives (the classic "dirty words") are considered indecent by the FCC. So are vulgar humor and sexual double entendres that hint at sexual activity without necessarily using expletives. Controversial radio personality Howard Stern—who has moved from over-the-air to satellite radio—has been subject to numerous FCC proceedings based on just such humor. Although such language would almost certainly be protected on cable, its broadcast over the airwaves can result in severe fines or other punishment for the broadcasting station. The FCC has become even more vigilant about broadcast indecency recently because of the controversy over singer Janet Jackson's "wardrobe malfunction" during the 2004 Super Bowl half-time show. However, broadcasters do have some leeway. Under current law, 10 P.M. until 6 A.M. is considered a "safe harbor" for broadcast indecency because of the reduced likelihood that children will be in the audience during those hours.

Broadcasters are under other content limitations as well. For example, *payola,* payments by record companies to programmers to play particular songs, is illegal. So is *plugola,* which is a payment to broadcasters to promote particular products during their regular programming. Broadcasters are also prohibited from airing hoaxes or other programming that might frighten listeners. In addition, federal law contains a number of important provisions that ensure access to the airwaves by political candidates.

CONCLUSION

This chapter has touched on a number of areas that can cause legal concerns for writers. Writers have a wonderful ally in the First Amendment. Nonetheless, legal minefields are plentiful. This need not result in abject fear for writers, but a healthy awareness of, and respect for, legal limitations is essential. Being involved in a legal proceeding can be a traumatic experience. Moreover, it can be detrimental to one's career and expensive. With care and thoughtfulness, writers can reduce the possibility that they will ever have an unpleasant encounter with the law.

FURTHER READING

Middleton, K. R., et al. (2004). *The Law of Public Communication* (6th ed.). New York: Longman.

Pember, D. R., & Calvert, C. (2006). *Mass Media Law.* New York: McGraw-Hill.

Student Press Law Center. (1994). *Law of the Student Press* (2nd ed.). Arlington, VA: Author.

WEBSITES

The Freedom Forum First Amendment Center: **www.fac.org**

The Reporters Committee for Freedom of the Press: **www.rcfp.org**

The Student Press Law Center: **www.splc.org**

Copy-Editing Symbols

Following is a standard listing of editing symbols that you should learn as quickly as possible.

Indent paragraph	⌐ The president said or ⌐
Take out letter	occassionally
Take out word	the ~~red~~ hat
Close up words	week‿end
Insert word	take it ∧ run *and*
Insert letter	encyclop∧dia *e*
Capitalize	president washington (cap)
Lowercase letter	the President's cabinet (lc)
Insert hyphen	up ∧ to ∧ date
Insert period	end of the sentence⊗ or ⊙
Insert quotation marks	the "orphan" quote
Abbreviate	the United States or Circle the word
Spell out	(Gov.) Sam Smith (sp)
Use figure	(one hundred fifty-seven) 157
Spell out figure	the (3) horses (sp)
Transpose letters	pejoartive
Transpose words	many |problems|difficult|
Circle any typesetting commands	(bfc) (clc)
Connect lines	the car wreck ~~XXXXXX~~ injured two people

Grammar and Diagnostic Exams

The exams in this appendix are meant to help students discover various writing, editing, and grammar problems. The answer key to these exams may be found in the Instructor's Manual for the book. That manual can be obtained from Allyn and Bacon or from the author of this text.

GRAMMAR EXAM

A note to instructors: This exam has been designed to test a student's ability to recognize correct grammatical formations. Students should be given about fifty minutes to complete the exam.

1. There _____ many possible candidates.
   (a) is
   (b) are
   (c) was
   (d) none of the above

2. None _____ so blind as he who will not see.
   (a) is
   (b) are
   (c) either of the above
   (d) none of the above

3. Both of your excuses _____ plausible.
   (a) sound
   (b) sounds
   (c) either of the above
   (d) none of the above

4. Several of the members _____ absent.
   (a) was
   (b) were
   (c) either of the above
   (d) none of the above

5. Few of my family really _____ me.
   (a) understand
   (b) understands
   (c) either of the above
   (d) none of the above

6. Many _____ surprised at the final score.
   (a) was
   (b) were
   (c) either of the above
   (d) none of the above

7. Some of the money _____ missing.
   (a) is
   (b) are
   (c) either of the above
   (d) none of the above

8. All of the cherries _____ ripe.
   (a) look
   (b) looks
   (c) either of the above
   (d) none of the above

9. _____ any of this evidence been presented?
   (a) Has
   (b) Have
   (c) either of the above
   (d) none of the above

10. Mary Sloan, one of the brightest girls, _____ to represent the school in the contest.
    (a) were chosen
    (b) was chosen
    (c) have been chosen
    (d) none of the above

11. Baker took the handoff, _____ his way within one foot of the goal line.
    (a) bulldozes
    (b) bulldozing
    (c) bulldozed
    (d) none of the above

12. I will _____ you to swim.
    (a) learn
    (b) teach
    (c) either of the above
    (d) none of the above

13. Fans cheered as the touchdown _____
    (a) had been made
    (b) was made
    (c) either of the above
    (d) none of the above

14. The team plans _____ tomorrow.
   (a) to celebrate
   (b) to have celebrated
   (c) either of the above
   (d) none of the above

15. _____ the tickets, Mr. Selby took the children to the circus.
   (a) Buying
   (b) Having bought
   (c) either of the above
   (d) none of the above

16. It is customary for ranchers _____ their cattle.
   (a) to have branded
   (b) to brand
   (c) either of the above
   (d) none of the above

17. The pond has begun freezing because the temperature _____.
   (a) has dropped
   (b) dropped
   (c) either of the above
   (d) none of the above

18. They _____ Mary from the invitation.
   (a) accepted
   (b) excepted
   (c) either of the above
   (d) none of the above

19. The citizens _____ many reforms.
   (a) affected
   (b) effected
   (c) either of the above
   (d) none of the above

20. A large _____ of disgruntled men barred the entrance.
   (a) amount
   (b) number
   (c) either of the above
   (d) none of the above

21. What honor is there _____ the forty thieves?
   (a) among
   (b) between
   (c) either of the above
   (d) none of the above

22. You have _____ friends than she.
    (a) fewer
    (b) less
    (c) either of the above
    (d) none of the above

23. Is an author to blame for what the public _____ from his work?
    (a) infers
    (b) implies
    (c) either of the above
    (d) none of the above

24. My house is _____ his.
    (a) different from
    (b) different than
    (c) either of the above
    (d) none of the above

25. It is handy for everyone to know how to cook for _____.
    (a) hisself
    (b) himself
    (c) theirselves
    (d) themselves

26. The old man fascinated _____ children with stories of his adventures.
    (a) them
    (b) us
    (c) we
    (d) none of the above

27. Between you and _____, the food could have been much better than it was.
    (a) I
    (b) me
    (c) she
    (d) none of the above

28. Why don't you get _____ some lunch?
    (a) your selves
    (b) yourselves
    (c) yourselfs
    (d) none of the above

29. Judy has just as much time to wash the dishes as _____.
    (a) I
    (b) me
    (c) them
    (d) none of the above

30. _____ and _____ dad have the same hobbies.
    (a) She, her
    (b) Him, his
    (c) Them, their
    (d) none of the above

31. The reforms _____ many citizens.
    (a) affected
    (b) effected
    (c) either of the above
    (d) none of the above

32. The construction of fallout shelters _____ being considered.
    (a) was
    (b) were
    (c) are
    (d) were not

33. Your contribution, in addition to other funds, _____ the success of our campaign.
    (a) have been assuring
    (b) assures
    (c) assure
    (d) were assuring

34. A combination of these methods _____ sure to succeed.
    (a) were
    (b) are
    (c) is
    (d) none of the above

35. Each of their children _____ a different instrument.
    (a) have
    (b) play
    (c) plays
    (d) either a or b

36. Val _____ me the very record I would have _____.
    (a) give, choosed
    (b) gave, choosed
    (c) give, chosen
    (d) gave, chosen

37. By the time the sun _____, we had _____ nearly a hundred miles.
    (a) rised, drove
    (b) raised, driven
    (c) rose, driven
    (d) had raised, driven

38. As I _____ there, my hat was _____ into the river.
    (a) sit, blowed
    (b) sit, blown
    (c) sat, blown
    (d) sat, blowed

39. Mr. Greenfield's lost eyeglasses _____ the object of everyone's search at the church picnic.
    (a) were
    (b) was
    (c) is
    (d) be

40. He is the one _____ broke it.
    (a) who
    (b) that
    (c) either of the above
    (d) none of the above

41. _____ of class standing, everyone will take the test.
    (a) Regardless
    (b) Irregardless
    (c) either of the above
    (d) none of the above

42. I must _____ find a job.
    (a) try and
    (b) try to
    (c) either of the above
    (d) none of the above

43. The theater was _____ full by seven o'clock.
    (a) already
    (b) all ready
    (c) either of the above
    (d) none of the above

44. The cast was _____ for the curtain call.
    (a) already
    (b) all ready
    (c) either of the above
    (d) none of the above

45. Everything will be _____.
    (a) alright
    (b) all right
    (c) either of the above
    (d) none of the above

46. Don't pay the bill _____ you received the goods.
   - (a) unless
   - (b) without
   - (c) but
   - (d) whether

47. Both the doctor and his nurse _____ to work on foot.
   - (a) come
   - (b) comes
   - (c) has come
   - (d) has came

48. If you _____, you would have passed easily.
   - (a) would have took my advice
   - (b) had taken my advice
   - (c) had taken my advise
   - (d) would have took my advise

49. If you will _____ me your radio, I'll fix it for you.
   - (a) bring
   - (b) take
   - (c) either of the above
   - (d) none of the above

50. Why don't you _____ someone else have a turn?
   - (a) let
   - (b) leave
   - (c) either of the above
   - (d) none of the above

51. Phil _____ and waited for his turn.
   - (a) sit
   - (b) set
   - (c) sat
   - (d) none of the above

52. Will they let _____ fellows use the pool?
   - (a) us
   - (b) we
   - (c) either of the above
   - (d) none of the above

53. Andy shot two more baskets than _____.
   - (a) he
   - (b) him
   - (c) her
   - (d) either b or c

54. I _____ back in my chair and relaxed.
   (a) lie
   (b) laid
   (c) layed
   (d) lay

55. Dick _____ his books on a vacant seat.
   (a) layed
   (b) laid
   (c) lay
   (d) lie

56. I _____ down and waited for the dentist to call me in.
   (a) set
   (b) sat
   (c) sit
   (d) sitted

57. I lay awake, wondering where I had _____ the receipt.
   (a) lay
   (b) laid
   (c) lain
   (d) layed

58. The meat was still frozen, though I had _____ it on the stove to thaw.
   (a) set
   (b) sat
   (c) sit
   (d) layed

59. Glen _____ me the pictures he had taken at the game.
   (a) brung
   (b) bringed
   (c) bring
   (d) brought

60. I _____ past a house on which a tree had fallen.
   (a) drived
   (b) drive
   (c) driven
   (d) drove

61. The new teacher, _____ I met today, came from the South.
   (a) who
   (b) whom
   (c) whose
   (d) who's

62. The new teacher, _____ has taken Mr. Breen's position, came from the South.
    (a) who
    (b) whom
    (c) in formal usage, either would be correct
    (d) none of the above

63. Leroy feels quite _____ about getting a scholarship.
    (a) hopeful
    (b) hopefully
    (c) either of the above
    (d) none of the above

64. The detective's solution to the crime was _____ right.
    (a) altogether
    (b) all together
    (c) all to gather
    (d) all too gather

65. Henry is the _____ of the two.
    (a) more strong
    (b) strongest
    (c) stronger
    (d) most strong

66. You cannot vote _____ you are eighteen.
    (a) unless
    (b) without
    (c) unless being
    (d) without being

67. Ann _____ three lessons.
    (a) taking
    (b) taken
    (c) has taken
    (d) has took

68. Cross the streets _____.
    (a) careful
    (b) carefully
    (c) most careful
    (d) carefuller

69. There is no use feeling sorry _____ the vase is shattered on the floor.
    (a) for
    (b) as
    (c) besides
    (d) because

70. The weather looks _____ it is about to change for the better.
    (a) like
    (b) as
    (c) like as
    (d) as if

71. The girl waved goodbye, _____ her mother did not see her.
    (a) because
    (b) whether
    (c) but
    (d) since

72. It was _____ paid the bill.
    (a) her who
    (b) she who
    (c) her whom
    (d) her who

73. The two students assigned to this project are you and me.
    (a) correct as is
    (b) you and I
    (c) I and you
    (d) me and you

74. Will you please tell me _____ I can solve this problem?
    (a) inasmuch as
    (b) whenever
    (c) with that which
    (d) so that

75. He walked right _____ the trap we set for him.
    (a) up on
    (b) in
    (c) into
    (d) in upon

76. She gets a larger allowance _____ she is older.
    (a) being that
    (b) because
    (c) being because of
    (d) none of the above

77. Too much food and rest _____ circus animals lazy.
    (a) make
    (b) makes
    (c) either of the above
    (d) none of the above

78. The footprints under the window _____ burglary.
    (a) suggests
    (b) suggest
    (c) either of the above
    (d) none of the above

79. Tracy Avenue is the only one of our streets that _____ from one end of the city to the other.
    (a) run
    (b) runs
    (c) either of the above
    (d) none of the above

80. The man acts as though he _____ the owner.
    (a) is
    (b) was
    (c) were
    (d) none of the above

81. If he _____ registered later, he would have had the right classes.
    (a) would have
    (b) had
    (c) either of the above
    (d) none of the above

82. Each one of the ladies _____ splashed by the passing car.
    (a) was
    (b) were
    (c) are
    (d) a and c above are correct

83. The natives believe that noise, smoke, and dancing _____ away the evil spirits.
    (a) drives
    (b) drive
    (c) drived
    (d) none of the above

84. Please tell me _____ you _____ during the winter.
    (a) at where, live
    (b) where, live at
    (c) where, live
    (d) where at, live

85. _____ he _____ yet?
    (a) Have, ate
    (b) Has, ate
    (c) Have, eaten
    (d) Has, eaten

86. The New York *Times* still _____ a wide circulation.
    - (a) has
    - (b) have
    - (c) either of the above
    - (d) none of the above

87. Athletics _____ required of every student.
    - (a) are
    - (b) is
    - (c) either of the above
    - (d) none of the above

88. On the wall _____ several posters.
    - (a) was
    - (b) were
    - (c) is
    - (d) either a or b

89. He failed _____ not studying.
    - (a) due to
    - (b) because of
    - (c) owing to
    - (d) because

90. She _____ her new clothes as if they made her superior to the rest of us.
    - (a) flouted
    - (b) flaunted
    - (c) had flouted
    - (d) flautened

91. He misspelled _____ words on this exam.
    - (a) less
    - (b) fewer
    - (c) lesser
    - (d) more fewer

92. Sue had _____ the cake on a kitchen chair.
    - (a) sat
    - (b) set
    - (c) sitted
    - (d) sit

93. The police will not _____ you park there.
    - (a) leave
    - (b) let
    - (c) either of the above
    - (d) none of the above

94. The gift from _____ and Bert came on Christmas Eve.
- (a) she
- (b) her
- (c) either of the above
- (d) none of the above

95. Norm and _____ share the same locker.
- (a) he
- (b) him
- (c) either of the above
- (d) none of the above

96. Ron doesn't live as far from the school as _____.
- (a) us
- (b) we
- (c) they
- (d) either b or c

97. The children amused _____ by asking riddles.
- (a) theirselves
- (b) themselves
- (c) either of the above
- (d) none of the above

98. I was sitting all by _____ in that last row.
- (a) my self
- (b) myself
- (c) either of the above
- (d) none of the above

99. Four of the committee members _____ married.
- (a) were
- (b) is
- (c) are
- (d) either a or c

100. _____ and _____ are good friends.
- (a) Her, me
- (b) He, she
- (c) She, I
- (d) either b or c

DIAGNOSTIC EXAM

A note to instructors: This test has been designed to help you determine levels of understanding about knowledge and use of the language. The final ten questions on copy-editing symbols may or may not be relevant to your instruction.

1. Robert _____ from his bike.
   - (a) had fell
   - (b) had fallen
   - (c) fallen
   - (d) falling

2. The plane with its crew _____ trying to take off now.
   - (a) is
   - (b) be
   - (c) are
   - (d) been

3. Is the atmosphere on the moon _____ the atmosphere here on earth?
   - (a) different from
   - (b) liken to
   - (c) different than
   - (d) as different as

4. Why is the referee so _____ the players?
   - (a) angry at
   - (b) angry with
   - (c) angry in
   - (d) angry over

5. Why _____ allowed to join?
   - (a) was Ann and he
   - (b) was Ann and him
   - (c) were Ann and he
   - (d) were Ann and him

6. Someone _____ turned on the automatic sprinkler.
   - (a) must of
   - (b) might of
   - (c) must to
   - (d) must have

7. I noticed the dog as he _____ on the porch.
   - (a) laid
   - (b) lay
   - (c) lain
   - (d) lied

8. Share the work _____ all the workers.
   - (a) between
   - (b) amongst
   - (c) betweens
   - (d) among

9. The trunk was _____ heavy _____ carry.
   - (a) to, to
   - (b) too, too
   - (c) too, to
   - (d) to, too

10. Will you _____ come?
    - (a) try and
    - (b) try to
    - (c) be trying and
    - (d) trying to

11. It was Ann who _____ the book on the table.
    - (a) layed
    - (b) laid
    - (c) lain
    - (d) lay

12. The committee _____ holding an open meeting on Thursday.
    - (a) are
    - (b) is
    - (c) been
    - (d) be

13. The new suit is _____.
    - (a) alright
    - (b) al right
    - (c) allright
    - (d) all right

14. I am happy to _____ your offer to go to the games.
    - (a) accept
    - (b) except
    - (c) have excepted
    - (d) having accepted

15. He spoke very _____.
    - (a) strange
    - (b) stranger
    - (c) strangest
    - (d) strangely

16. He speaks _____ .
   (a) good
   (b) goodly
   (c) well
   (d) more better

17. She _____ finished the job in half the time.
   (a) could of
   (b) can't of
   (c) could have
   (d) could had

18. Please _____ here.
   (a) set
   (b) sit
   (c) to be set
   (d) to be sitted

19. He _____ a pint of milk.
   (a) has drank
   (b) have drank
   (c) has drunk
   (d) have drunk

20. Either you or your friends _____ to blame for the accident.
   (a) is
   (b) are
   (c) been
   (d) was

21. Neither Barbara nor Sara _____ homework on Saturdays.
   (a) do
   (b) does
   (c) are doing
   (d) were doing

22. None of the programs _____ free from station breaks.
   (a) is
   (b) are
   (c) be
   (d) being

23. Why are you still angry _____ me?
   (a) at
   (b) with
   (c) by
   (d) against

24. If everyone does _____ share, we shall certainly finish on time.
    (a) their
    (b) his or her
    (c) there
    (d) they're

25. _____, the majority of the board members promises to support him.
    (a) Regardless of who is chosen
    (b) Regardless of whom is chosen
    (c) Irregardless of who is chosen
    (d) Irregardless of whom is chosen

Choose the correct style in Exercises 26 through 35:

26. (a) in a baptist church
    (b) in a Baptist Church
    (c) in a baptist Church
    (d) in a Baptist church

27. (a) a Mother's Day gift
    (b) a Mother's day gift
    (c) a mother's day gift
    (d) a Mother's Day Gift

28. (a) the new Fall colors
    (b) the new fall colors
    (c) the New Fall Colors
    (d) the New fall colors

29. (a) the Brother of mayor Bates
    (b) the brother of Mayor Bates
    (c) the Brother of Mayor Bates
    (d) the brother of mayor Bates

30. (a) a brazilian pianist
    (b) a Brazilian Pianist
    (c) a Brazilian pianist
    (d) a brazilian Pianist

31. (a) at Eaton High School
    (b) at Eaton high school
    (c) at Eaton high School
    (d) at eaton high school

32. (a) on the North Side of Pine Lake
    (b) on the north Side of Pine Lake
    (c) on the North side of Pine lake
    (d) on the north side of Pine Lake

33. (a) Dodd tool company
    (b) Dodd Tool company
    (c) Dodd tool Company
    (d) Dodd Tool Company

34. (a) any Sunday in July
    (b) any sunday in july
    (c) any Sunday in july
    (d) any sunday in July

35. (a) a College Football star
    (b) a college football star
    (c) a college Football star
    (d) a College Football Star

36. Mabel asked, "To which colleges has Joan _____
    (a) applied."
    (b) applied"?
    (c) applied".
    (d) applied?"

37. _____ should be free of loose dirt and paint.
    (a) Before you paint the surface, of course,
    (b) Before you paint the surface of course,
    (c) Before you paint, the surface, of course,
    (d) Before you paint, the surface, of course

38. All the _____
    (a) students, whose reports were not handed in, failed.
    (b) students, who's reports were not handed in, failed.
    (c) students who's reports were not handed in failed.
    (d) students whose reports were not handed in failed.

39. "Before starting to write your _____ Miss Wright advised.
    (a) composition plan what you are going to say,"
    (b) composition plan what you are going to say"
    (c) composition, plan what you are going to say,"
    (d) composition, plan what you are going to say",

40. Choose the correct possessive case:
    (a) everyones friend
    (b) childrens' toys
    (c) the school's reputation
    (d) Is this your's?

41. Built in 1832, _____ is now a museum of early American life.
    (a) Dunham Tavern at 6709 Euclid Avenue in Cleveland, Ohio,
    (b) Dunham Tavern, at 6709 Euclid Avenue in Cleveland, Ohio,
    (c) Dunham Tavern, at 6709 Euclid Avenue in Cleveland Ohio
    (d) Dunham Tavern, at 6709 Euclid Avenue in Cleveland, Ohio

42. "When you come to the stop _____ "make a full stop."
   (a) sign", Dad repeated,
   (b) sign: Dad repeated,
   (c) sign," Dad repeated
   (d) sign," Dad repeated,

43. Every _____ lose his license.
   (a) motorist, who is caught speeding, should
   (b) motorist who is caught speeding should
   (c) motorist who is caught speeding; should
   (d) motorist, who is caught speeding should

44. _____ stimulates the heart and raises blood pressure.
   (a) Caffeine which is present, in both tea and coffee,
   (b) Caffeine, which is present in both tea and coffee,
   (c) Caffeine, which is present in both tea, and coffee
   (d) Caffeine, which is present in both tea and coffee

45. Choose the correct possessive case:
   (a) Barton's and McLean's store
   (b) Jack and Tom's responsibility
   (c) moons rays
   (d) editor-in-chiefs' opinion

Choose the correct spelling in Exercises 46 through 65:

46. (a) fullfil   (b) fulfil   (c) fullfill   (d) fulfill

47. (a) seperate   (b) sepurate   (c) separate   (d) saperate

48. (a) defenitley   (b) defientely   (c) definitely   (d) definitly

49. (a) calander   (b) calandar   (c) calendar   (d) calender

50. (a) acomodat   (b) accomadate   (c) accommodate   (d) accomodate

51. (a) amatur   (b) ameteur   (c) amateur   (d) amater

52. (a) defisite   (b) deficit   (c) deficite   (d) defecite

53. (a) auxelary   (b) auxilary   (c) auxiliary   (d) auxilairy

54. (a) conceintous   (b) consientius   (c) conscientious   (d) consentious

55. (a) presedent   (b) presedant   (c) precedent   (d) precedant

56. (a) superentendent   (b) superintindent   (c) superintendint
   (d) superintendent

57. (a) recieve   (b) riceive   (c) ricieve   (d) receive

58. (a) adaptability   (b) adaptabilaty   (c) adaptibility   (d) adaptibilaty

59. (a) alegance   (b) allegance   (c) alegiance   (d) allegiance

60. (a) privilege   (b) priviledge   (c) previledge   (d) preveledge

61. (a) concede   (b) conceed   (c) consede   (d) conceede

62. (a) elegible   (b) eligible   (c) elegeble   (d) eligeble

63. (a) camoflauge   (b) camouglauge   (c) camouflage   (d) camalage

64. (a) athleet   (b) athlete   (c) athelete   (d) athilete

65. (a) genarosity   (b) generosity   (c) genatousity   (d) generousity

66. Copy-editing symbol for "new paragraph":

    (a) ⌐The   (b) ⌊The   (c) Par The   (d) The⟶

67. Copy-editing symbol for "deletion":

    (a) painǝted   (b) pain✗ted   (c) painˆted   (d) painᴖ̃ted

68. Copy-editing symbol for "spell out a number":

    (a) 6̲   (b) sp⃝6   (c) ⑥   (d) sp 6

69. Copy-editing symbol for "use numerals":

    (a) ⟨forty⟩   (b) ⌈forty⌉   (c) num forty   (d) ~~forty~~

70. Copy-editing symbol for "eliminate space":

    (a) ques/tion   (b) quesˆtion   (c) quesˆtion   (d) quesˆtion

71. Copy-editing symbol for "insert comma":

    (a) however①   (b) howeverˆ   (c) however˅   (d) however,

72. Copy-editing symbol for "retain copy":

    (a) stet ~~never~~   (b) never ~~never~~   (c) keep ~~never~~   (d) ⟨never⟩

73. Copy-editing symbol for "center copy":

    (a) ⌐John Doe⌝   (b) |John Doe| (c)]John Doe[(d) ⟶John Doe⟵

74. Proper mark to indicate that the story does not end on this page:

    (a) More,   (b) add,   (c) continued,   (d) —

75. Proper mark to indicate the end of the story:

    (a) end,   (b) —   (c) —30—   (d) —

Problem Words and Phrases

This section contains a variety of words and phrases that often give writers difficulty. Much of this section is about words that have similar sounds but different meanings.

accede, concede

To accede is to agree and is often used with the preposition *to*. *To concede* is to yield without necessarily agreeing.

access, excess

Access is a noun meaning "a way in"; *excess* is a noun meaning "too much."

adjured, abjured

To abjure is to renounce; *to adjure* is to entreat or to appeal.

afterward, afterwards

Use *afterward*. The dictionary allows use of *afterwards* only as a second form.

aisle, isle

Aisle is a noun referring to a passageway; *isle*, also a noun, is a shortened form of *island*.

all right

That's the way to spell it. The dictionary may list *alright* as a legitimate word, but it is not acceptable in standard usage.

altar, alter

An *altar* is a tablelike platform used in a church service; *to alter* is to change something.

annual

Don't use *first* with it. If it's the first time, it's not annual yet.

anyone, any one

Anyone means any person as in "Did anyone come?" *Any one* refers to any member of a group as in "Any one of you is welcome to come."

apprised, appraised

Apprise means to inform; *appraise* means to give or place a value on something.

arbitrator, mediator

An *arbitrator* is one who hears evidence from all persons concerned, then hands down a decision. A *mediator* is one who listens to arguments of both parties and tries by the exercise of reason to bring them to an agreement.

as, like

As is used to introduce clauses; *like* is a preposition and requires an object.

atheist, agnostic

An *atheist* is a person who believes that there is no God. An *agnostic* is a person who believes that it is impossible to know whether there is a God.

auger, augur

Auger, a noun, is a tool used for boring into wood or the ground. *Augur*, a verb, is used to imply foretelling.

adverse, averse

Adverse means unfavorable or hostile. One who is *averse* is reluctant.

biennial, biannual

Biennial means every two years. *Biannual* means twice a year and is a synonym for *semiannual*.

bloc, block

A *bloc* is a coalition of persons or a group with the same purpose or goal. Don't call it a *block*, which has some forty dictionary definitions.

bored, board

Bored is an adjective that means lacking interest. *Board* is a noun that may refer to lumber or food or a group of people.

bullion, bouillon

Bullion is gold or silver in the form of bars. *Bouillon* is a clear broth for cooking or drinking.

cannon, canon

A *cannon* is a weapon; a *canon* is a law or rule. The books that are in the Bible are referred to as the canon.

Capitol, capital

Capital refers to a seat of government, generally a city. A *Capitol* is the building in which a legislature sits. It should be capitalized.

carats, karats

Carats are used to measure the weight of precious stones. *Karats* measure the ratio of gold to the mixed alloy.

censor, censer

Censor, the verb, means to prohibit or restrict; as a noun, it means prohibitor. A *censer* is an incense burner or container.

chairwoman, chairman, chairperson

In AP style, *chairwoman* is used for a female; *chairman* is used for a man. *Chairperson* is used only when it is the organization's formal title.

cite, site

Cite is a verb that means to acknowledge; *site* is either a noun meaning location or a verb meaning to place.

complement, compliment

Complement is a noun or verb denoting completeness or the process of supplementing something. *Compliment* is a noun or verb that denotes praise or the expression of courtesy.

comprises, composes

Comprise means to contain, to include all, or to embrace. It is best used in active voice, followed by an object. *Compose* means to create or put together.

conscience, conscious

Conscience is a noun that means a sense of right and wrong; *conscious* is an adjective meaning "aware."

consul, counsel

A *consul* is a diplomatic emissary residing in a foreign country, overseeing his or her country's interests there. A *counsel* is an attorney or adviser.

continuous, continual

Continuous means unbroken. *Continual* means repeated or intermittent.

couple of

You need the *of*. It's never "a couple tomatoes."

demolish, destroy

They both mean to do away with completely. You can't partially demolish or destroy something; nor is there any need to say "totally destroyed."

denotes, connotes

Denotes implies a specific meaning; *connotes* means to suggest or imply.

dietitian, dietician

Dietitian is the correct spelling for someone trained in the field of nutrition planning, not *dietician*.

difference, differential

Difference is a noun that refers to the amount by which two things are dissimilar. *Differential* is an adjective that means distinctive or making use of a difference. The two words are not interchangeable.

different from

Things and people are *different from* each other. Don't write that they are *different than* each other.

discomfiture, discomfort

Discomfiture is uneasiness or embarrassment; *discomfort* is inconvenience or a physical lack of comfort.

discreet, discrete

Discreet means showing discernment or good judgment. *Discrete* means individually distinct and noncontinuous.

disinterested, uninterested

Disinterested means impartial; *uninterested* refers to someone who lacks interest or doesn't care.

dissent, descent

Dissent is disagreement; it can be a verb or a noun. *Descent* is the act or process of *descending,* meaning "going down."

drown

Don't say someone *was drowned* unless an assailant held the victim's head under water. Just that say the victim *drowned.*

due to, owing to, because of

The last is preferred. *Wrong:* The game was canceled due to rain. *Stilted:* Owing to rain, the game was canceled. *Right:* The game was canceled because of rain.

dyeing, dying

Dyeing refers to changing colors. *Dying* refers to death.

ecology, environment

They are not synonymous. *Ecology* is the study of the relationship between organisms and their environment. *Right:* The laboratory is studying the ecology of humans and the desert. *Right:* There is much interest in animal ecology these days. *Wrong:* Even as simple an undertaking as maintaining a lawn affects ecology. *Right:* Even as simple an undertaking as maintaining a lawn affects our environment.

effect, affect

Effect is a change or result; *affect* is usually a verb that means to pretend to feel or be, to like and display, or to produce an effect. (*Affect* in psychology can be a noun.)

effective, efficient

Effective means producing an effect with emphasis on the process of doing so; *efficient* means producing results with minimum effort or time.

either

It means one or the other, not both. *Wrong:* There were lions on either side of the door. *Right:* There were lions on each side of the door.

elude, allude

Elude means to escape from. *Allude* means to refer to or mention.

eminent, imminent

Eminent is an adjective meaning "prominent, important"; *imminent* is an adjective that refers to something about to happen.

enervate, energize

To *enervate* is to drain or weaken; *to energize* is to invigorate.

equal, equitable

Equal is an adjective that has no comparatives; that is, you cannot logically say that something is "more equal" or "less equal." The adjective *equitable* does have comparatives.

exaltation, exultation

Exaltation is high praise or to have raised in honor. *Exultation* is celebration or the act of rejoicing.

feign, fain

To *feign* is to pretend; *fain,* an adjective or adverb, means glad or willing.

fewer, less

Use *fewer* with countable items; use *less* with amounts or things that are not countable.

flare, flair

Flare is a verb meaning "to blaze with sudden, bright light" or "to burst out in anger"; it is also a noun meaning "a bright burst of light." *Flair,* a noun, is conspicuous talent.

fliers, flyers

Flier is the preferred term for both an aviator and a handbill.

flout, flaunt

Flout means to mock, to scoff, or to show disdain for. *Flaunt* means to display ostentatiously.

funeral service

A redundant expression. A funeral is a service.

gibe, jibe

To *gibe* means to taunt or sneer. *Jibe* means to shift in direction or, colloquially, to agree.

goodbye, goodby

It's *goodbye,* not *goodby.*

gourmet, gourmand

A *gourmet* is a person who appreciates fine food; a *gourmand* is a person who eats to excess, a glutton.

grisly, grizzly

Grisly means horrifying; *grizzly* refers to a type of bear.

hanged, hung

Hanged is used for people; *hung* refers to objects. One exception is the term *hung jury.*

head up

People don't *head up* committees. They *head* them.

half-mast, half-staff

On ships and at naval stations ashore, flags are flown at *half-mast.* Elsewhere ashore, flags are flown at *half-staff.*

hopefully

One of the most commonly misused words, in spite of what the dictionary may say. *Hopefully* should be used to describe the way the subject feels—for instance, "Hopefully, I shall present the plan to the president." This means that I will be hopeful when I do it, not that I hope I will do it. It is something else again when you attribute hope to a nonperson. You may write, "Hopefully, the war will end soon." What you mean is that you hope the war will end soon, but this is not what you are writing. What you should write is "I hope the war will end soon."

human, humane

Human means referring to people; *humane* is an adjective meaning "kindly."

illicit, elicit

An *illicit* activity is illegal or unseemly. *To elicit* is to invoke.

imply, infer

Imply means to suggest or indicate; *infer* means to draw a conclusion from.

in advance of, prior to

Use *before;* it sounds more natural than either of the above.

it's, its

It's is the contraction of *it is. Its* is the possessive form of the word *it.*

leave alone, let alone

Leave alone means to depart from or cause to be in solitude. *Let alone* means to allow to be undisturbed. *Wrong:* The man had pulled a gun on her, but Mr. Jones intervened and talked him into leaving her alone. *Right:* The man had pulled a gun on her, but Mr. Jones intervened and talked him into letting her alone. *Right:* When I entered the room, I saw that Jim and Mary were sleeping, so I decided to leave them alone.

lectern, podium, pulpit

A speaker stands *behind a lectern, on a podium or rostrum,* or *in the pulpit.*

Figure C.1

Mark Twain on the right word

The difference between the right word and the almost right word is the difference between lightning and the lightning bug.

lie, lay

Lie is a state of being (John chose to *lie* in the sun); *lay* is the action or work (He started to *lay* the books down). *Lay* needs an object to be used correctly.

like, as

Don't use *like* for *as* or *as if*. In general, use *like* to compare nouns and pronouns; use *as* in comparing phrases and clauses that contain a verb. *Wrong:* Jim blocks the linebacker like he should. *Right:* Jim blocks the linebacker as he should. *Right:* Jim blocks like a pro.

lineage, linage

Lineage means descent or ancestry. *Linage* means number of lines; newspapers often refer to the amount of advertising they have as *ad linage*.

mantel, mantle

A *mantel* is a shelf; a *mantle* is a cloak. *Mantle* also refers to a symbol of preeminence or authority.

marshall, marshal, martial

Generally, the first form is correct only when the word is a proper noun: John *Marshall*. The second form is the verb form: Marilyn will *marshal* her forces. The second form is also the one to use for a title: *fire marshal Stan Anderson, field marshal Erwin Rommel*. *Martial* means having to do with the military.

mean, average, median

Use *mean* as synonymous with *average*. Both words refer to the sum of all components divided by the number of components. *Median* is the number that has as many components above it as below it.

noisome, noisy

Noisome means offensive or noxious. *Noisy* means loud or clamorous.

off, off of

When using *off,* the word *of* is not necessary. *Off* is an adequate preposition to carry the phrase.

official, officious

Something that is *official* is formally authorized; one who is *officious* is impertinent or meddlesome.

opponent, adversary

While an *opponent* is simply on the opposite side, an *adversary* is openly hostile.

oral, verbal

Oral is used when the mouth is central to the idea, as in "He made an oral presentation." That means he spoke. *Verbal* may refer to spoken or written words.

over, more than

Over and *under* are best used for spatial relationships. When using figures, *more than* and *less than* are better choices.

palate, palette

Palate is the roof of the mouth. A *palette* is an artist's paint board.

parallel construction

Thoughts in series in the same sentence require parallel construction. *Wrong:* The union delivered demands for an increase of 10 percent in wages and to cut the work week to 30 hours. *Right:* The union delivered demands for an increase of 30 percent in wages and for a reduction in the work week to 30 hours.

parole, probation

Parole is the release of a prisoner before the sentence has expired, on condition of good behavior. *Probation* is the suspension of a sentence for a convicted person.

passed, enacted

Bills are *passed;* laws are *enacted.*

peacock, peahen, peafowl

Peacocks are male, *peahens* are female, and *peafowl* are both.

peddle, pedal

When selling something, you *peddle* it. When riding a bicycle or similar means of locomotion, you *pedal* it.

pour, pore

Pour means to flow in a continuous stream; *pore* means to gaze intently.

prescribe, proscribe

To *prescribe* is to order or recommend the use of. To *proscribe* is to forbid, denounce, or prohibit.

pretext, pretense

They are different, but it's a tough distinction. A *pretext* is that which is put forward to conceal a truth. *Right:* He was discharged for tardiness, but this was only a pretext for general incompetence. A *pretense* is a "false show," a more overt act that is intended to conceal personal feelings. *Right:* My profuse compliments were all pretense.

principal, principle

Principal means someone or something that is first in rank, authority, or importance. *Principle* means a fundamental truth, law, or doctrine.

prone, supine

Prone means lying face down; *supine* means lying face up. *Prone* can also mean inclined toward, and *supine* can also mean *passive*.

prophesy, prophecy

Prophesy is the verb; *prophecy* is the noun form.

ravaged, ravished

To *ravage* is to wreak great destruction; to *ravish* is to abduct, rape, or carry away with emotion. Buildings and towns cannot be ravished.

raze, raise

To *raze* is to destroy or to demolish. To *raise* is to lift up or to increase.

reeked, wreaked

To *reek* is to permeate with an offensive or strong odor. To *wreak* means to punish or to avenge; it connotes destructive activity.

refute

The word connotes success in argument and almost always implies an editorial judgment. *Wrong:* Father Bury refuted the arguments of the proabortion faction.

rein, reign

The leather strap for a horse is a *rein*. *Reign* is the period when a ruler is on the throne.

reluctant, reticent

If she doesn't want to act, she is *reluctant*. If she doesn't want to speak, she is *reticent*.

shut off, shut-off

Shut off is the verb form. The noun form, *shut-off,* is hyphenated.

stanch, staunch

Stanch is a verb that means to stop. *Staunch* is an adjective that means strong.

stationary, stationery

Stationary means to stand still; *stationery* is writing paper.

suite, suit

Suite refers to a set of rooms and furniture; a *suit* refers to clothes, cards, or a lawsuit.

survey, questionnaire

A *survey* is another word for a public opinion poll. A *questionnaire* is the set of questions that the respondents in the poll answer. *Survey* is not a synonym for *questionnaire*.

temperatures

They may get higher or lower, but they don't get warmer or cooler. *Wrong:* Temperatures are expected to warm up on Friday. *Right:* Temperatures are expected to rise on Friday.

that, which

That tends to restrict the reader's thought and direct it in the way you want it to go; *which* is nonrestrictive, introducing a bit of subsidiary information. For instance: The lawnmower that is in the garage needs sharpening. (Meaning: We have more than one lawnmower. The one in the garage needs sharpening.) The statue that graces our entry hall is on loan from the museum. (Meaning: Of all the statues around here, the one in the entry hall is on loan.) The statue, which was in the hallway, survived the fire. (Meaning: This statue survived the fire. It happened to be in the hallway.) Note that *which* clauses take commas, signaling that they are not essential to the meaning of the sentence.

their, there

Their is a possessive pronoun; *there* is an adverb indicating place or direction.

troop, troupe

A *troop* is a group of people or animals. A *troupe* is an ensemble of actors, singers, dancers, and so on.

under way

Use this form, not *underway*. But don't say that something *got under way*. Say that it *started* or *began*.

unique

Something that is *unique* is the only one of its kind. It can't be *very unique* or *quite unique* or *somewhat unique* or *rather unique*. Don't use this word unless you really mean unique.

up

Don't use it as a verb. *Wrong:* The manager said he would up the price next week. *Right:* The manager said he would raise the price next week.

venerable, vulnerable

Venerable means respected because of age or attainments; *vulnerable* means open to attack or damage.

versus, verses

Versus means to go against or aberrate; *verses* are lines of poetry.

whom, who

This is a tough one, but generally you're safe if you use *whom* to refer to someone who has been the object of an action. Example: A 19-year-old woman, to whom the room was rented, left the window open. *Who* is the word when the somebody has been the actor. Example: A 19-year-old woman, who rented the room, left the window open.

whose, who's

Whose is the possessive form of *who*. *Who's* is the contraction of *who is*.

would

Be careful about using *would* in constructing a conditional past tense. *Wrong:* If Smith would not have had an injured foot, Thompson wouldn't have been in the lineup. *Right:* If Smith had not had an injured foot, Thompson wouldn't have been in the lineup.

your, you're

Your is a pronoun that means belonging to you; *you're* is a contraction of *you are*.

COPY SHEET

Product:

Medium:

Client:

Writer:

Headline:

Subhead:

Body copy:

Subhead or slogan:

Signature:

RADIO SCRIPT SHEET

Product:

Client:

Title:

Writer:

Length:

Source	Audio

TELEVISION SCRIPT SHEET

Product:

Client:

Title:

Writer:

Length:

Video	Audio

TELEVISION STORYBOARD SHEET

Product:

Client:

Title:

Writer:

Length:

Video   Audio

Frame time

Frame time

Frame time

Frame time

Frame time

Frame time

Frame time

Glossary

Accuracy: the chief goal of media writing, which tries to present correct information in a context that allows the reader to interpret it accurately. Accuracy is one of the four major goals of media writing; the others are clarity, precision, and efficiency.

Active and passive voice: verb forms. Active voice verbs pass the action of the verb on to the object in the sentence. *Example:* John hit the ball. Passive voice structure turns the action back onto the subject. *Example:* The ball was hit by John. Generally, writers for the media want to use active rather than passive voice.

Actual malice: the standard of proof that a public figure who brings a libel suit must meet. Actual malice means that when the writer published the libelous statement, the writer either knew that the statement was false or had reckless disregard for the truth or falsity of the statement.

Antecedent: a noun in a sentence to which a pronoun later in the sentence refers. *Example:* The team boarded its bus after the game. In this sentence, *team* is the antecedent, the noun to which the pronoun *its* refers. Pronouns and their antecedents should agree in number; that is, singular antecedents require singular pronouns. The sentence in the example would be wrong if it said "The team boarded their bus after the game."

Attribution: telling the reader the source of the information the writer is using. Proper attribution is an important part of the media writing process.

Clarity: understandable, without confusion. Clear writing occurs when the writer and the reader have the same understanding about the words that are used.

Cliché: an overused expression. Using a cliché marks a writer as lazy and less than thoughtful.

Copy: a term referring to a particular piece of writing for a medium, such as broadcast copy or newspaper copy.

Copy platform: a form used in advertising to list some product characteristics and possible approaches to advertising the product. Copy platforms are a good starting point for advertising campaigns.

Copyright: protection given by the government to people who create literary or artistic works.

Deadline: the time when copy should be turned in for production. Deadlines are necessary for producing the organs of the mass media: newspapers, magazines, newscasts, websites, and so on. Adherence to deadlines is one of the chief requirements of a writer for the mass media.

Demographics: division of the population based on certain physical characteristics such as age or gender.

Dramatic unity: story structure used in most short broadcast news stories. Dramatic unity divides a story into three parts: climax, cause, and effect.

Editing: reworking or refining copy to make it better. Editing is an important part of the writing process; it should be done purposefully and systematically.

Efficiency: the quality of writing in which the writer conveys the most information with the fewest words.

Embargo: the time after which information in a news release can be used by the news media. Embargos are agreements between public relations practitioners and the news media about the use of information, but these agreements do not have legal force.

Fair use: the legal use of copyrighted material without permission or consent of the person who owns the copyright. Fair use is very limited and must meet a number of stringent conditions.

Fantasy: the use of unreal characters or abnormal situations in advertising. For example, the Jolly Green Giant is a fantasy character.

Headline: a few words in a print publication or on a website that tell the reader what is in an article. Because they are so short, accurate and informative headlines are difficult to write, but they are an essential part of the mass media.

HTML: hypertext mark-up language. This is a set of "tags" that instruct web browsers what to do and how to display text and images. Basic knowledge of HTML is essential for the web writer.

Inverted pyramid: structure of writing used for news stories for print and the Web. The inverted pyramid structure requires that the most important information be at the beginning of the story.

Lateral reporting: the concept of reporting that uses the characteristics of the Web to help journalists expand their work. Lateral reporting, or "thinking laterally," requires a reporter to consider the different ways in which a story could be reported beyond the basic written story.

Lead: the beginning of the story. It is sometimes referred to as the "lead paragraph" or the first paragraph of a story. Pronounced *LEED*.

Link: a device for getting from one web page to another. Links are an important part of writing for the Web; creating links helps to expand and enrich what the writer does.

Media: a plural noun that requires a plural verb: *media are,* not *media is.* The word is a catch-all term for the communication industry, and though it is widely used, its usefulness is limited because it is imprecise.

News: subjects and events that journalist deem worthy of writing about and disseminating to a wider audience. News events and subjects meet certain criteria called *news values.*

Objectivity, balance, fairness: the idea that journalists should present information that gives readers a complete picture of the event or subject they are trying to describe. That information should include differing points of view if appropriate. These terms represent ideals that writers should strive for; in reality, they often cannot be attained.

Plagiarism: using the words and ideas of others without giving appropriate credit or attribution. Plagiarism is one of the chief sins of a writer for the mass media.

Precision: the quality of writing in which the writing adheres to the commonly accepted standards of grammar, spelling, punctuation, and meaning.

Psychographics: division of the population based on how they feel or their outlook toward certain aspects of life.

Public figure: a class of people who must prove actual malice (*see definition*) in a libel suit. Public figures are generally considered to be people who hold public office or who thrust themselves into public forums or debates.

Publics: term describing the audiences to which public relations communications are directed. An organization can have internal publics (those within the organization) and external publics (those outside the organization).

Quotation: information that is attributed to a source. A direct quotation is one that uses the exact words of the source and puts them inside quotation marks; an indirect quotation uses the ideas and information of the source but not the exact words. An indirect quotation does not use quotation marks. Another term for indirect quotation is *paraphrase*.

Redundancy: an expression that uses more words than necessary. *Example:* the exact same thing.

Sound bite: a part of a broadcast news story in which there is audio or video. Sound bites are fairly short clips, usually only a few seconds.

Storyboard: a way of outlining a story or advertisement in broadcasting.

Style: a special case of English correctness that a publication adopts. It does so to promote consistency among its writers and to reduce confusion among its readers.

Summary: a short paragraph, sometimes only one sentence, that tells the reader of a website what is in a longer article. The summary is one of the basic forms of writing for the Web.

Testimonial: advertising that uses a well-known person to endorse a product.

Trademark: a symbol, word, or phrase that designates a commercial product.

Transition: a word or phrase that a writer uses to get readers from one sentence or idea to the next; used to build unity in writing.

Voiceover: a technique in a news story in which an anchor or reporter is speaking while a videotape is shown. The abbreviation for a voiceover in broadcast copy is *VO*.

Weblog: a website featuring the work of one writer (though sometimes more than one writer can contribute). A weblog (also known as a *blog*) allows the opinions and personality of the writer to be evident in the writing and is updated relatively often, even several times a day.

Index